ORGANISATION MONDIALE DE LA SANTÉ ANIM/
WORLD ORGANISATION FOR ANIMAL HEALTH
ORGANIZACIÓN MUNDIAL DE SANIDAD ANIMAL

Office International des Épizooties

REVUE
SCIENTIFIQUE ET TECHNIQUE

SCIENTIFIC AND TECHNICAL
REVIEW

REVISTA
CIENTÍFICA Y TÉCNICA

**Animal production food safety
challenges in global markets**

**Sécurité sanitaire des aliments
issus de la production animale
et commerce mondial**

**Los retos de la inocuidad de los alimentos
en los procesos de producción animal
y su comercio mundial**

Co-ordinated by
Coordonné par   S.A. Slorach
Coordinado por

VOL. 25 (2)
AUGUST – AOÛT – AGOSTO
2006

12, rue de Prony – 75017 Paris – France
Tél. : 33 (0)1 44 15 18 88 – E-mail : oie@oie.int – Fax : 33 (0)1 42 67 09 87

© Office international des épizooties, 2006

ISSN 0253-1933
ISBN 92-9044-662-5

Le papier choisi pour l'impression de cet ouvrage, étant recyclé à 50 % et exempt à 100 % de chlore et d'acide, ne peut pas nuire à l'environnement
This book is printed on 50% recycled, 100% chlorine and acid-free environmentally friendly paper
El papel escogido para la impresión de este libro está reciclado al 50% y no contiene cloro ni ácidos, por lo que no puede causar prejuicio al medio ambiente

■

Conception maquette / *Graphic design* / Diseño de la maqueta: J. Prieur – *Tous les chemins*
Conception couverture / *Cover design* / Diseño de cubierta: P. Blandin – OIE

Rev. sci. tech. Off. int. Epiz., **25** (2), 2006

Contents – Sommaire – Contenido

Animal production food safety challenges in global markets
Sécurité sanitaire des aliments issus de la production animale et commerce mondial
Los retos de la inocuidad de los alimentos en los procesos de producción animal y su comercio mundial

The global context of animal production and trade in animal food products – Le contexte mondial de la production animale et du commerce d'aliments d'origine animale – La producción animal y el comercio de sus subproductos en el contexto mundial

Rev. sci. tech. Off. int. Epiz., **25** (2)

Hazards occurring during the production stage and affecting the safety of food of animal origin – Les dangers en phase de production pouvant menacer la sécurité sanitaire des aliments d'origine animale – Los riesgos de la etapa de producción que pueden afectar a los alimentos de origen animal

Rev. sci. tech. Off. int. Epiz., **25** (2)

469

Challenges and responses: OIE Regions and Member Countries – Les enjeux et les réponses : régions et Pays Membres de l'OIE – Problemas y soluciones en las regiones y Países Miembros de la OIE

470

Rev. sci. tech. Off. int. Epiz., **25** (2)

Global perspectives: international standard-setting organisations
and stakeholders – Perspectives mondiales : les organisations internationales chargées
d'élaborer les normes et leurs partenaires – Las organizaciones internacionales
y demás partes en la perspectiva mundial

471

Rev. sci. tech. Off. int. Epiz., **25** (2)

Rev. sci. tech. Off. int. Epiz., 2006, **25** (2), 473-478

Preface

Animal production food safety challenges in global markets

Recognising that food safety is a vital public health issue for all countries and their consumers and also a matter of growing importance for international trade in foods of animal origin, the World Organisation for Animal Health (OIE) identified it as a high priority area in its Strategic Plan for 2001-2005. The organisation has been much more active in the food safety area in recent years: one manifestation of this was the establishment in 2002 of a permanent OIE Working Group on Animal Production Food Safety to coordinate its activities on food safety, focusing on measures applicable at the farm level. In addition, the Working Group promotes collaboration between the OIE, the Food and Agriculture Organization (FAO), the World Health Organization (WHO) and the Codex Alimentarius Commission (Codex). The latter, like the OIE, is specifically recognised as an international standard-setting organisation in the World Trade Organization's Agreement on the Application of Sanitary and Phytosanitary Measures (the SPS Agreement). The publication of this special issue of the OIE *Scientific and Technical Review* devoted to animal production food safety challenges in global markets and how these challenges can best be met is another example of the OIE's focus on food safety issues.

In this *Review* the scene is set by describing animal production systems in both the industrialised world and developing countries. In addition, the impact of animal diseases on international livestock markets and a producer's view on quality and efficiency in safe animal production are described. The second part of the review deals with various biological and chemical hazards that can occur during the primary production stage ('On-farm') or during transfer and can affect the safety of foods and feeds of animal origin. In addition to describing the food safety challenges, methods of controlling or eliminating the problems are discussed. The biological hazards covered include pathogenic bacteria (e.g. *Salmonella* spp., Shiga toxin-producing *Escherichia coli*, *Listeria monocytogenes* and *Campylobacter*) and food- and water-borne parasites. The chemical hazards reviewed include residues of veterinary medicinal products, growth-promoters and performance enhancers, dioxins and other persistent organic pollutants. The special food safety problems associated with fish and shellfish farming and captured fish are also reviewed.

For many developing countries, food export market development is a key requirement for rural income generation and rural growth and development. However, failure to achieve and maintain the high standards of food safety nowadays demanded by international markets can have dire economic and other consequences for food-exporting countries. This *Review* deals with some of the challenges involved in meeting the requirements of importing countries and how these can be met in both industrialised and developing countries, with special reference to implementation at farm level. Implementation of traceability systems is one such recently introduced requirement. Another important issue is how the growing problem with anti-microbial resistance can be tackled, with special reference again to on-farm measures.

National Veterinary Services play an important role worldwide in ensuring the safety and quality of food. The results of a recent global study on the organisation and functioning of Veterinary Services are presented and their role and functionality in food safety throughout the food chain is described. The SPS Agreement includes provisions related to technical assistance and special and differential treatment for developing countries. Public investment in strengthening Veterinary Services and other food safety authorities, including the Standards and Trade Development Facility (STDF) established in 2002 by FAO, the OIE, the World Bank, WHO and the WTO, is reviewed.

The standards developed by the OIE, Codex and the International Plant Protection Convention (IPPC) are specifically recognised by the SPS Agreement as international benchmarks in the areas of animal, human and plant health. It is important that the work of the OIE and Codex on food safety is well coordinated so that we avoid duplication of effort/overlap, gaps and, above all, conflicting standards. The policy and procedures of the OIE and Codex for the development of standards for food safety and how these standards complement each other are described in this *Review* and a *Guide to Good Farming Practices for Animal Production Food Safety*, developed by the Working Group is presented. Lastly, guidelines for the inspection of animals and meat at the abattoir are given.

I would like to express my sincere thanks to all the authors for their contributions to this *Review* on a subject of great importance for public health and international trade in food. I would especially like to thank Dr Stuart Slorach, past President of the Codex Alimentarius Commission and Chair of the OIE Working Group on Animal Production Food Safety, for accepting our invitation to coordinate this issue of the *Review*. I am very grateful for the way in which he undertook this task and for his invaluable contribution to the development of this publication.

Bernard Vallat
Director General

Préface

Sécurité sanitaire des aliments issus de la production animale et commerce mondial

Considérant que la sécurité sanitaire des aliments constitue désormais une question primordiale de santé publique pour tous les pays et pour leurs consommateurs, ainsi qu'un enjeu capital pour les échanges internationaux de denrées alimentaires d'origine animale, l'Organisation mondiale de la santé animale (OIE) a décidé de donner à cette question un traitement prioritaire dans le cadre de son plan stratégique pour la période 2001-2005. Les activités de l'Organisation dans le domaine de la sécurité sanitaire des aliments se sont considérablement intensifiées ces dernières années, avec notamment la mise en place, en 2002, d'un Groupe de travail permanent de l'OIE sur la sécurité sanitaire des aliments d'origine animale en phase de production, qui a reçu pour missions de coordonner les activités sur ce sujet en les centrant sur les mesures applicables au niveau de la ferme, et de promouvoir la collaboration entre l'OIE, l'Organisation des Nations unies pour l'alimentation et l'agriculture (FAO), l'Organisation mondiale de la santé (OMS) et la Commission du Codex alimentarius (CCA). Tout comme l'OIE, la CCA est reconnue spécifiquement comme organisation normative internationale aux termes de l'Accord sur l'Application des mesures sanitaires et phytosanitaires (Accord SPS) de l'Organisation mondiale du commerce (OMC). La publication de ce numéro spécial de la *Revue scientifique et technique* de l'OIE, consacré aux enjeux de la sécurité sanitaire des aliments issus de la production animale mis en marché au niveau mondial et aux moyens d'y faire face, offre un nouvel exemple de l'importance que l'OIE accorde à ces questions.

Ce numéro de la *Revue* commence par dresser le tableau de la situation, en décrivant les différents systèmes de production animale existant dans les pays industrialisés ainsi que dans ceux en développement. La question de l'impact des maladies animales sur les échanges internationaux des produits d'origine animale est ensuite examinée, ainsi que le point de vue des producteurs sur la qualité et l'efficacité d'un système de production animale garantissant la sécurité sanitaire des aliments. La deuxième partie de l'ouvrage traite des risques biologiques et chimiques qui peuvent survenir lors de la première phase de production (c'est-à-dire au niveau de la ferme) ou pendant le transport, et qui menacent la sécurité sanitaire des produits alimentaires issus de la production animale et destinés à la consommation humaine ou animale. Après avoir décrit les enjeux de la sécurité sanitaire des aliments, les auteurs examinent les moyens de maîtriser, voire de résoudre les problèmes dans ce domaine. Les risques biologiques envisagés sont notamment les infections bactériennes (dues à *Salmonella* spp., à *Escherichia coli* producteur de Shiga-toxines, à *Listeria monocytogenes* et à *Campylobacter*) et les parasites présents dans les aliments ou dans l'eau. Les dangers chimiques sont en premier lieu les résidus de médicaments vétérinaires, les promoteurs de croissance et les stimulants de performance, les dioxines et les autres polluants organiques persistants. Les problèmes de sécurité sanitaire associés spécifiquement à la pêche et aux élevages de poissons et de coquillages sont également étudiés.

Pour nombre de pays en développement, le renforcement du secteur d'exportation des aliments est un moyen essentiel d'accroître les revenus en milieu rural et d'en favoriser la croissance et le développement. Toutefois, l'incapacité que connaissent certains pays exportateurs de denrées alimentaires à se conformer aux exigences très strictes des marchés internationaux en matière de sécurité sanitaire des aliments, peut avoir des conséquences désastreuses, notamment sur le plan économique. Ce numéro analyse certains défis liés au respect des exigences des pays importateurs, et montre comment ces dernières peuvent être satisfaites, non seulement par les pays industrialisés, mais également par les pays en développement, en mettant l'accent sur les mesures applicables au niveau de la ferme. La mise en œuvre de systèmes de traçabilité est l'une des plus récentes parmi ces mesures. Une autre question importante est celle de la résistance aux antibiotiques et des moyens d'y remédier, ici encore en insistant sur ce qui peut être fait au niveau de la ferme.

Partout dans le monde, les Services vétérinaires nationaux ont un rôle crucial à jouer en matière de sécurité sanitaire et de qualité des aliments. Un article de ce numéro présente les résultats d'une enquête mondiale sur l'organisation et le fonctionnement des Services vétérinaires, où le rôle et les fonctions de ces Services tout au long de la chaîne alimentaire sont mis en avant. L'Accord SPS contient des dispositions relatives à l'assistance technique et au traitement spécial différentiel réservé aux pays en développement. Les investissements publics destinés à renforcer les Services vétérinaires et les autres autorités compétentes dans le domaine de la sécurité sanitaire des aliments sont également décrits, y compris ceux relevant du Mécanisme pour l'élaboration des normes et le développement du commerce (STDF), mis en place en 2002 par la FAO, l'OIE, la Banque mondiale, l'OMS et l'OMC.

Les normes élaborées par l'OIE, la CCA et la Convention internationale pour la protection des végétaux (CIPV) sont officiellement reconnues dans le cadre de l'Accord SPS comme des références internationales dans le domaine de la santé humaine, animale et

476

Rev. sci. tech. Off. int. Epiz., **25** (2)

végétale. Il importe de bien coordonner l'action de l'OIE et de la CCA en matière de sécurité sanitaire des aliments, afin d'éviter les chevauchements d'activités, les doubles emplois, les lacunes et, surtout, les divergences entre les normes. Un article du présent ouvrage décrit les politiques et les procédures mises en œuvre par l'OIE et par la CCA pour l'élaboration des normes visant la sécurité sanitaire des aliments, ainsi que la manière dont celles-ci se complètent mutuellement ; d'autre part, le Groupe de travail de l'OIE sur la sécurité sanitaire des aliments fait une présentation de son *Guide des bonnes pratiques d'élevage pour la sécurité sanitaire des aliments d'origine animale en phase de production.* Enfin, ce numéro contient des lignes directrices pour l'inspection des animaux et des viandes à l'abattoir.

J'aimerais exprimer ma gratitude à tous les auteurs de ce numéro de la *Revue* pour leurs contributions sur un sujet capital pour la santé publique et les échanges internationaux de produits alimentaires. J'adresse également au Docteur Stuart Slorach, ancien Président de la Commission du Codex alimentarius et Président du Groupe de travail de l'OIE sur la sécurité sanitaire des aliments d'origine animale en phase de production, mes plus vifs remerciements pour avoir accepté d'assurer la coordination de ce numéro spécial, tâche dont il s'est acquitté avec talent, et pour sa précieuse contribution à la réussite de cet ouvrage.

Bernard Vallat
Directeur général

Prólogo

Los retos de la inocuidad de los alimentos en los procesos de producción animal y su comercio mundial

Consciente de que la inocuidad de los alimentos es no sólo una cuestión de salud pública crucial para todos los países y sus consumidores, sino también un tema cada vez más importante para el comercio internacional de alimentos de origen animal, la Organización Mundial de Sanidad Animal (OIE) lo definió como una de sus líneas de trabajo prioritarias en su Plan Estratégico para 2001-2005. En los últimos años la Organización se ha mostrado cada vez más activa en este terreno. Buen ejemplo de ello fue la creación en 2002 de un Grupo de trabajo permanente sobre la seguridad sanitaria de los alimentos derivados de la producción animal para que se ocupara de coordinar las actividades de la OIE sobre el tema, centrándose en medidas aplicables a la escala de la explotación agrícola, y de promover la colaboración entre la OIE, la Organización de las Naciones Unidas para la Agricultura y la Alimentación (FAO), la Organización Mundial de la Salud (OMS) y la Comisión del Codex Alimentarius. Esta última, al igual que la OIE, está reconocida específicamente en el Acuerdo sobre la Aplicación de Medidas Sanitarias y

Fitosanitarias (Acuerdo MSF) de la Organización Mundial del Comercio como organismo con potestad normativa internacional. La publicación de este número especial de la *Revista científica y técnica* de la OIE, dedicado a los problemas de inocuidad alimentaria en los procesos de producción animal en relación con los mercados mundiales y a la forma idónea de afrontar esos problemas, constituye un nuevo ejemplo de la importancia que la OIE otorga a estos temas.

En este número de la *Revista* se empieza ofreciendo una panorámica de los sistemas de producción animal en países tanto industrializados como en desarrollo. Asimismo, se describen los efectos de las enfermedades animales sobre los mercados agropecuarios internacionales y se expone el punto de vista de los productores sobre cuestiones de calidad y eficacia en relación con los procesos de producción animal que ofrezcan garantías de inocuidad. La segunda parte está dedicada a una serie de peligros biológicos y químicos que pueden concurrir durante la fase de producción primaria (en las explotaciones) o las operaciones de traslado, y afectar con ello a la inocuidad de los alimentos o piensos de origen animal. Se describen los problemas que pueden plantearse al respecto y se examinan una serie de métodos para solventarlos o mantenerlos bajo control. En este sentido, se abordan peligros biológicos como la presencia de bacterias patógenas (por ejemplo *Salmonella* spp., *Escherichia coli* productoras de toxina Shiga, *Listeria monocytogenes* o *Campylobacter*) y de parásitos vehiculados por el agua o los alimentos. Se tratan igualmente peligros químicos como los residuos de productos medicamentosos veterinarios, los promotores del crecimiento y estimulantes del rendimiento, las dioxinas y otros contaminantes orgánicos persistentes. También se examinan los problemas especiales de inocuidad que se plantean en la pesca y la conchilicultura.

Para muchos países en desarrollo es indispensable ampliar sus mercados de exportación de alimentos para lograr que el medio rural genere ingresos y acceda así al crecimiento y el desarrollo. Sin embargo, la incapacidad de cumplir de forma permanente las estrictas reglas que en materia de inocuidad imponen hoy en día los mercados internacionales puede tener funestas consecuencias, tanto económicas como de otro tipo, para los países exportadores de alimentos. En este número de la *Revista* se examinan algunos de los problemas que surgen a la hora de cumplir los requisitos de los países importadores y la manera de resolverlos en países tanto industrializados como en desarrollo, haciendo especial hincapié en los aspectos relacionados con el trabajo en la propia explotación. La aplicación de sistemas de rastreabilidad es uno de esos requisitos impuestos recientemente. Otro problema cada vez más importante que hay que solventar es el de la resistencia a los antimicrobianos, cuya solución pasa sobre todo por la aplicación de medidas en las propias explotaciones.

En el mundo entero los Servicios Veterinarios nacionales desempeñan una importante función a la hora de garantizar la inocuidad y calidad de los alimentos. En uno de los artículos se presentan los resultados de un reciente estudio de alcance mundial sobre la organización y funciones de los servicios veterinarios, y se describen su papel y funcionamiento respecto a la cuestión de la inocuidad en toda la cadena alimentaria. El Acuerdo MSF contiene disposiciones relativas a la asistencia técnica y al tratamiento especial y diferenciado para los países en desarrollo. También se estudian las inversiones públicas destinadas a fortalecer los servicios veterinarios y otras instancias competentes en materia de inocuidad alimentaria, comprendido el Servicio de Elaboración de Normas y Fomento del Comercio (STDF) establecido en 2002 por la FAO, la OIE, el Banco Mundial, la OMS y la OMC.

En el Acuerdo MSF se reconocen específicamente las reglas elaboradas por la OIE, la Comisión del Codex y la Convención Internacional de Protección Fitosanitaria (CIPF) como referentes internacionales en materia de sanidad animal, humana y vegetal. Es importante que las respectivas labores de la OIE y del Codex sobre inocuidad de los alimentos estén bien coordinadas para evitar redundancias, lagunas y, sobre todo, reglas

Rev. sci. tech. Off. int. Epiz., **25** (2)

contradictorias. En este volumen se describen las políticas y procedimientos de la OIE y el Codex a la hora de formular reglas en la materia y se presenta una Guía de buenas prácticas ganaderas para la inocuidad de los alimentos derivados de la producción animal, elaborada por el mencionado grupo de trabajo de la OIE. Por último, se ofrecen pautas para la inspección de los animales y la carne en los mataderos.

Quisiera expresar mi sincera gratitud a todos los autores por sus aportaciones a este número de la *Revista*, dedicado a un tema de gran importancia para la salud pública y el comercio internacional de alimentos. Deseo agradecer especialmente al Dr. Stuart Slorach, ex Presidente de la Comisión del Codex Alimentarius y Presidente del Grupo de Trabajo de la OIE sobre Seguridad sanitaria de los alimentos derivados de la producción animal, que haya aceptado asumir la coordinación de este volumen y haya desempeñado esta labor como lo ha hecho. Su inestimable contribución ha hecho posible que la presente publicación viera la luz.

Bernard Vallat
Director General

Rev. sci. tech. Off. int. Epiz., 2006, **25** (2), 479-492

Introduction

Animal production food safety challenges in global markets

In recent years, the World Organisation for Animal Health (OIE) has given high priority to food safety and it is therefore timely to devote an issue of the *Review* to animal production food safety. In view of the increasing globalisation of trade in foods of animal origin, the subject has been examined in the context of global markets.

Animal production systems in the industrialised world are changing dramatically with respect to location, herd size and specialisation. The focus on food safety promotes systems with a higher degree of biosecurity, often associated with an increase in herd size and self-containment. The globalisation of agricultural trade and increased competition also favour an increase in herd size and specialisation. These trends also lead to some regions with livestock-dense areas, giving rise to environmental concerns.

The global context of animal production and trade in animal food products

In the first part of this *Review* the current status of livestock production systems in developing countries and the driving forces and major trends in global livestock production are described and assessed. Factors driving the livestock industry include economic growth and income, demographic and land use changes, dietary adjustments, and technological change. The rate of change and direction of livestock development vary greatly among world regions, with Asia showing the most rapid growth and structural change.

Global meat consumption has increased by nearly three-quarters since 1990, in line with global economic growth. Consumers in both developed and developing countries are requiring higher quality meat, a broader diversity of meat cuts, more ease in preparation and enhanced assurances of safety. However, escalating and pervasive outbreaks of animal diseases, for example bovine spongiform encephalopathy and avian influenza, are posing considerable challenges to livestock producers, industries and policymakers around the globe. Producers are becoming increasingly aware of their responsibility for the safety of the foods they produce and are developing and implementing, mainly in developed countries, farm-level quality assurance systems based on hazard analysis critical control point (HACCP) principles.

Hazards occurring during the production stage and affecting the safety of food of animal origin

The second part of the *Review* deals with the challenges posed by biological and chemical hazards occurring during the production stage and affecting the safety of foods of animal origin and how these challenges can be met.

Salmonellosis is the most common food-borne bacterial disease worldwide and the main source is *Salmonella*-infected food-producing animals; the herd prevalence varies from 0% to 90%, depending on animal species and region. The emergence of strains resistant to antimicrobials, often as a result of antimicrobial usage in animals, is a public health hazard of great concern. However, in a few countries the prevalence of *Salmonella* in foods of animal origin has been reduced to almost zero by the strict implementation of risk mitigation measures along the whole of the food production chain and several other countries are striving towards this goal.

Escherichia coli are one of the main inhabitants of the gastrointestinal tract of most mammalian species, including man. Shiga toxin-producing *E.coli* (STEC), also called verotoxinogenic *E.coli* (VTEC), do not usually cause disease in animals, but may cause watery diarrhoea, haemorrhagic colitis and/or haemolytic uraemic syndrome in humans. These zoonotic STEC include the O157:H7 strains and, more and more frequently, certain non-O157 strains. The importance of the latter is probably underestimated as they have been less well characterised and are more difficult to detect in samples than O157:H7. Cattle and other ruminants are the most important reservoir of the zoonotic STEC, which are transmitted to humans through the ingestion of foods or water contaminated with animal faeces, or through contact with infected animals or their environment.

In the past 25 years, *Listeria monocytogenes* has become increasingly important as a pathogen in food-borne infections. Because of its high fatality rate, listeriosis ranks among the most frequent causes of death due to food-borne illness. The ability to persist in food-processing environments and multiply under refrigeration temperatures makes *L. monocytogenes* a unique and significant threat to food safety and public health. Understanding how these organisms are able to successfully adapt their cellular physiology to overcome the various forms of stress is an important step in order to develop better ways of controlling *L. monocytogenes* in food environments.

Campylobacteriosis is one of the most important bacterial food-borne illnesses in humans. One of the principal sources for *Campylobacter* infections in humans is the handling and consumption of poultry meat and control of this pathogen in meat-producing poultry would reduce the human burden of illness. Although risk factors for the infection of flocks have been identified, preventive measures in primary production based on these risk factors have hitherto had limited and unpredictable effects.

Zoonotic parasites found in food animals include a wide variety of protozoa, nematodes, trematodes and cestodes. Many of these parasites are emerging or occurring globally due to increased movements of animals, food and people, and changes in farming practices. Some of the emerging or ubiquitous parasites, including *Toxoplasma*, *Cryptosporidium*, *Trichinella* and *Taenia*, present enormous risks to global food production and consumer health. Other important parasites include the trematodes, such as *Clonorchis* and *Paragonimus*, which are transmitted via fish or crustaceans and cause serious human disease in specific regions of the world, but there is potential for global occurrence.

Over the past three decades, aquaculture has developed to be the fastest growing food producing sector in the world. From its early development in Asia, aquaculture has experienced tremendous growth and is today highly diversified, consisting of a broad spectrum of systems ranging from small ponds to large-scale, highly intensified commercial systems. The Food and Agriculture Organization of the United Nations (FAO) has estimated that more than 30% of all fish for human consumption originates from aquaculture. Although only a few of the agents infecting fish are able to infect humans, some exceptions exist that may lead to fatalities. However, the greatest risk to human health is due to the intake of raw or insufficiently processed fish or fish products. Chemical hazards, which may be present in fish and pose a threat to human health, include persistent lipophilic compounds, for example dioxins and polychlorinated biphenyls (PCBs), methylmercury and residues of medicinal products used in aquaculture.

Shellfish culture is a major sector of aquaculture production throughout the world. Although many diseases are associated with shellfish, they do not appear to be transmissible to humans. The main hazards are associated with the farming methods for each animal species. The risk to human health is more commonly due to contamination by biotoxins produced by marine algae and protozoa. Another well-recognised problem associated with shellfish culture is the contamination of shellfish with domestic sewage, which contains human pathogenic bacteria and viruses, which cause diseases such as typhoid fever and hepatitis. In shrimp farming, potential food safety hazards are mainly due to zoonoses, chemical contamination and veterinary drug residues.

Rev. sci. tech. Off. int. Epiz., **25** (2)

481

Residues of veterinary medicinal products, growth promoters and performance enhancers in foods of animal origin are a potential threat to human health and differences in legislation on the use of such substances and maximum residue limits can result in barriers to international trade. Control of residues in meat and other animal foods and detection of illegal use in order to protect public health present considerable problems for the enforcement agencies.

At different points along the food chain from farm to fork, food may become contaminated with a wide variety of chemicals, including dioxins, PCBs and polycyclic aromatic hydrocarbons. Modern analytical techniques mean that we are now able to detect extremely low concentrations of such compounds in foods. Several incidents in which foods of animal origin have been found to be contaminated with dioxins and/or PCBs following accidents or criminal activity have lead to loss of consumer confidence in some food products and severe economic losses for food producers and stakeholders.

Physical, microbial and environmental hazards during transportation may adversely affect the safety and quality of meat, milk, poultry and egg products. Additionally, the stress level in live animals can be raised by transportation conditions, potentially causing increased pathogen shedding in carrier animals. The physiological effects of stress on animals can reduce the quality of meat, poultry and egg products, thus decreasing the economic value of the animal.

Challenges and responses: OIE Regions and Member Countries

The third section of this *Review* deals with responses to food safety challenges at the national, regional and international level and also considers the special problems faced by developing and in transition countries and how they can be tackled.

To achieve an acceptable level of food safety it is necessary for governments and industry to work collaboratively to provide quality assurance systems based on sound risk management principles throughout the food chain. Quality assurance systems on livestock farms should encompass food safety using good practices and HACCP principles. These systems should target areas such as biosecurity, disease monitoring and reporting, safety of feeds, use of agricultural and veterinary chemicals, potential food-borne pathogens and traceability.

Because of fast-growing demand, export markets can absorb high value-added products and bring high returns, and for many developing countries export market development is a key requirement for rural income generation and rural growth. The Agreement on the Application of Sanitary and Phytosanitary Measures ('SPS Agreement') of the World Trade Organization (WTO) sets out a number of basic rules regarding trade measures meant to protect human, animal or plant life or health, aimed at ensuring that such measures will not create unfair barriers to trade. Although in general terms the Agreement can be said to have triggered regulatory reform and prompted action to open markets, it has also raised concerns that it unduly favours advanced countries, because they are in a much better position to gain market access than those countries which lack sufficient capacity to meet sanitary and other safety and quality requirements.

During the negotiation of the SPS Agreement there was a clear recognition of the problems that developing countries would face in complying with the Agreement. The Agreement included provisions related to technical assistance and special and differential treatment for developing countries. The SPS Committee is currently considering proposals to make these provisions more precise, effective and operational. To improve the situation in developing countries, the Standards and Trade Development Facility (STDF) was established in 2002 as a coordinating mechanism and Trust fund and brings together five partner organisations each with specific expertise in the domain of

482

Rev. sci. tech. Off. int. Epiz., **25** (2)

SPS standards and trade: the OIE, FAO, World Bank, World Health Organization (WHO) and WTO.

Veterinary Services are generally involved in animal health and food safety controls at the farm level (including animal feed). They also are involved during primary and secondary processing, whether alone or in conjunction with other services. In addition, Veterinary Services have a central responsibility in the safety of international trade in animals and animal products. The traditional focus of veterinary involvement has also been in meat hygiene at the level of the slaughterhouse, including *ante-* and *post-mortem* inspection. While this role continues, the emerging new approach to food control demands increased involvement in other segments of the food chain as well as in other sectors of food production, e.g. production of milk, eggs and fish. This more extensive role requires a wider skill base and establishment of effective networks with a different range of stakeholders.

Animal identification and traceability systems are important tools in controlling, preventing and eradicating animal diseases and improving food safety. The European Union has already introduced a legal requirement for traceability in food production including live animals and several international and national organisations are developing standards or guidelines in this area.

The development at the farm level of bacteria resistant to antimicrobials poses an important threat to human health and is the subject of much scientific research and discussion at the international level. The WHO has already established a list of critically important antimicrobials for human use, as well as criteria for their selection and the OIE is developing a corresponding list of Veterinary Critically Important Antimicrobials.

Global perspectives: international standard-setting organisations and stakeholders

The last section of this *Review* deals with the work of the OIE and the Codex Alimentarius Commission (CAC) and the collaboration between these two international organisations, both of which set standards for food safety.

One manifestation of the OIE's increased activity in the area of food safety was the establishment in 2002 of a permanent Working Group on Animal Production Food Safety to coordinate OIE activities in food safety and provide advice to the Director General and the Specialist Commissions. In addition to experts from the OIE, the Working Group contains members well acquainted with the work of the CAC and its subsidiary bodies. The main focus of the Working Group is on food safety measures applicable at the farm level and one of the first results of its work was the production of a 'Guide to good farming practices for animal production food safety', which was published as an appendix for Member Country comments in the report of the meeting of the OIE Terrestrial Animal Health Standards Commission (January 2005).

International standards established by the OIE for animal health and zoonoses and by the CAC for food safety are specifically recognised as international benchmarks in the SPS Agreement. It is therefore vital that the OIE and the CAC work closely together to avoid duplication of effort, gaps and, above all, conflicting standards and guidelines, with the OIE concentrating on the 'farm' end of the food chain and CAC closer to the 'fork'.

Stuart A. Slorach
Chairperson of the Codex Alimentarius Commission (2003-2005)
Chairman of the OIE Working Group on Animal Production Food Safety
Stubbängsvägen 9A
SE-12553 Älvsjö, Sweden

■

Rev. sci. tech. Off. int. Epiz., **25** (2)

483

Introduction

Sécurité sanitaire des aliments issus de la production animale et commerce mondial

Le thème de la sécurité sanitaire des aliments étant depuis quelques années l'une des priorités de l'Organisation de la santé animale (OIE), il était naturel de consacrer un numéro de la *Revue scientifique et technique* à la sécurité sanitaire des aliments issus de la production animale. Compte tenu de la mondialisation croissante des échanges de denrées alimentaires d'origine animale, ce sujet est traité dans le contexte du commerce mondial.

Les systèmes de production animale des pays industrialisés se sont considérablement transformés, en termes d'implantation des élevages, de taille des troupeaux et de niveau de spécialisation. L'accent mis sur la sécurité sanitaire des aliments privilégie les systèmes dotés d'un niveau élevé de biosécurité, ce qui va souvent de pair avec un accroissement des troupeaux et une intégration des systèmes d'exploitation. La mondialisation des échanges de produits agricoles et l'intensification de la concurrence contribuent également à cet accroissement et spécialisation des troupeaux. Ces tendances se traduisent par de fortes densités d'animaux dans certaines régions, avec les problèmes environnementaux que cela comporte.

Le contexte mondial de la production animale et du commerce d'aliments d'origine animale

La première partie de l'ouvrage décrit et évalue la situation actuelle de la production animale dans les pays en développement ainsi que les éléments moteurs et les principales tendances de cette production dans le monde. Les éléments moteurs de l'élevage au niveau mondial sont la croissance et les revenus économiques, l'évolution démographique et l'utilisation des sols, les changements d'habitudes alimentaires et les mutations technologiques. Le rythme de ces changements et les orientations prises pour développer le secteur de l'élevage sont très variables d'une région à l'autre. C'est en Asie que la croissance et le changement structurel sont les plus rapides.

En quinze ans, la consommation mondiale de viande a augmenté de près de 75 %, parallèlement à la croissance économique. Les consommateurs des pays développés, mais aussi ceux des pays en développement recherchent une viande de meilleure qualité, une diversification des pièces de boucherie, des préparations plus faciles à réaliser et de solides garanties d'innocuité. En même temps, la gravité et le rythme de propagation de certains foyers de maladies animales telles que l'encéphalopathie spongiforme bovine et l'influenza aviaire représentent un défi considérable pour les éleveurs, les industriels et les responsables de l'élaboration des politiques partout dans le monde. Les producteurs, de plus en plus concernés par l'innocuité des aliments qu'ils produisent ont mis au point, surtout dans les pays développés, des systèmes d'assurance qualité des élevages, basés sur les principes de l'analyse des risques et la maîtrise des points critiques (HACCP).

Les dangers en phase de production pouvant menacer la sécurité sanitaire des aliments d'origine animale

La deuxième partie de la *Revue* examine les risques biologiques et chimiques survenant en phase de production et susceptibles d'affecter la sécurité sanitaire des aliments d'origine animale, ainsi que les réponses à ces défis.

La salmonellose est la bactériose d'origine alimentaire la plus répandue dans le monde. Les animaux d'élevage infectés par *Salmonella* sont la principale source d'infection. La prévalence au sein des troupeaux varie de 0 % à 90 % selon l'espèce animale et la région. L'émergence de souches résistantes aux agents antimicrobiens suite à l'administration inconsidérée de ces produits chez l'animal est un problème de santé publique extrêmement préoccupant. Toutefois, grâce à l'application rigoureuse de mesures de réduction des risques tout au long de la chaîne de production alimentaire, certains pays ont fait chuter la prévalence des *Salmonella* dans les aliments d'origine animale à des valeurs proches de zéro. Bien d'autres pays s'efforcent actuellement d'atteindre cet objectif.

Escherichia coli est l'un des microorganismes le plus souvent retrouvés dans l'appareil digestif de la plupart des espèces de mammifères, y compris l'homme. Les *E. coli* producteurs de Shiga-toxines (STEC) (ou producteurs de verocytotoxines) ne sont généralement pas pathogènes pour l'animal, alors que chez l'homme l'infection se manifeste par une diarrhée aqueuse, une colite hémorragique et/ou un syndrome hémolytique et urémique. Les infections à STEC zoonotiques sont souvent dues aux souches O157:H7, mais il est de plus en plus fréquent de retrouver l'implication d'autres souches. L'importance des souches autres que les O157:H7 a sans doute été sous-estimée, dans la mesure où leur caractérisation est moins aboutie que celle des O157:H7 et qu'elles sont plus difficiles à détecter dans les prélèvements. Les bovins et les autres ruminants constituent le principal réservoir des STEC zoonotiques, qui sont transmis à l'homme par ingestion d'aliments ou d'eau contaminés par des matières fécales animales, ou par contact direct avec des animaux infectés ou avec leur environnement.

L'importance de *Listeria monocytogenes* en tant qu'agent de toxi-infection alimentaire n'a pas cessé de croître depuis vingt-cinq ans. La listériose a un taux de létalité élevé qui en fait l'une des causes les plus fréquentes de décès parmi les maladies d'origine alimentaire. La capacité de *L. monocytogenes* à survivre aux divers stades de transformation des denrées alimentaires et à résister aux basses températures en fait une menace de premier ordre pour la santé publique. Il importe de bien comprendre comment la physiologie cellulaire de ces organismes s'adapte aux différentes agressions, afin de pouvoir maîtriser le risque de *L. monocytogenes* dans les milieux où sont élaborés les produits alimentaires.

La campylobactériose est l'une des principales maladies d'origine alimentaire chez l'homme. Les sources d'infection sont principalement la manipulation et la consommation de viande de volaille infectée, de sorte que la maîtrise de cet agent pathogène chez les volailles destinées à l'alimentation devrait réduire l'incidence de la maladie chez l'homme. Bien que les facteurs de risque d'infection des élevages de volaille soient désormais connus, les mesures de prévention appliquées à partir de ces facteurs de risque au niveau de la production primaire ont donné des résultats médiocres et imprévisibles.

De nombreux protozoaires, nématodes, trématodes et cestodes zoonotiques sont capables d'infester les animaux destinés à l'alimentation. L'émergence, ou la nouvelle dimension mondiale de nombre de ces parasitoses sont dues à l'intensification des déplacements d'animaux, de personnes et de produits alimentaires, ainsi qu'aux modifications des pratiques d'élevage. Certains parasites émergents ou ubiquistes, notamment *Toxoplasma, Cryptosporidium, Trichinella* et *Taenia* font peser un risque considérable sur la production mondiale de produits alimentaires et sur la santé des consommateurs. Des trématodes tels que *Clonorchis* et *Paragonimus* sont également des parasites importants pour la santé humaine ; transmis par ingestion de poisson ou de fruits de mer infestés, ils sont à l'origine de graves maladies chez l'homme, pour l'instant délimitées à certaines régions mais présentant un fort potentiel de distribution mondiale.

En une trentaine d'années, l'aquaculture s'est développée à un tel rythme qu'elle représente la plus forte croissance parmi tous les secteurs de production alimentaire dans le monde. Après une première phase de développement dans le continent asiatique et une croissance continue spectaculaire, le secteur est désormais fortement diversifié, avec une large variété de systèmes de production allant des petits bassins artisanaux aux élevages industriels à grande échelle et très intensifs. L'Organisation des Nations unies pour l'alimentation et l'agriculture (FAO) estime que plus de 30 % du poisson consommé par l'homme provient de l'aquaculture. Bien que les agents pathogènes affectant les poissons et capables d'infecter l'homme soient peu nombreux, il existe quelques exceptions, parfois fatales pour l'homme. Les plus grands dangers pour la santé publique résident néanmoins dans la consommation de poisson cru ou mal préparé ou dans la transformation défectueuse des produits de la pêche. Parmi les dangers chimiques associés aux poissons et pouvant menacer la santé humaine, citons notamment les composés organiques lipophiles persistants tels que les dioxines et les polychlorobiphényles (PCB), le méthyl-mercure et les résidus de produits vétérinaires utilisés en aquaculture.

L'élevage des mollusques et des crustacés représente un sous-secteur important de l'aquaculture dans le monde. Ces espèces sont sensibles à de nombreuses maladies qui ne semblent toutefois pas transmissibles à l'homme. Le principal danger réside plutôt dans les méthodes d'élevage pratiquées pour chaque espèce. Les risques associés aux fruits de mer pouvant menacer la santé publique sont le plus souvent liés à la contamination par les biotoxines produites par les algues marines et les protozoaires. Un autre problème parfaitement identifié affectant les élevages de mollusques et de crustacés est celui de la pollution par les eaux usées, qui contiennent des bactéries et des virus pathogènes pour l'homme et responsables d'épidémies de fièvre typhoïde et d'hépatite. S'agissant des élevages de crevettes, les principaux dangers potentiels menaçant la sécurité sanitaire sont les agents de certaines zoonoses, la contamination par des polluants chimiques et les résidus de médicaments vétérinaires.

La présence de résidus de médicaments vétérinaires, de promoteurs de croissance et d'additifs zootechniques dans les produits alimentaires d'origine animale est un danger potentiel pour la santé publique ; les différences réglementaires sur l'utilisation de ces substances et les limites maximales de résidus autorisées entraînent parfois des barrières aux échanges internationaux. Le contrôle des résidus dans la viande et les produits d'origine animale et la lutte contre les usages illicites de ces substances posent d'immenses problèmes aux agences chargées de la mise en œuvre.

La contamination chimique par des substances telles que les dioxines, les PCB et les hydrocarbonés polycycliques aromatiques peut se produire à différents stades de la chaîne alimentaire allant de l'étable à la table. Les techniques analytiques modernes nous permettent de détecter ces composés dans les aliments, même à de très faibles concentrations. Plusieurs incidents, accidentels ou d'origine criminelle impliquant des aliments d'origine animale contaminés à la dioxine et/ou aux PCB ont eu pour conséquences la méfiance des consommateurs à l'égard de certaines denrées alimentaires ainsi que des pertes économiques considérables pour les producteurs et les autres parties prenantes.

Les dangers physiques, microbiens et environnementaux associés au transport peuvent affecter de diverses manières l'innocuité et la qualité des viandes, du lait, des volailles et des œufs. En outre, les conditions de transport des animaux vivants, en leur occasionnant un stress supplémentaire, peuvent accroître l'excrétion d'agents pathogènes chez les individus porteurs. Les effets physiologiques du stress risquent d'affecter la qualité des viandes, de la volaille, des œufs et de leurs produits et font baisser d'autant la valeur marchande des animaux.

Les enjeux et les réponses : régions et Pays Membres de l'OIE

La troisième partie de cet ouvrage traite des réponses aux enjeux de la sécurité sanitaire des aliments, aussi bien au niveau national que régional et international, et s'intéresse tout particulièrement aux problèmes spécifiques rencontrés par les pays en

486

Rev. sci. tech. Off. int. Epiz., **25** (2)

développement ou en transition ainsi qu'aux différentes manières d'affronter ces problèmes.

Pour atteindre un niveau acceptable de sécurité sanitaire des aliments, les gouvernements et l'industrie agroalimentaire doivent travailler de concert afin de mettre au point des systèmes d'assurance qualité basés sur des principes rationnels de gestion des risques tout au long de la chaîne alimentaire. Les systèmes d'assurance qualité mis en place dans les élevages doivent garantir la sécurité sanitaire des aliments en appliquant les bonnes pratiques et les procédures HACCP. Ces systèmes doivent couvrir plusieurs domaines, dont la biosécurité, le suivi et la notification des maladies, l'innocuité des aliments pour animaux, les produits chimiques utilisés en médecine vétérinaire et en agriculture, les agents potentiels de toxi-infections alimentaires et la traçabilité.

En raison d'une demande en rapide augmentation, les marchés d'exportation sont capables d'absorber des produits à forte valeur ajoutée et rentabilité, de sorte que pour nombre de pays en développement, le soutien aux exportations représente un moyen essentiel de générer de nouvelles sources de revenus pour le secteur rural et d'y favoriser la croissance. L'Accord sur l'application des mesures sanitaires et phytosanitaires (Accord SPS) de l'Organisation mondiale du commerce (OMC) a établi une série de règles fondamentales relatives aux mesures applicables au commerce, en vue de préserver la santé humaine, animale et végétale tout en veillant à ne pas créer de barrières commerciales injustifiées. Bien qu'en règle générale l'Accord SPS ait donné une impulsion réelle aux réformes réglementaires et œuvré en faveur de l'ouverture des marchés, la crainte subsiste que les pays les plus avancés soient les seuls favorisés par cet accord, dans la mesure où ils sont bien mieux armés pour accéder aux marchés que les pays moins avancés dont les capacités sont insuffisantes pour se conformer aux critères sanitaires et autres exigences de sécurité et de qualité.

Les problèmes qui attendaient les pays en développement soucieux de se conformer aux termes de l'Accord SPS ont néanmoins été pris en compte durant les négociations préalables. L'Accord inclut des dispositions particulières en faveur des pays en développement, notamment l'assistance technique et le traitement différentiel. Des propositions visant à rendre ces dispositions encore plus détaillées, efficaces et opérationnelles sont actuellement à l'étude par le Comité SPS. Mis en place en 2002 en tant qu'outil de coordination et fonds spécial, le Mécanisme pour l'élaboration des normes et le développement du commerce (« STDF ») réunit cinq organisations partenaires dotées de compétences spécifiques dans le domaine des normes SPS et du commerce ; l'OIE, la FAO, la Banque mondiale, l'Organisation mondiale de la santé (OMS) et l'OMC.

Les Services vétérinaires sont généralement responsables de la santé animale et du contrôle de la sécurité sanitaire des aliments au niveau des exploitations (y compris pour ce qui concerne l'alimentation animale). Ils ont également un rôle à jouer, seuls ou en collaboration avec d'autres services, lors de la première et de la deuxième transformation. En outre, les Services vétérinaires ont une responsabilité centrale dans le domaine de la sécurité des échanges internationaux d'animaux et de produits d'origine animale. Les vétérinaires sont toujours intervenus dans l'inspection des viandes et l'hygiène des abattoirs, y compris lors des inspections ante-mortem et post-mortem. Cette fonction leur reste dévolue, mais une nouvelle approche de la sécurité sanitaire des aliments les invite à s'engager dans d'autres segments de la chaîne alimentaire et dans d'autres secteurs de la production alimentaire, par exemple les laiteries, la production d'œufs et la pisciculture. Cette extension de leur fonction suppose que les vétérinaires élargissent leur socle de compétences et mettent en place des réseaux efficaces avec différentes catégories de filières.

Les systèmes d'identification des animaux et la traçabilité sont des outils précieux pour contrôler, prévenir et éradiquer les maladies animales et pour assurer la sécurité sanitaire des aliments. L'Union européenne a déjà émis des directives sur la traçabilité des produits alimentaires, y compris les animaux vivants, et plusieurs organisations internationales et nationales mettent actuellement au point des normes et des lignes directrices en ce sens.

L'apparition de bactéries résistantes aux antimicrobiens dans les exploitations pose un défi considérable à la santé publique, ce qui justifie le nombre de travaux scientifiques et de discussions actuellement consacrés à ce thème au niveau international. L'OMS a mis au point une liste d'antimicrobiens d'importance prioritaire pour la médecine humaine et défini les critères de sélection de cette liste, et l'OIE travaille actuellement à l'élaboration d'une liste parallèle d'antimicrobiens importants en médecine vétérinaire.

Perspectives mondiales : les organisations internationales chargées d'élaborer les normes et leurs partenaires

La dernière partie de ce numéro de la *Revue* est consacrée aux activités de l'OIE et de la Commission du Codex alimentarius (CCA) ainsi qu'à la manière dont ces deux organisations internationales travaillent ensemble, chacune ayant des compétences normatives spécifiques dans le domaine de la sécurité sanitaire des aliments.

L'intensification des activités de l'OIE dans ce domaine s'est traduite, en 2002, par l'établissement d'un Groupe de travail permanent sur la sécurité sanitaire des aliments d'origine animale en phase de production, chargé de coordonner les travaux de l'OIE sur ce thème et de conseiller le Directeur général et les Commissions spécialisées. Le Groupe de travail est composé d'experts de l'OIE ainsi que de spécialistes connaissant bien le travail de la CCA et de ses différents comités. Les activités du Groupe sont axées sur les mesures de sécurité sanitaire des aliments applicables au niveau de la ferme. L'un des premiers aboutissements de ce travail a été la rédaction d'un *Guide des bonnes pratiques d'élevage pour la sécurité sanitaire des aliments d'origine animale en phase de production* qui a été publié en annexe au rapport de la réunion de janvier 2005 de la Commission des normes sanitaires pour les animaux terrestres de l'OIE.

L'Accord SPS reconnaît spécifiquement le caractère de références internationales des normes élaborées respectivement par l'OIE pour la santé animale et par la CCA pour la sécurité sanitaire des aliments. Il est donc capital que l'OIE et la CCA travaillent de concert, afin d'éviter les chevauchements d'activités, les doubles emplois, les lacunes et, surtout, les divergences entre normes et lignes directrices, l'OIE se préoccupant d'abord, à un bout de la chaîne alimentaire, de la sécurité de l'étable, et la CCA, à l'autre bout, de celle de la table.

Stuart A. Slorach
Président de la Commission du Codex Alimentarius (2003-2005)
Président du Groupe de travail de l'OIE sur la sécurité sanitaire des aliments d'origine animale en phase de production
Stubbängsvägen 9A
SE-12553 Älvsjö, Suède

Rev. sci. tech. Off. int. Epiz., **25** (2)

Introducción

Los retos de la inocuidad de los alimentos en los procesos de producción animal y su comercio mundial

En los últimos años, la inocuidad de los alimentos de origen animal se convirtió en uno de los temas de trabajo prioritarios de la Organización Mundial de Sanidad Animal (OIE). Por consiguiente, es oportuno dedicar un número de la *Revista* a la seguridad sanitaria de los alimentos de origen animal en la etapa de la producción. Vista la creciente mundialización del comercio de alimentos de origen animal, el tema se examina en el contexto de los mercados internacionales.

En el mundo industrializado, la ubicación y el tamaño de las manadas, así como la especialización de los sistemas de cría animal, que con frecuencia implican el aumento del número de cabezas y el confinamiento voluntario, están cambiando radicalmente. Al hacer hincapié en la inocuidad de los alimentos, se fomentan los sistemas de producción con un mayor grado de bioseguridad. La mundialización del comercio pecuario y la creciente competencia también favorecen el aumento de la especialización. Asimismo, los criaderos se han concentrado en determinadas regiones, provocando los consiguientes problemas medioambientales.

La producción animal y el comercio de sus subproductos en el contexto mundial

En la primera parte de este número de la *Revista* se exponen y evalúan la situación actual de los sistemas de cría de ganado de los países en desarrollo y las motivaciones principales de la producción pecuaria mundial. Los factores que condicionan la industria ganadera incluyen el crecimiento económico y de los ingresos, los cambios demográficos y de la explotación de la tierra, la modificación de los hábitos alimenticios y la evolución de las tecnologías. Tanto la velocidad a la que se modifica la producción pecuaria, como su orientación, difieren mucho en las distintas regiones del mundo. Asia es la que experimenta el crecimiento y los cambios estructurales más rápidos.

Como consecuencia del crecimiento económico internacional, desde 1990 el consumo mundial de carne se ha incrementado en aproximadamente un 75 por ciento. Los consumidores de los países desarrollados y en desarrollo exigen una mejora de la calidad de la carne, un aumento de la variedad de cortes, una mayor facilidad de preparación, así como el refuerzo de las garantías sobre su inocuidad. A su vez, los criadores, industrias y responsables de la formulación de políticas de todo el mundo enfrentan problemas considerables ocasionados por la escalada de los focos de enfermedades animales que se extienden por todo el planeta como, por ejemplo, la encefalopatía espongiforme bovina y la influenza aviar. Los productores tienen cada vez mayor conciencia de sus responsabilidades respecto de la inocuidad de los alimentos que producen y, en particular en los países desarrollados, elaboran y aplican sistemas de garantía de calidad basados en los principios del análisis de riesgos en puntos críticos de control (HACCP) en las explotaciones,.

Los riesgos de la etapa de producción que pueden afectar a los alimentos de origen animal

En la segunda parte de este número de la *Revista* se describen los problemas que plantean los peligros biológicos y químicos de la etapa de producción que pueden afectar la salubridad de los alimentos de origen animal, así como las soluciones posibles.

Rev. sci. tech. Off. int. Epiz., 25 (2)

489

La salmonelosis es la enfermedad de origen bacteriano transmitida por alimentos más común en todas partes del mundo. Los animales para consumo infectados por *Salmonella* son la principal fuente de transmisión dado que la prevalencia en las manadas varía, en función de las especies, animales y regiones, entre un 0% y un 90%. La emergencia de cepas resistentes a los antimicrobianos ocasionada, con frecuencia, por su administración a animales, constituye una amenaza muy importante para la salud pública. Sin embargo, algunos países han reducido la prevalencia de *Salmonella* en los alimentos de origen animal a prácticamente un 0% gracias a la aplicación estricta de medidas de reducción de riesgos en todas las etapas de la cadena de producción. Asimismo, varios países más se esfuerzan actualmente por alcanzar ese objetivo.

La *Escherichia coli* es uno de los principales huéspedes del tracto gastrointestinal de la mayoría de los mamíferos, incluidos los seres humanos. Habitualmente, la *E. coli* productora de toxina Shiga (STEC), también llamada *E. coli* verotoxigénica (VTEC), no provoca enfermedades en los animales, pero puede producir diarrea acuosa, colitis hemorrágica o síndrome hemolítico ureico en los seres humanos. Las STEC zoonóticas comprenden las cepas O157:H7 y, cada vez con mayor frecuencia, otras cepas distintas. Probablemente se subestima la importancia de estas últimas dado que no han sido tan bien caracterizadas como las cepas O157:H7 y son más difíciles de detectar en las muestras. Los bovinos y demás rumiantes son el principal reservorio de STEC zoonóticas, que se transmiten a los seres humanos por ingestión de alimentos o agua contaminados con heces animales, o por contacto directo con animales infectados o su entorno.

Desde hace 25 años, la *Listeria monocytogenes* se ha convertido en uno de los principales agentes patógenos transmitidos por los alimentos. Debido a su elevada tasa de letalidad, la listeriosis es una de las enfermedades de transmisión alimentaria que provoca mayor número de muertes. La capacidad para resistir a las condiciones existentes en las plantas de transformación y multiplicarse a temperaturas de refrigeración la convierte en una amenaza de excepcional gravedad para la inocuidad de los alimentos y la salud pública. A fin de mejorar los métodos de lucha contra la *Listeria monocytogenes* en las plantas de producción alimentaria es preciso comprender el mecanismo de adaptación de su fisiología celular para resistir a las distintas agresiones.

La campilobacteriosis es una de las enfermedades bacterianas de mayor importancia que transmiten los alimentos a los seres humanos. La manipulación y el consumo de aves de corral son las principales fuentes de infecciones humanas por el género *Campylobacter*. El control de estos agentes patógenos en los criaderos de aves para consumo reduciría la carga de la campilobacteriosis humana. Pero aunque ya se han identificado los factores de riesgo de infección en las bandadas, los las medidas de prevención que se aplican en su primera transformación han tenido efectos limitados e imprevisibles hasta la fecha.

Los parásitos zoonóticos que se hospedan en animales para consumo incluyen una amplia variedad de protozoarios, nematodos, trematodos y céstodes. Muchos de estos son parásitos emergentes, o que se encuentran en todas partes del mundo debido al incremento de los movimientos de animales, alimentos y personas, así como a la evolución de las prácticas de cría. Algunos de los parásitos emergentes o ubicuos, incluidos *Toxoplasma*, *Cryptosporidium*, *Trichinella* y *Taenia*, representan enormes amenazas para los productores de alimentos y la salud de los consumidores de todo el mundo. Los trematodos, como *Clonorchis* y *Paragonimus*, son otros importantes parásitos transmitidos por los peces y crustáceos que hasta ahora sólo han provocado enfermedades graves en los seres humanos de determinadas regiones, pero que podrían extenderse a todo el mundo.

En los últimos treinta años, la acuicultura se convirtió en el sector de producción alimentaria que más rápidamente crece en todas partes. Su desarrollo, que comenzó en Asia, experimentó un enorme crecimiento y hoy en día incluye una gran cantidad de

490

Rev. sci. tech. Off. int. Epiz., **25** (2)

sistemas sumamente diversificados, que comprenden desde estanques de pequeñas dimensiones, hasta prácticas comerciales a gran escala y sumamente intensivas. Según la Organización de las Naciones Unidas para la Agricultura y la Alimentación (FAO), más del 30% del pescado para consumo humano mundial proviene de criaderos. Aunque sólo unos pocos de los agentes patógenos que afectan a los peces pueden infectar a los seres humanos, algunos de ellos pueden provocar víctimas mortales. Pero el mayor riesgo para la salud humana proviene de la ingesta de pescado, o sus subproductos, crudo o insuficientemente cocido. Los compuestos lipofílicos persistentes como, por ejemplo, la dioxina y los bifenilos policlorados, el metilo de mercurio y los residuos de productos medicinales utilizados en acuicultura, son algunos de los productos químicos que pueden estar presentes en la carne de pescado y amenazar la salud humana.

La cría de mariscos es uno de los principales sectores de producción acuícola en todas partes del mundo. Esos animales sufren muchas enfermedades, pero aparentemente no son transmisibles a los seres humanos. Los principales peligros están vinculados con los métodos de cría de las diferentes especies. La amenaza más común para la salud humana es la contaminación con biotoxinas producidas por algas y protozoarios marinos. Y un problema bien conocido con que tropieza la cría de mariscos es la contaminación con aguas residuales domésticas que contienen bacterias y virus humanos patogénicos y provocan enfermedades como la fiebre tifoidea y la hepatitis. En el caso de la cría de camarones, unos patógenos zoonoticos, la contaminación con productos químicos y los residuos de medicamentos veterinarios son los principales peligros que pueden amenazar la inocuidad alimentaria.

Los residuos de medicamentos veterinarios, los promotores de crecimiento y los potenciadores de rendimiento presentes en alimentos de origen animal constituyen una amenaza potencial para la salud humana y las diferencias existentes entre las normativas relativas a su uso, así como a los límites máximos de administración autorizados, pueden convertirse en barreras al comercio internacional. Para proteger la salud pública, los organismos responsables de la aplicación de la legislación enfrentan problemas considerables, como el control de los residuos en la carne y otros alimentos de origen animal, así como la detección de la administración ilegal de productos medicinales veterinarios.

Una amplia variedad de productos químicos, incluyendo dioxinas, bifenilos policlorados e hidrocarbonos aromáticos policíclicos pueden contaminar los alimentos en distintos puntos de la cadena alimentaria, entre el criadero y la mesa del consumidor. Actualmente, las técnicas de análisis modernas posibilitan la detección de concentraciones sumamente bajas de esos compuestos en los alimentos. Varios casos de contaminación de alimentos, accidental o intencional, con dioxinas o bifenilos policlorados han provocado la pérdida de confianza de los consumidores en algunos productos alimenticios y, también, grandes pérdidas económicas a los fabricantes y demás partes interesadas.

Las amenazas materiales, microbianas y medioambientales que conlleva el transporte pueden afectar la salubridad y la calidad de la carne, la leche, las aves de corral y los productos a base de huevo. Además, las condiciones del transporte de animales vivos pueden aumentar su estrés e, incluso, incrementar la diseminación de agentes patógenos por parte de los animales portadores. Los efectos fisiológicos del estrés pueden disminuir la calidad de la carne, las aves de corral y los productos a base de huevo y, por consiguiente, reducir el valor económico del animal.

Problemas y soluciones en las regiones y Países Miembros de la OIE

En la tercera sección de este número de la *Revista* se analizan las soluciones a los problemas que plantea la seguridad sanitaria de los alimentos en las esferas nacional,

Rev. sci. tech. Off. int. Epiz., **25** (2)

491

regional e internacional. Asimismo, se exponen las dificultades especiales que enfrentan los países en desarrollo y en transición, y sus posibles soluciones.

Para que el nivel de inocuidad de los alimentos sea aceptable, es preciso que los gobiernos y la industria, en colaboración, elaboren sistemas de garantía de calidad basados en los sólidos principios de análisis de riesgos y aplicables a todas las etapas la cadena alimentaria. Para asegurar la inocuidad de los alimentos en las explotaciones pecuarias, los sistemas de garantía de calidad deben basarse en las prácticas idóneas y los principios del análisis de riesgos en puntos críticos de control. Estos sistemas deben aplicarse en ámbitos como la bioseguridad, el seguimiento y la notificación de las enfermedades, la inocuidad de los piensos, la utilización de productos químicos con fines agropecuarios, los posibles agentes patógenos transmisibles por los alimentos y la trazabilidad.

Debido al rápido aumento de la demanda, las plazas exportadoras pueden comercializar productos con un gran valor añadido y obtener importantes beneficios. Pero en muchos países en desarrollo, el incremento de las exportaciones constituye una condición esencial para generar ingresos en las zonas rurales y permitir su crecimiento. El Acuerdo sobre la Aplicación de las Medidas Sanitarias y Fitosanitarias (el "Acuerdo MSF") de la Organización Mundial del Comercio (OMC) incluye una serie de normas básicas sobre las medidas comerciales dirigidas a proteger la vida y la salud de los seres humanos, la fauna y la flora con objeto de impedir que esas medidas creasen barreras comerciales injustas. En líneas generales puede afirmarse que el Acuerdo puso en marcha una reforma normativa e impulsó la posibilidad de abrir mercados. Pero la eventualidad de que favoreciera injustamente a los países avanzados suscitó preocupación dado que estos últimos tienen mucho más posibilidades de exportar sus productos que los países que carecen de las capacidades necesarias para cumplir los requisitos sanitarios y demás condiciones relativas a la inocuidad y la calidad.

En el curso de las negociaciones relativas al Acuerdo MSF se determinaron claramente las dificultades que habrían de enfrentar los países en desarrollo para cumplir sus cláusulas. Por ello, el Acuerdo incluyó disposiciones sobre asistencia técnica y un trato especial y diferenciado para esos países. El Comité MSF estudia actualmente varias propuestas para reforzar la precisión, la eficacia y la puesta en práctica de esas disposiciones. Con objeto de mejorar la situación de los países en desarrollo, en 2002 se creó el Fondo para la Aplicación de Normas y el Fomento del Comercio ("STDF") en calidad de mecanismo de coordinación y fondo fiduciario. Cada una de las cinco organizaciones asociadas que componen el STDF – la OIE, la FAO, el Banco Mundial, la Organización Mundial de la Salud (OMS) y la OMC – cuenta con competencias específicas relacionadas con las normas MSF y el comercio.

Por lo general, los Servicios Veterinarios participan en los controles de la salud animal y la inocuidad de los alimentos, incluyendo los piensos, en las explotaciones. También actúan en el curso de la primera y segunda transformación de los productos alimenticios, ya sea solos, o en colaboración con otros servicios. Además, la responsabilidad de la seguridad en el comercio internacional de animales y sus subproductos recae fundamentalmente en los Servicios Veterinarios. Desde siempre, los veterinarios también se han ocupado de la higiene de la carne en los mataderos, comprendidas las inspecciones antemortem y postmortem. Si bien siguen desempeñando esa función, los nuevos métodos de control de los alimentos los llevan a participar más activamente en otros segmentos de la cadena de producción y otras esferas alimentarias como, por ejemplo, la transformación de leche, huevos y peces. Estas actuaciones más amplias requieren mayores competencias y la creación de redes eficientes con nuevos interlocutores.

Los sistemas de identificación y trazabilidad de los animales constituyen importantes instrumentos para el control, la prevención y la erradicación de enfermedades animales,

492

Rev. sci. tech. Off. int. Epiz., **25** (2)

y para la mejora de la inocuidad de los alimentos. En la normativa de la Unión Europea ya se ha incluido un requisito sobre la trazabilidad para la industria de transformación alimentaria que comprende a los animales vivos. A su vez, varias organizaciones internacionales y nacionales están formulando normas y directrices para este ámbito.

La presencia de bacterias resistentes a los antimicrobianos en las explotaciones constituye una importante amenaza para la salud humana; por ello, han sido objeto de numerosas investigaciones científicas y debates en el plano internacional. La OMS ya estableció una lista de antimicrobianos de importancia fundamental para su administración a los seres humanos, así como los criterios para su selección. Por su parte, la OIE está elaborando actualmente una lista correspondiente de Antimicrobianos de Fundamental Importancia para la Medicina Veterinaria.

Las organizaciones internacionales y demás partes en la perspectiva mundial

En la última sección de este número de la *Revista* se examina la labor de la OIE y la Comisión del Codex Alimentarius (CCA) y la colaboración entre ambas organizaciones internacionales encargadas de la formulación de normas sobre la seguridad sanitaria de los alimentos.

Una consecuencia directa del incremento de las actividades de la OIE en la esfera de la inocuidad de los alimentos fue la creación, en 2002, del Grupo de Trabajo de la OIE sobre Seguridad Sanitaria de los Alimentos derivados de la Producción Animal. Este Grupo de Trabajo, que está encargado de coordinar las actividades de la Organización en la materia y asesorar al Director General y las comisiones especializadas, está compuesto por expertos de la OIE y especialistas de la labor de la CCA y sus órganos subsidiarios. Las medidas aplicables en las explotaciones constituyen el ámbito principal de trabajo de este Grupo y uno de los primeros resultados de su labor fue la publicación de la Guía de buenas prácticas ganaderas para la obtención de alimentos de origen animal inocuos que se anexó al informe de la reunión de la Comisión de Normas Sanitarias para los Animales Terrestres de la OIE de enero de 2005.

En el Acuerdo MSF se reconoce específicamente que las normas internacionales sobre la sanidad animal y las zoonosis formuladas por la OIE, y la reglamentación de la CCA relativa a la inocuidad de los alimentos constituyen las referencias para los intercambios internacionales. Por consiguiente, para evitar duplicaciones y lagunas y, por sobre todo, la formulación de normas y directrices contradictorias, la estrecha colaboración entre la OIE y la CCA reviste fundamental importancia. La OIE habrá de concentrarse en el "campo", primera etapa de la cadena alimentaria, y la CCA trabajará en ámbitos más cercanos a la "mesa".

Stuart A. Slorach
Presidente de la Comisión del Codex Alimentarius (2003-2005)
Presidente del Grupo de Trabajo de la OIE sobre
Seguridad Sanitaria de los Alimentos derivados de la Producción Animal
Stubbängsvägen 9A
SE-12553 Älvsjö, Suecia

Rev. sci. tech. Off. int. Epiz., 2006, **25** (2), 493-503

Animal production systems in the industrialised world

J.T. Sørensen [1], S. Edwards [2], J. Noordhuizen [3] & S. Gunnarsson [4]

(1) Danish Institute of Agricultural Sciences, Department of Animal Health, Welfare and Nutrition, P.O. Box 50, DK-8830 Tjele, Denmark
(2) University of Newcastle, School of Agriculture Food and Rural Development, King George VI Building, Newcastle upon Tyne, NE1 7RU, United Kingdom
(3) University of Ghent, Faculty of Veterinary Medicine, Salisburylaan 133, B-9820 Merelbeke, Belgium
(4) Swedish University of Agricultural Science, Skara, Department of Animal Environment and Health, P.O. Box 234, 532 23 Skara, Sweden

Summary

The production of food from animal origin is relatively stable in the industrialised world. However, animal production systems are changing dramatically with respect to location, herd size and specialisation. Increased pressure from a critical public is moving animal-based production towards systems such as organic production and loose-housing systems which allow the animals to better express normal behaviour. The focus on food safety promotes systems with a high degree of biosecurity, often associated with an increase in herd size and self-containment. The globalisation of agricultural trade and increased competition also favours an increase in herd size and specialisation. These trends also lead to regions with livestock-dense areas, giving rise to environmental concerns. Therefore, good farming practice regulations and systems to provide a higher level of transparency, such as quality risk management programmes, are being developed.

Keywords

Animal production system – Cattle – Goat – Pig – Poultry – Sheep.

Introduction

Livestock production has been called the next food revolution (13), addressing the massive increase in world demand for food of animal origin. Although this increase is seen especially in developing countries, it also has a major influence in the industrialised world through the global economy.

Livestock production in the industrialised world is under pressure from two sides (46). On the one hand, the increased competition in the global market may decrease farmers' income through a decrease in product prices and increased costs; this encourages farmers to switch to more intensive production systems. Intensive animal production systems, on the other hand, often raise public criticism regarding their impact on the environment, and the public are worried about how such production affects animal welfare (4) and food safety. Food-borne diseases are a

significant source of morbidity and mortality in the developed world (47). A current review of research in the field of livestock systems identifies a greater focus on integrated livestock systems such as organic livestock systems (38). In the European Union (EU) there has been a 25% to 30% growth in organic livestock systems during the last decade and by 2001 there were 142,000 organic farms (53).

A large number of the animal production facilities in North America and in Europe are currently changing in location, size, and in the degree of specialisation. The overall production in the industrialised world is expected to increase very moderately (13). The enlargement of the EU from 15 to 25 countries in 2004 is expected to have a major effect on livestock farming systems in the former communist countries of Central and Eastern Europe. Since the collapse of the political system in these countries in 1989, livestock production in this area of the world has

494

Rev. sci. tech. Off. int. Epiz., **25** (2)

decreased to less than 50% (28). This shrinkage is due to changes in subsidies and a decrease in consumption.

The objective of this article is to describe current animal production systems in different regions in Europe, North America and Oceania, and also to assess the expected trends in development.

Cattle production systems

Dairy cattle production systems

Dairy cattle production systems in the industrialised world are generally characterised by a high level of specialisation and a relatively high milk yield. Large differences exist, however, in farming goals and management orientation, as well as husbandry methods, managerial skills and knowledge.

In Western Europe, a large proportion of the dairy production is concentrated along the coastal areas. Other areas with concentrated milk production in Europe are in southern Germany and in the Po-valley in Italy (9). Dairy farms in the Netherlands, Germany, Denmark and Sweden are typically intensive, whereas in the United Kingdom (UK) and Ireland the production is grassland-based and more extensive. More than 80% of all robotic milking farms in the world are located in North-Western Europe (12). Herd sizes in the 15 Member States of the pre-enlargement EU (EU-15) vary from 115 cows per herd in the UK to 15 cows per herd in Greece (Eurostat – http://epp.eurostat.cec.eu.int). In the new EU Member States (countries in Eastern and Central Europe) smallholder dairy farms with between one and 15 cows predominate. In the United States of America (USA), milk production is shifting to the western half of the USA. In recent years there has been a substantial increase in milk production in California, Idaho and New Mexico. In 2001, 39% of all the milk produced in the USA was from dairy cattle herds with more than 500 cows (50).

Dairy production in New Zealand differs from other parts of the industrialised world by being very extensive and almost purely grassland-based, with seasonal calving and a low rate of milk production per cow. Herd size is relatively large and the cows are often milked by carrousel systems. In recent years one-day milking has been introduced as a means to reduce production costs.

Diseases in dairy cattle can be classified as notifiable and/or epidemic in nature like foot and mouth disease, or as endemic in nature like mastitis and bovine herpes virus 1-infections. Examples of epidemic diseases which constitute a known public health hazard include brucellosis, bovine spongiform encephalopathy (BSE) and tuberculosis (8).

Endemic diseases commonly have multiple causes and, because the contributing causal factors differ between regions and farms, the prevalence of endemic diseases also varies greatly between regions and farms (48, 49). The probability of human health problems originating from cattle diseases is low in the industrialised world. The most predominant ones may cause occupational diseases in farmers, veterinarians or artificial insemination technicians (43).

For several zoonoses, eradication, prevention and control programmes are in place, e.g. blood or milk testing for salmonellosis (52), skin reaction testing for tuberculosis and slaughterhouse testing for BSE. Outbreaks of zoonoses can hence be considered as accidental. Most of the above-mentioned zoonoses will also cause disease signs in cattle. However, a disease caused by *Escherichia coli* O157:H7, a virulent serotype of verocytotoxigenic *E. coli* (VTEC – also known as Shiga toxin-producing *E. coli* [STEC]), represents a public health hazard for humans while the infection does not cause any signs of sickness in cattle (11, 45). The carrier-state of the animal should be detected in order to be able to effectively impose an eradication and control programme (10).

The predominant food safety concerns for the dairy cattle production industry are the contamination of milk, and, to a lesser extent, problems of meat/beef from culled dairy cows (11, 36). Contamination of milk may be (micro-) biological (bacteria, toxins, high somatic cell counts) or chemical (residues of anti-microbials, anthelmintics, chemicals such as disinfectants). Already, for a long time, formally imposed quality control programmes for milk involving laboratory testing have addressed these types of quality failures. Milk bulk tank samples testing positive for these failures will be rejected and will not be used in products destined for human consumption; moreover, the treatment of milk during processing will additionally eliminate certain problems, e.g. bacteria will be killed by pasteurisation. Farmers are required to respect withdrawal periods when they have used anti-microbials, for example to treat clinical mastitis cases, and to implement measures to maintain high standards of hygiene.

Trends in dairy cattle production systems

Milk production from cattle is stable in the industrialised world, and this situation is expected to continue in the future. However, it is also expected that farm size in general will increase and the number of holdings with dairy cows will decrease. In the EU-15, the number of holdings with dairy cows decreased by 31% between 1995 and 2001 (Eurostat), whilst the number of dairy herds in the USA decreased by 21% between 1997 and 2001 (50). It can be expected that many smallholder farms in Eastern and Central Europe will disappear.

Organic milk production has expanded during the last decade, especially in the EU. In Denmark more than 25% of all milk sold in shops is organic (3). In some regions, some dairy farming has a multifunctional operation, i.e. it provides recreational activities for civilians, or opportunities to involve mentally disabled people in farm work.

Beef production systems

Beef in the industrialised world derives from two production systems (35), namely, beef from dairy herds as a by-product and beef from suckler herds. Beef from dairy cattle herds is the main source of beef in Europe. Bull calves are traditionally used in young bull production, production of steers or in veal calf production. Veal is a pale meat from calves kept pre-ruminant on milk replacer until slaughter at 120 kg to 140 kg. Veal, which is traditionally used in France, Italy, Belgium and Switzerland, currently plays only a minor role in European beef consumption. In the UK and Ireland, most male dairy calves are reared as steers. They are produced on pasture until they are two years old. Dairy steers are also produced in the USA and in New Zealand. The predominant beef production from dairy cattle is young bull production (typically intensively fed on grain until they reach a carcass weight of 250 kg to 350 kg) and cull cows.

In beef production from suckler herds, cows are bred only to produce calves that are weaned at six to ten months of age. Suckler herds typically live on marginal land such as unploughable pastures. This type of production is the predominant source of beef in North America. Calves are typically sold after weaning and finished in feedlots on high energy diets.

The USA has 9.7% of the world cattle inventory; in 2004 it produced 12 million metric tonnes (Mt) of beef (the EU produced 8 million Mt in that same year) (51). Australia produces only 2 million Mt, but it has the highest proportion of exports – 22% of all the beef traded in the world is produced in Australia (29).

Organic beef production plays only a minor role in the EU, e.g. in Denmark the market share of organic beef is less than 2% (40).

Pig production systems

The major pigmeat producing countries in the world are as follows (the production figures for 2004 are given in brackets):

– the People's Republic of China (48.3 million Mt)

– the EU (25 Member States) (21.6 million Mt)

– the USA (9.3 million Mt)

– Brazil (3.1 million Mt)

– Canada (1.9 million Mt).

However, if one considers industrialisation as the production relative to the size of the human population it is apparent that EU countries predominate (production figures per 1,000 people in 2004 are given in brackets):

– Denmark (327.8 Mt)

– Belgium (101.6 Mt)

– Austria (80.5 Mt)

– the Netherlands (79.3 Mt)

– Spain (77.6 Mt)

– Canada (60.8 Mt)

– Poland (54.5 Mt)

– Germany (52.4 Mt) (FAOSTAT, 2005 – http://faostat. fao.org/).

Intensive production systems

A high level of intensity and management control generally characterises pig production systems in the industrialised world. They have historically been located in regions of high grain production, such as the American corn belt states and Canadian prairie provinces, or the major arable areas of Europe. However, significant concentrations of pigs can also develop around areas where cheap industrial by-products from human food processing are available for feeding, as seen in the Netherlands, or in regions where the activities of large integrator companies have stimulated growth, for example in North Carolina. Within the EU the major pig producing countries are Germany, Spain, Denmark, France and the Netherlands. Pig production has increased most in recent years in Spain, and is expected to increase again in the former communist countries in Central and Eastern Europe, which showed a big decrease in production during restructuring, whilst production in Western Europe is likely to fall. In all countries, economies of scale in production have resulted in a consistent decrease in the number of pig farms over recent decades, whilst the number of animals per unit has increased to compensate for this. Large concentrations of pigs in certain geographic areas have raised major concerns about waste management and the risk of adverse environmental impact from groundwater pollution, gaseous emissions and odour. Public concerns about animal welfare in large industrialised enterprises have also been growing. As a result, there is increasing legislative control on production in both Europe and North America.

496

Rev. sci. tech. Off. int. Epiz., **25** (2)

The production of pigmeat involves breeding, nursery (newly weaned piglets) and finishing phases. These may all take place on the same farm (so called farrow-to-finish operations), or may be split between different farms each specialising in only one or two phases. This latter strategy has become more common as herd size has increased, and as the advantages of split-site production for the control of disease spread have been demonstrated (32). For example, the proportion of total slaughter pigs produced from farrow-to-finish operations in the USA fell from 65% to 38% between 1992 and 1998 (37). Whilst this trend is not yet as pronounced in Europe, similar changes are taking place. There has been an associated increase in the number of pig-producing companies that contract out the nursery and finisher phases of production.

In intensive pig units biosecurity and health management are major priorities. Many intensive farms have a high health status, barrier fencing and restricted access. However, disease control is difficult in areas of high pig density and, once endemic diseases such as enzootic pneumonia, porcine respiratory and reproductive syndrome or postweaning multisystemic wasting syndrome arise within a herd, they can only be eradicated by full or partial destocking and repopulation, or controlled by the development and systematic use of vaccines. It has been common practice in the past to use in-feed antibiotics as a prophylactic and/or growth-promoting aid. However, whilst this practice is still common in the USA, EU legislation requires the removal of non-prescription antibiotics from feed from 2006.

The majority of pigs in industrialised countries are housed in buildings with fully or partially slatted floors and liquid manure (slurry) handling systems. Pregnant sows are most commonly housed in individual gestation crates, but animal welfare concerns have resulted in the requirement to phase out such systems within the EU by 2012 for all but the first four weeks after service, with some Member States already unilaterally imposing a complete ban. Whilst such legislation does not yet pertain in the major pig-producing states of North America, similar consumer pressures are growing. Alternative systems involve either group feeding, the use of temporary confinement in individual feeding stalls or automated systems using transponder identification and computer controlled feeding stations (17). From shortly before giving birth, and for the lactation period, sows are commonly housed in farrowing crates. Whilst animal welfare concerns are also expressed about the confinement during this period, the benefits of such systems for piglet survival in large-scale industrial units cannot yet be matched in higher welfare alternatives (19). In the EU, legislation specifies that piglets cannot be weaned at less than 28 days of age unless all-in all-out batch systems are employed to aid health management, in which case some litters may be weaned up to seven days earlier. However, in North America earlier

weaning, sometimes with piglets of less than two weeks of age, is commonly employed in some large enterprises as part of a veterinary strategy to break the infection cycle from sow to piglets (32). Weaned piglets and growing and finishing pigs are housed in groups varying in size from a single litter to several hundred animals, and are typically fed *ad libitum* until slaughter at five to six months of age. Whilst fully and partially slatted, unbedded systems are most common, other types of housing may be adopted depending on regional climate, availability of bedding materials such as straw, and legislation relating to animal welfare and environmental emissions which is in place in a number of different individual countries in Europe (27).

Alternative systems

In many European countries, and to a lesser extent in North America, alternative, less intensive systems of production may be adopted. These include deep litter, bedded indoor systems or outdoor production systems for both sows and growing pigs. Indoor bedded systems are often combined with cheaper building structures, such as uninsulated sheds in Northern Europe, or hoop (tent-like) structures in North America (34). Such systems are perceived by consumers to provide better welfare conditions because of the availability of straw or other bedding for occupations such as rooting, but they also pose risks of poorer hygiene, greater health challenges and persistence of zoonotic organisms such as *Salmonella* (27). Outdoor pig production systems come in many forms (18). In some European countries, notably the UK, and in a few mid-western states of the USA significant numbers of breeding sows are kept outdoors and supply pigs to conventional finishing systems. During both pregnancy and lactation periods, sows are kept in groups at pasture, with simple metal or wooden shelters for protection from the weather. This conventional outdoor production contrasts in scale with a small but growing number of farms producing pigs to organic standards, where it is a requirement that both sows and growing pigs have outdoor access. Whilst sows are usually kept at pasture, their piglets after weaning at six to eight weeks of age may either remain at pasture or be transferred to housing with an outdoor run area, depending on the climate and the precise requirements of the organic certifying body. The third major type of outdoor production is the traditional Mediterranean silvopastoral system, widely seen in some Southern European countries. This system involves indigenous breeds grazed in natural forest areas for the production of high-value dry-cured hams. Whilst all outdoor systems offer the animals much greater space and environmental complexity, welfare challenges from adverse climatic conditions, parasites and less prompt disease detection can occur. Similarly, whilst the lower animal density and greater volume of fresh air reduces disease challenge within the group, the open access for humans

Rev. sci. tech. Off. int. Epiz., **25** (2)

497

and wildlife can also make it more difficult to limit the spread of disease and transfer of zoonotic organisms.

Future trends in pig production

As with other livestock sectors, economic pressures will dictate the continued growth in unit size and reduction in number of units over time. However, the degree of intensification and the permitted housing systems are likely to be increasingly regulated by legislation to protect animal welfare and limit environmental impact. Such legislation is already in place in the EU, for example through Directives 2001/88/EC (24) and 2001/93/EC (23) on pig welfare, and 96/61/EC (20) on integrated pollution prevention and control, and growing public pressure is likely to lead to similar developments in North America. Whilst smaller traditional, and niche market systems are likely to grow in number to supply a high value market, they will always be a small minority of total pig production.

Poultry production systems

Broiler chickens and laying hens could be seen as two different farm animal species, although they have a common ancestor in the red jungle fowl (*Gallus gallus*). The chicken meat sector and egg sector are more or less separated in the industrialised world, with few connections except for control of contagious diseases.

Traditionally poultry production, both broiler meat and egg production, has been localised to grain-growing areas, but as trade has become more international other factors, such as access to cheap manpower, are influencing the location of the farms. The increasing farm size and flock size has raised concerns about the environmental effects of wastes from the operations. Furthermore, this development increases the risk of severe consequences should a huge farm be hit by an epizootic disease (e.g. avian influenza).

Broiler chickens

During the last two decades the annual world production of chicken meat has increased from 20 billion birds per year in 1984 to 47 billion birds in 2004 (FAOSTAT). The USA (8.9 billion), the People's Republic of China (7.2 billion), Brazil (5.3 billion), India (1.8 billion), Indonesia (1.4 billion) and Mexico (1.2 billion) are the main chicken meat producers in the world. Annually 6.4 billion broiler chickens are slaughtered in the EU (25 Member States). France, UK and Spain are the largest producers within the EU with an annual production of about 800 million each (FAOSTAT).

The predominant way to rear broiler chickens in the industrialised world is to keep the birds on littered floors in large window-less buildings. This system allows the farmer to house a large number of birds in an enclosed environment at a relatively low cost. The stocking density used in commercial broiler production is from about 30 kg/m^2 up to about 50 kg/m^2 (22, 44). The two predominant hybrids used in chicken meat production are the Cobb and the Ross.

In free-range broiler production the birds are typically kept indoors on a littered floor with access to an outdoor area. This can be a covered veranda (winter garden) that could be used all year round, or a free-range area. It is common that slow-growing broiler hybrids are used in free-range broiler rearing (e.g. Label Rouge in France), which means that the birds are slaughtered at 60 to 90 days compared to 30 to 50 days in conventional rearing. The market share of organic broiler rearing is still very restricted (22).

Future trends in broiler production

It seems unlikely that there will be any major change in basic housing practice in the near future, except for differences in stocking densities. The European Commission (25) is proposing that the stocking density of broilers should be restricted to 30 kg/m^2. If the farm is complying with a control programme, the stocking density may be increased to a maximum of 38 kg/m^2. Europe imports large quantities of broiler meat from other countries, e.g. Brazil and Thailand, which puts a lot of pressure on the national production within the EU. The trend has been for this trade to increase, although national concern for zoonotic diseases like salmonellosis and avian influenza may limit the import in future.

The market share for organic chicken may show a marginal increase in some countries, if challenges like the increased risk of parasitic diseases (e.g. coccidiosis) and other outdoor associated health and welfare problems can be overcome.

Laying hens

During the last two decades the annual number of laying hens has increased from 3.1 billion birds per year in 1984 to 5.4 billion birds in 2004, and egg production has increased from 29,266,307 Mt in 1984 to 58,205,376 Mt in 2004 (FAOSTAT). The People's Republic of China (2,134 million hens), the USA (344 million), Brazil (236 million), Indonesia (161 million), Mexico (154 million) and India (158 million) are the main egg producers in the world. In 2004, 407 million laying hens were producing eggs in the EU (25 Member States); France (61 million), Spain (50 million), Italy (46 million), Germany (45 million), Poland (45 million) are the largest egg producers within the EU (FAOSTAT).

Housing systems for laying hens can be categorised into cage systems and non-cage systems, as described below.

Cage systems

There are two types of cage system: battery cages and furnished cages. The battery cage is by far the most common housing system used internationally, although it is banned in Switzerland and Sweden. Battery cages are systems where a small group of hens is kept in an enclosure of welded wire mesh with a sloping floor. The system enables the farmer to keep a large number of birds in a restricted building space, but yet to keep them in small groups. The space allowance varies from 400 cm² to 750 cm² per bird (26, 33). The EU has planned to ban these battery cages by 1 January 2012 (21).

Furnished cages have the advantages of battery cages (small group size, wire mesh cage), but they also provide hens with access to important resources that enable them to express crucial behaviours such as perching, nesting and dustbathing. Usually the production results are more predictable in furnished cages than in non-cage systems. Different versions of the furnished cage have been tested, ranging from a battery cage supplied with a perch to larger cages supplied with a nest box, perch and dust bath. The cages are for five to nine birds at 600 cm² to 750 cm² of floor area per bird (26). By the 1 January 2012, the EU will only allow cages that give the birds the opportunity to perch, nest and dustbathe (21).

Non-cage systems

Non-cage systems are litter-based floor systems, usually with a separate manure area. They range from homemade simple deep litter systems, to prefabricated complex systems, where the birds are given an environment consisting of different levels of perches and nesting areas. Non-cage systems are very rarely used except in north-west and central Europe. The European Food Safety Authority categorises non-cage systems into single-tier systems and aviaries (26).

A single-level system consists of a littered floor which may also be perforated to allow droppings to pass through to a separate manure area. If a mechanical manure system is installed the manure can be cleaned out regularly during the production period. Otherwise, the manure is stored in the house and only removed between the batches. The single level system has nest boxes or colony nests for egg laying, and the birds have access to perches on a single level.

An aviary (or a multilevel system) consists of littered floor areas and tiers at different levels. Tiers consist of a perforated floor and/or perches, where the birds are offered food and water. The perforated area allows the droppings to pass through to a mechanical manure system, which allows regular cleaning out. The system has nest boxes or colony nests for egg laying. The nests can be separated from the tiers or they can be integrated within the tier system. The system makes it possible to house a large group of laying hens at a high stocking density, calculated as number of birds per unit of ground area.

In some non-cage systems hens are also given access to an outdoor environment. The outdoor area can also be combined with a covered veranda (winter garden), which can be used all year round. Sometimes the outdoor area is available all the time, but more commonly the birds are outside during a period of the day, typically the afternoon, in order to avoid mislaid eggs. In countries of the temperate or sub-arctic zone, birds in free-range systems are kept in the indoor area during the winter.

Future trends in egg production

It is reported that battery cages are probably the best choice from an economic point of view, although the feed conversion efficiency has been reported to be better in furnished cages (15, 26). Birds in non-cage systems, and in particular free-range systems, have been reported to have lower feed conversion and to produce fewer saleable eggs compared to layers kept in cages (1, 26). On the other hand, the barren environment of battery cages restricts the birds from satisfying their behavioural needs (15). The laying hens in furnished cages have improved welfare compared to battery hens, even if the furnished cages just allow the birds to express some behaviours and not others, e.g. wing flapping. The ideal situation from a welfare point of view is an aviary or a free-range system that gives the birds more opportunity to express natural behaviours, although these systems have a larger variation in productivity compared to cage systems (1). In addition to housing conditions, factors such as genetics, nutrition and rearing conditions for the pullets also have an influence on production and on the health and welfare of laying hens (26, 30, 31, 39).

In the EU, dramatic changes may occur within the next decade. Furnished cages and non-cage systems will replace battery cages, which will be banned from 1 January 2012. The replacement process will probably take two different directions. Some farmers may change to furnished cages, because they think these will give more predictable production results and require similar labour to battery cages. Other farmers may consider aviaries to be the less expensive alternative, offering more flexibility: a non-cage system can, for example, be turned into an organic farm. In future, furnished cages will probably be regarded as the baseline standard by consumers, once all battery eggs are out of the market.

The situation in North America may remain unchanged for a long time, i.e. most farmers will stick to the conventional battery cages. However, it is likely that a market-driven change from battery cages into furnished cages or non-cage systems could come. If so, the change could be more dramatic than the change in Europe. The adjustments in farming practice towards increased animal welfare in the EU are mainly driven by public and political opinions via legislation. Historically, this process has been a quite slow one (it has been going on for decades), whereas market-driven changes in animal welfare practice may happen over a couple of years.

Other animal production systems

Goat production systems

Although sheep and goats are very important livestock in the developing world, they are less important in the industrialised world (Table I). From 1993 to 2003 the world goat population increased by 26% (7). In the industrialised world, the goat population has been stable during the last 20 years. In Europe, dairy goats predominate and goat milk production has increased due to high performance in countries like Bulgaria, Cyprus, France and Spain (7). In the Mediterranean countries, goat products are associated with agrotourism in mountainous regions (14).

Table I
Number of live animals in the industrialised world in 2004 (million head) (FAOSTAT)

Type of animal	European Union [a]	North America	Oceania	World
		Location		
Goats	12	1	1	783
Sheep	103	7	135	1,059
Cattle	88	110	37	1,339
Pigs	152	75	5	948
Chickens	1,170	2,130	120	16,352

a) 10 new Member Countries joined the European Union on 1 May 2004, bringing the total to 25. Figures quoted here include information from all 25 countries

Sheep production systems

It appears from Table I, that the world sheep population is similar in number to the global cattle population. However, the world sheep population is decreasing (6). Sheep meat is still the most internationally traded type of meat; in total 15% of sheep meat production is exported.

This is mainly due to export from Australia and New Zealand. In the Mediterranean countries, the production of dairy sheep is the predominant type of sheep husbandry. Wool is the main purpose for sheep breeding in Australia, New Zealand and Eastern Europe. Lamb meat is, on average, the most expensive type of meat worldwide (6). However, there are major cultural differences in the products, from 6 kg lambs in Greece to 30 kg lambs in Australia. Sheep can be fed on pastoral range land for which opportunity costs are low. However, production systems vary between countries. Bouttonnet (6) has calculated that the average number of ewes per labour unit is 1,400 in New Zealand compared to 20 in Greece. In New Zealand, 76% of sales come from wool and 24% from meat. In Greece 42% come from milk, 34% from meat and 24% direct from subsidies. In North European countries, meat has become the main product of sheep (16).

Ways to improve food safety and the health and welfare of animals in future livestock production systems

There are different ways to improve food safety, public health and the health and welfare of livestock. First of all, regulations can be defined for health promotion (e.g. EU directives and regulations). Secondly, different organisations such as national livestock sector bodies, the meat/milk/egg processing industries and retailer organisations can set rules for good farming practice and develop information systems for food safety (2) or animal welfare (5). Thirdly, different actions can be taken at the local farm level to improve the issues named above. Such actions include better training to improve skills and knowledge, e.g. with regard to health and welfare hazards and their associated risks (10). Improving farmers' observational skills so that they can properly monitor their animals and their direct environment, and correctly interpretate the findings, contributes to the early detection of health and welfare problems on livestock farms. Farmers should also be encouraged to develop an attitude of focusing on high quality production, where quality refers to both the product and the production process. Quality risk management in such operations may be executed according to principles of the hazard analysis and critical control point concept (36, 41, 42) and integrates the tactical quality approach with operational farm management issues.

Rev. sci. tech. Off. int. Epiz., **25** (2)

Les systèmes de production animale dans le monde industrialisé

J.T. Sørensen, S. Edwards, J. Noordhuizen & S. Gunnarsson

Résumé

La production de denrées alimentaires d'origine animale dans le monde industrialisé est relativement stable. Par contre, les systèmes d'élevage ont subi des transformations radicales en ce qui concerne la localisation des élevages, la taille des troupeaux et le niveau de spécialisation. Suite aux critiques émanant de l'opinion publique, les systèmes de production animale évoluent progressivement vers des productions « bio » et des systèmes d'élevage à stabulation libre, favorisant l'expression du comportement naturel de l'animal. L'accent mis sur la sécurité sanitaire des aliments favorise les systèmes dotés d'un niveau élevé de biosécurité, souvent associé à une augmentation de la taille des troupeaux et à un système d'exploitation intégré. La mondialisation des échanges de produits agricoles et l'intensification de la concurrence sont d'autres facteurs contribuant à l'augmentation des troupeaux et à une spécialisation accrue. Ces tendances se traduisent par de fortes densités de bétail dans certaines régions, avec les problèmes environnementaux que cela suppose. Il est donc nécessaire de réglementer les bonnes pratiques d'élevage et d'établir des systèmes offrant une meilleure transparence.

Mots-clés

Système de production animale – Bovin – Caprin – Porcin – Volaille – Ovin.

■

Sistemas de producción animal en el mundo industrializado

J.T. Sørensen, S. Edwards, J. Noordhuizen & S. Gunnarsson

Resumen

En el mundo industrializado, la producción de alimentos de origen animal permanece en niveles relativamente estables. Sin embargo, los sistemas productivos están sufriendo cambios muy profundos por lo que respecta a su ubicación, al tamaño de los rebaños y a la especialización. La creciente presión de una opinion pública bastante crítica está reorientando la producción animal hacia sistemas que privilegien métodos como la producción biológica o la estabulación espaciosa, que inducen un comportamiento más normal de los animales. El hecho de poner el acento en la inocuidad de los alimentos favorece a los sistemas productivos que ofrezcan un elevado nivel de seguridad biológica, lo que suele ir ligado a rebaños más numerosos y a un mayor grado la autocontención. La mundialización del comercio agrícola y la creciente competencia también favorecen la especialización y el aumento del tamaño de los rebaños. Estas tendencias propician además la aparición de regiones con zonas de alta densidad ganadera, hecho que despierta inquietud por sus posibles repercusiones ambientales. En este sentido, se están elaborando reglamentos y sistemas de buenas prácticas ganaderas para ofrecer un mayor nivel de transparencia.

Palabras clave

Ave de corral – Bovino – Caprino – Ovino – Porcino – Sistema de producción animal.

■

References

1. Aerni V., Brinkhof M.W.G., Wechsler B., Oester H. & Fröhlich E. (2005). – Productivity and mortality of laying hens in aviaries: a systematic review. *World Poult. Sci. J.*, **61** (1), 130-142.

2. Althoff G.S. & Petersen B. (2004). – Improving quality and safety in pork chains addressing the challenge of chain wide information management. *In* Animal production in Europe: the way forward in a changing world. Proc. of 'In-between' Congress of the International Society for Animal Hygiene [ISAH], 11-13 October, Saint-Malo. Zoopole, Ploufragan, France, 475-476.

3. Anon. (2005). – Landøkonomisk Oversigt 2005. Dansk Landbrug.

4. Appleby M.C. (1999). – What should we do about animal welfare? Blackwell Science Ltd, Oxford.

5. Blockhuis H.J., Jones R.B., Geers R., Miele M. & Veissier I. (2003). – Measuring and monitoring animal welfare: transparency in the food product quality chain. *Anim. Welf.*, **12**, 445-456.

6. Boutonnet J.-P. (1999). – Perspectives of the sheep meat world market on future production systems and trends. *Small Rum. Res.*, **34**, 189-195.

7. Boyazoglu J., Hatziminaoglou Y. & Morand-Fehr P. (2005). – The role of the goat in society: past present and perspectives for the future. *Small Rum. Res.*, **60**, 13-23.

8. Brown C. (2004). – Emerging zoonoses and pathogens of public health significance – an overview. *In* Emerging zoonoses and pathogens of public health concern. *Rev. sci. tech. Off. int. Epiz.*, **23** (2), 435-442.

9. Clausen S. (2005). – From cow to business: globalization herd/size. Cattle Consultancy Days 2005, Best Western Hotel, Nyborg Strand, Denmark, 1-2 September. Published by Cattle Consultancy Days, c/o DDD-Kursus Emdrupvej 28A, DK-2100 København Ø, Denmark, 6-10.

10. Collins J.D. & Wall P.G. (2004). – Food safety and animal production systems controlling zoonoses at farm level. *In* Emerging zoonoses and pathogens of public health concern. *Rev. sci. tech. Off. int. Epiz.*, **23** (2), 685-700.

11. Cursons R.T., Williamson J. & Bean A. (2005). – Shiga toxin genes from *Escherichia coli* strains isolated from mastitic milk. *In* Mastitis in dairy production: current knowledge and future solutions (H. Hogeveen, ed.). Proc 4th IDF [International Diary Federation] International Mastitis Conference, 12-15 June, Maastricht. Wageningen Academic Publishers, Wageningen, the Netherlands, 671-676.

12. De Koning K. & Rodenburg J. (2004). – Automatic milking: state of the art in Europe and North America. *In* Automatic milking – a better understanding. Wageningen Academic Publishers, Wageningen, the Netherlands, 27-40.

13. Delgado C., Rosegrant A., Steinfeld H., Ehui S. & Courbois C. (1999). – Livestock 2020. The next food revolution. Vision Discussion Paper No. 28. International Food Policy Research Institute, Washington, DC.

14. Dubeuf J.-P., Rubino R. & Morand-Fehr P. (2004). – Situation, changes and future of goat industry around the world. *Small Rum. Res.*, **51**, 165-173.

15. Duncan I.J.H. (2001). – The pros and cons of cages. *World Poult. Sci. J.*, **57** (4), 381-390.

16. Dyrmundsson O.R. (2004). – Sustainability of sheep and goat production in North European countries – from the Arctic to the Alps. Paper presented at the 55th Annual Meeting of the European Association for Animal Production, Bled, Slovenia, 5-9 September 2004.

17. Edwards S.A. (1992). – Scientific perspectives on loose housing systems for dry sows. *Pig vet. J.*, **28**, 40-51.

18. Edwards S.A. (2005). – Product quality attributes associated with outdoor pig production. *Livest. Prod. Sci.*, **94**, 5-14.

19. Edwards S.A. & Fraser D. (1997). – Housing systems for farrowing and lactation. *Pig J.*, **39**, 77-89.

20. European Commission (1996). – Council Directive 96/61/EC of 24 September 1996 concerning integrated pollution prevention and control. *Off. J. Eur. Communities*, **L257**, 10/10/1996.

21. European Commission (1999). – Directive 99/74/EC of 19 July laying down minimum standards for the protection of laying hens. *Off. J. Eur. Communities*, **L203**, 3/8/1999.

22. European Commission (2000). – The welfare of chickens kept for meat production. Report of the Scientific Committee on animal health and animal welfare, 21 March. Health and Consumer Protection Directorate-General, European Commission, Brussels.

23. European Commission (2001). – Commission Directive 2001/93/EC of 9 November 2001 amending Directive 91/630/EEC laying down minimum standards for the protection of pigs. *Off. J. Eur. Communities*, **L316**, 1/12/2001.

24. European Commission (2001). – Council Directive 2001/88/EC of 23 October 2001 amending Directive 91/630/EEC laying down minimum standards for the protection of pigs. *Off. J. Eur. Communities*, **L316**, 1/12/2001.

25. European Commission (2005). – Proposal for a Council Directive laying down minimum rules for the protection of chickens kept for meat production. Interinstitutional file 2005/0099 (CNS), 31 May. European Commission, Brussels.

26. European Food Safety Authority (EFSA) (2004). – Welfare aspects of various systems for keeping laying hens. Report of the animal health and animal welfare panel of the European Food Safety Authority. EFSA, Parma.

502

Rev. sci. tech. Off. int. Epiz., **25** (2)

27. European Food Safety Authority (EFSA) (2005). – The welfare of weaners and rearing pigs: effects of different space allowances and floor types. Report of the animal health and animal welfare panel of European Food Safety Authority. EFSA, Parma.

28. Gibon A., Mihina S., Zervas G., Boyazoglu J., Maki-Hokkonen J. & Zjalic M. (2003). – Livestock farming systems diversity and challenges for sustainable livestock development in selected countries in Central and Eastern Europe. *In* Livestock farming systems in Central and Eastern Europe (A. Gibon & S. Mihina, eds). European Association for Animal Production, Technical Series no. 3. Wageningen Academic Publishers, Wageningen, the Netherlands, 1-22.

29. Griffith G.R. & Alford A.R. (2002). – The US cattle cycle and its influence on the Australian beef industry. *Aust. Agribus. Rev.* **10**. Available at: www. http://www.agrifood.info/review/2002/Griffith.pdf.

30. Gunnarsson S., Keeling L.J. & Svedberg J. (1999). – Effects of rearing factors on the prevalence of floor eggs, cloacal cannibalism and feather pecking in commercial flocks of loose housed laying hens. *Br. Poult. Sci.,* **40**, 12-18.

31. Häne M., Huber-Eicher B. & Fröhlich E. (2000). – Survey of laying hen husbandry in Switzerland. *World Poult. Sci. J.,* **56**, 21-31.

32. Harris D.L. & Alexander T.J.L. (1999). – Methods of disease control. *In* Diseases of swine (B.E. Straw, S. D'Allaire, W.L. Mengeling & D.J. Taylor, eds), 8th Ed. Iowa State University Press, Ames, Iowa, 1077-1110.

33. Hester P.Y. (2005). – Impact of science and management on the welfare of egg laying strains of hens. *Poult. Sci.,* **84** (5), 687-696.

34. Honeyman M.S. (2005). – Extensive bedded indoor and outdoor pig production systems in USA: current trends and effects on animal care and product quality. *Livest. Prod. Sci.,* **94**, 15-24.

35. Jarrige R. & Auriol P. (1992). – An outline of world beef production. *In* Beef cattle production (R. Jarrige & C. Beranger, eds), World Animal Science C5. Elsevier, Amsterdam, New York, 3-30.

36. Lievaart J.J., Noordhuizen J.P.T.M., van Beek E., van der Beek C., van Risp A., Schenkel J. & van Veersen J. (2005). – The hazard analysis critical control points (HACCP) concept as applied to some chemical, physical and microbiological contaminants of milk on dairy farms. A prototype. *Vet. Q.,* **27** (1), 21-29.

37. McBride W.D. & Key N. (2003). – Economic and structural relationships in US hog production. AER-818. Economic Research Service, United States Department of Agriculture, Washington, DC.

38. Maldonado B.L.R. & Schunemann A.A. (2003). – Achievements of research in the field of livestock systems. *In* A review on developments and research in livestock systems. WAAP [World Association for Animal Production] Book of the Year 2003 (A. Rosati, A. Tewolde & C. Mosconi, eds). Wageningen Academic Publishers, Wageningen, the Netherlands, 127-131.

39. Nicol C.J., Pötzsch C., Lewis K. & Green L.E. (2003). – Matched concurrent case-control study of risk factors for feather pecking in hens on free-range commercial farms in the UK. *Br. Poult. Sci.,* **44**, 515-523.

40. Nielsen B.K. & Thamsborg S.M. (2005). – Welfare, health and product quality in organic beef production: a Danish perspective. *Livest. Prod. Sci.,* **94**, 41-50.

41. Noordhuizen J.P.T.M. & Welpelo H.J. (1996). – Sustainable improvement of animal health care by systematic quality risk management according to the HACCP-concept. *Vet. Q.,* **18**, 121-126.

42. Noordhuizen J.P.T.M. & Metz J.H.M. (2005). – Quality control on dairy farms with emphasis on public health, food safety and animal health and welfare. *Livest. Prod. Sci.,* **94** (1-2), 51-59.

43. Oliver S.P., Murinda S.E., Nguyen L.T., Nam H.M., Almeida R.A. & Headrick S.J. (2005). – On-farm sources of foodborne pathogens: isolation from dairy farm environment. *In* Mastitis in dairy production: current knowledge and future solutions (H. Hogeveen, ed.). Proc. 4th IDF [International Dairy Federation] International Mastitis Conference, 12-15 June, Maastricht. Wageningen Academic Publishers, Wageningen, the Netherlands, 665-670.

44. Perry J., Banker D. & Green R. (1999). – Broiler farms' organization, management, and performance. Agriculture Information Bulletin no. 748, United States Department of Agriculture, Washington, DC.

45. Schouten J.M., Bouwknegt M., van de Giessen A.W., Frankena K., De Jong M.C.M. & Graat E.A.M. (2004). – Prevalence estimation and risk factors for *Escherichia coli* O157 on Dutch dairy farms. *Prev. vet. Med.,* **64**, 49-61.

46. Schwabenbauer K. (2004). – Livestock sector in Europe: the political standpoint. *In* Animal production in Europe: the way forward in a changing world. Proc. of 'In-between' Congress of the International Society for Animal Hygiene [ISAH], 11-13 October, Saint-Malo. Zoopole, Ploufragan, France, 3-5.

47. Thorns C.J. (2004). – Coordinated approach to controlling foodborne zoonoses – achievements and future prospects. *In* Animal production in Europe: the way forward in a changing world. Proc. of 'In-between' Congress of the International Society for Animal Hygiene [ISAH], 11-13 October, Saint-Malo. Zoopole, Ploufragan, France, 403-408.

48. Thrusfield M. (1995). – Veterinary epidemiology, 2nd Ed. Blackwell Science, Oxford.

49. Toma B., Dufour B., Sanaa M., Beret J.J., Ellis P. Moutou F. & Laura A. (1995). – Épidémiologie appliquée à la lutte collective contre les maladies animales transmissibles majeures. Association pour l'Étude de l'Épidémiologie des Maladies Animales, Maisons-Alfort, France.

50. United States Department of Agriculture (USDA) (2002). – US Dairy Herd Structure. Released September 26, 2002 by the National Agricultural Statistics Service (NASS), Agricultural Statistics Board, USDA, Washington, DC.

Rev. sci. tech. Off. int. Epiz., **25** (2)

503

51. United States Department of Agriculture (USDA) (2005). Livestock and Poultry: World Markets and Trade. Available at: http://www.fas.usda.gov/dlp/circular/2006/06-03LP/toc.htm

52. Veling J. (2004). – Diagnosis and control of *Salmonella* Dublin infections on Dutch dairy farms. PhD thesis. Utrecht University, Utrecht.

53. Von Borell E. & Sørensen J.T. (2004). – Organic livestock production in Europe: aims, rules and trends with special emphasis on animal health and welfare. *Livest. Prod. Sci.,* **90**, 3-9.

Rev. sci. tech. Off. int. Epiz., 2006, **25** (2), 505-516

Livestock production systems in developing countries: status, drivers, trends

H. Steinfeld, T. Wassenaar & S. Jutzi

Animal Production and Health Division, Food and Agriculture Organization of the United Nations, Viale delle Terme di Caracalla, 00100-Rome, Italy

Summary
This paper describes and assesses the current status of livestock production systems, the drivers of global livestock production, and the major trends in such production. The analysis covers the six major livestock species: cattle and buffaloes, goats and sheep, pigs and chickens. Global drivers of the livestock sector include economic growth and income, demographic and land use changes, dietary adjustments and technological change. The rate of change and direction of livestock development vary greatly among world regions, with Asia showing the most rapid growth and structural change. The paper also examines system dynamics, by analysing the ways livestock production has adjusted to external forces. A brief discussion of how these trends link to food safety concludes the paper.

Keywords
Driver – Livestock production system – Structural change.

Introduction

Livestock production is undertaken in a multitude of ways across the planet, providing a large variety of goods and services, and using different animal species and different sets of resources, in a wide spectrum of agro-ecological and socio-economic conditions. Within this wide variety of livestock production there are certain patterns that have been categorised into various livestock production systems (LPS). Most frequently, these systems have been defined on the basis of land use by livestock, and for this purpose the distinction between grazing systems, mixed farming systems and industrial (or landless) systems (12) has been widely accepted.

In order for decision-makers to address the livestock-related food safety challenges in global markets, it may be useful to look at LPS as the basic building blocks of the sector. Livestock production is undergoing rapid change, and this change manifests itself in the growing contribution that livestock makes to satisfying increasing

global demands for high-value food products, and in continuous adjustments at the level of resource-use intensity, size of operations, product orientation and marketing channels.

This paper describes the current status of LPS, and the drivers of and major trends in global livestock production. Due to the limitations of space, this cannot be more than a cursory analysis, highlighting the principal features and developments. Six major livestock species are covered (cattle and buffaloes, goats and sheep, pigs and chickens). First, the global drivers of the livestock sector are discussed, in particular economic growth and income, demographic and land-use changes, dietary adjustments and technological change. Second, the status of the main LPS is described, with some attention to regional differences. Third, system dynamics are examined, by analysing the adjustment of livestock production to external forces (this section is largely based on Costales *et al.*, 2006 [3]). A brief discussion of how these trends link to food safety concludes the paper.

Rev. sci. tech. Off. int. Epiz., **25** (2)

Global drivers of the livestock sector

Individual consumption of livestock products is closely related to per capita income. That is, with growing incomes people typically increase their consumption of meat, milk and eggs until these products become fully integrated into the daily diet. In high-income countries, per capita consumption of meat ranges between 80 kg and 130 kg per year; there is practically no further increase beyond that level. As incomes in many developing countries have grown rapidly over the past 20 years, consumption levels of meat and other livestock products have also increased. The economies of developing countries' achieved an average annual growth of 3.8% (1.8% per capita) from 1991 to 2001, up from 2.9% during the ten preceding years. Developing countries in East Asia, in particular, have experienced very strong economic growth, with an annual rate of 7.4% (6.2% per capita) over the decade between 1991 and 2001, with the People's Republic of China leading as the world's fastest growing economy. South Asia and the Near East follow, with gross domestic product growth rates of 5.5% and 4.4% over the same period. Economic expansion has been more modest in Latin America, at 2.9% annually, and in sub-Saharan Africa at 2.6% (Table I).

In addition to higher incomes, increases in human populations add to the demand for animal-source food products. Most developing countries still have rapidly growing populations even though percentage growth rates are below their peak in the 1970s. Each year, the human population in developing countries grows by 72 million, adding to the demand for food products. There are wide differences among developing countries; population growth has slowed down to 1.6% in East Asia whereas it remains high in sub-Saharan Africa (2.8%) and in the Near East/North Africa region (2.6%). In addition to population growth, the population structure is also changing: urbanisation is fast increasing and it is projected that by 2007 the majority of the human population will live in cities (13). Urban people adopt new eating habits, consuming higher amounts of animal protein, and eating a higher proportion of their food away from home. Furthermore, many populations in developed and developing countries are aging, with a declining proportion of the total population younger than 15 years. This also has an impact on total food demand and on the type of food consumed.

Table II gives an overview of the important changes that have occurred in the average diets of people in various world regions. People in industrialised countries derive more than 40% of their dietary protein intake from food of livestock origin (the figures do not include fish and other seafood), and little change occurred between 1980 and 2002. Changes have been most dramatic in Asia, where total protein supply from livestock for human diets increased by 131%, followed by Latin America, where per capita animal protein intake rose by nearly a third. In contrast, there has been a decline in livestock consumption in sub-Saharan Africa, reflecting economic stagnation and a decline in available incomes.

The increasing share of livestock products in the human diet in many developing countries is part of a dietary transition that has also included a higher intake of fats, fish, vegetables and fruit, at the expense of staple foods such as cereals and tubers.

Rapidly increasing demand for animal-source food products exerts pressures on the livestock sector, which needs to adapt fast in order to cope with such demand.

Table I

Economic growth rates, per capita gross domestic product (GDP) growth rates and human population growth rates (annual rates during the period 1991 to 2001)

Region	GDP growth rates (%)	Per capita GDP growth rate (%)	Population growth rate (%)
East Asia and Pacific	7.4	6.2	1.6
South Asia	5.5	3.6	2.1
Sub-Saharan Africa	2.6	0.0	2.8
Near East and North Africa	4.4	2.3	2.6
Latin America and Caribbean	2.9	1.3	2.0
OECD countries	2.5	1.9	0.7
EE and CIS	0.0	− 0.1	0.7
Developing countries	3.8	1.8	0.8
Developed countries	2.5	2.3	1.8
World	2.8	1.4	1.6

Source: World Bank (14)
CIS: Commonwealth of Independent States
EE: Eastern Europe
OECD: Organization for Economic Co-operation and Development

Table II

Daily protein supply from livestock and from all sources in 1980 and 2002 (in grams per capita)

Region	Total protein from livestock		Total protein	
	1980	2002	1980	2002
Sub-Saharan Africa	10.4	9.3	53.9	55.1
Near East	18.2	18.1	76.3	80.5
Latin America	27.5	34.1	69.8	77.0
Developing Asia	7.0	16.2	53.4	68.9
Industrialised countries	50.8	56.1	95.8	106.4
World	20.0	24.3	66.9	75.3

Source: FAOSTAT (7; accessed June 2006)

Rev. sci. tech. Off. int. Epiz., **25** (2)

507

These adjustments are based on a changing feed resource base, particularly feed concentrates. Current and projected levels of livestock production would not be possible without the expanding production and yield increase of crop agriculture. Traditionally, livestock production used to be based on locally available feed resources, including local fodder, crop residues and unconsumed parts of human food – resources that had no value as human food. Traditionally, natural pastures were the venue of livestock production. More recently, however, a growing proportion of pastureland in developing countries is in areas which are unfit or marginal for cropping, and degraded arable land is often converted into pastureland. The demand for arable land, and the fact that there is basically no additional available land that can readily be converted into pastures, except in parts of tropical Latin America, have important implications for the livestock sector. The lack of available new land prohibits a 'horizontal' expansion of existing modes of production, and forces the sector into rapid technological change and search for alternative resources.

Livestock production systems

Production environments, and the intensities and purposes of production, vary greatly within and across countries. Animal agriculture systems have been categorised on the basis of agro-ecological opportunities and demand for livestock commodities. In general, these systems are shaped by prevailing biophysical and socio-cultural environments, and without external inputs they have traditionally been mostly in sustainable equilibrium with such environments. In many of these systems, the livestock element is interwoven with crop production, as in the rice/buffalo or cereal/cattle systems of Asia. Animal manure is often essential for maintaining soil fertility, and the role of animals in nutrient cycling is often an important motivation for keeping animals, particularly where this involves a transfer of nutrients from common property resources to private land. In other cases, such as the semi-nomadic pastoral systems of the world's natural grassland regions, environmentally stable balances of human society, animal population and vegetative biomass have been maintained for centuries. Many of these systems that are the result of a long evolution are currently under pressure to adjust to rapidly evolving socio-economic conditions; large intensive livestock production units, in particular for pig and poultry production, have emerged over the last decades in many developing regions in response to the rapidly growing demand for livestock products.

To classify the resulting continuity of situations into a limited number of distinct LPS, the following criteria should ideally be considered:

– integration with crops

– relation to land

– agro-ecological zone

– intensity of production

– type of product.

The classification proposed by Seré and Steinfeld (12), which uses only the first three of these classification criteria, identifies ten broad categories of systems. In addition, the landless category defined by Seré and Steinfeld is split into landless ruminant and landless monogastric systems, bringing the total number of production system categories to eleven.

The LPS are considered a subset of farming systems. Seré and Steinfeld (12) distinguished two main groups of LPS: those solely based on animal production and those where cropping and livestock rearing are associated. The first group is defined as systems in which more than 90% of dry matter fed to animals comes from rangelands, pastures, annual forages and purchased feeds, and less than 10% of the total value of production comes from non-livestock farming activities. Mixed farming systems are livestock systems in which more than 10% of the dry matter fed to animals comes from crop by-products such as stubble, or where more than 10% of the total value of production comes from non-livestock farming activities.

Landless LPS are a subset of the pure livestock systems in which less than 10% of the dry matter fed to animals is farm produced and in which annual average stocking rates are above ten livestock units per hectare of agricultural land (on average at census unit level). Grassland-based systems are defined as systems in which more than 10% of the dry matter fed to animals is farm produced and in which annual average stocking rates are less than ten livestock units per hectare of agricultural land. A distinction is made between:

– temperate zones and tropical highland

– humid/sub-humid tropics and sub-tropics

– arid/semi-arid tropics and sub-tropics.

Rainfed mixed farming systems are mixed systems in which more than 90% of the value of non-livestock farm production comes from rainfed land use; these systems can be divided into the same agro-ecological sub-classes as given above. Irrigated mixed farming systems are systems in which more than 10% of the value of non-livestock farm production comes from irrigated land use, and again includes the same sub-classes.

The map in Figure 1 depicts the relative predominance of the broad groups of LPS around the world. The presence of industrial systems is connected to both demand factors and supply determinants; areas with high population density and purchasing power, in particular coastal areas in

508

Rev. sci. tech. Off. int. Epiz., **25** (2)

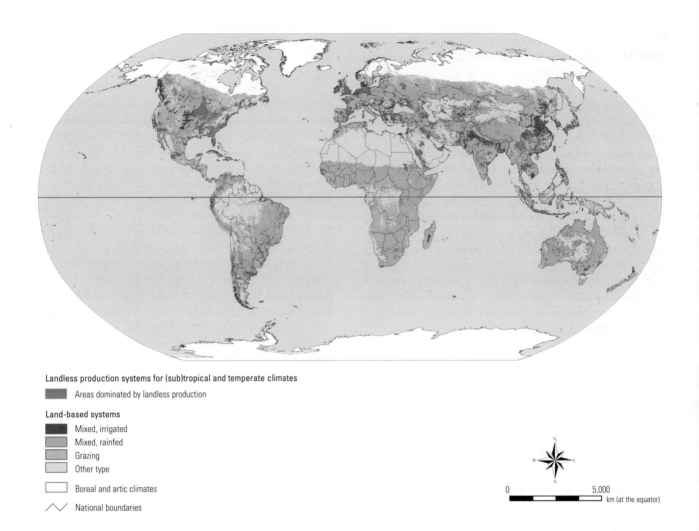

Landless production systems for (sub)tropical and temperate climates

▪ Areas dominated by landless production

Land-based systems

▪ Mixed, irrigated
▪ Mixed, rainfed
▪ Grazing
▫ Other type

▫ Boreal and artic climates

⋏⋏ National boundaries

0   5,000
          km (at the equator)

Fig. 1
Map of world livestock production systems

East Asia, Europe and North America, which also have access to ocean ports, show a high prevalence of industrial systems and import much of the necessary feed. In contrast, there are areas with ample feed supplies such as the mid-western United States of America (USA) and interior parts of Brazil and Argentina, where industrial systems rely mainly on local feed surpluses. East and Southeast Asia strongly dominate industrial monogastrics' production in the developing regions. Southern Brazil is another industrial production hot spot at world level, while important regional centres of industrial production are found, for example in Mexico, Colombia, Venezuela and Chile. Similarly there are major regional centres for the industrial production of chicken in Nigeria, South Africa and the Middle East.

Of the land-based system group, grazing systems cover the largest area and are currently estimated to occupy some 26% of the earth's ice-free land surface. This figure obviously includes a large variety of agro-ecological contexts with very different levels of biomass productivity. Grazing systems are primarily found in the more marginal areas which are unfit for cropping because of topography, low temperature or low rainfall. Mixed farming systems are prevalent in bio-climatically more favoured ecosystems. Most mixed farming systems are rain-fed, and they are particularly widespread in semi-arid and sub-humid areas of the tropics and in temperate zones. Mixed irrigated systems are found throughout the world, but in most cases are relatively small. Exceptions are the eastern parts of the People's Republic of China, northern India and Pakistan, where mixed irrigated systems extend over large areas.

Tables III and IV show the kinds of ruminant populations and animal production in the different production system groups, both globally and for the developing regions. The

Table III

Global livestock population and production in different production systems (averages 2001 to 2003)

Type of animal/ animal product	Livestock population (10⁶ heads) and production (10⁶ tonnes)			
	Grazing	Rainfed mixed	Irrigated mixed	Industrial
Animal				
Cattle and buffaloes	406	641	450	29
Sheep and goats	590	632	546	9
Animal product				
Total beef	14.6	29.3	12.9	3.9
Total mutton	3.8	4.0	4.0	0.1
Total pork	0.8	12.5	29.1	52.8
Total poultry meat	1.2	8.0	11.7	52.8
Total milk	71.5	319.2	203.7	–
Total eggs	0.5	5.6	17.1	35.7

Source: based on FAOSTAT data and calculations by J. Groenewold ('Classification and characterization of world livestock production systems'; unpublished report for the Food and Agriculture Organization, 2005)

Table IV

Livestock population and production in different production systems of the developing world (averages, 2001 to 2003)

Type of animal/ animal product	Livestock population (10⁶ heads) and production (10⁶ tonnes)			
	Grazing	Rainfed mixed	Irrigated mixed	Industrial
Animal				
Cattle and buffaloes	342	444	416	1
Sheep and goats	405	500	474	9
Animal product				
Total beef	9.8	11.5	9.4	0.2
Total mutton	2.3	2.7	3.4	0.1
Total pork	0.6	3.2	26.6	26.6
Total poultry meat	0.8	3.6	9.7	25.2
Total milk	43.8	69.2	130.8	0.0
Total eggs	0.4	2.4	15.6	21.6

Source: based on FAOSTAT data and calculations by J. Groenewold ('Classification and characterization of world livestock production systems'; unpublished report for the Food and Agriculture Organization, 2005)

1.5 billion head of cattle and buffaloes, and the 1.7 billion sheep and goats are fairly evenly distributed across the land-based systems, but average densities increase sharply from grazing systems to mixed irrigated systems; the latter have far greater livestock supporting capacities per unit area. Only a small fraction of the world's ruminant population is found in industrial feedlots, partly because this corresponds to only the final stage of the animal's life cycle, even in regions where intensive production is

common. Ruminant feedlots are predominantly a North American phenomenon, though they are used to a lesser extent in parts of Europe and the Near East. The vast majority of large and small ruminant populations are found in the developing regions: some 70% of small ruminants in grazing systems and over 80% of large ruminants in grazing systems are located in developing regions. These shares are respectively about 80% and 70% in rainfed mixed systems and 87% and 92% in irrigated mixed systems.

Ruminant productivity varies considerably within each system, but in grazing and mixed systems overall productivity is lower in developing countries than in developed ones: in grazing systems, for example, worldwide beef production per head averages 36 kg/head/year, but the average for developing countries is only 29 kg/head/year. In the mixed rainfed system, the difference between developed and developing regions is even more marked. By far the largest variation in intensity of production is found within this system, which is the largest producer of ruminant products. Even though the developing regions host the vast majority of the mixed rainfed ruminant population, they account for less than half of the system's production worldwide. In fact beef productivity in these regions averages 26 kg/head, as opposed to 46 kg/head at world level, and their milk production represents only 22% of the world total. Across all systems, developing regions account for half of the world's beef production, some 70% of mutton production and about 40% of milk production.

A sharply contrasting situation is found in the monogastric sector. More than half of the world's pork production currently originates from industrial systems, and over 70% of poultry meat. About half of this production originates from developing countries and, though reliable population figures are not available, variation in productivity between regions is probably much lower than for ruminants. Including the substantial monogastric production from irrigated mixed systems in developing regions, these regions account for the majority of the world's pork, poultry and egg production. Huge differences are found between the developing regions: although substantial, total production in Latin America is less than one tenth of that in Asia, and production in Africa and the Near East is almost non-existent. The developed countries and Asia together account for over 95% of the world's industrial pork production.

Table V shows the breakdown by agro-ecological zones. There has recently been a rapid growth in industrial production of monogastrics in the tropics and sub-tropics, leading to production levels that are similar to those of temperate regions. However, the situation is very different for ruminant production, partly because of its land-based nature; production and productivity are much higher in

510

Rev. sci. tech. Off. int. Epiz., **25** (2)

Table V
Livestock population and production in different
agro-ecological zones (global averages, 2001 to 2003)

Type of animal / animal product	Livestock population (10^6 heads) and production (10^6 tonnes)		
	Arid and semi-arid tropics and and sub-tropics	Humid and sub-humid tropics and sub-tropics	Temperate and tropical highlands
Animal			
Cattle and buffaloes	515	603	381
Sheep and goats	810	405	552
Animal product			
Total beef	11.7	18.1	27.1
Total mutton	4.5	2.3	5.1
Total pork	4.7	19.4	18.4
Total poultry meat	4.2	8.1	8.6
Total milk	177.2	73.6	343.5
Total eggs	4.65	10.2	8.3

Source: based on FAOSTAT data and calculations by J. Groenewold ('Classification and characterization of world livestock production systems'; unpublished report for the Food and Agriculture Organization, 2005)

the cooler climates. Small ruminant production in the (semi-)arid (sub-)tropics is a notable exception, explained by the large population and the relatively high rates of breeding, the latter being due to the fitness of these species, which are well adapted to harsh and marginal conditions. The relatively low productivity for milk in the more humid tropics relates to the strong dominance of mixed systems in these regions, where substantial use is still made of animals for draught power and other non-productive uses.

System dynamics

Intensification

Intensification of livestock production is taking place with regard to the use of most of the production inputs. In particular, the intensity of feed use has greatly increased over recent decades. While a growing number of people in the developing world are moving up the food chain, enjoying a richer and more diverse diet, so too are livestock; traditional fibrous and energy-rich feed stuffs are in relative decline, and protein-rich feeds together with sophisticated additives that enhance feed conversion are on the rise.

On balance, pastureland productivity has lagged far behind that of cultivated areas, although detailed estimates are difficult to make. A number of factors contribute to this trend. First, making more intensive use of the areas classified as pastures is often technically difficult and unprofitable. Constraints on the productivity of pastures most commonly relate to climatic features, topography,

shallowness and/or acidity of the soils, and disease pressure, among other factors. These constraints can be overcome only with massive investments to address them on various fronts. Additionally, in much of Africa and Asia, most pastures are used as common property, which further complicates attempts to intensify production. Without firm institutional arrangements, private investments in these areas are difficult to organise as returns accrue to individuals in proportion to the number of livestock they graze on communal land. Limited market access due to lack of infrastructure in these remote areas further contributes to the difficulty in achieving productivity improvements through individual investments. The harsh conditions of these pasturelands are exemplified by the pastoralist and agro-pastoralist areas in arid and semi-arid lands in sub-Saharan Africa.

As livestock production grows and intensifies, it depends less and less on locally available feed resources but increasingly on feed concentrates that are traded domestically and internationally. In 2004, a total of 690 million tonnes of cereals were fed to livestock (34% of the global cereal harvest) and another 18 million tonnes of oilseeds (mainly soya). In addition, 295 million tonnes of protein-rich processing by-products were used as feed (mainly bran, oilcakes and fish meal).

Species that can profitably make use of such feed concentrates (pigs and poultry) have an advantage over those that cannot do this to the same extent (cattle, sheep, goats). Among the monogastrics, it is poultry that shows the highest growth rates and lowest costs per unit of output, mainly because of efficient feed conversion. The use of feed concentrates for ruminants is limited to countries with low grain–meat price ratios. Where these ratios are high, typically in grain- or cereal-deficit developing countries, grain feeding to ruminants is usually not profitable.

What is driving the increasing use of feed grains? First, there is a decline in grain prices, a trend that is basically unchanged since the 1950s – which implies that global agriculture has been in a position to easily meet the growing demand over that period. The total supply of cereals increased by 46% over the 24 years from 1980 to 2004. In real terms (constant US dollars), international prices for grains are now half those in 1961. Expanding supply at declining prices has been brought about by intensification of existing crop-land use (not by expanding the crop area: globally, cereal crop-land declined by 5.2% between 1980 and 2004).

Intensification is a result of technological advances and greater use of inputs in crop production, notably in the areas of plant breeding, irrigation and water management, application of fertilisers and mechanisation. In contrast to developed countries, the expansion of the area dedicated to cereals has been an important contributor to increasing supplies in the developing countries, with rates highest in sub-Saharan Africa (64%) and East and Southeast Asia (15.2%) over the period 1980 to 2004. However, the vast majority of the additional supplies in these regions are used for food and not for feed. In Latin America, expansion of the area dedicated to cereal production has been slower (3.9%), but there was a 97% increase in the area under oil crops, notably soya. Here, however, the demand for feed crops has been a major determining factor in the expansion of arable land. Some countries have seen a particularly strong expansion of cropped area, most of it at the expense of the forests (Brazil and other Latin America countries). Large parts of this expansion are devoted to production of feed concentrates, notably soya and maize (8).

Intensification also draws on technical improvements in livestock production, such as genetics, health and farm management, which have contributed to raising resource-use efficiency and higher output per animal. Over the 24 years from 1980 to 2004, the pork, chicken and milk offtake per unit of stock increased by 61%, 32% and 21% respectively (7). Such biological and technical advances must be adapted to local conditions if they are to be profitably introduced. These advances are supported by increasing use of external services and by the specialisation of production, with a substantial shift from backyard and mixed systems to commercial, specialised, single-product operations.

Geographic concentration

Driven by growing demand and market opportunities, and supported by technological change, the distribution of production is no longer determined by the agro-ecological potential of a given location but by a variety of interacting factors. As well as local supply of feed and demand for livestock products, driving factors include transport costs, disease concerns, environmental regulations and a whole set of other policy factors.

As countries industrialise, they follow a pattern in relocating livestock production. Livestock production has traditionally been based on locally available feed resources, particularly those that have no other use or are of limited value, such as natural pasture and crop residues. In pre-industrialised contexts, the distribution of ruminant livestock can be explained by the availability of such resources, while the distribution of pigs and poultry closely matches that of humans, because of these animals' role as waste converters. For example, in Vietnam, a country that can be considered to be in the early stages of industrialisation, in 1991 90% of the poultry distribution pattern could be explained by the distribution of the human population ('Geographical shifts of livestock production: landuse and environmental impact

implications'; unpublished report for the Food and Agriculture Organization by P. Gerber and T. Wassenaar, 2005). As soon as urbanisation and economic growth translate rising incomes into 'bulk' demand for animal food products, large-scale operators emerge that are initially located close to towns and cities. Livestock products are among the most perishable products, and their conservation without chilling or processing poses serious problems. Therefore, food items from livestock have to be produced in the vicinity of demand – with concomitant human health and environmental problems stemming from the rapid urbanisation of both humans and animals in the same places.

In a subsequent phase, infrastructure and technology develop sufficiently to enable the production of livestock farther away from human populations, and livestock production shifts further away from demand centres, driven by a series of factors such as lower land and labour prices, access to feed, lower environmental standards in rural areas, tax incentives, and fewer disease problems. Figure 2 shows an example of this geographic shift that occurred around Bangkok between 1992 and 2000.

Vertical integration

There is rapid change also in the way value or food chains are organised in the livestock sector. Vertical integration provides economies of scope, ensures reliability of supply, and facilitates quality management and homogeneity of products. Importantly, it also allows producers to mitigate the wide host of pathogen threats to which the livestock sector and associated food chains are subject. At the same time, and in line with previous observations on dietary

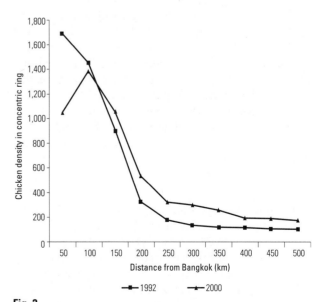

Fig. 2
The evolution of the geographical concentration of poultry around Bangkok from 1992 to 2000

changes, vertical integration accompanies the global sourcing of both livestock production inputs and outputs, and the important moves in trade liberalisation that have occurred over the last decade.

In many developing countries, particularly in rapidly developing countries in Asia and Latin America, the continued rise in per capita incomes together with the increasing urbanisation of populations has led to the westernisation of diets and transformation of food systems (9). The increasing affluence of urban consumers in developing countries is associated with an increase in the predominance and reach of large-scale retail stores, in particular supermarkets, responding to and also shaping the increasing demand for convenience, variety and quality assurance by individuals and households with more disposable income and increased opportunity-costs of time (4). While the main customer of the supermarkets in developing countries is the urban middle class, the competition among rival chains brings the prices of similar products down, thus also accommodating lower-income households seeking to stretch the purchasing power of their food budgets. The rapid expansion in supermarket penetration in developing countries is a fairly recent phenomenon, notable only over the last five to ten years, that is proceeding at different rates and depths in the various regions of the developing world (11).

The emergence of supermarkets in developing countries reflects a structural change in the way that meat, dairy products and eggs are collected, inspected, processed, packaged and supplied to consumers. It is a change that has deep impacts on livestock producers, particularly in determining who can and who cannot participate in the mainstream supply chains. A segmentation of markets can be observed, between the rapidly growing formal and the stagnating or declining informal supply chains, and between the 'wet' markets for fresh meat and the supermarket outlets of processed, frozen, packaged and branded meat. The relative significance of each market segment is tied to the level of economic development. It is closely linked to the purchasing power of households and individuals, their demand for leisure, their preferences with respect to the form and texture of meat upon purchase, and the relative value they give to notions of food that are considered 'safe'.

At the same time large-scale retailers compete in delivering consistent product quality that is demanded by their main market. The concept of 'quality' from the producers' perspective is complex, and its attributes evolve over time. The definition of quality varies according to suppliers' strategies on the one hand, and to cultural influences on the other. It includes food safety, nutrition and attributes related to the commercial differentiation of the products (11). Large retailers require a reliable supply of agricultural

products from their suppliers (producers) with consistency in volume and in quality.

Vertical coordination presents the opportunity to keep control of operating and transaction costs while at the same time meeting high standards of food safety. It demands organisational and institutional changes in the relationship between the primary producer and the agri-food processor or supermarket distributor, giving rise either to various forms of vertically coordinated transactions (the retailer contracts suppliers and/or processors), or in the extreme form, to fully integrated systems (all units in the food chain owned by one company). Large retailers in developing countries are increasingly tending towards vertical coordination, although vertically coordinated chains may interact with informal markets that supply inputs of live animals or products.

Increasing scales of production

Throughout developed and rapidly developing countries, there is a continuing tendency for production scales to grow. This is particularly pronounced for the production of monogastrics, and less so for ruminants. In contrast, certain areas with low economic growth, like parts of South Asia and sub-Saharan Africa, have not yet experienced an increase in average scale of production.

The process of ever-growing scales is triggered by economies of scale: average production costs decline with an expanding scale of operations at various stages of the production process. As a result, the number of producers rapidly diminishes even though the sector as a whole may expand. In emerging economies, the average size of operations is rapidly increasing and the numbers of livestock producers are in sharp decline. For chicken in Brazil, between 1985 and 1996, most of the growth occurred in the larger farms of the central western part of the country: farms with more than 10,000 head increased their proportion of the total population from 42% to 78% (1).

Similarly in Thailand, only the largest category of pig farms grew in number (Fig. 3) (10). However, in the Southern Luzon region of the Philippines, one of the main pig producing regions of the country, the pig numbers in commercial farms exhibited phenomenal growth between 1980 and 2000, while the number of pigs produced by smallholders as a whole also increased (3).

Smallholders can stay in business by providing their labour input to their own farms at below market price, which works well in countries where there are limited employment opportunities in other sectors (5). But as soon as employment opportunities in other sectors rise, many smallholder producers opt out of livestock production.

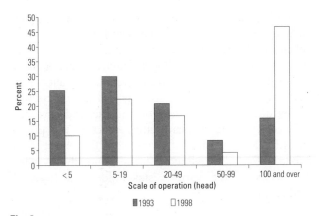

Fig. 3
Changes in the proportion of large and small-scale pig holdings in Thailand from 1993 to 1998

Different commodities and different stages in the production process reveal different potential for economies of scale. This potential tends to be high in the post-harvest sectors (e.g. slaughterhouses, dairy plants). In commodity production, poultry is most easily mechanised and shows a trend towards industrial forms of production even in the least-developed countries.

Livestock production system growth rates

The Livestock, Environment and Development Initiative has recently conducted an update ('Classification and characterization of world livestock production systems'; unpublished report for the Food and Agriculture Organization by J. Groenewold, 2005) of the world livestock production systems study by Seré and Steinfeld (12). The ten-year period between the two quantifications (which took averages of the periods 1991 to 1993 and 2001 to 2003) allows for a number of observations that among others confirm the importance of the above processes. Significant changes in resource endowment have brought about changes in the nature and extent of certain production systems. Permanent pastures show an increase at world level of about 3% in that period, particularly in Central/South America and western Asia/North Africa, while slight drops are observed in sub-Saharan Africa and in the countries of the Organization for Economic Co-operation and Development (OECD). Total arable land increased by about 5%, with almost all of this growth occurring in the developing regions. Major increases are observed in tropical highland grazing systems as well as in humid mixed irrigated systems. The irrigated area expanded by some 20% in ten years. This expansion has been particularly large in the arid and tropical highland grazing systems, as well as in the arid mixed rainfed systems.

As a consequence of the agricultural expansion, global cattle stocks are slightly up (5%), with considerable increases in stock numbers for sub-Saharan Africa, Asia

and Latin America. A sharp drop (almost 50%) in animal numbers occurred in Eastern Europe and the Commonwealth of Independent States (CIS, the former Soviet Union) following the collapse of the Soviet Union and political change in other countries. World output rose by about 10% in the period of observation, with very sharp differences at regional level; Asia almost doubled cattle meat output, sub-Saharan Africa increased by 30%, Latin America by 40%, and West Asia and North Africa (WANA), albeit from a lower absolute level, by about 20%. The strongest cattle output increases occurred in the mixed systems in the humid zones.

Total meat production from small ruminants increased by about 10%, while the overall stock numbers for small ruminants remained fairly constant for the two reference periods. There have been inter-regional shifts in distribution: stock numbers increased considerably in sub-Saharan Africa and Asia, and declined sharply in Latin America and the OECD, and in particular in Eastern Europe and the CIS. The increases occurred mainly in the mixed humid systems.

The changes in monogastric animal production are more notable. Total pig meat output rose by 30% at the world level, and this increase is accounted for almost entirely by the increased output in Asia. Most regional groupings show increases in pig meat production, while for Eastern Europe and the CIS there is a drop of about 30%. Industrial pig meat production grew at a pace of about 3% per annum. Major increases also occurred in the humid and temperate mixed irrigated systems.

The total production of poultry meat grew by about 75%, the greatest expansion of all livestock products. Regional differences are pronounced, with an extremely strong expansion in Asia (about 150% of added production, representing 9% yearly growth). The growth rates are generally positive, ranging between 2% and 10% across regions, the majority originating from the expansion of industrial systems. The global production of table eggs grew by about 40%. Asia more than doubled its egg production in the period and attained a share of about 50% of world production. The landless system grew by about 4% per year.

Implications for food safety

On a global average for 1997, animal products provided about 16% of the calories in the diet (6), representing around 25% in developed countries and around 12% in developing countries. For proteins over the same period the proportion was about 37%, being about 56% in developed countries and 29% in developing countries. Meat and other animal products also provide essential fatty

514

Rev. sci. tech. Off. int. Epiz., **25** (2)

acids, vitamins and minerals. The iron in meat and meat products is easily assimilated by humans and is a key to preventing iron deficiency anaemia, a high prevalence of which has been reported in, for example, Eastern Europe. The livestock industry therefore has great global economic and nutritional significance. While the global importance of animal food increases, the related changes in the livestock sector affect the security of the food provided in many ways. While being far from exhaustive, a few salient aspects of these consequences are highlighted below.

The production/demand trends described above have led to an increase in white meat consumption and a decline in red meat. This has important implications because it is the poultry, pig (requiring protein supplementation) and dairy industries that are the principal users of processed animal feeds. This feed must be of high quality to sustain efficient growth and feed conversion. It is important to realise, however, that the large and increasing volume of international trade in foods of animal origin as well as in feedstuffs adds an important international dimension to the control of animal feedstuffs. Given the direct links between feed safety and the safety of foods of animal origin, it is essential that feed production and manufacture be considered as an integral part of the food production chain. Feed production must therefore be subject, in the same way as food production, to quality assurance, including food safety systems based preferably on hazard analysis and critical control points. The Codex Alimentarius Commission has negotiated a *Code of Conduct on Safe Animal Feeding*, adopted in 2004, to help meet such requirements (2).

While in many developing countries LPS are subject to strong external forces and are in the process of rapid adjustment, little change is occurring in other countries. In a number of ways, it is the dichotomy that characterises livestock production in developing countries that poses the greatest challenge to food safety. Where traditional and modern forms of livestock production co-exist, with parallel market channels and outlets, uniform standards are difficult to enforce because of equity concerns, disease concerns, certification problems and other issues. This poses a formidable challenge to regulating and upgrading food safety in developing countries, particularly also because the two segments interact.

A recent Food and Agriculture Organization expert consultation on the dynamics of sanitary and technical requirements analysed the trends in food safety (8). Standards and regulations for animal health, food safety and food quality affect and are affected by the structure of livestock food chains. These standards are increasing in stringency, complexity and cost implications. They are variable in nature and driven by multiple forces, which include international agreements and bodies, national policies and laws, and the requirements of large-scale retailers. Consumers in affluent countries have a major impact on standard setting, yet the results may affect poor and marginal producers, processors and consumers who do not directly trade in the global market and have very little voice in the standard-setting process. The private sector has an increasing influence, while the impact of the public sector is limited and policies do not always reflect the needs of the various stakeholders in livestock food chains.

Food safety requirements are a major determinant shaping the structure of the livestock sector and associated food chains. One of the main aspects of the structural change process described above is the decoupling of production locations from consumption, and this has resulted in the risk through the food chain becoming an issue. Vertical integration, one of the other characteristics of structural change, also may affect food safety. The emergence of multinational food chains and a dramatic rise in the market share of supermarkets and the modern retail sector in many countries have created a number of effects, some of which may affect food safety:

– a shift toward cross-border systems, with corporations procuring goods in their different countries of operation

– a shift toward preferred-supplier systems to select producers who meet specific quality and safety standards and lower transaction costs

– a consolidation of production and processing which may have unexpected impacts on safety

– a shift toward safety and quality standards driven by the private sector.

While the speed and intensity of such effects vary by region – rapid in Eastern Europe, Latin America and the People's Republic of China, much slower in Africa – they suggest a trend that will continue. Other sectoral changes may take place in response to food safety concerns or in response to a crisis. In Thailand, for example, following the highly pathogenic avian influenza crisis, the poultry sector – and particularly the layer industry – showed signs of becoming more concentrated. Factors affecting this included producer liquidity, government policy and consumer risk perception towards food safety. The trend was already in evidence as a result of the export-oriented policy of one large company, but has been hastened by the avian influenza epidemic.

Les systèmes de production animale dans les pays en développement : statuts, moteurs, tendances

H. Steinfeld, T. Wassenaar & S. Jutzi

Résumé

Les auteurs décrivent et évaluent le statut actuel des systèmes de production animale ainsi que les moteurs de cette production au niveau mondial et les tendances dominantes dans ce secteur. L'analyse porte sur les six principales espèces d'élevage : les bœufs, les buffles, les chèvres, les moutons, les porcs et les poulets. Les moteurs impulsant le secteur de l'élevage au niveau mondial sont la croissance et les revenus économiques, l'évolution démographique et l'utilisation des sols, les changements d'habitudes alimentaires et les mutations technologiques. Le niveau de changement et les orientations prises pour développer le secteur de l'élevage sont très variables d'une région à l'autre. C'est en Asie que la croissance et le changement structurel sont les plus rapides. L'article aborde également la dynamique des systèmes en analysant la manière dont les systèmes de production animale se sont adaptés aux contraintes extérieures. L'article s'achève sur un bref examen des relations entre ces tendances et la sécurité sanitaire des aliments.

Mots-clés

Changement structurel – Moteur – Système de production animale.

■

Situación, fuerzas motrices y tendencias de los sistemas de producción agropecuaria en los países en desarrollo

H. Steinfeld, T. Wassenaar & S. Jutzi

Resumen

Los autores describen y evalúan la actual situación de los sistemas de producción agropecuaria, los factores que impulsan la producción a escala mundial y las tendencias básicas en este terreno. En su análisis estudian las seis principales especies que son objeto de producción industrial: vacas y búfalos, caprinos y ovinos, porcinos y pollos. Los factores que en el plano mundial ejercen de fuerza motriz del sector agropecuario son: el crecimiento económico y el nivel de renta, los cambios demográficos y de usos del suelo, la evolución de los regímenes alimentarios y los cambios tecnológicos. El ritmo y las orientaciones de la producción agropecuaria varían sobremanera según la región del mundo de que se trate. Asia, en este sentido, exhibe la mayor velocidad de crecimiento y el mayor nivel de cambios estructurales. Los autores se detienen también en la dinámica de los sistemas, analizando el modo en que la producción agropecuaria se ha adaptado a fuerzas externas. Para concluir, examinan brevemente la relación entre esas tendencias y la cuestión de la inocuidad de los alimentos.

Palabras clave

Cambio estructural – Fuerza motriz – Sistema de producción agropecuaria.

■

References

1. Camargo Barros G.S., Zen S.D., Piedade Bacchi M.R., Galvão de Miranda S.H., Narrod C. & Tiongco M. (2003). – Policy, technical, and environmental determinants and implications of the scaling-up of swine, broiler, layer and milk production in Brazil. Annex V, Final report of IFPRI-FAO Livestock Industrialization Project: phase II. International Food Policy Research Institute, Washington, DC.

2. Codex Alimentarius Commission (CAC) (2004). – Code of practice on good animal feeding. CAC report CAC/RCP 54-2004. Available at: http://www.codexalimentarius.net/download/standards/10080/CXC_054_2004e.pdf (accessed on 10 January 2006).

3. Costales A.C., Delgado C., Catelo M.A.O., Tiongco M., Chatterjee A., de los Reyes A. & Narrod C. (2003). – Policy, technical, and environmental determinants and implications of the scaling-up of broiler and swine production in the Philippines. Annex I, Final report of IFPRI-FAO Livestock Industrialization Project: phase II. International Food Policy Research Institute, Washington, DC.

4. Costales A., Gerber P. & Steinfeld H. (2006). – Underneath the livestock revolution. *In* Livestock report 2006. Food and Agriculture Organization, Rome, 15-27.

5. Delgado C., Narrod C. & Tiongco M. (2006). – Determinants and implications of the growing scale of livestock farms in four fast-growing developing countries. Research report (draft). International Food Policy Research Institute, Washington, DC.

6. Food and Agriculture Organization (FAO) (2000). – Food safety and quality as affected by animal feedstuffs. Agenda item 10.2, 22nd FAO regional conference for Europe, 24-28 July, Porto, Portugal. Available at: http://www.fao.org/docrep/meeting/x7320e.htm (accessed on 11 January 2006).

7. Food and Agriculture Organization (FAO) (2005). – FAO statistical databases. Available at: http://faostat.external.fao.org/ (accessed on 12 December 2005).

8. Food and Agriculture Organization (FAO) (2005). – The dynamics of sanitary and technical requirements: assisting the poor to cope. Proc. of an expert consultation, FAO-AGA, 22-24 June 2004, Rome. FAO, Rome.

9. Pingali P. (2004). – Westernization of Asian diets and the transformation of food systems: implications for research and policy. ESA Working Paper No. 04-17. Economic and Social Department, Food and Agriculture Organization, Rome.

10. Poapongsakorn N., NaRanong V., Delgado C., Narrod C., Siriprapanukul P., Srianant N., Goolchai P., Ruangchan S., Methrsuraruk S., Jittreekhun T., Chalermpao N., Tiongco M. & Suwankiri B. (2003). – Policy, technical, and environmental determinants and implications of the scaling-up of swine, broiler, layer and milk production in Thailand. Annex IV, Final report of IFPRI-FAO Livestock Industrialization Project: phase II. International Food Policy Research Institute, Washington, DC.

11. Reardon T. & Timmer C.P. (2005). – Transformation of markets for agricultural output in developing countries since 1950: how has thinking changed? *In* Handbook of agricultural economics, volume 3: agricultural development – farmers, farm production and farm markets (R. Evenson, P. Pingali & T.P. Schulz, eds). North Holland Press, Amsterdam, Chapter 13.

12. Seré C. & Steinfeld S. (1996). – World livestock production systems: current status, issues and trends. FAO Animal Production and Health Paper 127. Food and Agriculture Organization, Rome.

13. United Nations, Department of Economic and Social Affairs (UN-ESA) (2004). – World urbanization prospects: the 2003 revision. UN-ESA, New York. Available at: http://www.un.org/esa/population/publications/wup2003/WUP2003Report.pdf (accessed on 14 January 2006).

14. World Bank (2005). – World development indicators online. Available at: http://devdata.worldbank.org/dataonline/ (accessed on 12 December 2005).

Rev. sci. tech. Off. int. Epiz., 2006, **25** (2), 517-528

International livestock markets and the impact of animal disease

N. Morgan & A. Prakash

Food and Agriculture Organization, Commodity and Trade Division, Viale delle Terme di Caracalla, Rome, Italy

The views presented in this article are those of the authors and not necessarily those of the Food and Agriculture Organization.

Summary
Escalating and pervasive outbreaks of animal diseases are posing considerable challenges to livestock producers, industries, and policy-makers around the globe in a context of steadily rising demand for locally produced and imported livestock products. This paper reviews the factors and trends underpinning the growth in meat trade over the past decade and assesses the impact of animal diseases on international markets. The factors shaping the transmission of the impact of animal disease to global markets and back into domestic markets are identified and the potential global market impact of further animal disease outbreaks evaluated.

Keywords
Animal disease – Avian influenza – Bovine spongiform encephalopathy – Foot and mouth disease – Livestock – Meat trade.

Introduction

The global meat market has witnessed a profound transformation over the past 15 years, with rising incomes, changing consumption and demographic patterns prompting growth in consumption and trade that exceeds those of most other agricultural commodities (Fig. 1). Global meat consumption has increased by nearly three-quarters since 1990, in line with global economic growth. Consumers in both developed and developing countries are requiring a broader diversity and quality of meat cuts, more ease in preparation, and enhanced assurances about product safety.

Declines in feed prices in real terms and increases in productivity, achieved through specialisation, enhanced management and improved processing technologies, over the past decade, have led to progressively higher meat production and lower prices, particularly those of the poultry and pigmeat sectors (Fig. 2a). This is despite the concomitant increase in demand and the challenges posed by changing consumer requirements. This process was facilitated by increased cross-border movement of finance, knowledge and technology that permitted nearly three-quarters of this growth in global meat production to be concentrated in developing countries (Fig. 2b).

Among the major factors that have influenced the global livestock sector over the past few decades, the following are of particular relevance. Many of these factors are expected to continue to shape markets over the next decade.

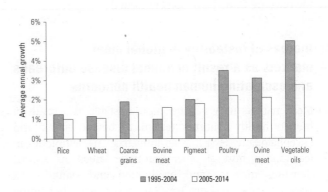

Fig. 1
The growth in the consumption and trade of meat compared with that of other agricultural commodities

Rev. sci. tech. Off. int. Epiz., **25** (2)

a) growth driven by gains in poultry/pork sectors

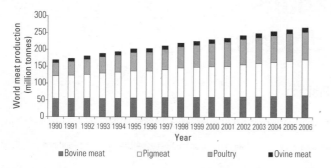

b) growth in developed and developing countries

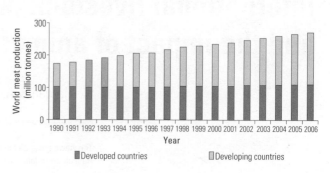

Fig. 2
World meat production, an historical perspective, 1990-2006

Structural changes in livestock industries, including improved genetics, upgraded animal housing, and enhanced management

In part these changes are a result of growing cross-border technology and investment flows into meat industries around the globe, particularly in strong growth markets or low-cost production regions. This trend is likely to continue in the future, leading to changing cost structures in industries in developing countries.

Changes in policy environment

Implementation of World Trade Organization (WTO) provisions for meat products over the past decade has led to a reduction in the use of export subsidies and expanding access to various markets. In particular, the transformation of tariff-rate quotas into *ad valorem* tariffs in many of the strongly growing Asia meat markets has had a significant and positive impact on trade. Policy developments that have stimulated trade flows have led to the increasing participation of developing countries in international markets as exporters. The gains are expected to continue, albeit at a slower pace, in the context of any agreement of the ongoing Doha Development Round.

Increased instability in global meat markets as a result of animal disease outbreaks and escalating human health concerns

Meat markets have become more unstable as a result of human health concerns related to bovine spongiform encephalopathy (BSE), avian influenza (AI), antibiotics in feed and a host of other non-trade issues. As animal densities increase and production and slaughtering systems change, disease outbreaks are becoming increasingly prevalent and widespread. In particular, the magnitude and the impact of these disease outbreaks have accelerated over the past five years with the imposition of disease-related import restictions, which had an immediate and visible impact on world meat trade.

The role of trade in the global meat economy

The evolution of meat trade since the 1990s has been, for the most part, resilient and dynamic, supported by developments in transportation, cold chain, and meat processing and packaging technology, which have all combined to push up trade nearly threefold since 1990 to an estimated 20 million tonnes in 2005. Meat trade as a share of production over this period rose from 5% to 8%. While gains in the volume of meat trade have exceeded most other agricultural products, the total value of global livestock and meat trade since 1990 has grown much more slowly than absolute trade volumes. This value was estimated at US$ 72 billion (source: FAOSTAT – http://faostat.fao.org) in 2004, which is up less than half from the 1990 level. The slower growth in the value versus the volume of trade is an indicator of the declining prices of meat and the changing meat product composition of livestock markets that have stimulated both trade and meat consumption around the globe. These price declines have been facilitated by technology and the ability of meat processors to produce a diverse combination of product cuts that are priced to sell to consumers in different markets characterised by a wide range of preferences and tastes.

Much of the growth in meat trade has been driven by growing demand for poultry cuts, due to both health and economic factors, such as lower relative prices. Poultry's share of the volume of global meat trade rose from 22% in 1990 to over 40% by 2005 (Fig. 3). Pork and beef trade has also grown, albeit more slowly, with increasing market access provisions under the WTO, as well as a plethora of bilateral and regional trade agreements.

Rev. sci. tech. Off. int. Epiz., **25** (2)

519

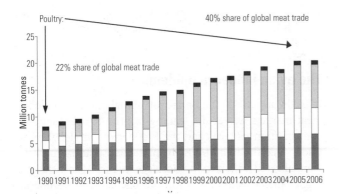

Fig. 3
Meat trade gains since 1990
Much of the growth in the meat trade has been driven by growing demand for poultry meat

Disease-related trade restrictions increasingly shape animal product markets

Over the past five years, the resilience of international meat markets has frequently been tested by the increasing and pervasive impacts of animal disease outbreaks. While many animal diseases, particularly foot and mouth disease (FMD) and most types of AI, are endemic in many parts of the developing world, only since 2001 has the severity of outbreaks of FMD (in Europe and Latin America) and more recently AI outbreaks in Asia (which have moved westward into Europe) had a significant impact on international meat markets.

Market disturbances induced by animal disease outbreaks have affected consumption and meat trading patterns, altered relative meat prices, and imposed ripple effects transcending the direct impact on livestock industries by imposing higher costs on the input industries and the broader economy. Worldwide import bans on meat from disease-infected areas, combined with heightened border inspections and testing, have limited trade gains over recent years, from the 7% annual gains witnessed during the late 1990s to only 2% annually over the past few years.

As a result of these outbreaks, meat producers, processors, traders and policy-makers are facing unprecedented challenges. Despite a context of relatively robust economic growth and growing demand for meat products, animal diseases are resulting in production losses and food safety-induced consumption shifts which limit potential industry gains. Trade disruptions resulting from import bans reinforce market segmentation, resulting in diverging meat prices within and between countries, and among products. Furthermore, the increasing complexity of global markets,

the uncertain nature of consumer demand, and the often prolonged and capricious imposition of market access conditions make it difficult to assess the duration and magnitude of a short-term market shock. Animal health and food safety issues, as well as those related to product quality, are expected to increase in complexity over the next decade, influencing consumption patterns and market access by competitive suppliers to global meat markets.

The impacts of animal diseases on international meat trade: an historical review

Prior to 2000, isolated disease outbreaks had short-lived and less dramatic impacts on global markets. These included the United Kingdom (UK) BSE crisis which since the mid-1990s, while causing temporary shifts in world beef demand to other meat products due to human health concerns, has had only a limited direct impact on beef shipments as the UK was not a significant exporter outside the European Union (EU). Similarly, in 1997, the EU classical swine fever outbreak significantly affected intra-EU trade, as the Netherlands was a major exporter of pork and live pigs within the EU, but global pork trade was largely unaffected since the Netherlands, as well as Germany, Belgium, France, Italy and Spain, were not major exporters of pork outside the EU. By contrast, the global pigmeat market was affected by the outbreak of foot and mouth disease in Taipei China when its pork exports, valued in 1996 at US$ 1.6 billion, fell to US$ 234 million in 1997. The broader impact of the disease was the major realignment of pigmeat destined for the Japanese market. The drop in product movement from Taipei China resulted in expanding pork shipments into the Japanese market from the United States of America (USA), Denmark, Canada and the Republic of Korea. However, the Republic of Korea's outbreak of foot and mouth disease in 2000 ended its recent growth in trade with Japan, valued at US$ 300 million, allowing other major exporters to increase their share of the Japanese market.

These relatively isolated animal disease outbreaks do not appear to have resulted in long-term market disruptions. This is partly because reduced exportable supplies from one producing country have typically been compensated by rapid increases in supplies elsewhere. From an international trade perspective, the increasingly pervasive outbreaks of transboundary animal diseases over the past five years and the consequential imposition of disease-related export restrictions have had much more immediate and visible impacts on world meat trade.

Foot and mouth disease in the United Kingdom and Latin America

In 2001 the severity and visibility of the FMD pandemic that affected major meat markets led to countries around the globe closing their borders to at least one-quarter of world beef trade and nearly 40% of global pork exports. These were imposed firstly to meat products originating in the countries of the EU and, later on, to those from Argentina, Uruguay, and parts of Brazil.

Global meat trade, disrupted by temporary market closures and food-safety-induced shifts in consumer preferences, grew only fractionally, registering the slowest gains in 13 years. Beef trade, in particular, destabilised by FMD outbreaks and escalating reports of BSE cases outside the UK, fell by 3% while demand and prices for meats other than beef, particularly poultry, rose. Trade losses for Argentina and Uruguay are estimated at US$ 400 million and US$ 150 million respectively. While the value of lost trade opportunities for the UK meat industries is estimated at only US$ 300 million, this amount pales compared to the total cost of the disease outbreak to the economy, estimated at US$ 9.2 billion (Table I).

While trade, with the exception of some markets for Argentinean beef, has recovered, the magnitude of the consequential losses, in particular in the UK, highlights the serious adverse impact that animal disease can have for the wider economy and the process of economic growth in both developed and developing countries.

The avian influenza epidemic

In 2004 and 2005, the impact of animal disease on global meat markets was acute, leading to price shocks, shifting consumption patterns and the first decline in global meat trade since the mid-1980s. In particular, poultry markets were affected with export shortages due to AI in Asia and higher prices leading to an unprecedented 8% decline in global poultry trade. Limitations on fresh/chilled/frozen products from disease-affected Asian exporters (in particular Thailand and the People's Republic of China) caused a decline in Asian exports from 1.8 million tonnes in 2003 to less than 1 million tonnes in 2004, a loss of approximately US$ 1 billion of export earnings for the region. These AI outbreaks followed on the heels of an H7N7 AI outbreak in the Netherlands in 2003 that, although quickly contained, cost the government nearly €150 million. The Dutch Agricultural Research Institute estimates that total costs for the Dutch farm sector, including related industries, were 500 million. While the impact of the outbreak reduced EU poultry production slightly in 2003, there was only a limited impact on global markets, with most of the impact on intra-European regional trade flows.

Table I
Cost of recent animal disease outbreaks (US$ million) (FAO study [1])

| Cost | BSE United Kingdom 1996/1997 | CSF Netherlands 1997/1998 | Foot and mouth disease | | | |
			Uruguay 2000 and 2001	United Kingdom 2001	Republic of Korea 2000	Japan 2000	Taipei China 1997
Direct costs							
Compensation	2,433	1,183	n.a.	2,223	377	0.5	188
Control measures	n.a.	138	20	1,335	66	14.5	66
Sub-total	2,433	1,321	20	3,558	433	15	254
Indirect costs							
Agricultural sector	n.a.	423	n.a.	489	n.a.	n.a.	2,202
Related industries	n.a.	596	60	267	n.a.	n.a.	3,212
Other	n.a.	n.a.	n.a.	4,890	n.a.	n.a.	949
Sub-total	1,395	1,019	60	5,646	n.a.	n.a.	6,363
Total costs	3,828	2,340	80	9,204	433	15	6,617
Impact on GDP	− 0.4% [a]	− 0.75%	n.a.	− 0.2% [b]	n.a.	n.a.	− 0.64%
Cost to public sector	63.5%	43.5%	25.0%	38.6%	n.a.	n.a.	3.8%
Cost to private sector	36.5%	56.5%	75.0%	61.4%	n.a.	n.a.	96.2%

a) − 0.1% to − 0.2% if the cost of compensation, which accounts for 64% of total costs, is excluded
b) the impact on United Kingdom (UK) gross domestic product (GDP) is relatively low because the cancellation of tourism and leisure to the countryside (53% of total costs), was largely offset by increased consumer spending in other sectors of the UK economy (4)
BSE: bovine spongiform encephalopathy
CSF: classical swine fever
n.a.: not available

It is clear that meat markets affected by animal disease outbreaks are characterised by considerable instability as governments are forced to adopt policies to protect their livestock sectors, including import bans, tighter sanitary border control measures, and stronger domestic regulations. Prices tend to become more volatile as importers scramble to procure meat products from disease-free zones. In 2001, beef trade dropped; however, some of the pressure on international beef prices was mitigated by a shift in trading patterns with non-disease affected markets increasing shipments and stronger import demand for other meats. In 2004, however, the pervasive impact of AI outbreaks led to a more than 30% increase in international poultry prices. The overall price impact on poultry prices has been additionally aggravated by shortages of other meats, particularly beef from North America; a region that, while traditionally supplying one-quarter of world beef trade, faced bans over the same period (2004-2005) from many countries due to BSE-concerns. Recent market developments since late 2005, however, have dramatically changed price developments in international meat markets. In particular, AI outbreaks in approximately 40 previously unaffected countries, many of which are the major poultry consuming and importing countries of Europe, the Middle East, and Africa, have prompted a decline in the FAO poultry price index by 22 points (Fig. 4). Dramatic consumer responses as consumers shifted their consumption patterns to include alternative protein sources are affecting market developments in global meat markets in 2006.

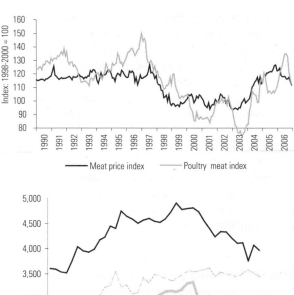

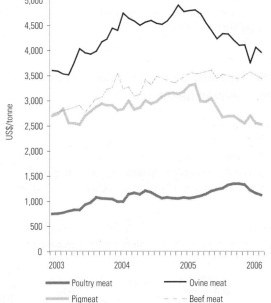

Fig. 4
Increased meat price volatility as a result of animal disease outbreaks

Policy challenges related to animal disease outbreaks

Key to the challenges being confronted by industries is the policy dimensions surrounding the issue of controlling animal diseases. Until recently animal diseases have been relatively localised in terms of their cost and impact on international livestock markets. Increasingly, as livestock production and trade have grown and markets have become more integrated, it is clear that national commodity strategies addressing animal disease issues need to be reinforced by international policies and guidelines that facilitate livestock trade while providing guidance on animal disease prevention and control.

Policy-makers need to have a good understanding of the overall market impact of animal diseases, both globally and locally, to be able to attribute costs to various sectors of the economies, covering producers, traders, feed and service industries, as well as the general economy etc., and to understand the socio-economic/equity implications of policy interventions which potentially reshape the structure of livestock industries. Animal disease outbreaks need to be recognised as problems that affect economies as

a whole, with policy intervention developed within a context of comprehensive cost information and tailored to deal with their socio-economic consequences. The development of tools to understand and analyse these linkages requires a solid understanding of how local livestock markets are linked to other sectors of the economy and to international markets. The next sections identify some of the factors determining those linkages and attempt to analyse the impact of further animal disease outbreaks on both local and international markets.

What puts global markets at risk from localised disease outbreaks?

The livestock sector is rapidly globalising as meat demand increases, structures of production change, and trade

522

Rev. sci. tech. Off. int. Epiz., **25** (2)

increases not only in absolute volume but also as a share of global production. In addition, the segmentation of meat markets that previously characterised trading patterns is gradually being eroded by disease eradication, policies on zoning and technologies that allow exporters to ship products in a form that minimises the risk of disease transmission, e.g. cooked product or beef aged to reduced FMD risk. Consequently, the impacts of localised animal disease outbreaks are quickly transposed into the global marketplace as a result of diverging trading patterns, changing consumption patterns (including shifts between different meats), and price shocks. Some of the key factors influencing the overall duration and impact of animal diseases are discussed below

Disease type and consumer response to potential human health issues

The potential risks of animal to human disease transmission posed by zoonotic diseases, including the H5N1 AI virus and BSE which is linked to variant Creutzfeldt-Jakob disease, have had a more durable impact on global meat markets than those resulting from other animal diseases

such as FMD or non-H5N1 AI outbreaks. A case in point is the prolonged ban on North American beef after the discovery of three BSE-infected cows in 2003. The USA and Canada normally account for more than one-quarter of global beef exports (around 1.6 million tonnes, valued at approximately US$ 4 billion). Two-year bans by major Asian importing countries contributed to nearly 20% gains in international beef prices over the same period. History seems to reveal that changing consumption and trade patterns related to zoonotic animal diseases tend to recover within two years. However, consumer and government responses to the human health implications of animal diseases make any type of market assessment of the overall impacts extremely complicated because of the difficulties of estimating consumption impacts in different markets.

Disease outbreak location/ duration and global market concentration

Despite the increasing shift in the percentage of global trade being provided by developing countries and growing export gains from non-traditional middle-income exporters, the degree of market concentration in the global

Table IIa
Largest meat exporters: share of global trade (percentage)

Poultry	United States of America	Brazil	European Union (EU-15)	People's Republic of China including Hong Kong	Thailand	Total market share of the five largest exporters	Developed countries	Developing countries
1980-1990	29	21	31	1	5	87	67	33
1990-2000	41	12	17	9	5	84	66	34
2000-2004	36	22	13	7	6	84	56	44
2004	34	36	11	3	3	87	52	48

Bovine meat	Australia	United States of America	European Union (EU-15)	New Zealand	Brazil	Total market share of the five largest exporters	Developed countries	Developing countries
1980-1990	24	7	32	11	9	83	66	34
1990-2000	21	15	19	8	5	68	76	24
2000-2004	21	15	8	8	15	67	66	34

Pigmeat	European Union (EU-15)	Canada	United States of America	People's Republic of China	Brazil	Total market share of the five largest exporters	Developed countries	Developing countries
1980-1990	40	18	6	17	1	82	74	26
1990-2000	35	15	13	8	3	74	77	23
2000-2004	27	20	18	8	11	84	75	25

Total meat	United States of America	Brazil	European Union (EU-15)	Australia	Canada	Total market share of the five largest exporters	Developed countries	Developing countries
1980-1990	11	8	30	14	5	68	70	30
1990-2000	23	7	20	10	5	65	73	27
2000-2004	24	16	14	14	7	75	64	36

Rev. sci. tech. Off. int. Epiz., **25** (2)

523

meat market is high, with five major exporters accounting for nearly three-quarters of global meat exports (Table II). This high degree of concentration in global meat markets, in the context of any market shocks, including those resulting from animal disease outbreaks, can translate into large swings in international prices. Of particular note is the rapid escalation of meat exports from Brazil, which has risen from less than 10% of global meat trade in 2000 to an estimated 35% by 2005.

Links to international markets

The extent to which a country or region is impacted by a disease is dependent on their linkages to international livestock markets and the meat product trade.

A heavy export dependency by some countries can lead to significant market disruptions, both internationally and domestically. Such examples include the Canadian cattle industry which exported 12% of their live animals and nearly 50% of total beef production prior to the identification of a BSE-infected animal in May 2003. After two years, at a cost of over US$ 4 billion, exports of meat are finally recovering but live animal exports are still languishing. In 2003 alone, the value of Canadian beef and

cattle exports declined by over US$ 1.3 billion. In Asia, the Thai poultry industry, prior to the AI outbreaks in late 2003 was the fourth largest poultry exporter after the USA, Brazil, and the EU. With approximately 40% of Thailand's estimated production of 1.5 million tonnes destined for export markets, market closures resulted in a 40% decline in export earnings in 2004, from US$ 1.1 billion to US$ 674 million. Such trade losses, the cost of animal disease surveillance and control, and livelihood losses to poultry producing households are estimated to have resulted in a 1.5% gross domestic product (GDP) loss for the country (2).

The net trade position of a major trading country and the trade share of production/consumption will also determine how localised the impact of an animal disease will be, as well as how global trading patterns are likely to be shaped. Animal disease outbreaks in countries that are both large importers and exporters of the same products, such as the USA for beef or the EU for poultry, have a very different impact on global markets than outbreaks in countries that are only exporters. For example, the discovery of BSE-infected cattle in Canada and the USA resulted in different impacts in the two markets due to differing characteristics of the two respective beef markets. While the USA is one of the world's largest beef exporters, exports account for only 10% of production and it is a net beef and live cattle

Table IIb
Largest meat importers: share of global trade (percentage)

Poultry	Russia	Hong Kong	Japan	People's Republic of China	European Union (EU-15)	Total market share of the five largest importers	Developed countries	Developing countries
1980-1990	n.a	12	23	2	17	54	44	56
1990-2000	20	14	13	10	6	64	48	52
2000-2004	16	11	10	8	8	54	49	51

Bovine meat	United States of America	Japan	Russia	European Union (EU-15)	Mexico	Total market share of the five largest importers	Developed countries	Developing countries
1980-1990	38	12	n.a.	16	1	66	69	31
1990-2000	22	16	12	8	4	63	69	31
2000-2004	24	13	10	8	6	61	65	35

Pigmeat	Japan	Russia	United States of America	People's Republic of China including Hong Kong	Mexico	Total market share of the five largest importers	Developed countries	Developing countries
1980-1990	26	n.a.	39	8	2	75	78	22
1990-2000	29	20	14	6	5	75	75	25
2000-2004	26	11	12	7	8	64	67	33

Total meat	Japan	United States of America	European Union (EU-15)	Mexico	People's Republic of China including Hong Kong	Total market share of the five largest importers	Developed countries	Developing countries
1980-1990	18	28	21	1	5	73	66	34
1990-2000	17	11	8	4	7	48	62	38
2000-2004	14	11	8	6	7	46	58	42

importer. The value of US beef exports, as a result of the discovery of two BSE-cows led to a drop of export earnings of US$ 2.6 billion in 2004 while the absence of US beef in global markets contributed to higher international prices. However, domestic prices remained relatively high as imports adjusted. This contrasts with the domestic impact in Canada where a more dramatic dependence on international export markets, as indicated above, immediately translated into cattle prices dropping by approximately 50% and reduction of cattle and calf receipts for 2003 by 33% from the previous year's level (3). Since Canada is not a net beef importing country, imports could not adjust sufficiently to maintain stable prices.

In the case of countries which are neither importers nor exporters, the impact of an animal disease outbreak will be linked to the structure of the industry and the contribution of the livestock sector to GDP. The extent of the losses beyond the production sector depends on linkages with other sectors within the agricultural supply chain. In most cases, animal disease outbreaks in these cases will only have a limited impact on international markets, with the glaring exception being the potential consumption shocks generated by the H5N1 AI which is aggravated by the human-to-human health concerns.

Industry structure and the degree to which the industry is linked to other sectors of the economy

Livestock industries in many developed, and increasingly developing countries, have a high degree of vertical linkages with upstream and downstream industries as well as horizontal linkages between industries in different countries through foreign investment. Livestock industries can be significant users of raw materials from upstream industries and are a major provider of raw materials for downstream industries. Any shock to highly concentrated industries that undertake further processing and move packaged products to numerous outlets around the country will have knock-on effects throughout the supply chain. Consequently, the broader impact of animal diseases needs to be examined to identify the market impacts on other sectors of the economy.

Further outbreaks of avian influenza: what are the market implications?

Identifying the scenario

After the AI outbreaks of 2004 and 2005 and BSE-concerns about North American beef over the same period,

meat markets are expected to recover in 2006, with consumption rising and increased production in disease-free countries mitigating the pressure for upward price movements. However, considerable uncertainty clouds any potential market impact of further outbreaks of AI, particularly in Europe where its close proximity to recent outbreaks raises concerns about the risk of disease transmission. In the current situation, a key issue for the global poultry sector is the vulnerability of poultry markets to any major market shocks, in particular any potential outbreak in the EU, a significant player in world poultry markets. This has led the Food and Agriculture Organization (FAO) to evaluate the impact that any extensive outbreak of avian influenza that spreads over the major EU producing countries (five countries account for two-thirds of EU poultry production: France, the UK, Spain, Germany and Italy) would have on global poultry markets as countries around the globe ban imports from the EU (a summary of this evaluation, including the difficulties of undertaking such a study, is discussed below).

Reviewing any complicating factors

Any straightforward assessment of the potential global impact of AI in Europe is, however, complicated by the recent outbreaks of FMD in Brazil – the world's largest meat exporter of both beef and poultry – which will also influence world meat markets over the short term. The market impact of poultry shortages in international markets, in particular relative price movements, would be heightened by reduced exportable beef supplies from Brazil which was expected to account for more than one-quarter of the global beef shipments in 2005. The combination of these two events would be expected to put considerable upward pressure on all meat prices, similar to the situation in 2004 when the absence of North American beef due to BSE-concerns led to hikes in all meat prices.

A factor complicating the analysis is the net trade position of a country. Whereas Brazil has limited imports, the EU is both a major importer and exporter of poultry meat. The EU ships approximately 1 million tonnes of fresh/chilled/frozen poultry products, valued at over US$ 1 billion, to more than 150 markets around the world with three-quarters of these shipments destined for Russia (23%), Middle Eastern markets (27%) and developing countries in Africa (26%). Meanwhile, they also import approximately 500,000 tonnes of frozen fillets and other chicken products. These imports would be expected to drop as internal EU prices decline relative to rising world prices. Similarly, the EU is increasingly a net beef importer. With a large percentage of imports sourced from FMD-affected Brazil, any shortfalls would prompt a rise in domestic beef prices as bans are imposed on Brazilian beef products.

Rev. sci. tech. Off. int. Epiz., **25** (2)

525

Working through the possible market impacts of a scenario analysis

With the EU accounting for approximately 13% of global poultry production and exports, and Brazil supplying nearly one-third of global beef shipments, international poultry and beef prices would be expected to move up sharply. Meanwhile, internal prices in these two disease-affected markets would decline as would production prospects and feed prices as meat products intended for exports, approximately 10% of production for EU poultry and 25% of Brazilian beef, move back into local markets. Differing production structures for the two livestock species, in particular the ability of producers to hold cattle back from slaughter, could, however, imply different supply availabilities on local markets.

Measuring the impacts of a potential market shock

Assessing the overall impact of an animal disease on both global meat markets and other sectors, such as the feed industry, ideally necessitates the use of a framework that links markets, both spatially and cross-commodity. In the absence of such a framework, it is somewhat difficult to disentangle the impacts that specific disease outbreaks have because of the complexities in determining trade developments that would have occurred in the absence of disease outbreaks. To evaluate the short-term global impact of a potential outbreak of AI in the EU, FAO's short-term commodity model (STM) was used. The STM is a dynamic, multi-commodity, partial-equilibrium, global trade model, which provides one-year-ahead projections for demand, imports, exports, stocks and prices, given predetermined supply for 18 basic foodstuffs, covering 50 countries /regions. Four meat categories, sub-divided into FMD-affected and FMD-free markets, are included in the model alongside a comprehensive coverage of the feed sector. Changes in real income, population and exchange rates are the principal exogenous variables driving global agricultural commodity markets.

Conditioning the impact assessment are the various assumptions underpinning the analysis. The scenario in the FAO study assumes that AI outbreaks in the EU are spread out over the major producing areas, thus inducing import bans on poultry products from the entire region. Producers in the EU, in response to lower prices, are expected to lower production levels. While AI is expected to result in changes in poultry consumption as consumers shift to alternative protein sources, it is assumed that this is only of a short duration as risk communication strategies ensure that consumers are aware of the minimal risks of avian influenza transmission through poultry consumption. Consequently poultry consumption over the period of the shock is assumed to remain relatively stable.

This scenario evaluates the impact of two major shocks to global meat markets that are imposed exogenously:

a) EU poultry exports drop to 0 from 1 million tonnes while imports adjust based on demand

b) Brazilian exports of beef decline by 200,000 tonnes (down 10% from their projected exports of 1.8 million tonnes). (This assumption is a moderate case scenario which reflects Mato Grosso do Sul's and Parana's [the FMD-affected states] position as suppliers of nearly half of Brazil's beef exports. In actual fact, due to the FMD outbreak in October 2005, Brazilian beef exports in 2005 grew at only 16%, half of the trade gains registered over the past five years and less than FAO's estimated gains of nearly 22%.)

Market implications

Any extensive AI outbreak in the EU, combined with reduced exportable beef supplies from Brazil, would have immediate implications on global meat and feed markets. Preliminary results of the FAO analysis indicate that the potential short-term impact would be higher meat prices for all meats on world markets (ranging from 9% and 11% for poultry and beef respectively and 6% for pigmeat), lower global meat consumption, and a shift in trading patterns with some markets moving to fill the gap left by Europe (for chicken) and Brazil (for beef). In addition, spillover effects would be evident in the feed industry as lower meat production pushes down grain and protein feed consumption, resulting in price drops of 2% and 5%, respectively (Table III).

The results of this short-term analysis have been shaped on the basis of rather extreme assumptions including the total loss of the EU export market in the context of AI outbreaks and expectations that European consumers and others will not reduce their consumption of poultry products. In fact, poultry consumption in the EU was already affected in 2005 despite the absence of an actual outbreak in the EU. Sales of poultry dropped in many European countries with poultry prices, production, and feed use reported down. In addition, trade flows within Europe have been affected with markets such as the Netherlands, heavily dependent on intra-European trade, reporting poultry price declines of up to 25% and falling animal feed exports.

With potential outbreaks and consumer responses uncertain, the above scenario is only one possible impact assessment. Consumption responses are very difficult to anticipate as is the ability of other major exporting

Table III
The projected implications for global meat
and feed markets of any extensive outbreak of avian influenza

Type of change	Percentage change		
	World	European Union (EU-25)	Brazil
Bovine meat			
Production	− 0.19	0.00	− 1.51
Consumption	− 0.19	− 0.05	+ 2.69
Exports	+ 4.45	0.00	− 17.05
Imports	+ 4.28	− 0.59	0.00
Price	+ 11.41	+ 0.80	− 2.57
Poultry			
Production	− 1.93	− 14.35	0.00
Consumption	− 1.92	− 0.55	− 3.20
Exports	+ 0.46	− 100.00	+ 7.15
Imports	+ 0.46	− 6.25	0.00
Price	+ 9.02	− 7.08	+ 7.16
Pigmeat			
Production	0.00	0.00	0.00
Consumption	+ 0.01	+ 0.23	+ 0.41
Exports	+ 1.61	− 3.30	− 1.48
Imports	+ 1.58	+ 0.23	0.00
Price	+ 6.83	+ 0.26	+ 0.75
Wheat feed			
Consumption	− 0.68	− 1.19	− 0.90
Price	− 1.91	− 1.91	− 0.58
Corn feed			
Consumption	− 0.37	− 2.54	− 0.37
Price	− 2.08	− 0.63	− 0.63
Protein feed			
Consumption	− 0.21	− 2.04	+ 2.17
Price	− 4.55	0.00	0.00

countries, particularly the USA and Brazil who supply nearly 70% of global poultry trade, to step up production and exports of poultry meat in the short-term. The ability of these countries to respond to market shocks and higher prices would obviously mitigate upward price shocks. This, of course, assumes that there are no supply constraints in these countries and they themselves do not experience any AI outbreaks.

Conclusions

International meat markets have been increasingly affected by animal disease outbreaks which have caused trade diversion and shifting market shares between exporters of the same and different types of meat products. History as an indicator has, however, shown us that global meat markets are very resilient to these shocks, with markets typically recovering within a few years. The short-term costs to economies, however, are considerable and even short-term market impacts have long-term implications for trading patterns, policy formulation and industry and sector development. Increasing recognition is being paid to the fact that the continual emergence and re-emergence of disease outbreaks are increasingly resulting in frequent short-term market disruptions which impose significant costs to producers, industries, and economies around the globe. Economic models are a useful tool that take into account the factors affecting the market fundamentals and may provide useful indications of the potential impact on livestock prices and trading patterns.

The broader implications of the proliferation of animal diseases, including an assessment of the localised costs of the animal disease outbreaks, cannot, however, be measured by an econometric model. Increasing attention is being placed on the costs, both direct and indirect, of animal diseases for producers, industries and consumers, as well as to the broader economy. A previous review undertaken by FAO (1) demonstrates the enormous financial and economic losses that can accrue to both developed and developing nations following the outbreak of a transboundary animal disease (Fig. 5). In many cases, the costs of animal diseases to the livelihoods of households and industries linked to the livestock sector are underestimated.

One of the long-term consequences of the costs imposed by animal diseases is that longer-term investment in the

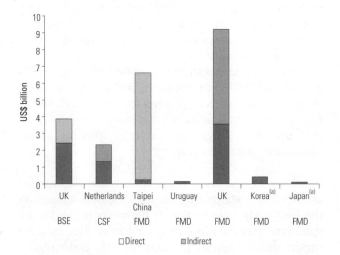

a) indirect costs not available
BSE: bovine spongiform encephalopathy
CSF: classical swine fever
FMD: foot and mouth disease
UK: United Kingdom

Fig. 5
The cost of animal disease outbreaks

Rev. sci. tech. Off. int. Epiz., **25** (2)

527

sector will be shaped by the increased market volatility engendered by disease outbreaks. Whereas in developed countries, governments have the ability to compensate a given sector, the invisible impact of such diseases in developing countries on small producers have implications for livelihoods and food security. Increasingly, and very acutely in the case of AI which has implications for human health, policy-makers are faced with the difficult question of how the livestock sector should be structured and what needs to be done to limit the damaging impact of animal disease outbreaks.

■

Impact des maladies animales sur les échanges internationaux d'animaux d'élevage et de leurs produits

N. Morgan & A. Prakash

Résumé
Partout dans le monde, la gravité et l'extension croissantes des foyers épizootiques posent d'immenses difficultés aux éleveurs, au secteur agroalimentaire et aux responsables politiques, dans un contexte d'augmentation constante de la demande en produits d'origine animale issus des productions locales ou des marchés internationaux. Après avoir expliqué les facteurs et les tendances qui soutiennent la croissance du marché de la viande depuis une dizaine d'années, les auteurs évaluent l'impact des maladies animales sur les échanges internationaux. Les facteurs déterminant que l'impact d'une épizootie puisse se répercuter sur les marchés mondiaux, puis affecter de nouveau le marché intérieur d'un pays, sont ainsi identifiés ; l'impact potentiel de nouveaux foyers épizootiques sur le marché mondial est également évalué.

Mots-clés
Animal d'élevage – Commerce de la viande – Encéphalopathie spongiforme bovine – Fièvre aphteuse – Influenza aviaire – Maladie animale.

■

528

Rev. sci. tech. Off. int. Epiz., 25 (2)

Influencia de las enfermedades animales en los mercados agropecuarios internacionales

N. Morgan & A. Prakash

Resumen

En todo el planeta, la proliferación de brotes zoosanitarios cada vez más agresivos plantea considerables problemas al sector de la producción y la industria agropecuarias, así como a los organismos de planificación, en un contexto en el que viene aumentando, sin prisa pero sin pausa, la demanda de productos ganaderos, ya sean importados o de origen local. Tras describir los factores y tendencias que han impulsado el crecimiento del comercio de carne en el último decenio, los autores evalúan la influencia de la situación zoosanitaria en los mercados internacionales. También examinan los factores que hacen que las repercusiones de las enfermedades animales se transmitan a los mercados mundiales para después incidir de vuelta en los mercados nacionales. Asimismo, evalúan las posibles consecuencias de nuevos brotes zoosanitarios para los mercados mundiales.

Palabras clave

Comercio de carne – Enfermedad animal – Encefalopatía espongiforme bovina – Fiebre aftosa – Ganado – Influenza aviar.

■

Referènces

1. Food and Agriculture Organization (FAO) (2002). – Animal diseases: implications for international meat trade. Nineteenth session of the intergovernmental group of meat and dairy products 27-29 August, Rome. FAO, Rome.

2. McLeod A., Morgan N., Prakash A. & Hinrichs J. (2005). – Economic and social impacts of avian influenza, November. Food and Agriculture Organization, Rome.

3. Statistics Canada, Agriculture Division (2004). – Canada's beef cattle sector and the impact of BSE on farm family income, 2000-2003. Agriculture and Rural Working Paper Series Working Paper No. 69, June. Statistics Canada, Ottawa.

4. Thompson D. (2001). – Economic consequences of the FMD outbreak on the wider economy in the UK. Paper presented at the international conference on control and prevention of foot and mouth disease, 12-13 December, Brussels.

Rev. sci. tech. Off. int. Epiz., 2006, **25** (2), 529-539

Food safety begins on the farm: the viewpoint of the producer

K.E. Olson & G.N. Slack

National Institute for Animal Agriculture, 1910 Lyda Drive, Bowling Green, KY 42104, United States of America

Summary

Consumers expect the food they purchase to be safe. Governments seek to provide them with assurances of food safety through regulation, but additional steps are needed to more fully address the issue. Producers are increasingly aware of their responsibility in this area and are working in concert with other segments of the agri-food industry. Hazard analysis critical control point-based (HACCP) quality assurance programmes are being developed and implemented at the farm level for most species, in many countries. These approaches will enhance food safety for consumers everywhere. Producers continue to demonstrate that they respond positively to programmes based on science and good management practices. The authors conclude that the use of HACCP programmes will continue to increase.

Keywords

Farm-based programmes – Food safety – Hazard analysis critical control point – Pre-harvest – Producer survey – Producers – Quality assurance – Survey.

Introduction

Everyone in the food production chain, 'from the stable to the table', or from pre-harvest to post-harvest, has a role and responsibility in ensuring the safety of the food supply. Producers around the world recognise that food safety begins with them and take this responsibility seriously. Regulations on food safety may not be as obvious on the farm or ranch as they are in processing plants, stores or eating establishments, but they already exist in many areas (7, 19). While regulations address food safety issues by enforcing standards, producers are, in many cases, taking active steps to ensure food safety by establishing species-specific programmes to deal effectively with potential concerns. The standards that govern international trade (1, 4, 6) are also concerned with food safety and affect the actions of producers and food processors.

Background

'Food safety' generally refers to all hazards that may make food injurious to the consumer, while 'quality' includes those attributes that influence the value of a product. Food quality normally has a range of values that may be acceptable and this range is typically driven by market forces. Producers receive price incentives, positive or negative, that are intended to reflect the value that consumers place on their products. On the other hand, food safety is seen as non-negotiable. It is expected by consumers and thus supervised by government officials. As a result, a mixture of national and international agencies and regulations seek to protect the safety of the food supply in most countries (1, 7, 11, 20).

In spite of a variety of regulations, and good intentions on the part of all, food safety problems do arise. These range from microbial contamination to pesticide and antimicrobial residues (5, 20). In addition to traditional food safety issues, concern is being raised over newer issues, such as:

– new production technologies

– bioterrorism

– emerging or re-emerging zoonotic diseases (4, 5).

530

Rev. sci. tech. Off. int. Epiz., **25** (2)

Producer awareness

The primary concern of producers is to maintain the economic viability of their farm or ranch, as they and their families depend on this for their livelihood. Production practices are typically judged by the impact that they have on the productivity and efficiency of the animals and the overall production unit. A general perspective in the producer community is that producers are the most interested parties in assuring the health and well-being of their animals, since only healthy, well-cared-for animals are productive. Maintaining healthy animals also helps to ensure the production of 'safe' food. Producers have demonstrated that they respond positively to product quality incentives that reflect consumer demand (see, 'What producers are doing', below).

Leaner cattle and pigs/hogs, reduced somatic cell levels in milk, greater emphasis on protein in milk and a reduction in injection-site lesions are a few examples of concerns that producers have addressed through changes in livestock management. Although these items primarily reflect quality issues, producers are also concerned about food safety.

One of the most comprehensive efforts to assess the attitudes and actions of producers and animal professionals toward food safety was a survey (8) conducted under the auspices of the Livestock Conservation Institute (LCI), in conjunction with the University of Kentucky Survey Research Center, for the United States Department of Agriculture (USDA). This survey was designed to evaluate food safety education programmes developed for food animal producers. A combination of state veterinarians, extension veterinarians, extension specialists and producers were included in the survey. A total of 1,299 responses were received out of 2,500 surveys distributed. The following farming interests were represented in the final tally:

– beef (68.8%)

– dairy (51.7%)

– pork (43.6%)

– lamb (29.8%)

– broilers (17.4%)

– eggs (14.8%)

– turkeys (10.9%)

– veal (6.9%).

As expected from a survey population, many respondents covered multiple species. A summary of all questions and responses is included as Appendix 1.

The first question in the survey (*Regarding food safety and food safety policy, which of the following do you feel are of significant importance?*) presented a variety of items and asked respondents to indicate which were the most significant for food safety and food safety policy. Strong majorities of respondents felt that 'microbial pathogens' (80.4%), 'public perceptions' (76.6%) and 'antimicrobial residues' (67.2%) were of significant importance. Also important to a majority were: 'good production practices' (61.7%) and 'imported foods' (56.1%).

Fewer respondents thought that 'water quality' (47.4%), 'on-farm hazard analysis critical control point (HACCP)' (41.2%), 'maintenance of markets' (33.8%) and 'international trade barriers' (29.5%) were of significant importance. In addition, 5.6% indicated that other factors were important, with 'food handling practices' being the most common response.

As a group, veterinarians were significantly more likely than educators to cite:

– antibiotic residues

– imported foods

– international trade barriers

– water quality

– maintenance of markets

– good production practices.

Veterinarians were also significantly more likely than producers to cite:

– antibiotic residues

– microbial pathogens

– on-farm HACCP

– water quality

– good production practices.

Educators were more likely to cite microbial pathogens, on-farm HACCP and water quality than producers. Producers were more likely to cite international trade barriers than educators.

Table I summarises the responses of all survey participants. These responses reflect both real food safety issues and factors that potentially affect the livelihood of a producer.

Another question asked: *What quality assurance/food safety assurance tools have you found that producers use the most? (Please circle all that apply.)*

Strong majorities of all respondent groups cited 'antibiotic/chemical residue avoidance programmes' (75.3%) and 'water quality programmes' (64.1%).

Table I
Items indicated as significant for food safety by respondents to the survey

Item	Frequency	Percentage
Antibiotic residues	871	67.2
Microbial pathogens	1,043	80.4
Imported food	727	56.1
On-farm hazard analysis critical control point	534	41.2
International trade barriers	382	29.5
Water quality	615	47.4
Public perceptions	993	76.6
Maintenance of markets	438	33.8
Good production practices	800	61.7

Source: report on Livestock Conservation Institute Food Safety Survey of Food Animal Production Professionals (8)

Majorities also cited:

– dead animal disposal system (58.4%)

– general hygiene/sanitation (57.7%)

– injection site selection/management (56.4%)

– waste disposal management (51.3%).

Significant numbers also cited:

– rodent control (45.9%)

– general biosecurity practices (40.4%)

– feed bunk (manger) management (35.7%)

– routine veterinary inspection (34.8%)

– isolation/quarantine of incoming animals (32.3%).

Fewer than 30% of respondents reported the use of:

– colostrum management (28.3%)

– limited access to the farm (27.7%)

– feed control measures and facility design to avoid muddy lots (26.5%)

– pathogen reduction programmes (25.4%)

– segregated housing (22%)

– bird control system (19.3%)

– flush system management (11.3%).

In addition, 2.6% cited various other tools in use.

Producers were significantly more likely than veterinarians to identify:

– water quality programmes

– isolation/quarantine of incoming animals

– feed control measures

– waste disposal management

– facility design

– limited access to the farm.

Producers were also significantly more likely than educators to identify:

– water quality programmes

– general biosecurity practices

– feed control measures

– waste disposal management

– rodent control

– dead animal disposal

– limited access to the farm

– routine veterinary inspection.

Veterinarians were more likely than educators to identify:

– antibiotic/chemical residue avoidance programmes

– general biosecurity practices

– rodent control

– colostrum management

– dead animal disposal

– routine veterinary inspection.

Veterinarians were also more likely to identify 'colostrum management' than producers. Educators were more likely to identify 'isolation/quarantine of incoming animals' and 'feed control measures' than veterinarians. Veterinarians were significantly more likely to mention programmes to reduce the risk of residues than producers or educators.

Based on their responses, both producers and food animal production professionals demonstrated a good awareness of food safety issues that were likely to concern consumers and regulators alike. To further explore this area, the survey asked: *How important are the following incentives for producers to participate in quality assurance/food safety programmes in your area, state or region? Would you say they are very important, somewhat important, or not important at all?*

There was substantial agreement that all of the incentives listed were at least somewhat important, with over 90% of the respondents placing each of them in that category. An interesting pattern emerged, however, when examining how many respondents rated the incentives as 'very important'. The most important incentives appeared to be the avoidance of penalties or sanctions:

– avoiding a penalty in price for the product (71.5% cited this as 'very important')

– maintaining market access (62.8%)

– reducing the risk of residue violations (62.7%).

Production factors appeared to be the next most important incentive:

– production of a quality product (57.4%)

– enhanced production performance (53.6%)

– marketing a 'value-added' product (50.6%).

Fewer than half of the respondents cited a 'reduction in food-borne disease' (44.9%) or 'personal satisfaction' (34.6%) as important incentives to participate in these programmes. Two percent (2.2%) cited some other incentive as being 'very important', with 'price increases' being the one most often mentioned.

Producers were significantly more likely to mention a reduction in food-borne disease, producing a quality product, marketing a 'value-added' product and enhanced production performance as important incentives than either veterinarians or educators. This may be interpreted as indicating that the desire to produce a safe product is a major incentive for producers.

Overall results are included in Table II.

This issue was examined in further detail by asking participants to identify: *The characteristics that make a programme effective include: (please circle all that apply).*

The top five characteristics of an effective programme, as identified by the respondents, are:

– economical to implement (80.8%)

Table II
Incentives ranked as important for implementing quality assurance and food safety programmes by respondents to the survey

Incentive	Very important (%)	Somewhat important (%)	Not important (%)
Reduce food-borne disease	44.9	49.5	5.7
Gain personal satisfaction	34.4	57.9	7.8
Reduce risk-residue violations	62.7	34.7	2.7
Produce quality product	57.4	41.2	1.5
Produce value-added product	50.6	39.9	9.4
Maintain market access	62.8	33.4	3.8
Avoid price penalty	71.5	24.3	4.1
Enhance performance	53.6	41.8	4.5

Source: report on Livestock Conservation Institute Food Safety Survey of Food Animal Production Professionals (8)

– based on scientific data (71.6%)

– evidence of increased product quality (67.4%)

– satisfactory benefit-to-cost ratio (67.3%)

– broad participation by producers (64.6%).

Characteristics cited by almost half the respondents were: 'industry operated' (46%) and 'voluntary' (44.9%). 'Government mandated' (14.5%) and 'government operated' (2.9%) were much less desirable characteristics. In addition, 7.4% of respondents identified some other characteristic.

Producers were significantly more likely than veterinarians to point to programmes based on scientific data, which were voluntary and industry operated. Producers were also more likely than educators to point to such programmes.

Educators were more likely to point to programmes that were based on scientific data and voluntary than veterinarians. Veterinarians were more likely than producers to point to programmes that were economical to implement and government mandated. Veterinarians were also more likely than educators to point to programmes that were government mandated.

What producers are doing

Increasingly, buyers are recognising that actions other than regulation are required to improve food safety. Regulations can set a 'baseline' or basic standard, but other actions are likely to be more effective in enhancing overall food safety. Large buyers are more frequently imposing requirements above the regulatory standards for processors and, ultimately, the producers who supply them (15).

As found in the LCI survey, producers have a strong desire to produce safe products. In reality, food producers have been working to find better ways to do this for decades, both in the United States of America (USA) and around the world. They want to 'do the right thing', but producers also want to ensure that the programmes they implement and the regulations they must meet are firmly based on science (3, 14, 17, 18). Just as regulatory programmes have evolved to embrace HACCP (11) principles, producers have introduced programmes based on these principles to their production facilities to improve the safety of their food products.

In 1982, beef producers recognised the need for an organised approach to avoid violative residues in food. The result was the development of the beef quality assurance (BQA) programme (12), under the auspices of the National Cattlemen's Beef Association. The BQA education programme is active in 47 states and has been effective in continuing to reduce residue rates in red meat.

Rev. sci. tech. Off. int. Epiz., **25** (2)

533

In 1989, pork producers worked together through the National Pork Board, a producer-funded education and promotion group, to create the pork quality assurance programme (13). The current programme, based on HACCP principles, is focused on good production practices. It stresses:

– good management

– proper use of animal health products

– working with animal health professionals

– accurate record-keeping

– proper swine care

– proper feed processing practices.

Participating producers complete a quality assurance checklist each year and meet educational requirements every two years.

The dairy industry, which is already well regulated at the farm level (19), has also undertaken an HACCP-based quality assurance programme. The dairy quality assurance (DQA) programme (2) was launched in 1991 as an educational initiative directed at decreasing antibiotic residues in milk and dairy beef. It has been expanded from the initial effort to include dairy animal care and environmental issues. It has thus become a more comprehensive programme, but still one that actively addresses food safety concerns. In its present form, it is known as the 'DQA Five-Star Program'.

Sheep producers in the USA initiated an industry-wide quality assurance programme in 1991 through their membership organisation, the American Sheep Industry (ASI) Association. Working with university and industry partners, the ASI has continued to refine the programme as research makes new information available (16). This programme addresses a wide range of concerns, including pathogens, antibiotic residues and other potential food safety issues.

Egg producers have taken action, often in conjunction with state agencies, to address specific concerns about *Salmonella enterica*, serovar Enteritidis. The Centers for Disease Control and Prevention, a part of the US Department of Health and Human Services, have found that these voluntary on-farm programmes based on HACCP principles have been effective in reducing the incidence of *S.* Enteritidis infections (10). The Centers have also concluded that scientific data, public health concerns, and public relations and marketing concerns are all potential underlying reasons for the adoption of these programmes by producers.

Australia has moved to more fully integrate on-farm quality assurance as part of the meat inspection system at federally inspected establishments (1, 9). A combination of documented, nationally consistent, HACCP-based quality assurance programmes, supported by auditing, laboratory testing and a flexible design, allow the system to address meat safety issues as well as contemporary and emerging public health risks. This is part of the Australian effort to meet the national and international expectations of consumers, while also supporting its animal health programmes. This approach, which continuously works toward improvement, is applied to all species.

Conclusions

Producers recognise the significant role they play in ensuring a safe food supply. Programmes that are based on science are generally embraced by producers. Producer commitment to a safe food supply is demonstrated by the fact that species groups in many developed countries have adopted HACCP-based programmes. Such programmes have been effective in addressing specific food safety concerns. Producers generally find that these programmes are consistent with good management practices, and thus make good economic sense, while also helping them to meet their objective of providing consumers with a safe supply of food. It is likely that these producer-led programmes will continue to complement regulations, thus enhancing food safety for everyone. This has already occurred in Australia, and is increasingly expected by major commercial buyers.

Appendix 1

Report on Livestock Conservation Institute Food Safety Survey of Food Animal Production Professionals

[Taken from the 1998 Report on the Livestock Conservation Institute Food Safety Survey by R.E. Langley (8)]

Results summary
Question 1

Regarding food safety and food safety policy, which of the following do you feel are of significant importance? (Please circle all that apply.)

– antimicrobial residues

– on-farm HACCP

– public perceptions

– microbial pathogens

– international trade barriers

– maintenance of markets

– imported food

– water quality

– good production practices.

Strong majorities of respondents felt 'microbial pathogens' (80.4%), 'public perceptions' (76.6%), and 'antimicrobial residues' (67.2%) were of significant importance. Also of importance to a majority were 'good production practices' (61.7%) and 'imported foods' (56.1%). Fewer respondents thought 'water quality' (47.4%), 'on-farm HACCP' (41.2%), 'maintenance of markets' (33.8%), and 'international trade barriers' (29.5%) were of significant importance. Additionally, 5.6% indicated other factors were important, with 'food-handling practices' being the most common response.

Question 2

In your opinion, how important a role do food animal producers have in ensuring food safety?

Virtually all respondents thought food animal producers play an important role, with 67.4% stating it is a 'very important' role and 32.4% stating 'somewhat important'.

Veterinarians were more likely to see an important role than producers.

Question 3

What quality assurance/food safety assurance tools have you found that producers use the most? (Please circle all that apply.)

Strong majorities cited 'antibiotic/chemical residue avoidance programmes' (75.3%) and 'water quality programmes' (64.1%). Majorities also cited 'dead animal disposal system' (58.4%), 'general hygiene/sanitation' (57.7%), 'injection site selection/management' (56.4%), and 'waste disposal management' (51.3%). Significant numbers also cited 'rodent control' (45.9%), 'general biosecurity practices' (40.4%), 'feed bunk management' (35.7%), 'routine veterinary inspection' (34.8%), and 'isolation/quarantine of incoming animals' (32.3%). Fewer than 30% reported use of 'colostrum management' (28.3%), 'limited access to farm' (27.7%), 'feed control measures and facility design to avoid muddy lots' (26.5%), 'pathogen reduction programmes' (25.4%), 'segregated housing' (22%), 'bird control system' (19.3%), or 'flush system management' (11.3%). Additionally, 2.6% cited various other tools in use.

Question 4

In your opinion, how important for producers are each of the following sources of information about food safety issues and concerns in your area, state or region? Would you say they are very important, somewhat important, or not important at all?

There appeared to be significant agreement among respondents about the most valuable information sources for food safety issues. Over 95% cited four different sources as being 'very important' or 'somewhat important': 'veterinarian' (97.2%), 'newspaper/news magazines (farm/food industry)' (98.2%), 'producer meetings' (97.4%), and 'extension service' (95.9%). In addition, four other sources garnered at least 70% mention as being important sources: 'association/company newsletters' (92.3%), 'farm cooperative' (87.8%), 'newspaper/news magazines (popular press)' (82.2%), and 'TV news/news shows' (72.3%). Seventy-one percent (71%) also cited the 'Internet/world wide web' as an important information source, although only 10.4% deemed it 'very important'. Finally, a majority also thought that 'scientific/veterinary journals' (59.8%) and 'radio news/talk shows' (68.4%) were at least somewhat important sources. A little over 5% cited some other important source of information as well.

Question 5

How important are each of the following methods of delivery for educating producers on their role in food safety in your area, state or region? Would you say they are very important, somewhat important, or not important at all?

All of the delivery systems listed were cited as being at least 'somewhat important' by 75% or more of the respondents. There was much greater variability, however, in the percentage of respondents who cited each as being 'very important'. The delivery method with the most intense support was 'cooperative extension programmes/meetings' (61.8%: 'very important'), followed by 'producer meetings' (59.2%) and 'commodity quality assurance programmes' (51.5%). Methods with substantially more lukewarm support were: 'adult farmer classes' (24.1%), 'farm cooperative programmes' (23.3%), 'TV/radio farm shows' (17.7%), and 'USDA information sheets' (15.1%). Fewer than 5% cited some other method of delivery, with 'veterinarian' being the most common response.

Question 6

To the best of your knowledge, what percent of food animal producers in your area, state or region currently participate in a programme designed to enhance quality assurance/food safety?

When offered broad categories to estimate the percentage of producers in their area that participated in such programmes, about one-third of the respondents (33.7%) indicated 25% or fewer participate. Roughly another third

(30.3%) said 26% to 50% participate, with the remaining third estimating 51% to 75% (20.2%) or 76% to 100% (15.8%) participation. It should be noted that 14.5% of the sample did not venture a guess on this question.

Question 7

Producers in my area, state or region are participating in a quality assurance/food safety programme operated by: (Please circle all that apply).

Most producers were reported to be participating in programmes operated by either a 'national/state commodity organisation' (55.3%) or a 'university/ extension service' (54.1%). Fewer were in programmes operated by the 'state department of agriculture' (29.1%), 'packer/processors' (25.4%), or 'farm cooperatives' (16.7%). In addition, 9.8% cited some other programme operator, with 'veterinarians' and 'trade associations' getting the most mention.

Question 8

What programmes are you aware of that are being implemented and used to educate producers on residues and medications?

For this type of programme, 57.9% mentioned 'national-level commodity quality assurance programmes' and 57.1% mentioned 'state-level commodity quality assurance programmes'. In addition, 12.7% specified some other type of programme with those implemented by 'extension', 'trade associations' and 'the state' getting the most mention.

Question 9

Among the programmes you are familiar with in your area, region or state, who helps to administer producer participation in quality assurance/food safety programmes? (Please circle all that apply.)

It appears that 'veterinarians' were most likely to help administer these programmes with mention by 76.6% of the respondents. Significant roles were also played by 'extension agents' (59.4%) and 'state extension personnel' (59.1%). To a lesser degree, programmes were also administered by a 'field man'/company representative (38.9%), with very little identification of assistance by an 'adult farmer instructor' (6.2%). In addition, 11.2% mentioned some other entity with 'trade associations', the 'state', and 'drug company representatives' being cited most often.

Question 10

The characteristics that make a programme effective include: (Please circle all that apply).

The top five characteristics of effective programmes, as identified by the respondents, were: 'economical to implement' (80.8%), 'based on scientific data' (71.6%), 'evidence of increased product quality' (67.4%), 'satisfactory benefit-to-cost ratio' (67.3%), and 'broad participation by producers' (64.6%). Characteristics cited by almost half of the respondents were: 'industry operated' (46%), and 'voluntary' (44.9%). 'Government-mandated' (14.5%) and 'government-operated' (2.9%) were much less desirable characteristics. In addition, 7.4% identified some other characteristic.

Question 11

How important are the following incentives for producers to participate in quality assurance/food safety programmes in your area, state or region? Would you say they are very important, somewhat important, or not important at all?

There was substantial agreement that all of the incentives listed were at least somewhat important, with over 90% of the respondents citing each of them as such. An interesting pattern emerges, however, when comparing the options on how many respondents rated them as 'very important' incentives. The most important incentives appeared to be avoidance of penalties or sanctions: 'avoid penalty in price for product' (71.5%: 'very important'), 'maintain market access' (62.8%), and, 'reduced risk of residue violations' (62.7%). Production factors appeared to be next most important: 'production of quality product' (57.4%), 'enhanced production performance' (53.6%), and 'market a "value-added" product' (50.6%). Fewer than half of the respondents cited 'reduction in food-borne disease' (44.9%) and 'personal satisfaction' (34.6%) as important incentives to participate in these programmes. Two percent (2.2%) cited some other incentive as being 'very important' with 'price increases' being the most mentioned.

Respondents were then queried as to what type of programme format they would most prefer, and then asked a subtly different question regarding what type of programme format would be best to get participation in these programmes from producers who currently do not participate. Some interesting differences appeared between what food animal production professionals think is the ideal, and what they think will actually work to increase participation.

Question 12

Which one of the following programme formats comes closest to your ideal?

The overwhelming favourite as the ideal programme format was: 'voluntary quality assurance programme – commodity based', with 41.7% of the 'vote'. Next, with virtually identical support, were: 'voluntary quality assurance programme – supervised by cooperative extension system' (13.7%), 'voluntary quality assurance programme – supervised by private veterinarians' (12%), and 'voluntary quality assurance programmes – supervised by state department of agriculture' (11.7%). The less-favoured options were 'programmes that are buyer developed and supervised (i.e. packer/processor)' (9.8%), 'federal-mandated quality assurance programmes' (5.7%), and 'state-mandated quality assurance programme' (4%). The remaining 1.3% who answered the question selected 'none of the above, we do not need on-farm quality assurance/food safety programmes'.

Question 13

What one type of programme would work BEST for producers who are NOT participating in a quality assurance/food safety programme in your area, state or region?

When asked what type of format would work best to attract more participation, once again the top choice was 'voluntary quality assurance programme – commodity based' but with only 20.9% supporting this option. Interestingly, the statistically indistinguishable second choice, 'programmes that are buyer developed and supervised (i.e. packer/processor)' (19.9%), was seen as being the ideal format by fewer than half of those who thought it was the most workable. The third favourite response to this question was 'state-mandated and supervised quality assurance programme' (17.1%), with the remaining four options receiving similar support: 'voluntary quality assurance programme – supervised by cooperative extension system' (12.5%), 'federal-mandated and supervised quality assurance programme' (10.9%), 'voluntary quality assurance programme – supervised by state department of agriculture' (8.7%), and, 'voluntary quality assurance programme – supervised by private veterinarians' (8.5%). Again, 1.4% selected 'none of the above, we do not need on-farm quality assurance/food safety programmes'.

Question 14

The current amount of information producers in my area, state or region are receiving about food safety is adequate.

A majority agreed with this statement (60.9%), although only 7.3% 'strongly agreed'. There was no significant difference of opinion on this statement.

Question 15

The education programmes that I am familiar with have been effective.

A majority agreed with this statement (77%), although only 15.4% 'strongly agreed'. In addition, veterinarians were significantly more likely to disagree with this statement than both producers and educators.

Question 16

Animal production or on-farm food safety systems are necessary to maintain access to international markets for USA products.

A strong majority agreed with this statement (89.6%), with over half (53.2%) marking 'strongly agree'. In addition, veterinarians were significantly more likely to strongly agree with this statement than both producers and educators.

Question 17

Animal production or on-farm food safety systems are necessary to maintain domestic demand of USA products.

A strong majority agreed with this statement (93.3%), with over half (56.3%) marking 'strongly agree'. Veterinarians were significantly more likely to strongly agree with this statement than educators.

Question 18

Pathogen reduction activities at processing, such as irradiation/cold pasteurisation, would make production level activity unnecessary.

Only 20% agreed with this statement, while 54.2% marked 'strongly disagree'. Both veterinarians and educators were more likely to strongly disagree than producers.

Question 19

There should be a national system to provide basic provisions that would lend uniformity to production food safety systems across the country.

A fairly strong majority agreed with this statement (69.5%), with 23% marking 'strongly agree'. Veterinarians were more likely to strongly agree with this than producers.

While there was substantial agreement that there should be a national system, there was little agreement on who should develop it. Furthermore, although asked to select only one response, almost 100 respondents were apparently unable to limit themselves to one choice.

Question 20

In your opinion, if a national system were provided, who should develop it? (Please circle only one.)

Rev. sci. tech. Off. int. Epiz., **25** (2)

537

The top choice for who should develop a national system was 'various commodity/farm organisations' (26.7%), with 'USDA, Animal and Plant Health Inspection Service, Veterinary Services' (22.3%), 'USDA, Food Safety and Inspection Service' (16.7%), and 'USDA Cooperative Extension Service' (11.8%) also getting substantial mention. The remaining options garnered less than 5% mention each: 'national packer/processor associations' and 'USA Animal Health Association' (3.9%), 'Livestock Conservation Institute' (3.5%) and 'Food and Drug Administration' (0.6%). As mentioned above, significant numbers of respondents felt several of these entities should collaborate to develop a national system (if provided), and among these, 'all of the above' was the most common suggestion.

The main pattern that emerged when comparing group responses to this question was that producers appeared to more heavily favour a system developed by various commodity/farm organisations, with almost half (48.8%) giving this response. Alternatively, veterinarians and educators appeared more in favour of some aspect of USDA involvement in the development of a national system, as witnessed by their stronger support, in general, for the USDA Animal and Plant Health Inspection Service, Veterinary Services, USDA Food Safety and Inspection Service, and USDA Cooperative Extension Service.

La sécurité sanitaire des aliments commence à la ferme : le point de vue du producteur

K.E. Olson & G.N. Slack

Résumé

Les consommateurs doivent pouvoir compter sur l'innocuité des denrées alimentaires qu'ils achètent. Les réglementations nationales visent à leur fournir une certaine garantie en matière de sécurité sanitaire des aliments, mais des mesures complémentaires s'avèrent nécessaires pour que cette question soit traitée de manière exhaustive. Les producteurs sont de plus en plus conscients des responsabilités qui leur incombent dans ce domaine et travaillent de concert avec d'autres segments du secteur agroalimentaire. Dans de nombreux pays, des programmes d'assurance qualité basés sur le système d'analyse des risques et de maîtrise des points critiques (HACCP) ont été mis au point et sont appliqués dans les élevages pour la plupart des espèces animales. Ces approches garantiront aux consommateurs, partout dans le monde, un meilleur niveau de sécurité sanitaire des aliments. Les producteurs sont disposés à s'engager activement dans des programmes fondés scientifiquement et qui reposent sur de bonnes pratiques de gestion. Les auteurs en concluent que les programmes HACCP seront de plus en plus utilisés à l'avenir.

Mots-clés

Analyse des risques et maîtrise des points critiques – Assurance qualité – Enquête – Enquête auprès des producteurs – Phase avant l'abattage – Producteurs – Programmes appliqués au niveau des fermes – Sécurité sanitaire des aliments.

538

Rev. sci. tech. Off. int. Epiz., **25** (2)

El punto de vista del productor: la seguridad sanitaria empieza en la granja

K.E. Olson & G.N. Slack

Resumen

El consumidor espera que los alimentos que compra sean inocuos. Aunque los gobiernos instituyen reglamentos para tratar de ofrecerle garantías en este sentido, un trabajo global sobre la cuestión requiere además medidas de otro tipo. Los productores, cada vez más conscientes de su responsabilidad en este terreno, trabajan concertadamente con otros segmentos de la industria agroalimentaria. Ahora mismo se están elaborando programas de garantía de calidad basados en el análisis de riesgos y puntos críticos de control (HACCP), programas que en muchos países se aplican en las propias explotaciones a la mayoría de las especies. La aplicación de este tipo de métodos acrecentará el nivel de seguridad sanitaria de los alimentos, lo que por doquier redunda en beneficio de los consumidores. Los productores siguen demostrando que son capaces de responder positivamente a programas basados en datos científicos y en buenas prácticas de gestión. Los autores llegan a la conclusión de que cada vez se utilizará más el HACCP.

Palabras clave

Análisis de riesgos y puntos críticos de control – Antes del sacrificio – Encuesta – Encuesta entre productores – Garantía de calidad – Inocuidad de los alimentos – Productores – Programas en las explotaciones.

■

References

1. Butler R.J., Murray J.G. & Tidswell S. (2003). – Quality assurance and meat inspection in Australia. *In* Veterinary Services: organisation, quality assurance, evaluation (E. Correa Melo & F. Gerster, eds). *Rev. sci. tech. Off. int. Epiz.,* **22** (2), 697-712.

2. Carlson K. (2005). – Looking back: the history behind the dairy quality assurance (DQA) center. Available at: http://www.dqacenter.org/history.htm (accessed on 24 February 2006).

3. Cummings T.S. (2006). – Stakeholder position paper: poultry. *Prev. vet. Med.,* **73** (2-3), 209-212. Epub.: 21 November 2005.

4. Filipic M. (2003). – Survey reveals Ohioans' food safety concerns, 29 May. Ohio State University Extension. Available at: http://www.ag.ohio-state.edu/~news/story.php?id=2529 (accessed on 15 March 2006).

5. Food and Agriculture Organization of the United Nations (FAO) (2001). – Food quality and safety. FAO factsheet. FAO, Rome.

6. Johnson R., Hillman J. & Petrey A. (2001). – Food safety issues, protection and trade (with respect to meat products). International Agricultural Trade Research Consortium Symposium on Trade in livestock products, Auckland, New Zealand, 18-19 January. Available at: http://www.geocities.com/rwmj2001/foodsafe.html?200624 (accessed on 24 February 2006).

7. Joint Food and Agriculture Organization of the United Nations (FAO)/World Health Organization (WHO) (2003). – Assuring food safety and quality: guidelines for strengthening national food control systems. FAO Food and Nutrition Paper No. 76. FAO/WHO, Rome, Geneva.

8. Langley R.E. (1998). – Report on LCI food safety survey of food animal production professionals, 14 December. University of Kentucky, Survey Research Center, Lexington, United States of America.

9. Meat and Livestock Australia (2006). – Livestock production assurance (LPA) [on-farm food safety certification programme]. Available at: http://www.mla.com.au/TopicHierarchy/IndustryPrograms/LivestockQualitySystems/Default.htm (accessed on 15 March 2006).

10. Mumma G.A., Griffin P.M., Meltzer M.I., Braden C.R. & Tauxe R.V. (2004). – Egg quality assurance programs and egg-associated *Salmonella enteritidis* infections, United States. *Emerg. infect. Dis.*, **10** (10), 1782-1789. Available at: http://www.cdc.gov/ncidod/EID/vol10no10/04-0189.htm (accessed on 9 May 2006).

11. National Advisory Committee on Microbiological Criteria for Foods (1997). – Hazard analysis and critical control point principles and application guidelines. United States Food and Drug Administration/United States Department of Agriculture, Washington, DC. Available at: http://www.cfsan. fda.gov/~comm/nacmcfp.html (accessed on 15 March 2006).

12. National Cattlemen's Beef Association (NCBA) (2001). – Beef Quality Assurance (BQA) national guidelines. NCBA, Centennial, Colorado. Available at: http://www.bqa.org (accessed on 24 February 2006).

13. National Pork Board (NPB) (2004). – Pork quality assurance [brochure]. NPB, Des Moines, Iowa. Available at: http://www.pork.org/Producers/PQA/PQA.aspx (accessed on 15 March 2006).

14. Noordhuizen J.P.T.M. & Frankena K. (1999). – Epidemiology and quality assurance: applications at farm level. *Prev. vet. Med.*, **39** (2), 93-110.

15. Ollinger M. & Ballenger N. (2003). – Weighing incentives for food safety in meat and poultry. United States Department of Agriculture, Economic Research Service, Washington, DC. Available at: http://www.ers.usda.gov/AmberWaves/April03/ Features/WeighingIncentives.htm (accessed on 24 February 2006).

16. Roeber D.L., Belk K.E., LeValley S.B., Scanga J.A., Sofos J.N. & Smith G.C. (2002). – Producing customer products from sheep: the sheep safety and quality assurance program. American Sheep Industry Association/Colorado State University, Denver, Colorado. Available at: http://www. colostate.edu/programs/SSQA/ (accessed on 9 May 2006).

17. Sischo W.M. (2006). – Stakeholder position paper: dairy producer. *Prev. vet. Med.*, **73** (2-3), 203-208. Epub.: 15 November 2005.

18. Sundberg P. (2006). – Stakeholder position paper: pork producer perspective on antibiotic use data. *Prev. vet. Med.*, **73** (2-3), 213-215.

19. United States Food and Drug Administration (FDA) (2004). – Grade 'A' pasteurized milk ordinance – 2003 revision. Center for Food Safety & Applied Nutrition, FDA/Office of Compliance, Washington, DC. Available at: http://www.cfsan. fda.gov/~ear/pmo03toc.html (accessed on 15 March 2006).

20. Unnevehr L. & Hirschhorn N. (2000). – Designing effective food safety interventions in developing countries. The World Bank Group, Washington, DC. Available at: http://www-wds.worldbank.org/servlet/WDS_IBank_Servlet?pcont=detail s&eid=000094946_00072805374210 (accessed on 15 March 2006).

Rev. sci. tech. Off. int. Epiz., 2006, **25** (2), 541-554

Salmonella contamination: a significant challenge to the global marketing of animal food products

L. Plym Forshell [1] & M. Wierup [2]

(1) Swedish National Food Administration, Box 622, 75126 Uppsala, Sweden
(2) Swedish University of Agricultural Sciences, Faculty of Veterinary Medicine and Animal Science, Box 7084, 75007 Uppsala, Sweden

Summary

Salmonellosis is the most common food-borne bacterial disease in the world. *Salmonella* is a significant pathogen for food-producing animals and these animals are the primary source of salmonellosis. It is estimated that herd prevalence varies between 0% and 90%, depending on the animal species and region. The pathogen is spread by trade in animals and non-heated animal food products. The emergence of strains that are resistant to antimicrobials, often as a result of antimicrobial usage in animals, is a public health hazard of great concern. It is increasingly accepted that the prevalence of *Salmonella* in animal production must be decreased and, in the European Union, plans to achieve this are currently being implemented. In this paper, the authors propose various risk mitigation strategies. Successful control must focus on a range of preventive actions because there is no simple 'silver bullet' solution to reduce *Salmonella* contamination. The authors conclude that the key to controlling *Salmonella* is to follow the general rules that have been successfully applied to other infectious diseases.

Keywords

Animal products – Antimicrobial resistance – Control – Disease – Epidemiology – Monitoring – Pre-harvest control – Risk mitigation – Salmonella – Salmonella contamination – Salmonella pathogenicity island – Salmonellosis – Virulence.

Introduction

In most parts of the world, countries have seen dramatic and continuous increases in human outbreaks of salmonellosis, caused by infections in animals. In 2004, in the European Union (EU) alone, 192,703 human cases of salmonellosis were reported (17). These and similar data from other countries almost certainly underestimate the magnitude of the problem, as many cases of salmonellosis are not reported. Often, the infected person does not visit a doctor, or no specimen is obtained for laboratory tests or laboratory findings are not reported. Taking into account this degree of under-reporting, the Centers for Disease Control estimate the annual number of non-typhoidal salmonellosis cases in the United States of America (USA) to be approximately 1.4 million (41).

In addition to human health implications, *Salmonella* is a pathogen of significant importance in worldwide animal production and the emergence of antibiotic-resistant strains, due principally to the therapeutic use of antimicrobials in animals, is a further threat to human and animal health. Increasing attention has been focused on the prevention and control of *Salmonella* in animal production, as this is the main source of outbreaks in humans (19, 66, 75). The need for global co-operation in controlling salmonellosis was emphasised at an early stage by the World Health Organization (WHO) (8). This is readily understandable since *Salmonella* infections are also

542

Rev. sci. tech. Off. int. Epiz., **25** (2)

spread through international trade in animal feed, live animals and food. The control of *Salmonella* is thus an urgent challenge confronted by Veterinary Services and producers as they seek to produce safe foods of animal origin. A 'stable-to-the-table' approach is needed to implement stringent disease control measures. In this paper, the authors examine preventive measures at the pre-harvest level.

Salmonella

Nomenclature/taxonomy

The genus *Salmonella* belongs to the family Enterobacteriaceae. *Salmonellae* are facultative anaerobic, Gram-negative, oxidase-negative, rod-shaped bacteria. The genus *Salmonella* consists of two species, *Salmonella enterica* and *S. bongori*. *Salmonella enterica* is further divided into six subspecies:

– *S. enterica* subsp. *enterica*

– *S. enterica* subsp. *salamae*

– *S. enterica* subsp. *arizonae*

– *S. enterica* subsp. *diarizonae*

– *S. enterica* subsp. *houtenae*

– *S. enterica* subsp. *indica*.

More than 2,400 serovars are known. Serovars that are frequently isolated in human or veterinary medicine have historically been given names denoting syndrome (e.g. *S.* Typhi), host-specificity (e.g. *S.* Choleraesuis) or the geographical origin of the first isolation of a new serovar (e.g. *S.* Dublin).

Salmonellae cause disease in both humans and animals. The serovar *S.* Typhi and most *S.* Paratyphi strains (A, B and C), which cause serious systemic infections in humans, are specific human pathogens. These pathogens have no animal reservoir and so are not dealt with in this paper. Instead, the authors focus on the remaining serovars, usually known as the 'zoonotic *Salmonella* spp.', which cause so-called non-typhoidal salmonellosis in humans and sometimes also in animals.

Virulence

Understanding the mechanisms behind the survival of *Salmonella* bacteria, as they invade an exposed animal, and their ability to cause disease would enable researchers to prevent much of the suffering and economic losses caused by this pathogen. However, despite substantial research efforts, progress has been limited. The current knowledge may be summarised as follows.

Following oral uptake, *Salmonella* is successively exposed to:

a) low pH in the stomach

b) the strong antimicrobial effect of bile

c) decreasing oxygen supply

d) normal gut flora and metabolites

e) intestinal peristalsis

f) cationic antimicrobial peptides present on the surface of epithelial cells (50).

These encounters with stressful environments induce the expression of a number of genes whose products are essential for *Salmonella* to invade the intestinal epithelium and infect the host.

The ability to cause disease relies on several virulence determinants. Some of these may be seen as virulence determinants in the broad sense, including genes involved in nutrient biosynthesis/uptake, stress response (both in and outside the host) and repair of cell damage. These genes may be considered 'housekeeping' genes and are present in other closely related bacteria, such as *Escherichia coli* (5).

Another group of virulence genes specific for the genus *Salmonella* encode adaptations to overcome host defence mechanisms and may therefore be called true virulence determinants.

The expression of both groups of virulence genes is regulated in response to environmental signals in the host. The regulatory genes mediating this control may also be considered virulence determinants (5).

The genetic control of *Salmonella* virulence is not fully known. However, both plasmid and chromosomal genes are involved. Many of the virulence genes of *S. enterica* are located on pathogenicity islands of the chromosomes, referred to as '*Salmonella* pathogenicity islands' (SPI). These genes are believed to have been acquired by *Salmonella* from other bacterial species through horizontal gene transfer (62). They include functions such as host cell invasion and intracellular pathogenesis. Thus far, 12 different SPI have been described. The roles of some SPI in the pathogenesis of *Salmonella* spp. are well described but the function in virulence of many genes within SPI is not yet understood (27).

At least six serovars of *Salmonella* (Abortusovis, Choleraesuis, Dublin, Enteritidis, Gallinarum/Pullorum and Typhimurium) harbour a virulence plasmid (although not all isolates of these serovars do). These plasmids vary

Rev. sci. tech. Off. int. Epiz., **25** (2)

543

in size among the serovars. All these plasmids contain the *Salmonella* plasmid virulence (spv) locus. This locus harbours five genes designated spvRABCD (62). The first gene spvR encodes an activator of spvABCD, but the exact function of the encoded proteins is not fully known. These genes are induced by growth restriction, reduced nutrient supply or lowered pH and are involved in intra-macrophage survival of *Salmonella* (51).

Other virulence factors of *Salmonella* include the production of endotoxins and exotoxins, and the presence of fimbriae and flagellae. The role of these factors in the pathogenesis of *Salmonella* spp. is not fully established (62).

Salmonella infections

Salmonella infections in humans

Non-typhoid salmonellosis in humans is usually manifested as a localised enterocolitis. The incubation period ranges from five hours (h) to seven days, but clinical signs usually begin 12 h to 36 h after ingestion of a contaminated food. Shorter incubation periods are generally associated with either higher doses of the pathogen or highly susceptible people. Clinical signs include diarrhoea, nausea, abdominal pain, mild fever and chills. The diarrhoea varies from a few thin vegetable-soup-like stools to massive evacuations with accompanying dehydration. Vomiting, prostration, anorexia, headache and malaise may also occur. The syndrome usually lasts for two to seven days. Systemic infections sometimes occur, and usually involve the very young, the elderly or the immuno-compromised. A fatal outcome is rare. The excreta of infected patients contain large numbers of *Salmonella* spp. at the onset of illness. Those numbers decrease with the passing of time. Some patients become carriers, and some are still excreting *Salmonella* spp. after three months. Non-typhoid salmonellosis can later give rise to chronic diseases, including localised infections in specific tissues or organs and reactive arthritis, as well as neurological and neuromuscular illnesses. Subclinical infections and/or carriers also occur and investigations have found that 7% to 66% of infected humans are subclinical carriers (2).

Salmonella infections in animals

As with humans, *Salmonella*-infected animals may or may not develop disease. Those serovars that were initially observed to cause disease were found to be adapted to specific animal species, that is:

– *S.* Abortus ovis (sheep)

– *S.* Cholerae suis (pigs)

– *S.* Gallinarum (poultry)

– *S.* Abortus equi (horses)

– *S.* Dublin (cattle).

These serovars cause disease in the species to which they are adapted and are considered less pathogenic to people. However, when humans become infected, the same serovars often cause severe septicaemia (1, 54). These host-adapted serovars primarily cause abortions or severe gastroenteritis in their animal hosts.

A group of more frequently isolated serovars, such as *S.* Typhimurium, *S.* Enteritidis, *S.* Hadar and *S.* Infantis (among others), readily affect both humans and animals. In food animals, these serovars manifest themselves clinically through per-acute septicaemia, acute enteritis or chronic enteritis. In the subclinical form of the disease, the animal may either have a latent infection or become a temporary or persistent carrier (47).

The remaining, less frequently isolated serovars can colonise animals, usually without significant clinical signs, but they are all considered capable of causing gastro-intestinal infection of varying severity in humans.

In summary, in most food animal species, *Salmonellae* usually establish a clinically inapparent infection of variable duration, which is significant as a potential zoonosis. However, under various stress conditions, serovars that are usually non-pathogenic may also cause disease in food animal species.

No data are available to give the true prevalence of *Salmonella* in animal production or to provide true comparisons between countries. Existing data indicate that the herd prevalence, depending on animal species and region, may vary between 0% and 90% (in swine, cattle and poultry) (10, 11, 17, 56). Interestingly, Sweden, Finland and Norway have achieved virtually *Salmonella*-free animal production as the result of an intervention strategy, implemented some time ago, which proposed zero tolerance for *Salmonella* (17).

Serovars involved in human illness

Any serovar is considered capable of causing gastro-intestinal illness of varying severity in humans. In a global survey covering the years 1990 and 1995, *S.* Enteritidis and *S.* Typhimurium were the two most frequently isolated serovars among human isolates (29). These serovars were also the most frequently found in human outbreaks of salmonellosis in Europe in the period 1993 to 1998, being responsible for 77.1% of the recorded outbreaks and occurring in a ratio of approximatively 3:1 (77). In 2004, *S.* Enteritidis and *S.* Typhimurium were still the

544

Rev. sci. tech. Off. int. Epiz., 25 (2)

most frequently reported serovars, accounting for 76% and 14%, respectively, of human isolates reported in the EU (17).

However, the current situation could easily change, as exemplified when an apparently new virulent strain of S. Enteritidis appeared in the 1980s, with the ability to infect the eggs of poultry. This resulted in a pandemic spread, combined with severe outbreaks in poultry but also in humans, with contaminated eggs and egg products being the principal vehicle (30). Similarly, the spread of the multi-antibiotic-resistant strain of S. Typhimurium (see below) demonstrated that dynamic spread of certain strains of Salmonella can easily occur. In particular, the pandemic spread of S. Enteritidis prompted a more active approach to the control of Salmonella (48).

Epidemiology

Animals infected after exposure to infected animals, feed or environmental conditions excrete Salmonella bacteria by faecal shedding. Faecal/intestinal contamination of carcasses is the principal source of human food-borne infections. The exception is when Salmonella is directly transmitted into the food product, for example, S. Enteritidis into eggs and sometimes other Salmonella serovars into milk. Humans excrete the microbe as animals do. Salmonella bacteria can survive for long periods in the environment, although in general no significant multiplication occurs. Salmonella infections in wild fauna, such as rodents, are usually secondary to the infection of farm animals, even though infection cycles may continue independently of any continuous input of Salmonella bacteria from farm animals, as described by Henzler and Opitz (28). In a review on the survival of Salmonella in the environment, Murray (43) concludes that control of Salmonella must start with a significant decrease in the number of organisms that are discharged into the environment. Animal and human faecal contamination of water and soil is also part of the epidemiological cycle and can contaminate, for example, vegetables, which then also become a source of food-borne human infections.

Animal sources of food-borne salmonellosis

An EU scientific committee concluded that the food categories that possibly pose the greatest hazard to public health include:

– raw meat and some meat products intended to be eaten raw

– raw or undercooked poultry meat products

– eggs and products containing raw eggs

– unpasteurised milk and some milk products.

Sprouted seeds, unpasteurised fruit juices and home-made mayonnaise are also of concern (54).

More correctly estimating the contributions of various food products to human outbreaks of Salmonella would require more detailed data. Situations are likely to vary between countries, according to different levels of Salmonella contamination and patterns of consumption. Two examples are available.

In the Netherlands, the estimated contributions of travel, farm animals and various animal products towards human salmonellosis are presented in the 2003 annual report of the Netherlands National Institute for Public Health and the Environment. Using typing data of Salmonella spp. isolates from laboratory surveillance, researchers estimated which fractions of human salmonellosis cases were attributable to which category of farm animals and their products, as well as which fraction was of unknown origin, including the possible cause of travel (Fig. 1). In 2003, the assessed total number of human salmonellosis cases amounted to 50,000 (308 cases per 100,000 head of population).

The estimated mean number of human cases in Denmark (per 100,000 inhabitants) that could be attributed to various sources is presented in Figure 2.

Transmission through trade and travelling

Salmonella is spread by the trade of live animals within and between countries. In Europe, the spread of infection with S. Typhimurium is typically seen as a result of trade in calves (7), and by parent and grandparent flocks in poultry production (45). Trade in contaminated animal feed products has also significantly contributed to the spread of Salmonella (59, 66), and several large outbreaks in humans have been traced back to contaminated animal feed (12). However, Salmonella is also spread by non-heat-treated animal products. In Sweden, in the 1950s, 500 people were reported to have been infected by S. Montevideo from meat imported from South America (55). Moreover, recent data from Denmark estimate the contribution from imported non-heat-treated meat (duck, turkey, chicken, beef and pork) to human cases of salmonellosis to be between 13.8% and 26.8% (Fig. 2).

Many countries have trade restrictions for Salmonella and trade between countries has often been interrupted by Salmonella-contaminated consignments (40). There have also been numerous alerts concerning Salmonella-contaminated meat, meat products and poultry notified through the rapid alert system for food and feed (RASFF) (49).

Salmonella is additionally spread between countries by humans as a result of food-borne infections acquired

Rev. sci. tech. Off. int. Epiz., **25** (2)

545

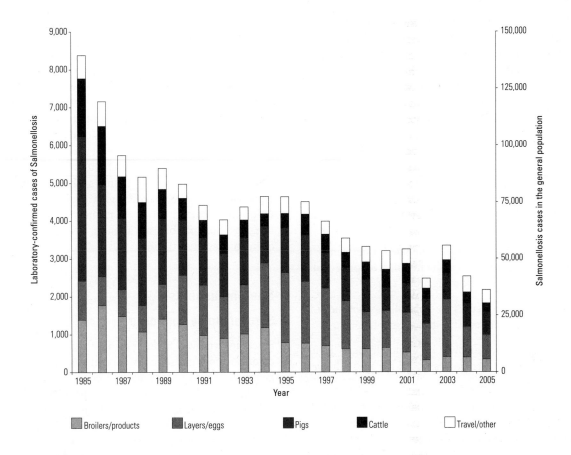

Fig. 1
Estimated contributions of travel and farm animals and their products to laboratory-confirmed human salmonellosis cases and estimated salmonellosis cases in the general population of the Netherlands, 1995-2005 (33, 34)

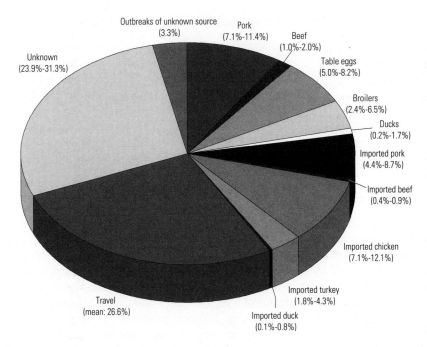

Fig. 2
Estimated sources of 1,538 cases of human salmonellosis in Denmark, 2004 (3)

546

Rev. sci. tech. Off. int. Epiz., **25** (2)

abroad. The overall importance of this route of transmission may reflect the prevalence of *Salmonella* contamination of food (including food of animal origin) in a particular country. In low-prevalence countries, such as Finland, Norway and Sweden, > 80% of human cases of salmonellosis are attributed to visits abroad (3). This is in marked contrast to countries such as Denmark and the Netherlands (Figs 1 and 2), where roughly the opposite situation exists.

Risk mitigation options

In 1980, WHO had already formulated three lines of defence against *Salmonella*, which still comprise valid strategic approaches to risk mitigation (71):

a) the first approach focuses on controlling *Salmonella* in the food-producing animal (pre-harvest control)

b) the second approach involves improving hygiene during the slaughter and further processing of the meat (harvest control)

c) the third approach targets the final preparation of food by educating the food industry and consumers about good hygiene practices (post-harvest control).

Successful prevention of food-borne salmonellosis originating from animal production must involve all three lines of defence. The previously supported strategy that it is possible to control *Salmonella* only at consumer level, i.e. only at the third line of defence, has been abandoned (67).

Pre-harvest control of *Salmonella* at the farm level has long been considered an important part of pathogen reduction schemes (61), not least because traditional meat inspection cannot control *Salmonella*-contaminated carcasses. Indeed, the latter demonstrate how the industrialisation of animal production 'opened the door' of the food chain to pathogens like *Salmonella*.

Pre-harvest control

General aspects

There have been numerous international workshops and consultations on microbiological control and *Salmonella* reduction schemes in farming (35, 72, 73, 74, 75, 76). In addition, national inquiries directed principally at controlling *Salmonella* in poultry have been conducted in several countries in Europe, as well as Canada and the USA. A presentation of the Swedish *Salmonella* programme, supported by WHO, was of special interest (45).

In a review for the World Organisation for Animal Health (OIE) (66), on knowledge and experience in the prevention of salmonellosis on livestock farms, it was concluded that *Salmonella* control programmes should follow the same general rules that have been successfully applied to other infectious diseases (69). It is fundamental that monitoring programmes should be established to identify *Salmonella*-infected herds and animals and that efforts are made to find and control the sources of infection and prevent further spread. The ultimate objective is to produce *Salmonella*-free animals. It should also be emphasised that *Salmonella* is a pathogen and not a ubiquitous bacterium or a normal inhabitant of the intestinal flora of domestic animals, as has sometimes been claimed previously (66).

Specific aspects

Serovars to be controlled

Since any serovar, including those that infect animals or colonise their intestine, is a potential hazard to human health, measures to prevent food-borne salmonellosis must be directed at all serovars of *Salmonella*. However, a *Salmonella* reduction strategy which is limited to a few selected serovars should also have a preventive effect on most other serovars since the same advice for reducing any serovar applies. If such a strategy is implemented, a supporting surveillance programme will also be needed to detect the prevalence of zoonotic serovars and prevent their build-up in the production chain. If no interventions are made at this early stage, these serovars could later spread widely, perhaps reaching epidemic proportions.

Live animals as a source of infection

Salmonella-infected food-producing animals excrete *Salmonella* bacteria in large numbers, sometimes intermittently during their entire economic life. Excreted bacteria infect neighbouring animals on the farm and contamination of the environment takes place, with infections being transmitted to rodents and other wild fauna. When moved, the *Salmonella*-infected animals are effective at introducing the infection into their new holdings.

In the absence of 'guaranteed *Salmonella*-free replacement animals', other methods must be used to limit the risk of introducing *Salmonella* with incoming animals. In general, animals should be introduced only from herds of the same or a higher health status. Integrated production limits the need to introduce animals from other herds and thus the risk of introducing *Salmonella*-infected livestock. Networking between producers is an effective way to prevent respiratory and enteric infections in pig production, and should also prove suitable for limiting the risk of *Salmonella*.

Diagnosis and monitoring methods

To combat the source of infection, the first requirement is to identify all *Salmonella*-infected animals on a livestock farm. Methods for this have been summarised in a WHO consultation report (76) on poultry production. Corresponding detailed guidelines have not yet been developed for other areas, e.g. for swine or beef/dairy production, but have long been applied successfully in Scandinavian countries.

Two principal methods are available:

- bacteriological

- immunological.

Bacteriological methods express the actual infection status of the animal, including recent transmission or contamination. They detect all serovars. The actual infectious agent (or, in the case of multiple infections, agents) is isolated, which makes further characterisation (e.g. serovar and antimicrobial resistance profile) possible. However, the analytical procedure is laborious.

Immunological methods identify previous exposure by detecting the presence of specific antibodies against *Salmonella*. This method can identify carriers or animals that are already clear of infection. It detects only those (most common) serogroups (O-antigens) included in the test and therefore new emerging serovars may not be detected. These methods are automated and less laborious.

A control programme also needs a supporting monitoring programme. Monitoring using bacteriological methods is needed to obtain a true picture of *Salmonella* status (38). Serological methods can be recommended, especially in medium- and high-prevalence countries, since they are cheap, fast and suitable for large-scale use, but their limitations should also be considered. They should be supplemented by the strategic use of bacteriological methods to ensure that emerging serovars, which might not otherwise be included in the tests, are also detected.

Hygiene and husbandry

Optimal hygiene and management routines are of major importance in aiding animals to withstand exposure to *Salmonella*, and to minimise the possible subsequent spread of the agent on the farm. Improvements in hygiene and management procedures must be continually implemented as a natural part of *Salmonella* control. Guidelines and recommendations have been presented by WHO (72), Blood and Radostits (7) and Schwartz (53).

Raising livestock in separate groups, without mixing animals from different sources and ages, has proved to be an effective health measure. The 'all-in, all-out' system, with careful cleaning and disinfection between batches, has long been essential in broiler production (6), and is now also routine in *Salmonella* control programmes for beef and swine production. (This involves entirely emptying the stable/pen of animals before any new ones are introduced, so that infection cannot be passed on to incoming livestock.)

Violating these procedures has been empirically shown to result in deteriorating health status. In the advanced *Salmonella* control policies applied in poultry production, good hygiene routines have proved to be of basic importance (66). In a study involving several EU Member States, it was found that the risk of swine at slaughter testing seropositive for *Salmonella* infection was twice as high in herds with a continuous production system as in herds with a batch production system (37). The importance of providing good herd and pen hygiene in pig production, especially by limiting the faecal-oral transmission route, is further emphasised in a recent report by the European Food Safety Authority (EFSA) (16).

The control and eradication of immunodeficiency-causing diseases have been found to have significant health-supporting effects, in addition to the direct gains due to the absence of clinical disease. These diseases include the following:

- bovine virus diarrhoea

- enzootic bovine leukosis

- caprine arthritis/encephalitis in goats

- maedi-visna in sheep

- infectious bursal disease in poultry

- Aujeszky's disease (pseudorabies) in pigs.

Other enzootic diseases can thus predispose or increase the susceptibility of animals to *Salmonella* exposure.

Biosecurity systems should also prevent the introduction of *Salmonella* into a herd through, for example, wild animals, visitors or machinery (63). The importance of hygienic handling of manure is obvious, particularly considering that *Salmonella* is transmitted by faecal shedding and that the average number of animals per farm is increasing. Jones (31) reviewed the question of *Salmonella* in animal waste and presented recommendations for the storage and spread of manure, especially slurry.

According to several studies, improving hygiene and husbandry management programmes, as described above, is generally very cost effective (64).

Feed

In all countries, there is a constant risk that animals will be exposed to *Salmonella* through their feed (14, 21).

548

Rev. sci. tech. Off. int. Epiz., **25** (2)

Considerable efforts should therefore be made to limit this exposure to an absolute minimum. Feed controls should follow the procedure described by Häggblom (24, 25). As *Salmonella* can seldom be detected in the final feed, unless the feed is heavily contaminated, it cannot be emphasised enough that control measures must be implemented before that stage. Programmes to prevent *Salmonella* in feedstuffs must be based on detecting the bacterium as early as possible in the production chain. A protocol involving hazard analysis at critical control points in the feed mill, including procedures for efficient cleaning and disinfection, should ensure that the processing line is not contaminated with *Salmonella* (59).

As shown by Edel *et al.* (13), pelleting can greatly reduce *Salmonella* contamination of the finished feed.

Certain feeds, such as fermented liquid feed used as a wet feeding system, and acidified feed or drinking water, have been found to reduce *Salmonella* in pig production (63).

Competitive exclusion

The use of competitive exclusion, in which the normal intestinal flora protects the host against invading pathogens, is a valuable part of *Salmonella* control in poultry farming. Competitive exclusion cultures have been used and tested in various countries, as reviewed by Schneitz and Mead (52). Positive results from the use of competitive exclusion have also been reported in pigs (22).

Vaccines

Many efforts have been made to find effective vaccines against *Salmonella* infections, especially in cattle and poultry but also in swine. A live attenuated vaccine against *S.* Gallinarum in poultry is available and there is currently demand for a vaccine to control *Salmonella* infections associated with human food poisoning, in particular, *S.* Enteritidis (20). However, due to the complicated pathogenesis of *Salmonella* infection, no significant breakthrough has been achieved (9). Vaccines to control *Salmonella* infections, especially inactivated vaccines, are in use all over the world. In recent years, increasing numbers of live vaccines have been developed but most of them are not yet authorised. Vaccination can play an important role in intervening against *Salmonella* in high-prevalence herds (23, 39, 46, 58). However, immunisation should not be conducted in isolation but always in combination with other measures, such as veterinary hygiene and improved management.

Antimicrobials

The use of antimicrobials to prevent suffering and economic losses in individual animals and herds can be justified, but should always be combined with other *Salmonella* reduction measures. Antibiotics have sometimes been used to prevent animals shedding *Salmonella* (36), but the use of antibiotics in pigs with enterocolitis has not been found to reduce the prevalence, magnitude or duration of *Salmonella* shedding by sick or recovered animals (70). Earlier, similar observations were made for experimental and natural *S.* Dublin infections in cattle (65). Both these findings agree with results from the use of antibiotics in human salmonellosis, i.e. that they have long been recognised to prolong the carrier state (4).

The use of antimicrobials for therapy or growth promotion may also disrupt the gut flora, which often increases the susceptibility of pigs to *Salmonella* infection. The use of antibiotics may thus act as a trigger to spread *Salmonella* infection throughout a herd, which would not have occurred if the animals remained untreated. This phenomenon has been thoroughly documented in poultry (57) and is also likely to occur in other animal species. The EFSA recently gave an opinion on the use of antibiotics to control *Salmonella* in poultry (15), which concurred with that of WHO (74), i.e. that *Salmonella* control should not be based on antibiotics. The emergence of antibiotic resistance is another serious reason why antibiotics should be used with great care, as demonstrated by the emergence and fast spread of the multi-resistant *S.* Typhimurium definitive phage type (DT) 104 (60).

In developed countries, it is also becoming increasingly accepted that a majority of the resistant strains of zoonotic *Salmonella* spp. have acquired that resistance in an animal host before being transmitted to humans through the food chain (42, 60). The prevalence of resistant isolates in countries where intensive animal production is practised is between 10% and 30%. When herds are held under strong antibiotic selective pressures, due to the intensive use of antibiotics, the prevalence of resistant strains rises to between 60% and 90% (26). As these bacterial strains are of considerable potential clinical importance to human health, this is a matter of real concern.

Strategies for implementation

The implementation of the mitigation options summarised above should all have a *Salmonella*-preventing effect. However, effective interventions also need specific targets and strategies for their application. In addition, if *Salmonella* does occur, despite these interventions, a progressive disease control plan should already have been prepared. Possible strategies for such approaches to control *Salmonella* have previously been formulated (66, 68). An intervention strategy should be based on the situation in the targeted herd, region or country.

In summary, the control of *Salmonella* at pre-harvest level must focus on preventive action because there is no 'silver bullet' through which the level of *Salmonella* contamination can be simply reduced. No single vaccine

Rev. sci. tech. Off. int. Epiz., **25** (2)

549

can prevent the infection, and the use of antimicrobials not only results in prolonged carriership but is also associated with the risk of developing antimicrobial-resistant strains. Both consequences pose public health hazards. Preventive action should follow the general rules that have already been successfully applied to control other infectious diseases.

In poultry production, rapid and positive results were demonstrated after the introduction of nationwide *Salmonella* reduction schemes. In Denmark, the prevalence of infection in broiler flocks declined from 12.9% in 1997 to 1.5% in 2002, resulting in an estimated 78% reduction of human cases related to domestically produced poultry products (44). Corresponding results have also been demonstrated in swine production, e.g. from Denmark (10). However, due to the more complex nature of swine, beef and dairy production, achieving positive results on a national basis would probably require a more long-term control programme, covering all steps of the production chain (32). A step-by-step approach to targeted interventions is advisable. The results should be viewed from a long-term perspective and the programme should be regularly re-evaluated to ensure compliance, efficacy and modification, if necessary.

Valuable experience can be gained from the EU, whose focus on preventing the spread of *Salmonella* in poultry is now directed to other animal species. Detailed rules are being established for harmonised *Salmonella* monitoring throughout the Community, to be followed by targets for reducing the prevalence of *Salmonella* serotypes with public health significance in pig herds. These will be based on appropriate legislation (18, 19). Within 18 months of these targets being set, Member States shall prepare and submit national control programmes to be approved by the Commission. The deadline for setting targets in pig production is December 2007 for breeding pigs and December 2008 for slaughter pigs.

Follow-up at harvest and post-harvest levels

If such pre-harvest *Salmonella* reduction interventions are supported by similar measures at harvest and post-harvest levels (which are, however, outside the scope of this paper), human exposure to *Salmonella* bacteria from animal food products should be considerably reduced. In Denmark, the herd prevalence of *Salmonella* in swine is estimated to have decreased from 22% to 11% in the four years following the implementation (1993/1994) of a *Salmonella* control programme (10). Through further interventions during slaughter, primarily hygienic killing procedures which avoid faecal contamination of carcasses, the prevalence of *Salmonella* in swine carcasses has been brought down to approximately 1% (17).

Infection à *Salmonella* : une grave menace pour le commerce mondial des produits alimentaires d'origine animale

L. Plym Forshell & M. Wierup

Résumé

La salmonellose constitue la maladie bactérienne d'origine alimentaire la plus fréquente du monde. *Salmonella* est un agent pathogène important des animaux destinés à la consommation et ces animaux sont la source principale de salmonellose. Selon les estimations, la prévalence à l'échelle des troupeaux varie entre 0 et 90 %, selon l'espèce animale et la région. L'agent pathogène se propage lors du commerce d'animaux et de produits alimentaires d'origine animale non cuits. L'apparition de souches résistantes aux antimicrobiens, souvent à la suite de l'utilisation d'antimicrobiens chez les animaux, représente une menace grave pour la santé publique. Il est de plus en plus admis que la

550

Rev. sci. tech. Off. int. Epiz., **25** (2)

prévalence de *Salmonella* dans la production animale doit être réduite et, dans l'Union européenne, des plans visant cet objectif sont actuellement mis en œuvre. Dans cet article, les auteurs proposent différentes stratégies d'atténuation du risque. Une prophylaxie réussie doit être axée sur un ensemble d'actions préventives car il n'existe pas de solution miracle pour réduire la contamination par *Salmonella*. Les auteurs concluent que pour lutter contre *Salmonella*, il faut suivre les règles générales qui ont été appliquées avec succès à d'autres maladies infectieuses.

Mots-clés

Atténuation du risque – Épidémiologie – Îlot de pathogénicité liés à Salmonella – Maladie – Produit d'origine animale – Prophylaxie – Prophylaxie avant abattage – Résistance aux antimicrobiens – Salmonella – Salmonellose – Suivi – Virulence.

■

La salmonelosis: un importante problema para la comercialización a escala mundial de productos alimentarios de origen animal

L. Plym Forshell & M. Wierup

Resumen

La salmonelosis es la más frecuente de las enfermedades bacterianas que se transmiten por vía alimentaria en el mundo. *Salmonella* es un patógeno importante para los animales de los que se alimenta el hombre, animales que son a su vez la fuente primaria de salmonelosis. Se estima que la prevalencia del patógeno en los rebaños oscila entre un 0% y un 90%, según la especie animal y la región de que se trate. La actividad comercial es el cauce por el que las salmonelas se transmiten entre animales y contaminan productos alimentarios no cocinados. La aparición de cepas resistentes a los antimicrobianos, que suele ser consecuencia del uso de estos fármacos en animales, constituye un riesgo de salud pública que suscita gran preocupación. Cada vez está más claro que hay que reducir la prevalencia de *Salmonella* en la producción animal, y actualmente se están aplicando planes para lograr ese objetivo en la Unión Europea. Los autores proponen varias estrategias para mitigar riesgos. Dado que no existe una única solución "mágica" que pueda reducir los niveles de contaminación, la lucha contra la enfermedad, para resultar eficaz, debe integrar un conjunto de medidas preventivas. Los autores llegan a la conclusión de que la clave para luchar contra *Salmonella* estriba en seguir las reglas generales que se han aplicado con éxito en el caso de otras enfermedades infecciosas.

Palabras clave

Control – Control previo al sacrificio – Enfermedad – Epidemiología – Isla de patogenicidad de Salmonella – Mitigación de riesgos – Productos de origen animal – Resistencia a los antimicrobianos – Salmonella – Salmonelosis – Vigilancia – Virulencia.

■

Rev. sci. tech. Off. int. Epiz., **25** (2)

551

References

1. Acha P.N. & Szyfres B. (1987). – *Salmonella. In* Zoonoses and communicable diseases common to man and animals. Pan American Health Organization (PAHO), Washington, DC, 147-155.

2. Anon. (1999). – *Salmonella*, strategidokument [in Swedish]. Socialstyrelsen, Stockholm.

3. Anon. (2005). – Erratum. *In* Annual report of zoonoses in Denmark 2004. Ministry of Family and Consumer Affairs, Copenhagen, 11-12.

4. Aserkoff B. & Bennett J.V. (1969). – Effect of antibiotic therapy in acute salmonellosis on the fecal excretion of salmonellae. *N. Engl. J. Med.*, **281** (12), 636-640.

5. Bäumler A.J., Tsolis R.M. & Heffron F. (2000). – Virulence mechanisms of *Salmonella* and their genetic basis. *In Salmonella* in domestic animals (C. Wray & A. Wray, eds). CABI Publishing, Wallingford, Oxfordshire, 57-72.

6. Berndtson E. (1996). – *Campylobacter* in broiler chickens: the mode of spread in chicken flocks with special reference to food hygiene. Dissertation. Swedish University of Agricultural Sciences, Uppsala, Sweden.

7. Blood D.C. & Radostits O.M. (1989). – Diseases caused by bacteria, III. *In* Veterinary medicine: a textbook of the diseases of cattle, sheep, pigs, goats and horses (D.C. Blood, O.M. Radostits, J.H. Arundel & C.C. Gay, eds), 7th Ed. Ballière Tindall, London, 643-655.

8. Bögel K. (1991). – Global cooperation in the control of salmonellosis. *In* Proc. Symposium on the Diagnosis and Control of *Salmonella* (G.H. Snoeyenbos, ed.), San Diego, California, 29 October. United States Animal Health Association, Richmond, Virginia, 1-5.

9. Chiu C.H., Su L.H. & Chu C. (2004). – *Salmonella enterica* serotype Choleraesuis: epidemiology, pathogenesis, clinical disease, and treatment. *Clin. Microbiol. Rev.*, **17** (2), 311-322.

10. Christensen J., Baggesen D.L., Nielsen B. & Stryhn H. (2002). – Herd prevalence of *Salmonella* spp. in Danish pig herds after implementation of the Danish *Salmonella* control program with reference to a pre-implementation study. *Vet. Microbiol.*, **88** (2), 175-188.

11. Cook A.J.C., Miller A., Snow L. & Davies R.H. (2005). – Epidemiological studies of *Salmonella* infection in pigs. *In* Proc. Med-Vet-Net 1st General Scientific Meeting, Winchester, United Kingdom, 29 June – 1 July. Available at: www.medvetnet.org/cms/ (accessed on 13 July 2006).

12. Crump J.A., Griffin P.M. & Angulo F.J. (2002). – Bacterial contamination of animal feed and its relationship to human foodborne illness. *Clin. infect. Dis.*, **35** (7), 859-865. Epub.: 5 September 2002.

13. Edel W., van Schothorst M., Guinee P.A.M. & Kampelmacher E.H. (1970). – Effect of feeding pellets on the prevention and sanitation of *Salmonella* infections in fattening pigs. *Zentralbl. Veterinärmed.*, B, **17** (7), 730-738.

14. Edel W., van Schothorst M., Guinee P.A.M. & Kampelmacher E.H. (1974). – *Salmonella* in pigs on farms feeding pellets and on farms feeding meal. *Zentralbl. Bakteriol., Orig. A*, **226** (3), 314-323.

15. European Food Safety Authority (EFSA) (2004). – Opinion of the scientific panel on biological hazards on a request from the Commission related to the use of antimicrobials for the control of *Salmonella* in poultry. *EFSA J.*, **115**, 1-76.

16. European Food Safety Authority (EFSA) (2005). – Opinion of the scientific panel on animal health and welfare on a request from the Commission related to welfare of weaners and rearing pigs: effects of different space allowances and floor types. Adopted on 13 September, Question No. EFSA-Q-2004-077. Available at: www.efsa.eu.int/science/ahaw/ahaw_opinions/1203_en.html (accessed on 23 April 2005).

17. European Food Safety Authority (EFSA) (2006). – Trends and sources of zoonoses, zoonotic agents and antimicrobial resistance in the European Union in 2004. *EFSA J.*, **310**, 10; 23-95.

18. European Union (2003). – Directive 2003/99/EC of the European Parliament and of the Council of 17 November 2003 on the monitoring of zoonoses and zoonotic agents, amending Council Decision 90/424/EEC and repealing Council Directive 92/117/EEC. *Off. J. Eur. Union*, **L 325** of 12.12.2003, 31-40.

19. European Union (2003). – Regulation (EC) No. 2160/2003 of the European Parliament and of the Council of 17 November 2003 on the control of salmonella and other specified food-borne zoonotic agents. *Off. J. Eur. Union*, **L 325** of 12.12.2003, 1-15.

20. Feberwee A., de Vries T.S., Hartman E.G., de Wit J.J., Elbers A.R. & de Jong W.A. (2001). – Vaccination against *Salmonella enteritidis* in Dutch commercial layer flocks with a vaccine based on a live *Salmonella gallinarum* 9R strain: evaluation of efficacy, safety, and performance of serologic *Salmonella* tests. *Avian Dis.*, **45** (1), 83-91.

21. Fedorka-Cray P.J., Hogg A., Gray J.T., Lorenzen K., Velasquez J. & von Behren P. (1997). – Feed and feed trucks as sources of *Salmonella* contamination in swine. *J. Swine Hlth Prod.*, **5** (5), 189-193.

22. Genovese K.J., Anderson R.C., Harvey R.B., Callaway T.R., Poole T.L., Edrington T.S., Fedorka-Cray P.J. & Nisbet D.J.S. (2003). – Competitive exclusion of *Salmonella* from the gut of neonatal and weaned pigs. *J. Food Protec.*, **66** (8), 1353-1359.

23. Haesebrouck F., Pasmans F., Chiers K., Maes D., Ducatelle R. & Decostère A. (2004). – Efficacy of vaccines against bacterial diseases in swine: what can we expect? *Vet. Microbiol.*, **100** (3-4), 255-268.

24. Häggblom P. (1994). – Cleaning of feed mills. *In* Report of the National Veterinary Institute (NVI) (Sweden)/World Health Organization (WHO) International Course on *Salmonella* control in animal production and products (S. Öijeberg-Bengtsson, ed.), Malmö, Sweden, 21-27 August 1993. WHO/CDS/ VPH/93.126. NVI, Uppsala, Sweden, 185-188. Available at: www.sva.se (accessed on 13 July 2006).

25. Häggblom P. (1994). – Monitoring and control of *Salmonella* in animal feed. *In* Report of the National Veterinary Institute (NVI) (Sweden)/World Health Organization (WHO) International Course on *Salmonella* control in animal production and products (S. Öijeberg-Bengtsson, ed.), Malmö, Sweden, 21-27 August 1993. WHO/CDS/VPH/ 93.126. NVI, Uppsala, Sweden, 127-137. Available at: www.sva.se (accessed on 13 July 2006).

26. Helmuth R. (2000). – Antibiotic resistance in *Salmonella*. *In Salmonella* in domestic animals (C. Wray & A. Wray, eds). CABI Publishing, Wallingford, Oxfordshire, 89-106.

27. Hensel M. (2004). – Evolution of pathogenicity islands of *Salmonella enterica*. *Int. J. med. Microbiol.*, **294** (2-3), 95-102.

28. Henzler D.J. & Opitz H.M. (1992). – The role of mice in the epizootiology of *Salmonella enteritidis* infection on chicken layer farms. *Avian Dis.*, **36** (3), 625-631.

29. Herikstad H., Motarjemi Y. & Tauxe R.V. (2002). – *Salmonella* surveillance: a global survey of public health serotyping. *Epidemiol. Infect.*, **129** (1), 1-8.

30. Humphrey T. (2000). – Public-health aspects of *Salmonella* infection. *In Salmonella* in domestic animals (C. Wray & A. Wray, eds). CABI Publishing, Wallingford, Oxfordshire, 245-263.

31. Jones P.W. (1992). – Salmonellas in animal wastes and hazards for other animals and humans from handling animal wastes. *In* Proc. Int. Symposium on *Salmonella* and salmonellosis, Ploufragan, France, 15-17 September. Zoopole, Ploufragan, 280-284.

32. Kaesbohrer A. (1999). – Control strategies for *Salmonella* in the pig to pork chain in the European Union. *In* Proc. 3rd International Symposium on the epidemiology and control of *Salmonella* in pork (ISECSP), Washington, DC, 5-7 August. College of Veterinary Medicine, University of Illinois, Urbana-Champaign, United States of America, 358-361.

33. Korver H., Mooijman K.A., Nagelkerke N.J.D., van de Giessen A.W. & Henken A.M. (2003). – European Union collaborative study VI (2002) on bacteriological detection of *Salmonella* spp. Report No. 330300 001. National Institute for Public Health and the Environment, Bilthoven, the Netherlands.

34. Korver H., Nagelkerke N.J.D., van de Giessen A.W. & Mooijman K.A. (2005). – European Union interlaboratory comparison study VII (2003) on bacteriological detection of *Salmonella* spp. Report No. 330300 004. National Institute for Public Health and the Environment, Bilthoven, the Netherlands.

35. Larsen E. (ed.) (1984). – Priority aspects of salmonellosis research. Commission of the European Communities (CEC), Luxembourg.

36. Laval A., Morvan H., Disperez G. & Corbion B. (1992). – Salmonellosis in swine. *In* Proc. International Symposium on *Salmonella* and salmonellosis, Ploufragan, France, 15-17 September. Zoopole, Ploufragan, 164-175.

37. Lo Fo Wong D.M., Dahl J., von Altrock A., Grafanakis S., Thorberg B.M. & van der Wolf P.J. (1999). – Herd-level risk factors for the introduction and spread of *Salmonella* in pig herds. *In* Proc. 3rd International Symposium on the epidemiology and control of *Salmonella* in pork (ISECSP), Washington, DC, 5-7 August. College of Veterinary Medicine, University of Illinois, Urbana-Champaign, United States of America, 151-154.

38. Lo Fo Wong D.M., Dahl J., Stege H., van der Wolf P.J., Leontides L., von Altrock A. & Thorberg B.M. (2004). – Herd-level risk factors for subclinical *Salmonella* infection in European finishing-pig herds. *Prev. vet. Med.*, **62** (4), 253-266.

39. Lumsden J.S. & Wilkie B.N. (1992). – Immune response of pigs to parenteral vaccination with an aromatic-dependent mutant of *Salmonella typhimurium*. *Can. J. vet. Res.*, **56** (4), 296-302.

40. Matthews K.H. Jr., Bernstein J. & Buzby J.C. (2003). – International trade of meat/poultry products and food safety issues. *In* International trade and food safety: economic theory and case studies (J.C. Buzby, ed.), Chapter 4. United States Department of Agriculture (USDA)/Economic Research Service (ERS) Agricultural Economic Report No. 828. USDA/ERS, Washington, DC, 48-74.

41. Mead P.S., Slutsker L., Dietz V., McCaig L.F., Bresee J.S., Shapiro C., Griffin P.M. & Tauxe R.V. (1999). – Food-related illness and death in the United States. *Emerg. infect. Dis.*, **5** (5), 607-625.

42. Mølbak K., Gerner-Smidt P. & Wegener H.C. (2002). – Increasing quinolone resistance in *Salmonella enterica* serotype Enteritidis. *Emerg. infect. Dis.*, **8** (5), 514-515.

43. Murray C.J. (1991). – *Salmonellae* in the environment. *In* Animals, pathogens and the environment. *Rev. sci. tech. Off. int. Epiz.*, **10** (3), 765-785.

44. Mygind J. (2004). – The Danish *Salmonella* control programme for the production of table eggs and broilers: an overview. *In* Proc. Symposium of the Public Danish Plan for control of *Salmonella* in poultry, Danish Veterinary and Food Administration, Copenhagen, 23 March. Available at: http://www.uk.foedevarestyrelsen.dk/Animal/Zoonoses/Symp osium_on_Salmonella_Control.htm (accessed in 2006).

Rev. sci. tech. Off. int. Epiz., **25** (2)

553

45. National Veterinary Institute (NVI) (Sweden)/World Health Organization (WHO) (1993). – Report of the National Veterinary Institute (NVI) (Sweden)/World Health Organization (WHO) International Course on *Salmonella* control in animal production and products (S. Öijeberg-Bengtsson, ed.), Malmö, Sweden, 21-27 August 1993. WHO/CDS/ VPH/93.126. NVI, Uppsala, Sweden. Available at: www.sva.se (accessed on 13 July 2006).

46. Ortmann R. (1999). – Immunisierungsversuche mit der *Salmonella* Typhimurium Lebendvakzine Salmoporc R zur Bekämpfung von Salmonellen Infektionen in Ferkelerzeugerbetrieben. Hanover, Tierärztl. Hochsch., Diss., 1999.

47. Quinn P.J., Markey B.K., Carter M.E., Donnelly W.J.C. & Leonard F.C. (2002). – Veterinary microbiology and microbial disease. Blackwell Science, Oxford.

48. Rabsch W., Tschäpe H. & Bäumler A.J. (2001). – Non-typhoidal salmonellosis: emerging problems. *Microbes Infect.*, **3** (3), 237-247.

49. Rapid Alert System for Food and Feed (RASFF) (2005). – Annual report of the functioning of the RASFF 2002, 2003, 2004. Available at: http://europa.eu.int/comm/food/rapidalert/resources/publications_en.htm_(accessed in 2006).

50. Rychlik I. & Barrow P.A. (2005). – *Salmonella* stress management and its relevance to behaviour during intestinal colonisation and infection. *FEMS Microbiol. Rev.*, **29** (5), 1021-1040. Epub.: 29 June 2005.

51. Rychlik I., Gregorova D. & Hradecka H. (2006). – Distribution and function of plasmids in *Salmonella enterica*. *Vet. Microbiol.*, **112** (1), 1-10. Epub.: 21 November 2005.

52. Schneitz C. & Mead G.C. (2000). – Competitive exclusion. *In Salmonella* in domestic animals (C. Wray & A. Wray, eds). CABI Publishing, Wallingford, Oxfordshire, 301-322.

53. Schwartz K.J. (1999). – Salmonellosis. *In* Diseases of swine (B.E. Straw, S. D'Allaire, W.L. Mengeling & D.J. Taylor, eds), 8th Ed. Blackwell Science, Oxford, 535-551.

54. Scientific Committee on Veterinary Measures relating to Public Health (SCVPH) (2003). – European Union (EU)/SANCO. Opinion of the SCVPH on *Salmonellae* in foodstuffs. Adopted on 14-15 April. SCVPH, Brussels.

55. Silverstolpe L. & Wranne N. (1955). – *Salmonella* outbreaks in Sweden in the county of Östergötland in 1953 [in Swedish]. *Nord. Hyg. Tidskr.*, **36** (11-12), 213-229.

56. Smith B.P., Da Roden L., Thurmond M.C., Dilling G.W., Konrad H., Pelton J.A. & Picanso J.P. (1994). – Prevalence of salmonellae in cattle and in the environment on California dairies. *JAVMA*, **205** (3), 467-471.

57. Smith H.W. & Tucker J.F. (1978). – The effect of antimicrobial feed additives on the colonization of the alimentary tract of chickens by *Salmonella typhimurium*. *J. Hyg. (Lond.)*, **80** (2), 217-231.

58. Springer S., Lindner T., Steinbach G. & Selbitz H.J. (2001). – Investigation of the efficacy of a genetically-stabile live *Salmonella typhimurium* vaccine for use in swine. *Berl. Münch. tierärztl. Wochenschr.*, **114** (9-10), 342-345.

59. Sternberg S., Boqvist S., Engström B. & Häggblom P. (2005). – The effective control of hazards in Swedish poultry: the case for Sweden. *In* Food safety control in the poultry industry (G.C. Mead, ed.). Woodhead Publishing, Cambridge, 195-215.

60. Threlfall E.J. (2002). – Antimicrobial drug resistance in *Salmonella*: problems and perspectives in food- and water-borne infections. *FEMS Microbiol. Rev.*, **26** (2), 141-148.

61. United States Department of Agriculture (USDA) (1993). – Proc. World Congress on meat and poultry inspection, Texas, 10-14 October. USDA, Washington, DC.

62. Van Asten A.J.A.M. & van Dijk J.E. (2005). – Distribution of 'classic' virulence factors among *Salmonella* spp. *FEMS Immunol. med. Microbiol.*, **44** (3), 251-259.

63. Van der Wolf P.J., Lo Fo Wong D.M., Wolbers W.B., Elbers A.R., van der Heijden H.M., van Schie F.W., Hunneman W.A., Willeberg P. & Tielen M.J. (2001). – A longitudinal study of *Salmonella enterica* infections in high- and low-seroprevalence finishing swine herds in the Netherlands. *Vet. Q.*, **23** (3), 116-121.

64. Wallgren P.T. (1994). – The importance of diseases for daily growth of pigs. *Proc. Nord. Vet. Congr.*, **17** (2), 106-110.

65. Wierup M. (1983). – *Salmonella* och antibiotika [the influence of antibiotics on *Salmonella* infections] [in Swedish]. *In* Allmänt Veterinärmöte Kompendium. Sveriges Veterinärförb [Swedish Veterinary Association], Uppsala, 115-122.

66. Wierup M. (1994). – Control and prevention of salmonellosis in livestock farms. *In* Comprehensive report on technical items presented to the International Committee or to Regional Commissions. World Organisation for Animal Health (OIE), Paris, 249-269.

67. Wierup M. (1995). – Preharvest control of salmonellosis. World Health Organisation (WHO)/USAA Consultation on economical implication of foodborne disease and consequences on animal production food hygiene, Washington, DC, 8-10 June. WHO, Geneva

68. Wierup M. (1997). – Principles for integrated surveillance and control of *Salmonella* in swine production. *In* Proc. 2nd International Symposium on epidemiology and control of *Salmonella* in pork (ISECSP), Copenhagen, 20-22 August. Danish Bacon & Meat Council, Copenhagen, 42-49.

554

Rev. sci. tech. Off. int. Epiz., **25** (2)

69. Wierup M. (2002). – Strategies for avoiding health problems of farmed animals: sustainable animal production. *In* Proc. Workshop on Sustainable Animal Production (F. Ellendorff, V. Moennig, J. Ladewig & L. Babiuk, eds), Institute for Animal Science and Animal Behaviour and Federal Agricultural Research Centre (FAL), Mariensee, Germany, 4-5 September 2000. Landbauforschung (FAL), Sonderheft 227, 103-105.

70. Wilcock B.P. & Schwartz K.J. (1992). – Salmonellosis. *In* Diseases of swine (A. Leman, B.E. Straw, W.L. Mengelin, S. D'Allaire & D.J. Taylor, eds). Iowa State University Press, Ames, Iowa, 570-583.

71. World Health Organization (WHO) (1980). – Report of the WHO/World Association of Veterinary Food Hygienists (WAVFH) round table conference on the present status of the *Salmonella* problem (prevention and control), Bilthoven, the Netherlands, 6-10 October. WHO/VPH/81.27. WHO, Bilthoven.

72. World Health Organization (WHO) (1983). – Guidelines on prevention and control of salmonellosis (A. Linton, ed.). WHO, Geneva.

73. World Health Organization (WHO) (1989). – Report of WHO Consultation on epidemiological emergency in poultry and egg salmonellosis, Geneva, 20-23 March. WHO, Geneva.

74. World Health Organization (WHO) (1992). – Report on WHO Consultation on national and local schemes of *Salmonella* control in poultry, Ploufragan, France, 18-19 September. WHO/CDS/VPH/92.110. WHO, Geneva.

75. World Health Organization (WHO) (1993). – Report of the WHO Consultation on control of *Salmonella* infections in animals: prevention of foodborne *Salmonella* infections in humans, Jena, Germany, 21-26 November. WHO/CDS/VPH/93.129. WHO, Geneva.

76. World Health Organization (WHO) (1994). – Guidelines on detection and monitoring of *Salmonella* infected poultry flocks with particular reference to *Salmonella* Enteritidis: report of a WHO Consultation on strategies for detection and monitoring of *Salmonella* infected poultry flocks (C. Wray & R.H. Davies, eds), Graz, Austria, 11-15 April. WHO/ZOON/94.173. WHO Veterinary Public Health Unit, Geneva.

77. World Health Organization (WHO) (2001). – WHO Surveillance Programme for control of foodborne infections and intoxications in Europe, 7th Report 1993-1998 (K. Schmidt & C. Tirado, eds). Federal Institute for Health Protection of Consumers and Veterinary Medicine, Berlin.

Rev. sci. tech. Off. int. Epiz., 2006, **25** (2), 555-569

Escherichia coli: on-farm contamination of animals

J.M. Fairbrother & É. Nadeau

The *Escherichia coli* Laboratory, Faculté de médecine vétérinaire, Université de Montréal, 3200 Sicotte, Saint-Hyacinthe (Québec) J2S 7C6, Canada

Summary

Escherichia coli is one of the main inhabitants of the intestinal tract of most mammalian species, including humans, and birds. Shiga toxin-producing *E. coli* (STEC), also called verotoxinogenic *E. coli*, usually do not cause disease in animals but may cause watery diarrhoea, haemorrhagic colitis, and/or haemolytic uraemic syndrome in humans. Zoonotic STEC include the O157:H7 strains and, with increasing frequency, certain non-O157 strains. The importance of non-O157 zoonotic strains is probably underestimated as they have been less well characterised and are more difficult to detect in samples than O157:H7. Another large subset of STEC strains has been isolated from animals but has not, at the present time, been associated with disease in animals or humans. Cattle and other ruminants are the most important reservoir of zoonotic STEC, which are transmitted to humans through the ingestion of foods or water contaminated with animal faeces, or through direct contact with the infected animals or their environment. The main sources of STEC infection of cattle on-farm are the drinking water, the feed, and the immediate environment of the animal. Risk factors that have been identified for infection of animals with O157 STEC include age, weaning, movement of the animals, season, feed composition, and the ability of the bacteria to persist in the environment. On-farm control of the zoonotic risk of human infection with STEC should primarily target the main source of contamination: the animal reservoir. Various strategies to reduce intestinal colonisation of cattle by zoonotic STEC have been tried with varying results, including vaccination, treatment with probiotics, such as direct-fed microbials or competitive exclusion, administration of bacteriophages, and modification of the diet.

Keywords

Escherichia coli – Haemolytic uraemic syndrome – Haemorrhagic colitis – Non-O157 strain – O157:H7 strain – Probiotic – Shiga toxin – Shiga toxin-producing Escherichia coli – Vaccination – Verotoxin – Verotoxinogenic Escherichia coli.

Introduction

Escherichia coli is one of the main inhabitants of the intestinal tract of most mammalian species, including humans and birds. Most *E. coli* are harmless, but a small proportion are an important cause of disease worldwide. These potentially harmful *E. coli* are classified into categories based on the production of virulence factors and on the clinical manifestations that they cause.

Pioneering work in the 1970s demonstrated that certain *E. coli* strains produced a toxin, which was initially called verotoxin because of its distinct effect on Vero cells (27). This family of toxins was subsequently also called Shiga-like toxins, and more recently Shiga toxins (Stx), because of the close relation to the Stx of *Shigella dysenteriae* type 1. The latter nomenclature is now more universally accepted and will be used throughout the present review. The category of *E. coli* strains producing this family of toxins is

556

Rev. sci. tech. Off. int. Epiz., **25** (2)

referred to as both verotoxinogenic *E. coli* and Stx-producing *E. coli* (STEC). The latter designation will be used throughout this review.

STEC are commonly found in a wide range of farm and wild animal species and, for the most part, do not seem to cause disease in animals (Table I) (6). However, strains of one subset of STEC are responsible for oedema disease in pigs (i.e. oedema disease *E. coli* – EDEC), and another group of STEC (i.e. non-O157 enterohaemorrhagic *E. coli* – EHEC) cause dysentery in young calves. Certain STEC strains are also zoonotic. Infection in humans is mainly associated with the ingestion of foods contaminated with the zoonotic bacteria, and clinical signs include watery diarrhoea, haemorrhagic colitis (HC), and/or haemolytic uraemic syndrome (HUS). These strains were originally named enterohaemorrhagic *E. coli* because of the associated clinical signs. In this review, the authors will refer to them as zoonotic STEC, which the authors feel is a more logical designation and results in a less confusing classification system for the unfamiliar reader (Table I). Another large subset of STEC strains have been isolated from animals, but have not as yet been associated with disease in animals or humans.

The common feature of all STEC is the production of bacteriophage-encoded Stx. These toxins belong to one of two main families, each with several variants. *Escherichia coli* strains belonging to over 200 serotypes can express Stx, but within most serotypes both Stx-positive and Stx-negative strains can be found (43).

In 1983, STEC strains of serotype O157:H7 were definitively linked for the first time to several major outbreaks of HC and HUS in the United States of America (USA) and Canada. Zoonotic STEC-related disease has been observed worldwide, and in most industrialised countries O157:H7 remains the predominant serotype. In addition, an increasing association has been observed between certain zoonotic non-O157 STEC strains, most often of the serogroups O26, O103, and O111, and outbreaks or sporadic cases of HC and HUS. Cattle are the main reservoir for zoonotic STEC throughout the world. The advent of selective media and kits for the rapid identification of O157:H7 strains has permitted a more accurate assessment of the role of this serotype in human disease outbreaks and the transmission of the infection from animal reservoirs. However, a lack of similar tests for the rapid and easy identification of zoonotic non-O157 STEC and of other STEC, which are found in the intestinal tract of animals but have not yet been implicated in human infections, has impeded assessment of the geographical distribution of these strains, the mode of transmission to humans, and the prevalence of these strains in human outbreaks and in animal reservoirs. Also, because of the use in many laboratories of selective media for the specific detection of O157:H7, on which most non-O157 STEC are not readily identified, the prevalence of non-O157 STEC is probably underestimated.

Hazard identification and characterisation

Characteristics of zoonotic Shiga toxin-producing *Escherichia coli*

More than 60 of the 200 Stx-positive *E. coli* serotypes have been associated with HC or HUS in humans, the predominant serotype being O157:H7. The most common

Table I
Classification of Shiga toxin-producing *Escherichia coli* (STEC) found in animals

Type	STEC subsets: common designation	Common serotypes/ serogroups	Geographical distribution	Animal reservoir	Site of isolation in animals and derived products
Zoonotic	O157 EHEC	O157:H7	Worldwide, more common in industrialised countries	Cattle, sheep, goats, pigs [c]	Intestine, faeces, meat, milk, cheese
	Non-O157 EHEC	O26 [b], O111 [b], O103, O113, O145	Worldwide	Cattle, sheep, goats, pigs, chickens	Intestine, faeces, meat, milk, cheese
Potentially zoonotic [a]	None	O17, O56, O87, O108, O109, O130, O136, O149	Worldwide	Cattle, sheep, goats, pigs	Intestine, faeces, meat
Animal pathogenic	EDEC	O138, O139, O141	Worldwide	Pigs	Intestine

a) not as yet associated with disease in animals or humans; few data are available on the characterisation of the virulence factors associated with these strains. Source: website of MicroBioNet, serotypes of verotoxinogenic *E. coli* (http://www.microbionet.com.au/vtectable.htm)
b) strains of some serotypes also cause haemorrhagic enteritis in cattle
c) probably an accidental host
EDEC: oedema disease *E. coli* which causes oedema disease in pigs
EHEC: enterohaemorrhagic *E. coli*

non-O157:H7 serotypes associated with human disease include O26:H11, O103:H2, O111:NM, and O113:H21. STEC of many other serotypes have been found in animals, but they have not as yet been associated with disease in animals or humans (2) (Table I). The zoonotic potential of these strains is not yet known. The O157:H7 STEC and many of the zoonotic non-O157 STEC possess in their chromosome a large multi-gene pathogenicity island, called the locus for enterocyte effacement (LEE), which contains the genes that enable the bacteria to attach to the gut epithelium and efface the microvilli. However, it is now recognised that some of the zoonotic non-O157 strains, such as some of the O111 (42) and the O113 (49) strains, do not possess the LEE and, hence, adhere to and colonise the gut epithelium by means of other uncharacterised adhesins. The O157:H7 STEC and many of the zoonotic non-O157 strains possess a large plasmid that contains the genes for several possible adhesins and for an enterohaemolysin, which may be involved in causing disease. Sequencing of the entire O157:H7 genome and genome-based studies have facilitated the identification of several additional possible virulence factors that are also present on many zoonotic non-O157 STEC, although the role of these virulence factors in the development of disease has not yet been determined. The elucidation of the role of the various virulence factors in causing human disease could eventually enable laboratories to predict the zoonotic potential of a strain based on its virulence factor profile.

In human cases, identification of the zoonotic STEC, the suspected food sources of infection, and the potential animal reservoirs is based on the detection of strains producing one or more of the Stx. This has traditionally been accomplished by observation of the effects of the Stx produced by the bacteria, using time-consuming cell culture or immunological techniques. More and more laboratories are using highly sensitive and rapid molecular techniques, such as polymerase chain reaction (PCR), to detect the genes encoding the Stx: the original sample or a direct broth culture of the sample are used as the test material and the STEC colonies are isolated and identified by PCR. As many STEC have not yet been associated with disease in humans, detection of genes for virulence factors, in addition to identification of the Stx, will provide more information on the pathogenic potential of the strain, and serotyping will confirm the identification. It is important to keep in mind that the increasing reliance on molecular techniques used to initially screen for STEC may result in a failure to identify emerging STEC producing new variants of the Stx which are less closely related genetically. Hence, it will be important that at least some reference laboratories continue to screen for toxin production via observation of the biological effects of the toxin.

The use of selective growth media, which facilitates selective growth of the bacteria based on the characteristic ability of the strain to slowly ferment sorbitol, and of immunomagnetic separation techniques, which detect the O157 antigen, has permitted the rapid and sensitive detection of O157:H7. These methods are particularly useful in small laboratories that are not equipped to carry out molecular or tissue culture techniques. However, these techniques do not detect non-O157 STEC, which usually ferment sorbitol and do not contain the O157 antigen. Immunomagnetic separation techniques and selective media are being developed for non-O157 STEC, such as O26, O103, O111 and O145 (7, 23, 51), which will facilitate rapid identification of these serotypes. O157:H7 isolates have been further characterised and sub-typed by pulse-field gel electrophoresis. Standardisation of this technique by the Centers for Disease Control and Prevention (CDC) in the USA and the establishment of PulseNet, a database and network into which strain profiles are deposited by laboratories throughout the USA and Canada, permits, by cluster analysis, the rapid tracing of O157:H7 isolates to non-human sources and identification of common source outbreaks (16, 64).

How zoonotic Shiga toxin-producing *Escherichia coli* cause disease

Zoonotic STEC cause non-bloody to bloody diarrhoea in humans. Concurrent HUS may lead to acute kidney failure, especially in children and elderly patients. The steps in the development of disease are shown in Figure 1.

The clinical course and outcome of disease due to O157 and non-O157 STEC appears to be similar, but O157 STEC may be more frequently associated with HC. The risk of disease associated with O157:H7 can be high, even at doses of < 1,000 bacteria (66), although this may be related to a variety of factors, including acid resistance of the bacteria and, hence, the ability to survive in acidic foods, which varies greatly between isolates. The infectious dose for O111 strains appears to be similar (50) but is unknown for other non-O157 STEC.

The geographical distribution of zoonotic Shiga toxin-producing *Escherichia coli* infections

STEC infections occur worldwide but are most commonly reported in the USA and Canada (43). In the USA, it is estimated that every year O157 STEC infection causes 73,000 cases of illness and approximately 61 deaths, and that zoonotic non-O157 STEC infections are responsible for about half this number of cases and deaths (40). The estimates for zoonotic non-O157 STEC are considered to be less accurate because these cases are not routinely reported and few laboratories are capable of identifying non-O157 STEC strains. The number of reported outbreaks of O157 STEC infections began rising in 1993,

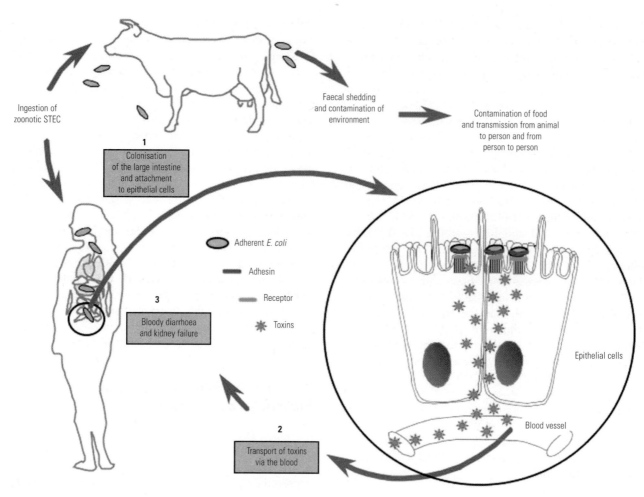

Fig. 1

How zoonotic Shiga toxin-producing *Escherichia coli* (STEC) cause bloody diarrhoea and haemolytic uraemic syndrome in humans

Zoonotic STEC principally colonise the large intestine (1). The adherent bacteria produce Shiga toxin which is transported across the epithelial cells and via the blood (2). This toxin acts on the endothelial cells of blood vessels and causes non-bloody to bloody diarrhoea and abdominal cramps (3)

Source: website of the *Escherichia coli* Laboratory (www.ecl-lab.ca)

peaked in 2000, and has subsequently decreased (55). On the other hand, the size of outbreaks steadily declined from 1982 to 2002. The increase in the number of outbreaks and the corresponding decrease in the size of the outbreaks is probably a result of greater public awareness of the association between STEC infections and illness, improved techniques for the detection and identification of O157:H7, increased testing for O157:H7 following its designation as a notifiable infection (and the subsequent requirement for the mandatory reporting of cases), and improved tracing of outbreaks due to the introduction of molecular subtyping and PulseNet. Most outbreaks occurred from May to November, and outbreaks appeared to be more common in the northern states of the USA and western provinces of Canada.

Zoonotic STEC is also an important cause of disease in many other countries, particularly Japan, Australia, Argentina and European countries (8, 21, 43, 45, 70). It appears that the prevalence of HUS is similar in Australia, Europe, and North

America and that the association between HUS and *E. coli* infection is similar in the different parts of the world (70). The proportion of human cases in which zoonotic non-O157 STEC are involved varies from 20% to 70% among geographical regions (69). In Japan, between 1991 and 1995, more than 80% of *E. coli* isolates were identified as O157:H7. The other most important isolates identified were the non-O157 serotypes O26 and O111 (21). By 2004, O157:H7 isolations had decreased by about 50%, while O26 and O111 isolations had increased by 24% and 8.2%, respectively. Nevertheless, in 2004, O157:H7 was the predominant serotype among STEC isolates causing HUS in Japan. In Australia, from 2002 to 2004, O157 was the predominant isolate from zoonotic STEC infections, except for infections manifesting HUS (45). Little information is available regarding HUS-associated infections, and non-O157 O86 and O111 were the only two serotypes identified upon STEC isolation from these cases. Data compiled from different countries in Europe indicated that about 80% of STEC isolated from cases of diarrhoea were non-O157: the

Rev. sci. tech. Off. int. Epiz., **25** (2)

559

most common isolates identified were O26, O91, O103, O111, O113, O128, and O145 (5). On the other hand, STEC isolated from HUS cases were mostly O157:H7. In Argentina, the frequency of HUS appears to be very high (36, 46). In this country, as well as in Chile and Uruguay, O157 STEC appeared to be less predominant in HUS than non-O157 STEC, using data collected since 2000 (little data is available for cases occurring before 2000).

There are fewer reports on zoonotic STEC infections from other countries. In the People's Republic of China, a national network for the detection of O157:H7 was set up in 1997 (71). Only a few sporadic cases of diarrhoea associated with O157 STEC have been identified. Involvement of non-O157 zoonotic STEC is less well-defined, but there is some indication that these infections may be more predominant than O157 STEC infections. In countries in Africa from which data have been reported, including Kenya, Nigeria, Côte d'Ivoire, and the Central African Republic, O157 STEC have been isolated from sporadic cases of diarrhoea and HUS, and have also been

associated with some diarrhoeal disease outbreaks, especially in southern Africa (12, 54). Non-O157 STEC have also been associated with sporadic cases and outbreaks of diarrhoea in Nigeria (44). Conversely, STEC were not frequently involved in cases of diarrhoea in Uganda (26). STEC do not appear to be an important cause of diarrhoea in India, at least in Calcutta, where non-O157 STEC were isolated from only a small proportion of cases (28). Similarly, STEC do not seem to be an important cause of bloody or non-bloody diarrhoea in Bangkok, Thailand (34).

Exposure assessment

Humans are infected with zoonotic STEC mostly through the consumption of foods contaminated with faeces containing the bacteria (Fig. 2). A large amount of data are available on the mode of transmission of O157 STEC, particularly in the USA (55). Food has remained the predominant transmission route: the most important food

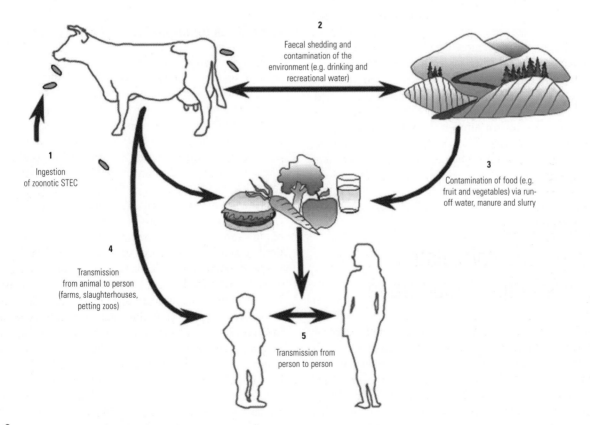

Fig. 2
How humans are exposed to zoonotic Shiga toxin-producing *Escherichia coli* (STEC)
Zoonotic STEC are ingested by cattle and other ruminants (1) and colonise the intestinal tract but do not cause any disease in these animals. The bacteria are shed in the faeces and contaminate the environment, including drinking and recreational water used by the human population (2). There may also be contamination of foods, such as fruits and fruit juices, vegetables, sprouts, and lettuce via run-off water, manure, or slurry (3). There may be contamination of milk during milking and of carcasses at slaughter such that bacteria will be mixed into ground beef. Persons working on farms or in slaughterhouses or visiting farms or petting zoos may also be infected with the bacteria through direct contact with animals (4). There may also be direct spread of bacteria from person to person (5)
Source: website of the *Escherichia coli* Laboratory (www.ecl-lab.ca)

Rev. sci. tech. Off. int. Epiz., 25 (2)

sources being undercooked hamburgers and ground beef products. Raw milk and milk products, such as cheese curds, butter, and ice cream bars, have also been a source of infection. Since 1991, produce has been an increasingly important cause of outbreaks: high risk products include lettuce, unpasteurised apple cider and juice, salad, coleslaw, melons, and sprouts. Outbreaks of O157 STEC most commonly occurred in restaurants, often due to cross-contamination during food preparation. Person-to-person transmission via the faecal-oral route has been an important mode of transmission, particularly since the early 1990s, and occurs mostly in child day care centres, individual homes, communities, and schools. Waterborne outbreaks of O157 STEC associated with recreational waters, such as lakes, swimming pools, and contaminated drinking water, have been increasingly reported since the early 1990s. Outbreaks associated with contaminated water tend to be larger in size and have been attributed to local well, municipal, and spring water systems. Since 1996, outbreaks resulting from a new transmission mode have been recognised, i.e. direct contact between humans and cows or calves at farms, fairs, or petting zoos. For the most part, the modes of transmission in other industrialised countries appear to be similar to those observed in the USA. As more data become available from developing countries, other modes of transmission specific for the environmental, demographic, and farming conditions in these countries will certainly be elucidated. For instance, a large outbreak of bloody diarrhoea due to O157 STEC in southern Africa in 1992 was the result of a combination of carriage of O157 STEC by pastured cattle, cattle deaths due to drought, and ensuing heavy rains resulting in contamination of surface waters (12).

Exposure to *Escherichia coli* related to international food trade

There is a high potential for multinational food-borne outbreaks of illness following international trading of foods contaminated with zoonotic STEC, especially ground beef and beef products. This is well illustrated by the example of the 2004 outbreak of O157:H7 infections in humans in Japan following commercial distribution of contaminated ground beef that had been produced in the USA (30). Use of PulseNet protocols during the public health investigation by Japanese authorities enabled international comparison of isolates and facilitated detection of presumptively associated *E. coli* O157:H7 infections in the USA. The six-month lag between production of the beef products in the USA and sale of the products in Japan, with intervening cases in the USA, demonstrates the prolonged survival of O157:H7 STEC in frozen ground beef and the

potential for outbreaks to occur over an extended time period and have a wide geographical distribution. PulseNet has now been established in several regions of the world. The use of standardised methods of molecular subtyping for O157:H7 and eventually for other non-O157 STEC will be invaluable in permitting the international collaboration necessary for investigation of these outbreaks.

Animal reservoirs

STEC are found in the intestinal tract and are shed in the faeces of a wide variety of animal species, including cattle, sheep, goats, pigs, water buffalo, and wild ruminant species (6). Ruminants are the most important reservoir of the zoonotic STEC (Fig. 2), which are transmitted to humans through the ingestion of food or water contaminated with animal faeces or through contact with the infected animals or their environment.

O157 Shiga toxin-producing *Escherichia coli*

O157 STEC mostly originate from cattle. Faecal shedding appears to occur for longer periods and the number of bacteria shed in the faeces is greater in young calves and at weaning, compared to adult cattle (10). The amount of faecal shedding is the greatest in both young and adult cattle during the summer (19). O157 STEC are found in dairy cattle and in both pastured and feedlot beef cattle. The prevalence of infection in individual animals is low (often less than 1%), although the herd prevalence may be higher and is often between 10% and 20% in the USA (18). A similar prevalence has been observed in studies carried out in various European countries (6), although the rate of positive animals was as high as 17% in Italy. O157 STEC has been found in cattle in many other countries, including Japan (29), Korea (24), the People's Republic of China (73, 74), Argentina (41), and Brazil (22). On the other hand, O157 STEC were not found in cattle in studies conducted in India (28) and Thailand (47), where cases of diarrhoea in humans attributed to zoonotic STEC do not appear to be frequent. In the few reports from Africa, O157 STEC have been found in beef meat products in Botswana (38) and in cattle associated with a major outbreak of diarrhoea in humans in southern Africa in 1992, but have not been detected in cattle in Uganda (26).

O157 STEC are also isolated sporadically from non-ruminant species on farms, such as rabbits, pigs, horses, and dogs. It is not clear if these species are hosts of O157 STEC or if they become accidentally colonised due to contact with infected ruminants. Pigs are not considered a major source of O157 STEC (the prevalence rate is usually very low), although reports from certain countries,

Rev. sci. tech. Off. int. Epiz., **25** (2)

561

such as Chile (56) and the People's Republic of China (71, 74), demonstrate a much higher prevalence of up to 10%, which could reflect different farming and slaughter practices and could represent an important hazard in countries where the consumption of pork is high.

Non-O157 Shiga toxin-producing *Escherichia coli*

Non-O157 STEC has been found in the animal population worldwide, including in Africa and the People's Republic of China (2, 6, 26, 35, 52). Non-O157 STEC are mostly associated with cattle but have also been isolated from sheep, goats, pigs, and chickens. The prevalence rate varies considerably, depending on the technique used for sampling and detection, but is usually between 10% and 20% and may be as high as 80% to 90%. The prevalence rate of zoonotic non-O157 STEC is often difficult to assess because in many studies detection is based only on the presence of the Stx, and the serotype of the isolate and presence of other virulence factors are not determined by the investigators. In studies in which serotyping has been performed, zoonotic STEC belonging to serogroups such as O26, O103, O111, and O145 have been found in the USA, the United Kingdom, Canada, Europe, Australia, Argentina, Hong Kong and Japan in different animal species: cattle were the most common species in which these serotypes were detected (1, 52) (Table I). When determined, prevalence rates for STEC of these serotypes were usually around 1% to 2%. However, this prevalence may be underestimated compared to that observed for O157 STEC cases in which techniques to concentrate the sample in order to detect the bacteria are often used. Prevalence rates for O26 and O103 STEC were 94% and 51%, respectively, in calves examined over a period of five months in Scotland using an immunomagnetic separation technique (51). Testing for certain virulence factors, which provides a means of more accurately assessing the prevalence of zoonotic STEC in animal populations and, hence, the potential hazard to human health, has been carried out in some studies and has demonstrated much lower prevalence rates of zoonotic STEC than those for total STEC (22, 29, 48, 57, 61). This approach will become more valuable as virulence factor profiles of these strains are identified and rapid high-throughput tests become available.

Sources of infection in animals

The main sources of STEC infection in cattle are drinking water, feed, and the environment of the animal (Fig. 3).

The environment may be contaminated by cattle carrying the bacteria as well as by production animals of other species (e.g. sheep, goats, or pigs), by companion animals (e.g. dogs, cats, or horses), by wild animal species (e.g. deer), or by insects (e.g. flies). Infection may also occur through direct contact with other cattle or animals of other species.

Run-off of water from dairies or from pastures where cattle carrying zoonotic STEC have been grazing can contaminate surface drinking waters, such as rivers, ponds, lakes, and ground water supplying wells and springs. Pastures where slurry or manure originating from cattle carrying zoonotic STEC has been spread as fertiliser may also be a source of contamination. Contamination of drinking troughs may originate from the water source or occur following faecal contamination or often, when troughs are covered, following oral contamination of the drinking water by cattle carrying STEC in their tonsils (62). O157 STEC can survive in water, faeces, or sediment from drinking troughs for several months (6, 60).

Contamination of feeds, such as grain pellets, soybean meal, silage grasses, and grass hay, may occur at the source of the feed (i.e. in the crop fields) following run-off of contaminated water, spreading of manure and slurries as fertiliser or via wild bird or mammalian faeces. Feeds may also be contaminated during transport by truck to a feed mill (11). Poor silage management may permit the survival of STEC found on faecally-contaminated grasses: proper silage processing normally eliminates STEC (13). Contamination of feed troughs may occur through saliva or following defecation in the troughs by cattle, wildlife, rodents, birds, or insects, such as flies.

Contamination of the environment of cattle, including pastures, feed and water troughs, and pen floors, is mostly a result of faecal contamination by the cattle living in the environment. Most importantly, it has been shown that some O157 STEC strains may persist for more than two years in a particular farm environment (62). The type of environment greatly influences the persistence of the bacteria. For instance, calves kept indoors in pens continued to shed O157 STEC for four months, whereas no shedding of O157 STEC was detected (over a period of six months) in calves on the same farm kept on pasture, possibly due to a reduced exposure of the pasture-raised calves to the bacteria (25). Poor husbandry will also affect STEC persistence. Cattle kept in feedlot pens with wet, muddy floors demonstrated a higher prevalence rate of shedding of O157 STEC than cattle raised in pens under normal conditions (63).

Risk factors for infection of animals

Risk factors that have been associated with the infection of animals with O157 STEC include age, weaning, movement

562

Rev. sci. tech. Off. int. Epiz., **25** (2)

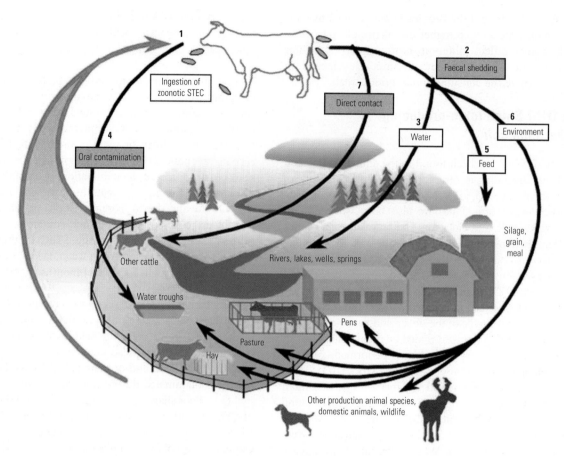

Fig. 3
Sources of zoonotic Shiga toxin-producing *Escherichia coli* (STEC) infection in farm animals
Zoonotic STEC are ingested by cattle and other ruminants (1) and colonise the intestinal tract but do not cause any disease in these animals. The bacteria are shed in the faeces (2). Contamination of drinking water from rivers, lakes, wells, and springs occurs following run-off of contaminated water from dairies and from pastures where cattle have been grazing or cattle manure has been spread (3). Contamination of water troughs may also originate from the saliva of cattle carrying the STEC in their tonsils (4). Contamination of feeds may occur at the source (i.e. in the crop fields) following run-off of contaminated water, spreading of manure and slurries as fertiliser, or via wild bird or mammalian faeces (5). Cattle faeces containing zoonotic STEC can also contaminate the immediate environment of the animals, including pastures, feed and water troughs, and pen floors (6). Other farm and wild animal species may be infected via the water, feed, or environment and, in turn, infect cattle via their faeces. Infection of cattle may also occur by direct contact with other cattle (7)
Source: website of the *Escherichia coli* Laboratory (www.ecl-lab.ca)

of animals, season, feed composition, and the ability of the bacteria to persist in the environment. Faecal shedding was higher in dairy calves at weaning than before weaning in studies conducted in the western USA and Denmark (15, 58) and was higher in weaned heifers than in calves or adults in a longitudinal study of cattle herds conducted in the northwestern USA (19). In the latter study, carried out over a period of more than one year, faecal shedding was highest in the summer months. In a risk-factor study of dairy herds in Denmark, calves up to two years old that had been moved to a new location within the previous two weeks had a higher risk of faecal shedding of O157 STEC (58). In a cross-sectional study of feedlot cattle close to their market date in the Midwestern USA (59), a positive association was observed between the heat index (combining heat and humidity) and levels of O157 STEC

in feed sampled from feed bunks in feedlot pens. Interestingly, no difference in faecal shedding of O157 STEC was observed between cattle produced on conventional versus organic dairy farms in Switzerland (33).

Feed composition is also a possible risk factor for infection of animals with STEC. It has been shown that zoonotic O157 and non-O157 STEC survive in acid conditions and persist in rumen contents (3), which supports the proposal that a grain-rich diet may induce acid resistance of STEC in the rumen and permit the bacteria to survive in the abomasum, leading to increased faecal shedding. However, numerous field studies have demonstrated the opposite effect: hay-fed sheep (31) and cattle (20) shed O157 STEC for longer periods than grain-fed animals of the same species. In another study, (17) no difference in faecal shedding of O157 STEC was observed between hay-fed and grain-fed cattle. On the other hand, in the aforementioned risk-factor study of dairy herds in Denmark (58), cows fed grain or molasses had a higher risk of shedding O157 STEC.

The type of grain used in a feed may also influence the risk of infection of cattle with STEC. For instance, in the cross-sectional study of feedlot cattle that were close to their market date in the Midwestern USA (59), a positive association was noted between the use of cottonseed meal and levels of O157 STEC in feed sampled from feed bunks in feedlot pens. It is not known if this effect is due to an ability of the cottonseed meal to enhance O157 STEC survival in the intestinal tract of the cattle or to contamination of the meal with the bacteria.

The ability of zoonotic STEC to survive and persist in faeces, manure, and soil in the environment can be considered as a risk factor for the infection of animals and humans. It has been shown that O157 STEC can survive for several months in water or sediment from drinking troughs. These bacteria can also survive for long periods in cattle faeces, particularly when the moisture content remains high (68), and in cattle or sheep manure piles and manure slurry (32). O157 STEC can survive in soil for long periods, particularly in the presence of manure, and during rainfall can be leached out of the soil and travel below the top layers of the soil for more than two months, increasing the probability of contamination of groundwater, which is recycled for crop irrigation, vegetable cleansing, or as drinking water for animals and the human population (14). Hence, run-off from manure piles contaminated with zoonotic STEC and using manure and slurries contaminated with zoonotic STEC as fertiliser on land used for animal grazing, crop or silage production for animal feed, or food crops for human consumption may result in persistent animal infection and a greater risk of human exposure.

Controlling the zoonotic risk at farm level

On-farm control of zoonotic STEC should primarily target the main source of contamination: the animal reservoir. Complete eradication of zoonotic STEC-positive farm animals would not be feasible due to the high prevalence rate of O157 STEC, the transient nature of the infection, and the difficulty in detecting low numbers of zoonotic STEC found in animal faeces (6). A more realistic aim would be to reduce intestinal colonisation of, and consequent faecal shedding by, animals. Such a measure would minimise STEC contamination of water sources used for human consumption and recreational activities; of food crops used for human consumption; and of meat, meat products, and milk. It would also minimise the possibility of infection of humans through direct contact with animals. At the same time, measures should be taken to limit the persistence of STEC in the farm environment.

Various strategies to reduce intestinal colonisation of cattle by zoonotic STEC have been attempted, including vaccination, treatment with probiotics (e.g. direct-fed microbials or competitive exclusion), administration of bacteriophages, and modification of the diet (4). There has been at least one report of field testing of a vaccine in cattle based on the virulence factors of O157 STEC. Vaccination resulted in decreased faecal shedding in experimentally infected cattle and in clinical trials in feedlot cattle, demonstrating the potential benefits of such an approach (53). Nevertheless, this approach still requires some optimisation as faecal shedding was not reduced after administration of the same vaccine to feedlot cattle in commercial operations (67). Another promising approach is feeding ruminants egg yolk antibodies purified from chickens immunised with specific virulence factors of zoonotic STEC. This approach resulted in a decrease in the duration and level of faecal shedding of O157 STEC in experimentally infected sheep (9).

Treatment with different probiotic strains has had variable effects on faecal shedding of STEC in cattle. Encouragingly, daily treatment of finisher beef cattle with direct-fed microbials, such as certain strains of *Lactobacillus acidophilus* (72), reduced faecal shedding of O157 STEC by over 50%. Treatment with a competitive exclusion probiotic containing *E. coli* strains reduced faecal shedding of both O157 and O111 but not O26 zoonotic STEC in weaned calves (65). Hence, these results suggest that a judicious choice of probiotic bacterial strains for the treatment of cattle could eventually permit a reduction in faecal shedding of not only O157 STEC but also a variety of zoonotic non-O157 STEC serotypes.

Antibacterial viruses, known as bacteriophages, that specifically target O157 STEC appear to be able to control the growth of these bacteria under laboratory conditions and have shown promising results in sheep; however, further work is necessary before the viruses can be considered a feasible approach for the control of STEC in cattle (4).

The application of epidemiological models to prevalence data on faecal shedding of O157 STEC in cattle in Scotland has demonstrated that only about 20% of the infections are responsible for 80% of the transmission to the cattle population (39). Hence, control strategies aimed at the 5% of animals in the population with high levels of intestinal carriage of the bacteria or interventions aimed at preventing high bacterial loads could very effectively

564

Rev. sci. tech. Off. int. Epiz., **25** (2)

reduce the prevalence of O157 STEC. Such control measures could include testing and removal of high shedding individuals, vaccination or probiotic treatment.

The effect of changing abruptly from a grain diet to a hay diet on faecal shedding of O157 STEC has not been consistent (4). In general, there appeared to be a decrease in the intestinal *E. coli* population; however, the percent reduction in the bacterial population was not consistent between animals.

Manure piles and slurries are a potential source of zoonotic STEC contamination if manure-based fertilisers are used on food crops destined for human consumption or if fields and recreational waters become polluted by run-off water. Hence, reduction in the levels of STEC in the manure would be a logical strategy to reduce the risk of human infection. Composting has been shown to be very effective for the elimination of O157 STEC from manure and should be considered as a routine practice prior to spreading the manure (37).

Good management practices, such as routinely cleaning water troughs, chlorinating or ozonating the water supply, reducing the faecal contamination and humidification of cattle feeds, avoiding overcrowding and muddy pen floors in feedlots, and correctly preparing silage, will greatly contribute to minimising the spread and persistence of zoonotic STEC on the farm.

To control the risk of human infection through direct contact with farm animals, strict hygiene practices should be established, including controlling the movement of visitors to farms, restricting access to farm animals, making washing facilities readily available, providing a means of disinfection in case visitors come into contact with the animals, and segregating eating areas from areas where the animals are kept.

Conclusions

Great strides have been made in recent years in the detection, identification, and molecular characterisation of O157:H7 STEC, which has led to a more accurate assessment of the role of this serotype in human disease outbreaks and the transmission of infection from animal reservoirs. A major challenge will now be to better understand how these bacteria colonise the gut of the animal hosts. Such an understanding will permit the development of effective strategies to eliminate or greatly reduce the numbers of the bacteria in the animal reservoir.

In recent years, it has become apparent that certain non-O157 STEC can also cause human infections. Another challenge will be to more definitively identify and characterise these non-O157 STEC strains, which will allow a more thorough surveillance of the prevalence of the bacteria in animal populations, assessment of the importance of these bacterial species in human infections, and development of effective on-farm control strategies.

Acknowledgements

The authors thank Jacinthe Lachance for assistance in the preparation of the manuscript and for the design of the diagrams.

■

Escherichia coli : la contamination des animaux à la ferme

J.M. Fairbrother & É. Nadeau

Résumé
Escherichia coli est l'un des principaux microorganismes présents dans l'intestin de la plupart des espèces de mammifères, y compris les êtres humains, et des oiseaux. Les *E. coli* producteurs de Shiga-toxines (STEC), appelés aussi producteurs de verocytotoxine, ne sont généralement pas pathogènes pour l'animal, alors que chez l'homme l'infection se manifeste par une diarrhée aqueuse, une colite hémorragique et/ou un syndrome hémolytique et urémique (SHU). Si les souches O157:H7 sont le plus souvent incriminées lors des infections à STEC zoonotiques, il est de plus en plus fréquent de retrouver

d'autres souches. L'importance de souches autres que les O157:H7 a sans doute été sous-estimée, dans la mesure où leur caractérisation est moins aboutie que celle des O157:H7 et qu'elles sont plus difficiles à détecter dans les prélèvements. Un sous-type comprenant de nombreuses souches STEC a été isolé à partir de prélèvements animaux mais à ce jour il n'a été associé à aucune pathologie chez l'animal ni chez l'homme. Les bovins et les autres ruminants constituent le principal réservoir des STEC zoonotiques, qui sont transmis à l'homme par ingestion d'aliments ou d'eau contaminés par des matières fécales animales, ou par contact direct avec des animaux infectés ou avec leur environnement. Dans les exploitations, la contamination des bovins par des STEC se fait à travers l'eau, l'alimentation et l'environnement immédiat. Les facteurs de risque d'infection des animaux avec des STEC de sérotype O157 sont l'âge, les conditions de sevrage, les déplacements des animaux, la saison, la composition de la ration alimentaire, ainsi que la capacité de la bactérie à survivre dans l'environnement. Pour maîtriser le risque zoonotique de contamination par des STEC au niveau de l'exploitation, il convient de se concentrer sur la principale source de contamination, à savoir le réservoir animal. Plusieurs stratégies ont été tentées pour limiter les colonies de STEC zoonotiques dans l'intestin de bovins, avec des résultats variables : la vaccination, le recours aux probiotiques en administrant des agents microbiens dans l'alimentation ou en faisant intervenir le mécanisme d'exclusion compétitive, l'administration de bactériophages ou la modification de la ration alimentaire.

Mots-clés

Colite hémorragique – Escherichia coli – Escherichia coli producteur de Shiga-toxine – Escherichia coli producteur de verocytotoxine – Probiotique – Sérotype autre que O157 – Sérotype O157:H7 – Shiga-toxine – Syndrome hémolytique et urémique – Vaccination – Verotoxine.

■

Contaminación de animales por *Escherichia coli* en la finca

J.M. Fairbrother & É. Nadeau

Resumen
Escherichia coli es uno de los principales huéspedes del tracto intestinal de la mayoría de mamíferos, comprendidos los seres humanos, y las aves. Habitualmente, *E. coli* productora de toxina Shiga (STEC), también llamada *E. coli* verotoxigénica, no provoca enfermedades en los animales, pero puede producir diarrea acuosa, colitis hemorrágica o síndrome hemolítico ureico en los seres humanos. La STEC zoonótica comprende las cepas O157:H7 y, con una frecuencia cada vez mayor, otras cepas distintas. Probablemente se subestima la importancia de estas últimas dado que no han sido tan bien caracterizadas como las cepas O157:H7 y son más difíciles de detectar en las muestras. Se ha aislado en animales otro importante subconjunto de cepas de STEC, pero hasta el momento no se lo ha asociado con la aparición de enfermedades animales o humanas. Los bovinos y demás rumiantes son el principal reservorio de STEC zoonótica, que se transmite a los seres humanos por ingestión de alimentos o agua contaminados con heces animales, o por contacto directo con animales infectados o su entorno. Las principales fuentes de infección del ganado por STEC en las explotaciones son el agua de beber, los piensos y el entorno

inmediato de los animales. Los factores de riesgo de infección de animales por la cepa O157 de STEC identificados hasta la fecha comprenden la edad, el destete, los movimientos de animales, el celo, la composición de los piensos y la capacidad de la bacteria para resistir al entorno. En las explotaciones, el control del riesgo zoonótico de infección por STEC en los seres humanos debe concentrarse fundamentalmente en el reservorio animal, principal fuente de contagio. Se han probado, con mayor o menor éxito, distintas estrategias para reducir el establecimiento de colonias zoonóticas de STEC en los animales, comprendidas la vacunación, los tratamientos con probióticos, como la alimentación directa con microbianos y la exclusión competitiva, la administración de bacteriófagos y la modificación de la dieta.

Palabras clave

Cepa O157:H7 – Cepa distinta de la O157 – Colitis hemorrágica – Escherichia coli – Escherichia coli productora de toxina Shiga – Escherichia coli verotoxigénica – Probiótico – Síndrome hemolítico ureico – Toxina Shiga – Vacunación – Verotoxina.

■

References

1. Bettelheim K.A. (2003). – Non-O157 verotoxin-producing *Escherichia coli*: a problem, paradox, and paradigm. *Experim. Biol. Med.*, **228**, 333-344.

2. Beutin L., Geier D., Steinruck H., Zimmermann S. & Scheutz F. (1993). – Prevalence and some properties of verotoxin (Shiga-like toxin)-producing *Escherichia coli* in seven different species of healthy domestic animals. *J. clin. Microbiol.*, **31** (9), 2483-2488.

3. Boukhors K., Pradel N., Girardeau J.P., Livrelli V., Ou Saïd A.M., Contrepois M. & Martin C. (2002). – Effect of diet on Shiga toxin-producing *Escherichia coli* (STEC) growth and survival in rumen and abomasum fluids. *Vet. Res.*, **33**, 405-412.

4. Callaway T.R., Anderson R.C., Edrington T.S., Genovese K.J., Bischoff K.M., Poole T.L., Jung Y.S., Harvey R.B. & Nisbet D.J. (2004). – What are we doing about *Escherichia coli* O157:H7 in cattle? *J. Anim. Sci.*, **82** (E. suppl.), 93-99.

5. Caprioli A. & Tozzi A.E. (1998). – Epidemiology of Shiga toxin-producing *Escherichia coli* infections in continental Europe. *In Escherichia coli* O157:H7 and other Shiga toxin-producing *E. coli* strains (J.B. Kaper & A.D. O'Brien, eds). ASM Press, Washington, DC, 38-48.

6. Caprioli A., Morabito S., Brugère H. & Oswald E. (2005). – Enterohaemorrhagic *Escherichia coli*: emerging issues on virulence and modes of transmission. *Vet. Res.*, **36**, 289-311.

7. Catarame T.M., O'Hanlon K.A., Duffy G., Sheridan J.J., Blair I.S. & McDowell D.A. (2003). – Optimization of enrichment and plating procedures for the recovery of *Escherichia coli* O111 and O26 from minced beef. *J. appl. Microbiol.*, **95** (5), 949-957.

8. Combs B.G., Raupach J.C.A. & Kirk M.D. (2005). – Surveillance of Shiga toxigenic in Australia. *Communic. Dis. Intell.*, **29** (4), 366-369.

9. Cook S.R., Bach S.J., Stevenson S.M.L., DeVinney R., Frohlich A.A., Fang L. & McAllister T.A. (2005). – Orally administered anti-*Escherichia coli* O157:H7 chicken egg yolk antibodies reduce fecal shedding of the pathogen by ruminants. *Can. J. anim. Sci.*, **85**, 291-299.

10. Cray W.C. Jr & Moon H.W. (1995). – Experimental infection of calves and adult cattle with *Escherichia coli* O157:H7. *Appl. environ. Microbiol.*, **61** (4), 1586-1590.

11. Davis M.A., Hancock D.D., Rice D.H., Call D.R., DiGiacomo R., Samadpour M. & Besser T.E. (2003). – Feedstuffs as a vehicle of cattle exposure to *Escherichia coli* O157:H7 and *Salmonella enterica*. *Vet. Microbiol.*, **95**, 199-210.

12. Effler P., Isaäcson M., Arntzen L., Heenan R., Canter P., Barrett T., Lee L., Mambo C., Levine W., Zaidi A. & Griffin P.M. (2001). – Factors contributing to the emergence of *Escherichia coli* O157 in Africa. *Emerg. infect. Dis.*, **7** (5), 812-819.

13. Fenlon D.R. & Wilson J. (2000). – Growth of *Escherichia coli* O157 in poorly fermented laboratory silage: a possible environmental dimension in the epidemiology of *E. coli* O157. *Lett. appl. Microbiol.*, **30** (2), 118-121.

14. Gagliardi J.V. & Karns J.S. (2000). – Leaching of *Escherichia coli* O157:H7 in diverse soils under various agricultural management practices. *Appl. environ. Microbiol.*, **66** (3), 877-883.

Rev. sci. tech. Off. int. Epiz., **25** (2)

567

15. Garber L.P., Wells S.J., Hancock D.D., Doyle M.P., Tuttle J., Shere J.A. & Zhao T. (1995). – Risk factors for fecal shedding of *Escherichia coli* O157:H7 in dairy calves. *J. Am. vet. med. Assoc.*, **207** (1), 46-49.

16. Gerner-Smidt P., Kincaid J., Kubota K., Hise K., Hunter S.B., Fair M.A., Norton D., Woo-Ming A., Kurzynski T., Sotir M.J., Head M., Holt K. & Swaminathan B. (2005). – Molecular surveillance of shiga toxigenic *Escherichia coli* O157 by PulseNet USA. *J. Food Protec.*, **68** (9), 1926-1931.

17. Grauke L.J., Wynia S.A., Sheng H.Q., Yoon J.W., Williams C.J., Hunt C.W. & Hovde C.J. (2003). – Acid resistance of *Escherichia coli* O157:H7 from the gastrointestinal tract of cattle fed hay or grain. *Vet. Microbiol.*, **95**, 211-225.

18. Hancock D.D., Besser T.E., Kinsel M.L., Tarr P.I., Rice D.H. & Paros M.G. (1994). – The prevalence of *Escherichia coli* O157:H7 in dairy and beef cattle in Washington State. *Epidemiol. Infect.*, **113** (2), 199-207.

19. Hancock D.D., Besser T.E., Rice D.H., Herriott D.E. & Tarr P.I. (1997). – A longitudinal study of *Escherichia coli* O157 in fourteen cattle herds. *Epidemiol. Infect.*, **118** (2), 193-195.

20. Hovde C.J., Austin P.R., Cloud K.A., Williams C.J. & Hunt C.W. (1999). – Effect of cattle diet on *Escherichia coli* O157:H7 acid resistance. *Appl. environ. Microbiol.*, **65** (7), 3233-3235.

21. Infectious Disease Surveillance Center (2005). – Enterohemorrhagic *Escherichia coli* infection as of May 2005. *Infect. Agents Surv. Rep.*, **26** (6), 137-138.

22. Irino K., Kato M.A.M.F., Vaz T.M.I., Ramos I.I., Souza M.A.C., Cruz A.S., Gomes T.A.T., Vieira M.A.M. & Guth B.E.C. (2005). – Serotypes and virulence markers of Shiga toxin-producing *Escherichia coli* (STEC) isolated from dairy cattle in São Paulo State, Brazil. *Vet. Microbiol.*, **105**, 29-36.

23. Jenkins C., Pearce M.C., Smith A.W., Knight H.I., Shaw D.J., Cheasty T., Foster G., Gunn G.J., Dougan G., Smith H.R. & Frankel G. (2003). – Detection of *Escherichia coli* serogroups O26, O103, O111 and O145 from bovine faeces using immunomagnetic separation and PCR/DNA probe techniques. *Lett. appl. Microbiol.*, **37** (3), 207-212.

24. Jo M.Y., Kim J.H., Lim J.H., Kang M.Y., Koh H.B., Park Y.H., Yoon D.Y., Chae J.S., Eo S.K. & Lee J.H. (2004). – Prevalence and characteristics of *Escherichia coli* O157 from major food animals in Korea. *Int. J. Food Microbiol.*, **95**, 41-49.

25. Jonsson M.E., Aspan A., Eriksson E. & Vagsholm I. (2001). – Persistence of verocytotoxin-producing *Escherichia coli* O157:H7 in calves kept on pasture and in calves kept indoors during the summer months in a Swedish dairy herd. *Int. J. Food Microbiol.*, **66** (1-2), 55-61.

26. Kaddu-Mulindw D.H., Aisu T., Gleier K., Zimmermann S. & Beutin L. (2001). – Occurrence of Shiga toxin-producing *Escherichia coli* in fecal samples from children with diarrhea and from healthy zebu cattle in Uganda. *Int. J. Food Microbiol.*, **66** (1-2), 95-101.

27. Karmali M.A. (1989). – Infection by verocytotoxin-producing *Escherichia coli*. *Clin. Microbiol. Rev.*, **2** (1), 15-38.

28. Khan A., Yamasaki S., Sato T., Ramamurthy T., Pal A., Datta S., Chowdhury N.R., Das S.C., Sikdar A., Tsukamoto T., Bhattacharya S.K., Takeda Y. & Nair G.B. (2002). – Prevalence and genetic profiling of virulence determinants of non-O157 Shiga toxin-producing *Escherichia coli* isolated from cattle, beef, and humans, Calcutta, India. *Emerg. infect. Dis.*, **8** (1), 54-62.

29. Kobayashi H., Shimada J., Nakazawa M., Morozumi T., Pohjanvirta T., Pelkonen S. & Yamamoto K. (2001). – Prevalence and characteristics of Shiga toxin-producing *Escherichia coli* from healthy cattle in Japan. *Appl. environ. Microbiol.*, **67** (1), 484-489.

30. Kudaka J., Asato R., Itokazu K., Nakamura M., Taira K., Kuniyosi H., Kinjo Y., Terajima J., Watanabe H., Kobayashi J., Swaminathan B., Braden C.R. & Dunn J.R. (2005). – *Escherichia coli* O157:H7 infections associated with ground beef from a US military installation – Okinawa, Japan, February 2004. *MMWR*, **54** (02), 40-42.

31. Kudva I.T., Hunt C.W., Williams C.J., Nance U.M. & Hovde C.J. (1997). – Evaluation of dietary influences on *Escherichia coli* O157:H7 shedding by sheep. *Appl. environ. Microbiol.*, **63** (10), 3878-3886.

32. Kudva I.T., Blanch K. & Hovde C.J. (1998). – Analysis of *Escherichia coli* O157:H7 survival in ovine or bovine manure and manure slurry. *Appl. environ. Microbiol.*, **64** (9), 3166-3174.

33. Kuhnert P., Dubosson C.R., Roesch M., Homfeld E., Doherr M.G. & Blum J.W. (2005). – Prevalence and risk-factor analysis of Shiga toxigenic *Escherichia coli* in faecal samples of organically and conventionally farmed dairy cattle. *Vet. Microbiol.*, **109**, 37-45.

34. Leelaporn A., Phengmak M., Eampoklap B., Manatsathit S., Tritilanunt S., Siritantikorn S., Nagayama K., Iida T., Niyasom C. & Komolpit P. (2003). – Shiga toxin- and enterotoxin-producing *Escherichia coli* isolated from subjects with bloody and nonbloody diarrhea in Bangkok, Thailand. *Diagn. Microbiol. infect. Dis.*, **46**, 173-180.

35. Leung P.H., Yam W.C., Ng W.W. & Peiris J.S. (2001). – The prevalence and characterization of verotoxin-producing *Escherichia coli* isolated from cattle and pigs in an abattoir in Hong Kong. *Epidemiol. Infect.*, **126** (2), 173-179.

36. Lopez E.L., Contrini M.M. & De Rosa M.F. (1998). – Epidemiology of Shiga toxin-producing *Escherichia coli* in South America. *In Escherichia coli* O157:H7 and other Shiga toxin-producing *E. coli* strains (J.B. Kaper & A.D. O'Brien, eds). ASM Press, Washington, DC, 30-37.

37. Lung A.J., Lin C.M., Kim J.M., Marshall M.R., Nordstedt R., Thompson N.P. & Wei C.I. (2001). – Destruction of *Escherichia coli* O157:H7 and *Salmonella enteritidis* in cow manure composting. *J. Food Protec.*, **64** (9), 1309-1314.

38. Magwira C.A., Gashe B.A. & Collison E.K. (2005). – Prevalence and antibiotic resistance profiles of *Escherichia coli* O157:H7 in beef products from retail outlets in Gaborone, Botswana. *J. Food Protec.,* **68** (2), 403-406.

39. Matthews L., Low J.C., Gally D.L., Pearce M.C., Mellor D.J., Heesterbeek J.A.P., Chase-Topping M., Naylor S.W., Shaw D.J., Reid S.W.J., Gunn G.J. & Woolhouse M.E.J. (2006). – Heterogeneous shedding of *Escherichia coli* O157 in cattle and its implications for control. *PNAS,* **103** (3), 547-552.

40. Mead P.S., Slutsker L., Dietz V., McCaig L.F., Bresee J.S., Shapiro C., Griffin P.M. & Tauxe R.V. (1999). – Food-related illness and death in the United States. *Emerg. infect. Dis.,* **5** (5), 607-625.

41. Meichtri L., Miliwebsky E., Gioffré A., Chinen I., Baschkier A., Chillemi G., Guth B.E.C., Masana M.O., Cataldi A., Rodríguez H.R. & Rivas M. (2004). – Shiga toxin-producing *Escherichia coli* in healthy young beef steers from Argentina: prevalence and virulence properties. *Int. J. Food Microbiol.,* **96**, 189-198.

42. Morabito S., Karch H., Mariani-Kurkdjian P., Schmidt H., Minelli F., Bingen E. & Caprioli A. (1998). – Enteroaggregative, Shiga toxin-producing *Escherichia coli* O111:H2 associated with an outbreak of hemolytic-uremic syndrome. *J. clin. Microbiol.,* **36** (3), 840-842.

43. Nataro J.P. & Kaper J.B. (1998). – Diarrheagenic *Escherichia coli. Clin. Microbiol. Rev.,* **11** (1), 142-201.

44. Okeke I.N., Ojo O., Lamikanra A. & Kaper J.B. (2003). – Etiology of acute diarrhea in adults in Southwestern Nigeria. *J. clin. Microbiol.,* **41** (10), 4525-4530.

45. OzFoodNet Working Group (2005). – Reported foodborne illness and gastroenteritis in Australia: annual report of the OzFoodNet network, 2004. *Communic. Dis. Intell.,* **29** (2), 164-190.

46. Pan American Health Organization (PAHO) (2001). – Executive Summary. 4th Meeting of the Emerging Disease Surveillance Network of the Southern Cone, Paraguay. PAHO, Washington, DC.

47. Panutdaporn N., Chongsa-nguan M., Nair G.B., Ramamurthy T., Yamasaki S., Chaisri U., Tongtawe P., Eampokalarp B., Tapchaisri P., Sakolvaree Y., Kurazono H., Thein W.B., Hayashi H., Takeda Y. & Chaicumpa W. (2004). – Genotypes and phenotypes of Shiga toxin-producing *Escherichia coli* isolated from healthy cattle in Thailand. *J. Infection,* **48**, 149-160.

48. Parma A.E., Sanz M.E., Blanco J.E., Blanco J., Viñas M.R., Blanco M., Padola N.L. & Etcheverría A.I. (2000). – Virulence genotypes and serotypes of verotoxigenic *Escherichia coli* isolated from cattle and foods in Argentina. *Eur. J. Epidemiol.,* **16**, 757-762.

49. Paton A.W., Woodrow M.C., Doyle R.M., Lanser J.A. & Paton J.C. (1999). – Molecular characterization of a Shiga toxigenic *Escherichia coli* O113:H21 strain lacking eae responsible for a cluster of cases of hemolytic-uremic syndrome. *J. clin. Microbiol.,* **37** (10), 3357-3361.

50. Paton J.C. & Paton A.W. (1998). – Pathogenesis and diagnosis of Shiga toxin-producing *Escherichia coli* infections. *Clin. Microbiol. Rev.,* **11** (3), 450-479.

51. Pearce M.C., Jenkins C., Vali L., Smith A.W., Knight H.I., Cheasty T., Smith H.R., Gunn G.J., Woolhouse M.E.J., Amyes S.G.B. & Frankel G. (2004). – Temporal shedding patterns and virulence factors of *Escherichia coli* serogroups O26, O103, O111, O145, and O157 in a cohort of beef calves and their dams. *Appl. environ. Microbiol.,* **70** (3), 1708-1716.

52. Pearce M.C., Evans J., McKendrick I.J., Smith A.W., Knight H.I., Mellor D.J., Woolhouse M.E.J., Gunn G.J. & Low J.C. (2006). – Prevalence and virulence factors of *Escherichia coli* serogroups O26, O103, O111, and O145 shed by cattle in Scotland. *Appl. environ. Microbiol.,* **72** (1), 653-659.

53. Potter A.A., Klashinsky S., Li Y., Frey E., Townsend H., Roganc D., Erickson G., Hinkley S., Klopfenstein T., Moxley R.A., Smith D.R. & Finlay B.B. (2004). – Decreased shedding of *Escherichia coli* O157:H7 by cattle following vaccination with type III secreted proteins. *Vaccine,* **22**, 362-369.

54. Raji M.A., Jiwa S.F., Minga M.U. & Gwakisa P.S. (2003). – *Escherichia coli* O157:H7 reservoir, transmission, diagnosis and the African situation: a review. *East Afr. med. J.,* **80** (5), 271-276.

55. Rangel J.M., Sparling P.H., Crowe C., Griffin P.M. & Swerdlow D.L. (2005). – Epidemiology of *Escherichia coli* O157:H7 outbreaks, United States, 1982-2002. *Emerg. infect. Dis.,* **11** (4), 603-609.

56. Rios M., Prado V., Trucksis M., Arellano C., Borie C., Alexandre M., Fica A. & Levine M.M. (1999). – Clonal diversity of Chilean isolates of enterohemorrhagic *Escherichia coli* from patients with hemolytic-uremic syndrome, asymptomatic subjects, animal reservoirs, and food products. *J. clin. Microbiol.,* **37** (3), 778-781.

57. Rogerie F., Marecat A., Gambade S., Dupond F., Beaubois P. & Lange M. (2001). – Characterization of Shiga toxin-producing *E. coli* and O157 serotype *E. coli* isolated in France from healthy domestic cattle. *Int. J. Food Microbiol.,* **63**, 217-223.

58. Rugbjerg H., Nielsen E.M. & Andersen J.S. (2003). – Risk factors associated with faecal shedding of verocytotoxin-producing *Escherichia coli* O157 in eight known-infected Danish dairy herds. *Prev. vet. Med.,* **58**, 101-113.

59. Sargeant J.M., Sanderson M.W., Griffin D.D. & Smith R.A. (2004). – Factors associated with the presence of *Escherichia coli* O157 in feedlot cattle water and feed in the Midwestern USA. *Prev. vet. Med.,* **66**, 207-237.

60. Scott L., McGee P., Sheridan J.J., Earley B. & Leonard N. (2006). – A comparison of the survival in feces and water of *Escherichia coli* O157:H7 grown under laboratory conditions or obtained from cattle feces. *J. Food Protec.*, **69** (1), 6-11.

61. Shaw D.J., Jenkins C., Pearce M.C., Cheasty T., Gunn G.J., Dougan G., Smith H.R., Woolhouse M.E.J. & Frankel G. (2004). – Shedding patterns of verocytotoxin-producing *Escherichia coli* strains in a cohort of calves and their dams on a Scottish beef farm. *Appl. environ. Microbiol.*, **70** (12), 7456-7465.

62. Shere J.A., Bartlett K.J. & Kaspar C.W. (1998). – Longitudinal study of *Escherichia coli* O157:H7 dissemination on four dairy farms in Wisconsin. *Appl. environ. Microbiol.*, **64** (4), 1390-1399.

63. Smith D., Blackford M., Younts S., Moxley R., Gray J., Hungerford L., Milton T. & Klopfenstein T. (2001). – Ecological relationships between the prevalence of cattle shedding *Escherichia coli* O157:H7 and characteristics of the cattle or conditions of the feedlot pen. *J. Food Protec.*, **64** (12), 1899-1903.

64. Swaminathan B., Barrett T.J., Hunter S.B., Tauxe R.V. & CDC PulseNet Task Force (2001). – PulseNet: the molecular subtyping network for foodborne bacterial disease surveillance, United States. *Emerg. infect. Dis.*, **7** (3), 382-389.

65. Tkalcic S., Zhao T., Harmon B.G., Doyle M.P., Brown C.A. & Zhao P. (2003). – Fecal shedding of enterohemorrhagic *Escherichia coli* in weaned calves following treatment with probiotic *Escherichia coli*. *J. Food Protec.*, **66** (7), 1184-1189.

66. United Kingdom Advisory Committee on the Microbiological Safety of Food (1995). – Report on verocytotoxin-producing *Escherichia coli*. Her Majesty's Stationery Office, London.

67. Van Donkersgoed J., Hancock D., Rogan D. & Potter A.A. (2005). – *Escherichia coli* O157:H7 vaccine field trial in 9 feedlots in Alberta and Saskatchewan. *Can. vet. J.*, **46**, 724-728.

68. Wang G., Zhao T. & Doyle M.P. (1996). – Fate of enterohemorrhagic *Escherichia coli* O157:H7 in bovine feces. *Appl. environ. Microbiol.*, **62** (7), 2567-2570.

69. World Health Organization (WHO) (1998). – Zoonotic non-O157 Shiga toxin-producing *Escherichia coli* (STEC). Report of a WHO Scientific Working Group Meeting. WHO/CSR/APH/98.8. WHO, Geneva.

70. World Health Organization & Food and Agriculture Organization (2002). – Risk profile for enterohemorrhagic *E. coli* including the identification of the commodities of concern, including sprouts, ground beef and pork. Codex Committee of Food Hygiene CX/FH 03/5-Add 4. Food and Agriculture Organization of the United Nations, Rome.

71. Xu J.G., Cheng B.K. & Jing H.Q. (1999). – *Escherichia coli* O157:H7 and Shiga-like-toxin-producing *Escherichia coli* in China. *World. J. Gastroenterol.*, **5** (3), 191-194.

72. Younts-Dahl S.M., Osborn G.D., Galyean M.L., Rivera J.D., Loneragan G.H. & Brashears M.M. (2005). – Reduction of *Escherichia coli* O157 in finishing beef cattle by various doses of *Lactobacillus acidophilus* in direct-fed microbials. *J. Food Protec.*, **68** (1), 6-10.

73. Zheng H., Jing H., Wang H., Xia S., Hu W., Cui S., Bi Z., Yang J., Pang B., Zhao G., Zhang J., Li H. & Xu J. (2005). – *stx2vha* is the dominant genotype of Shiga toxin-producing *Escherichia coli* O157:H7 isolated from patients and domestic animals of three regions of China. *Microbiol. Immunol.*, **49** (12), 1019-1026.

74. Zhou Z., Nishikawa Y., Zhu P., Hong S., Hase A., Cheasty T., Smith H.R., Zheng M. & Haruki K. (2002). – Isolation and characterization of Shiga toxin-producing *Escherichia coli* O157:H7 from beef, pork and cattle fecal samples in Changchun, China. *J. vet. med. Sci.*, **64** (11), 1041-1044.

Rev. sci. tech. Off. int. Epiz., 2006, **25** (2), 571-580

Listeria monocytogenes: food-borne pathogen and hygiene indicator

T. Jemmi [1] & R. Stephan [2]

(1) Swiss Federal Veterinary Office, Schwarzenburgstrasse 161, CH-3003 Bern, Switzerland
(2) Institute for Food Safety and Hygiene, Vetsuisse Faculty University of Zurich, CH-8057 Zurich, Switzerland

Summary

In the past 25 years, *Listeria monocytogenes* has become increasingly important as a food-associated pathogen. Most European Union countries have an annual incidence of human listeriosis of between two and ten reported cases per million. Because of its high case fatality rate, listeriosis ranks among the most frequent causes of death due to food-borne illness. *Listeria monocytogenes* infections are responsible for the highest hospitalisation rates (91%) amongst known food-borne pathogens and have been linked to sporadic episodes and large outbreaks of human illness worldwide.

The ability to persist in food-processing environments and multiply under refrigeration temperatures makes *L. monocytogenes* a significant threat to public health. *Listeria monocytogenes* contamination is one of the leading microbiological causes of food recalls, mainly of meat, poultry, seafood and dairy products.

Prevention and control measures are based on hazard analysis and critical control point programmes throughout the food industry, and on specific recommendations for high-risk groups.

Understanding how these micro-organisms adapt their cellular physiology to overcome stress is important in controlling *L. monocytogenes* in food environments.

Keywords

Ecology – Food safety – Food-borne disease – Listeria monocytogenes – Occurrence – Virulence.

Introduction

The genus *Listeria* is grouped with other Gram-positive non-spore forming bacilli. Members of the genus *Listeria* are generally aerobes or facultative anaerobes, catalase positive and oxidase negative. *Listeria* are motile via a few peritrichous flagella when grown at temperatures below 30°C. The genus includes six species:

– *L. monocytogenes*

– *L. innocua*

– *L. ivanovii*

– *L. seeligeri*

– *L. welshimeri*

– *L. grayi*.

Differentiation of the *Listeria* species can be made based on haemolytic activity and sugar fermentation (Table I).

The genomes of both *L. monocytogenes* and *L. innocua* have been sequenced. The genome of *L. monocytogenes* strain EGD (serotype 1/2a) is 2,944,528 base pairs (bp) long with 2,853 open reading frames and a guanine-cytosine (G + C) content of 39%. The genome of *L. innocua* is 3,011,209 bp long with 2,973 open reading frames and a G + C content of 37%. Surprisingly, many encoded proteins are similar to those of the soil bacterium *Bacillus subtilis*. *Listeria monocytogenes* has a single circular chromosome, while *L. innocua* also contains a plasmid of 81,905 bp.

Listeria monocytogenes is a food-borne pathogen that is distributed in a wide variety of environments. Human

Table I
Biochemical differentiation of *Listeria* species (25)

Listeria spp.	Haemolysis	CAMP	Acid production from:		
			ᴅ-Xylose	ʟ-Rhamnose	Mannitol
L. monocytogenes	+	+	–	+	–
L. seeligeri	+	+/–	+	–	–
L. ivanovii	++	–	+	–	–
L. innocua	–	–	–	V	–
L. welshimeri	–	–	+	V	–
L. grayi	–	–	–	V	+

+: positive
+/–: weakly positive
–: negative
CAMP: is an acronym for Christie, Atkins, Munch, Petersen; the discoverers of this haemolysis phenomenon
V: variable

infection may lead to a serious and potentially life-threatening illness known as listeriosis (36). Reports from the United States of America (USA) show that *L. monocytogenes* infections are responsible for the highest hospitalisation rates (91%) amongst known food-borne pathogens (31). *Listeria monocytogenes* infections have been linked to both sporadic episodes and large outbreaks of human illness in various parts of the world (10). The general severity of the human clinical disease, coupled with the high case fatality rate associated with *L. monocytogenes* infections (10, 31), emphasise the critical importance of effective control measures against this food pathogen. However, the organism's ubiquity in food processing, distribution and storage environments, as well as its efficient stress adaptation capabilities make the control of this microbe in food a great challenge.

From the viewpoint of food safety, understanding how *Listeria* organisms are able to adapt their cellular physiology to overcome various forms of stress as well as current control measures is an important step in developing better methods of controlling *L. monocytogenes* in food-producing environments. Cold stress adaptation is one of the fundamental attributes of *L. monocytogenes* that is essential for its dissemination. The organism's robust cold adaptation capacity renders the use of low temperatures and refrigeration ineffective as control measures.

Ecology

All members of the genus *Listeria* are widely distributed in nature and have been isolated from soil, vegetation, sewage, water, animal feed, fresh and frozen meat, slaughterhouse wastes and the faeces of healthy animals. Thus, farm animals and their environment may present an important source of food contamination and infections for humans.

There have been suggestions that *L. monocytogenes* subtypes and lineages differ in their association with specific host and non-host environments. Epidemiological data from different countries show that the majority of human outbreaks are associated with three *L. monocytogenes* serotypes (1/2a, 1/2b and 4b), despite the fact that there are 13 serotypes potentially capable of infecting humans (59). This may reflect the greater adaptation of certain *L. monocytogenes* subtypes to food-associated environments and human infection.

Due to their ubiquitous presence, *Listeria* in general and *L. monocytogenes* in particular are also used as hygiene indicators in all stages of the food processing chain. Single *Listeria* strains can spread in manufacturing plants and even establish themselves as endemic organisms (45).

Pathogenesis and virulence factors

Listeria monocytogenes is pathogenic for animals and human beings without showing any significant host specificity. Infection occurs in several steps:

a) entry of the bacterium into the host

b) lysis of the phagosomal vacuole

c) multiplication in the cytosol

d) direct cell-to-cell spread using actin-based motility.

Each step requires expression of specific virulence factors. The major virulence genes are located in a cluster of genes on two different DNA loci and are mainly influenced by the positive regulatory factor A protein.

Several groups of virulence factors which are thought to be important in the pathogenicity of *Listeria monocytogenes* strains have recently been characterised:

a) the internalines, encoded by different internaline genes (*inl*), which take part in the invasion of epithelial cells and seem to be jointly responsible for the tissue tropism of *L. monocytogenes* (6, 42)

b) listeriolysin O, encoded by the gene *hlyA*, and phosphatidylinositol-specific phospholipase C (PI-PLC), encoded by the gene *plcA*, which take part in lysis of the phagosomes of the host cell and thus make the intracellular growth of *Listeria* cells possible (29, 46)

c) act A-protein, which is involved in motility (4)

d) enzymes such as lecithinase, zinc metal protease and serine protease (15, 37, 54)

e) a fibronectin-binding protein, FbpA, has been recently described as a novel multifunctional *L. monocytogenes*

Rev. sci. tech. Off. int. Epiz., **25** (2)

573

virulence factor which seems to be involved in intestinal and liver colonisation processes (7).

Listeriosis in animals

Many animal species can be infected with *L. monocytogenes*. Nevertheless, clinical disease is rare and mainly found in ruminants, in which it presents as meningoencephalitis, septicaemia, and abortions. Feeding of grass silage with high pH, which can be contaminated with large amounts of *Listeria*, is normally incriminated. Furthermore, *Listeria* spp. are a rare cause of mastitis in cattle and sheep (41, 48, 56). In these cases, contamination of milk can be due to direct shedding of *Listeria*.

Listeria spp. are shed in the faeces of asymptomatic animal carriers. Therefore, contamination of milk and meat is normally due to faecal contamination during the milking or slaughtering process.

Listeriosis in humans

Human infections primarily result from eating contaminated food and may lead to serious and potentially life-threatening listeriosis (36). Pregnant women, neonates, and elderly or immunocompromised adults are particularly susceptible to listeriosis, which typically presents as septicaemia, meningitis, or meningoencephalitis (36). In pregnant women, *Listeria monocytogenes* takes advantage of the natural localised immunosuppression at the maternal-fetal interface and causes abortions. A milder form of listeriosis that presents as febrile gastroenteritis was recognised in the 1990s (39). This disease state is induced when otherwise healthy hosts consume large numbers of *L. monocytogenes* organisms (14).

A minimal infective dose has not been determined in human infection studies and estimates vary from 10^2 colony-forming units (cfu) to 10^9 cfu, depending on the immunological status of the host. The incubation period for the disease varies from 11 to 70 days (median 21 days) in humans.

Most countries within the European Union have an annual incidence of listeriosis of between two and ten reported cases per million per year. Because of its high case fatality rate, listeriosis ranks among the most frequent causes of death due to food-borne illness. Reports from the USA show that *L. monocytogenes* infections are responsible for the highest hospitalisation rates (91%) amongst known food-borne pathogens (31). *Listeria monocytogenes* infections have been linked to both sporadic episodes and large outbreaks (Table II) of human illness in various parts of the world.

Table II
Examples of outbreaks of human food-borne listeriosis (28)

Country	Year	Food	Cases	Deaths	Serotype
United States of America	1976	Raw salad (?)	20	5	4b
New Zealand	1980	Fish (?)	22	7	1/2a
Canada	1981	Coleslaw	41	18	4b
United States of America	1983	Milk (?)	49	14	4b
United States of America	1985	Soft cheese	142	30	4b
Switzerland	1983-1987	Soft cheese	122	34	4b
United Kingdom	1987-1989	Pâté	355	94	4b
France	1993	Pork tongue in aspic	279	NK	4b
France	1993	Pork rillettes	38	10	4b
United States of America	1994	Milk	45	0	1/2b
Sweden	1994-1995	Fish	9	2	4b
France	1995	Soft cheese	17	4	4b
Canada	1996	Crab meat	2	0	1/2a
Italy	1997	Salad	1566	0	4b
United States of America	1998-1999	Hot dogs	50	>8	4b
Finland	1998-1999	Butter	25	6	3a
Finland	1999	Fish	5	NK	1/2a
France	1999-2000	Pork rillettes	10	2	4b
France	1999-2000	Pork tongue in jelly	32	10	4b
United States of America	2000	Turkey meat	29	7	NK
Switzerland	2005	Soft cheese	3	1	NK

NK: not known

Rev. sci. tech. Off. int. Epiz., **25** (2)

Occurrence in foods, source and mode of transmission

Products such as raw milk, soft cheese produced from raw milk, raw meat products and salads are frequently implicated in the literature (23, 43, 44). Summarised data for the prevalence of *L. monocytogenes* in raw meat and raw milk are given in Tables III and IV. In this context, hygiene weak points during the slaughtering and milking processes are the main critical points for *Listeria* contamination.

Cross-contamination, which can occur within the environment of food-processing equipment, is considered to be a possible source of *Listeria* contamination in processed food. *Listeria monocytogenes* is able to attach to and survive on various working contact surfaces. One reason may be its ability to form biofilms (3, 60).

Table III
Prevalence of *Listeria monocytogenes* in raw meat

Country	Meat	Number of samples tested	Prevalence (%)	References
Italy	NK	113	8	27
Belgium	Poultry	772	38	52
United Kingdom	Poultry	100	60	35
Denmark	Minced meat	67	28	47
France	NK	112	17	40
Japan	Minced beef meat	41	12	19
	Minced pork meat	34	21	19
Switzerland	Minced meat	400	11	8

NK: species not known

Table IV
Prevalence of *Listeria monocytogenes* in raw milk

Country	Number	Prevalence (%)	References
Italy	40	0	30
Switzerland	310	0	49
Spain	95	45	5
Sweden	294	1	55
United States of America	861	7	53
	131	5	21
Canada	445	12	9
Brazil	440	13	32

Growth, survival and stress resistance

Generally, *Listeria* spp. strains grow between 1°C and 45°C under aerobic and facultative anaerobic conditions. Their optimal growth temperature is between 30°C and 37°C. *Listeria* spp. have the unusual ability to grow at refrigeration temperatures (57, 58). Minimal growth temperatures were determined for 100 strains of *Listeria* (24). The mean minimum temperature for *L. monocytogenes* growth was 1.7°C. No differences in growth temperature were observed among strains isolated from different sources.

Studies of growth models for *L. monocytogenes* have been published in recent years (e.g. 13, 26). These models include the effect of temperature, aqueous phase salt/water activity, pH, and other intrinsic or extrinsic factors on the growth of *L. monocytogenes*.

The thermotolerance of the organism has been examined in different studies in broth cultures and various food matrices. An overview of results obtained from broth cultures is given in Table V. The reported D-value (the decimal reduction time: the time interval required for one decimal reduction [90%] in the number of organisms surviving) at 64°C for *L. monocytogenes* is 2.1 min, with a z-value (the temperature difference required to change the D-value by a factor of 10) of 7.5°C. A more comprehensive overview for different food matrices is given in *Microorganisms in Foods 5: Characteristics of Microbial Pathogens* published by the International Commission on Microbiological Specifications for Foods (20).

Table V
Heat inactivation of *Listeria monocytogenes*

Temperature (°C)	Time for 6D reduction (min)
63	17
64	12.7
65	9.3
66	6.8
67	5.0
68	3.7
69	2.7
70	2.0
71	1.5
72	1.0
73	0.8
74	0.6
75	0.4

Source: Food and Drug Administration, Hazards and Controls Guidance (2001) (12)

Current transmission models assume that consumption of contaminated food products is the main route of human infection (38), and therefore that the epidemiological trends observed may reflect better adaptation of certain *L. monocytogenes* subtypes to food environments and subsequent human infection (17, 33). *Listeria monocytogenes* is endowed with numerous adaptive physiological traits that enable it to survive under a wide range of environmental conditions. It can overcome various types of stress, including the cold stress associated with the low temperatures of food production environments. The organism's robust cold adaptation capacities render the current use of low temperatures and refrigeration, which control most food-borne pathogens in food environments, ineffective.

The cold tolerance phenomenon in these microorganisms is a function of multiple genetic and physiological factors that sense the cold stress threat and efficiently induce appropriate cellular responses. The exact nature of molecular cold adaptation in *L. monocytogenes*, as in most psychotropic microbes, remains elusive, but certain molecular and physiological aspects of this phenomenon have been illuminated in model microorganisms (reviewed in 62). In the case of *L. monocytogenes*, research over the past few years has revealed various aspects of cold stress adaptation mechanisms in these organisms (for a review see 50). An improved understanding of how cold stress is sensed and adaptation measures implemented by *L. monocytogenes* may facilitate the development of better ways of controlling these pathogens in food and related environments.

Diagnostics

A wide variety of methods are available for the detection of *L. monocytogenes*, either in animal feed, in human food, or in clinical specimens. Classical bacteriological techniques are still considered to be the 'gold standard'. In food, detection of *L. monocytogenes* is generally performed in a two-step cultural enrichment process and it takes on average one week for biochemical identification of a suspected *L. monocytogenes* colony. The bacteriological culture methods commonly used for detection and identification of *L. monocytogenes* include esculin and ferric iron in enrichment or plating media, which results, through the hydrolysation capacity of *Listeria*, in the formation of an intense black colour (Fig. 1a). More recently, chromogenic media have been developed that take advantage of the PI-PLC activity that is present in *L. monocytogenes* and *L. ivanovii*, but not the other *Listeria* spp. (Fig. 1b).

A variety of combinations of enrichment and plating media have been evaluated for the isolation of *L. monocytogenes*. Even if no single method is ideal for all types of food,

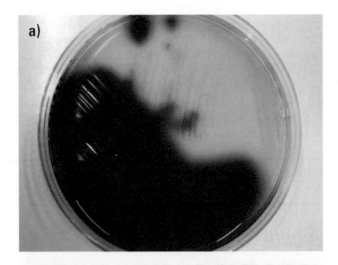

Fig. 1
Listeria monocytogenes
a) on Oxford medium
b) on Ottaviani Agosti medium

regulatory agencies provide guidance through the publication of standardised methods for the isolation of *L. monocytogenes* (e.g. the Food and Drug Administration [FDA] method, the United States Department of Agriculture [USDA] method, and the International Organization for Standardization/Association Française de Normalisation [AFNOR] method).

Food-processing companies increasingly depend on rapid quality control tests, which deliver results within a shorter time and allow batches to be released following completion of the test. Advances in research have led to the development of more rapid *L. monocytogenes* detection assays that utilise immunological and nucleic acid-based techniques (61).

The use of serological tests for diagnostic purposes is largely considered to be unreliable (61). Nevertheless, serology can be used for epidemiological studies in defined populations (2).

576

Rev. sci. tech. Off. int. Epiz., **25** (2)

A range of subtyping methods is available to distinguish between strains of *L. monocytogenes*. These methods include the more traditional techniques of serotyping, phage typing and isoenzyme analysis, as well as those based on the characterisation of DNA, such as pulsed field gel electrophoresis, ribotyping, and polymerase chain reaction-based methods. However, the differences in the potential of the various strains to cause disease are still, as yet, poorly understood.

Impact of *Listeria monocytogenes* on the food industry

A comprehensive assessment of the impact of *L. monocytogenes* on the food industry is not available from the literature. However, an initial approach was made in the Food and Agriculture Organization (FAO) expert consultation report on the trade impact of *Listeria* in fish products (11).

The impact on the food industry is partly due to recalls, which result in large economic losses. As an example, the FDA in the USA has taken firm action against many processors due to the presence of *L. monocytogenes* in their products. Since 1985, Class I recalls (i.e. those that could cause serious health problems or death) have been imposed on many ready-to-eat food products contaminated with *L. monocytogenes*, including cheeses, ice-cream, milk, fish, prepared salads, sandwiches, crab meat, smoked fish, and bakery products. From 1987 to 1992, there were recalls on 970 ready-to-eat products from 109 firms because of contamination with this organism. Between 1987 and August 1998 there were 112 Class I recalls for domestic or imported ready-to-eat seafood products (11). Examples of significant recent recalls are the *Listeria*-related recall of 4.2 million pounds (approximately 1.9 million kg) of egg salad on Vienna bread sandwiches (51), and a recall of a total of 2.8 million pounds (approximately 1.3 million kg) of various sausage, ham and turkey lunch products due to possible contamination with *L. monocytogenes* (1).

Furthermore, *L. monocytogenes* contamination may affect the food industry through rejection or detention of products. In addition to the direct costs of rejection and detention, there are economic costs that result from inspection/re-inspection, delays in distribution, transportation, expiry of shelf-life, and the opportunity cost of holding products.

Risk reduction strategies

Until recently, most available data derived from the results of prevalence studies based on the concept 'from farm to fork'. However, studies systematically analysing such data are rare. A recent approach aims to establish national and international studies to inform a comprehensive risk analysis. The purpose of one such study, carried out by Pak *et al.* (34), was to identify the main hazards associated with the spread of *L. monocytogenes* in dairy products in Switzerland and to determine the changes in the predominant serotypes of the isolates, using a database covering the years 1990 to 1999. Another study combined data on 2,053 imported and 164 exported meat and fish products from 425 production plants investigated for the presence of *L. monocytogenes* over a nine-year period (1992 to 2000) (22). The highest isolation risk was for marinated fish; the lowest was in cured and dried-meat products. Unconditional fixed-effects logistic regression analysis was used to identify the main hazards associated with the presence of *L. monocytogenes*. The production plant-level model considered potential risk factors for a positive culture by including a random effect for plant and year. Food category was the only significant factor; sampling site, country of origin and season were not significant. The authors concluded that control measures should be focused on specific food items in each production plant.

Risk management strategies are pursued at different levels along the food production chain. The faecal carriage of food-borne pathogens by livestock is strongly correlated with the hazard of milk and carcass contamination. In order to reduce the risk represented by *Listeria*, the maintenance of milking and slaughter hygiene is of central importance in food animal production (16, 18). Prevention and control measures are also based on the implementation of hazard analysis and critical control point (HACCP) programmes throughout the food industry, and specific recommendations to high-risk groups.

From the food safety point of view, understanding how *Listeria* organisms are able to successfully adapt their cellular physiology to overcome various forms of stress and current control measures is an important step in developing better ways of controlling *L. monocytogenes* in food environments. Cold stress adaptation is one of the fundamental attributes of *L. monocytogenes* that is essential for its dissemination in food environments.

Rev. sci. tech. Off. int. Epiz., **25** (2)

577

Listeria monocytogenes – agent de toxi-infection alimentaire et indicateur d'hygiène

T. Jemmi & R. Stephan

Résumé

L'importance de *Listeria monocytogenes* en tant qu'agent de toxi-infection alimentaire n'a pas cessé de croître depuis vingt-cinq ans. Dans la plupart des États membres de l'Union européenne, l'incidence annuelle de la listériose humaine varie de deux à dix cas par million d'habitants. La listériose a un taux de létalité élevé qui en fait l'une des causes les plus fréquentes de décès parmi les maladies d'origine alimentaire. L'infection à *L. monocytogenes* est à l'origine de la plupart des hospitalisations (91 %) dues à des agents de toxi-infection alimentaire, et reste associée aussi bien à des cas isolés qu'à des épidémies qui surviennent partout dans le monde.

La capacité de *L. monocytogenes* à survivre aux conditions de transformation des denrées alimentaires et à résister aux basses températures en fait une menace de premier ordre pour la santé publique. La contamination par *L. monocytogenes* est l'une des principales causes de saisie de produits alimentaires, et concerne aussi bien la viande, la volaille, les fruits de mer que les produits laitiers.

La maîtrise des risques associés à *Listeria* passe par la surveillance de l'hygiène dans les laiteries et les abattoirs. Les mesures de prévention et de prophylaxie reposent sur l'application de programmes d'analyse des risques et de maîtrise des points critiques tout au long de la chaîne de production alimentaire et sur la prise en compte de recommandations spécifiques pour les groupes à haut risque.

Il importe de bien comprendre comment la physiologie cellulaire de ces micro-organismes s'adapte aux agressions, afin de pouvoir maîtriser le risque lié à *L. monocytogenes* dans les milieux où sont élaborées les denrées alimentaires.

Mots-clés

Cas – Écologie – Listeria monocytogenes – Sécurité sanitaire des aliments – Virulence.
■

La *Listeria monocytogenes*, un agente patógeno transmitido por los alimentos que también sirve de indicador de higiene

T. Jemmi & R. Stephan

Resumen

Desde hace 25 años, la *Listeria monocytogenes* se ha convertido en uno de los principales agentes patógenos transmitidos por los alimentos. En la mayoría de los países de la Unión Europea, la incidencia anual de la listeriosis en seres humanos oscila entre dos y diez casos notificados por millón. Debido a su elevada tasa de letalidad, la listeriosis es una de las enfermedades de transmisión alimentaria que provoca mayor número de muertes. Asimismo, de los agentes patógenos transmitidos por alimentos conocidos, es el que ocasiona

Rev. sci. tech. Off. int. Epiz., **25** (2)

mayores porcentajes de hospitalización (91%). Esta bacteria ha sido asociada tanto a brotes esporádicos, como a grandes focos de listeriosis humana, en todas partes del mundo.

La capacidad para resistir a las condiciones existentes en las plantas de producción de alimentos y multiplicarse a temperaturas de refrigeración convierte a la *L. monocytogenes* en una grave amenaza para la salud pública. La contaminación con *L. monocytogenes* es una de las principales causas microbiológicas de devolución de alimentos, en particular de carne, aves de corral, mariscos y productos lácteos.

El mantenimiento de la higiene en las granjas lecheras y mataderos es capital para reducir el riesgo de presencia de la *L. monocytogenes*. Las medidas de prevención y control se basan en análisis de riesgos y programas de control de puntos críticos en todas las etapas de la industria alimentaria y, también, en la formulación de recomendaciones específicas para grupos de riesgo elevado.

Para luchar contra estos microorganismos en las plantas de producción alimentaria es preciso comprender cómo adaptan su fisiología celular para resistir a las agresiones.

Palabras clave
Ecología – Enfermedad transmitida por alimentos – Frecuencia – Inocuidad de los alimentos – Listeria monocytogènes – Virulencia.

■

References

1. Anon (2005). – Missouri firm expands recall of meat lunch maker's products for possible *Listeria* contamination. Available at: http://forums.chef2chef.net/showflat.php?Cat= 0 &Number=382583&an=0&page=0#382583 (accessed on 5 December 2005).

2. Boerlin P., Boerlin-Petzold F. & Jemmi T. (2003). – Use of listeriolysin O and internalin A in a seroepidemiological study of listeriosis in Swiss dairy cows. *J. clin. Microbiol.*, **41**, 1055-1061.

3. Borucki M.K., Peppin J.D., White D., Loge F. & Call D.R. (2003). – Variation in biofilm formation among strains of *Listeria monocytogenes*. *Appl. environ. Microbiol.*, **69**, 7336-7342.

4. Domann E., Wehland J., Rohde M., Pistor S., Hartl M., Goebel W., Leimeister-Wachter M., Wuenscher M., Chakraborty T. (1992). – A novel bacterial virulence gene in *Listeria monocytogenes* required for host cell microfilament interaction with homology to the proline-rich region of vinculin. *EMBO J.* **11**, 1981-90.

5. Dominguez Rodriguez L., Fernández Garayzabal J.F., Vazquez Boland J.A., Rodriguez Ferri E. & Suárez Fernández G. (1985). – Isolation of microorganisms of the species *Listeria* from raw milk intended for human consumption. *Can. J. Microbiol.*, **31**, 938-941.

6. Dramsi S., Dehoux P., Lebrun M., Goossens P.L. & Cossart P. (1997). – Identification of four new members of the internalin multigene family of *Listeria monocytogenes* EGD. *Infect. Immunol.*, **65**, 1615-1625.

7. Dramsi S., Bourdichon F., Cabanes D., Lecuit M., Fsihi H. & Cossart P. (2004). – FbpA, a novel multifunctional *Listeria monocytogenes* virulence factor. *Molec. Microbiol.*, **53**, 639-649.

8. Fantelli K. & Stephan R. (2001). – Prevalence and characteristics of Shigatoxin-producing *E. coli* (STEC) and *Listeria monocytogenes* strains isolated from minced meat in Switzerland. *Int. J. Food Microbiol.*, **70**, 63-69.

9. Farber J.M., Sanders G.W. & Malcolm S.A. (1988). – The presence of *Listeria* spp. in raw milk in Ontario. *Can. J. Microbiol.*, **34**, 95-100.

10. Farber J.M. & Peterkin P.I. (1991). – *Listeria monocytogenes*, a food-borne pathogen. *Microbiol. Rev.*, **55**, 476-511.

11. Food and Agriculture Organization (FAO) (1999). – Report of the FAO expert consultation on the trade impact of *Listeria* in fish products, 17-20 May, Amherst, Massachusetts. FAO Fisheries Report no. 604. Available at: http://www.fao.org/documents/show_cdr.asp?url_file=/DOCREP/003/X3018E/X 3018E01.HTM (accessed on 12 March 2006).

Rev. sci. tech. Off. int. Epiz., 25 (2)

579

12. Food and Drug Administration Center for Food Safety and Applied Nutrition (2001). – Fish and Fisheries Products Hazards and Controls Guidance. Third Ed. Available at: http://www.cfsan.fda.gov/~comm/haccp4x4.html (accessed on 12 March 2006).

13. Francois K., Devlieghere F., Smet K., Standaert A.R., Geeraerd A.H., Van Impe J.F. & Debevere J. (2005). – Modelling the individual cell lag phase: effect of temperature and pH on the individual cell lag distribution of Listeria monocytogenes. Int. J. Food Microbiol., 100, 41-53.

14. Frye D.M., Zweig R., Sturgeon J., Tormey M., LeCavalier M., Lee I., Lawani L. & Mascola L. (2002). – An outbreak of febrile gastroenteritis associated with delicatessen meat contaminated with Listeria monocytogenes. Clin. infect. Dis., 35, 943-949.

15. Gaillot O., Pellegrini E., Bregenholt S., Nair S. & Berche P. (2000). – The ClpP serine protease is essential for the intracellular parasitism and virulence of Listeria monocytogenes. Molec. Microbiol., 35, 1286-1294.

16. Gobat P.F. & Jemmi T. (1990). – Epidemiological studies on Listeria spp. in slaughterhouses. Fleischwirtschaft, 70, 1448-1450.

17. Gray M.J., Zadoks R.N., Fortes E.D., Dogan B., Cai S., Chen Y., Scott V.N., Gombas D.E., Boor K.J. & Wiedmann M. (2004). – Listeria monocytogenes isolates from foods and humans form distinct but overlapping populations. Appl. environ. Microbiol., 70, 5833-5841.

18. Husu J.R., Seppanen J.T., Sivela S.K. & Rauramaa A.L. (1990). – Contamination of raw milk by Listeria monocytogenes on dairy farms. Zentralbl. Veterinärmed., B, 37, 268-275.

19. Inoue S., Nakama A., Arai Y., Kokubo Y., Maruyama T., Saito A., Yoshida T., Terao M., Yamamoto S. & Kumagai S. (2000). – Prevalence and contamination levels of Listeria monocytogenes in retail foods in Japan. Int. J. Food Microbiol., 59, 73-77.

20. International Commission on Microbiological Specifications for Foods (1996). – Microorganisms in foods 5: characteristics of microbial pathogens. Blackie Academic & Professional, London.

21. Jayarao B.M. & Henning D.R. (2001). – Prevalence of foodborne pathogens in bulk tank milk. J. Dairy Sci., 84, 2157-2162.

22. Jemmi T., Pak S.I. & Salman M.D. (2002). – Prevalence and risk factors for contamination with Listeria monocytogenes of imported and exported meat and fish products in Switzerland, 1992-2000. Prev. vet. Med., 54, 25-36.

23. Johansson T., Rantala L., Palmu L. & Honkanen-Buzalski T. (1999). – Occurrence and typing of Listeria monocytogenes strains in retail vacuum-packed fish products and in a production plant. Int. J. Food Microbiol., 47, 111-119.

24. Junttila J.R., Niemela S.I. & Hirn J. (1988). – Minimum growth temperatures of Listeria monocytogenes and non-haemolytic Listeria. J. appl. Bacteriol., 65, 321-327.

25. Linnan M.J., Mascola L., Lou X.D., Goulet V., May S., Salminen C., Hird D.W., Yonekura M.L., Hayes P. & Weaver R. (1988). – Epidemic listeriosis associated with Mexican-style cheese. N. Engl. J. Med., 319, 823-828.

26. Lu Z., Sebranek J.G., Dickson J.S., Mendonca A.F. & Bailey T.B. (2005). – Application of predictive models to estimate Listeria monocytogenes growth on frankfurters treated with organic acid salts. J. Food Protec., 68, 2326-2332.

27. Luppi A., Bucci G., Maini P. & Rocourt J. (1988). – Ecological survey of Listeria in the Ferrara area (northern Italy). Zentralbl. Bakteriol. Mikrobiol. Hyg., A, 269, 266-275.

28. McLauchlin J., Mitchell R.T., Smerdon W.J. & Jewell K. (2004). – Listeria monocytogenes and listeriosis: a review of hazard characterisation for use in microbiological risk assessment of foods. Int. J. Food Microbiol., 92, 15-33.

29. Marquis H., Doshi V. & Portnoy D.A. (1995). – The broad-range phospholipase C and a metalloprotease mediate listeriolysin O-independent escape of Listeria monocytogenes from a primary vacuole in human epithelial cells. Infect. Immunol., 63, 4531-4534.

30. Massa S., Cesaroni D., Poda G. & Trovatelli L.D. (1990). – The incidence of Listeria spp. in soft cheeses, butter and raw milk in the province of Bologna. J. appl. Bacteriol., 68, 153-156.

31. Mead P.S., Slutsker L., Dietz V., McCaig L.F., Bresee J.S., Shapiro C., Griffin P.M. & Tauxe R.V. (1999). – Food-related illness and death in the United States. Emerg. infect. Dis., 5, 607-625.

32. Moura S.M., Destro M.T. & Franco B.D. (1993). – Incidence of Listeria species in raw and pasteurized milk produced in São Paulo, Brazil. Int. J. Food Microbiol., 19, 229-237.

33. Norrung B. & Skovgaard N. (1993). – Application of multilocus enzyme electrophoresis in studies of the epidemiology of Listeria monocytogenes in Denmark. Appl. environ. Microbiol., 59, 2817-2822.

34. Pak S.I., Spahr U., Jemmi T. & Salman M.D. (2002). – Risk factors for L. monocytogenes contamination of dairy products in Switzerland, 1990-1999. Prev. vet. Med., 1663, 1-11.

35. Pini P.N. & Gilbert R.J. (1988). – The occurrence in the UK of Listeria species in raw chickens and soft cheeses. Int. J. Food Microbiol., 7, 331-337.

36. Posfay-Barbe K.M. & Wald E.R. (2004). – Listeriosis. Pediatr. Res., 25, 151-159.

37. Raveneau J., Geoffroy C., Beretti J.L., Gaillard J.L., Alouf J.E. & Berche P. (1992). – Reduced virulence of a Listeria monocytogenes phospholipase-deficient mutant obtained by transposon insertion into the zinc metalloprotease gene. Infect. Immunol., 60, 916-921.

38. Rocourt J. & Bille J. (1997). – Foodborne listeriosis. *World Hlth Stat. Q.*, **50**, 67-73.

39. Salamina G., Dalle Donne E., Niccolini A., Poda G., Cesaroni D., Bucci M., Fini R., Maldini M., Schuchat A., Swaminathan B., Bibb W., Rocourt J., Binkin N. & Salmaso S. (1996). – A foodborne outbreak of gastroenteritis involving *Listeria monocytogenes*. *Epidemiol. Infect.*, **117**, 429-436.

40. Salvat G., Toquin M.T., Michel Y. & Colin P. (1995). – Control of *Listeria monocytogenes* in the delicatessen industries: the lessons of a listeriosis outbreak in France. *Int. J. Food Microbiol.*, **25**, 75-81.

41. Schoder D., Winter P., Kareem A., Baumgartner W. & Wagner M. (2003). – A case of sporadic ovine mastitis caused by *Listeria monocytogenes* and its effect on contamination of raw milk and raw-milk cheeses produced in the on-farm dairy. *J. Dairy Res.*, **70**, 395-401.

42. Schubert W.D., Urbanke C., Ziehm T., Beier V., Machner M.P., Domann E., Wehland J., Chakraborty T. & Heinz D.W. (2002). – Structure of internalin, a major invasion protein of *Listeria monocytogenes*, in complex with its human receptor E-cadherin. *Cell*, **111**, 825-836.

43. Schuchat A., Swaminathan B. & Broome C.V. (1991). – Epidemiology of human listeriosis. *Clin. Microbiol. Rev.*, **4**, 169-183.

44. Schwarzkopf A. (1996). – *Listeria monocytogenes* – aspects of pathogenicity. *Pathol. biol. (Paris)*, **44**, 769-774.

45. Senczek D., Stephan R. & Untermann F. (2000). – Pulsed-field gel electrophoresis (PFGE) typing of *Listeria* strains isolated from a meat processing plant over a 2-year period. *Int. J. Food Microbiol.*, **62**, 155-159.

46. Sibelius U., Schulz E.C., Rose F., Hattar K., Jacobs T., Weiss S., Chakraborty T., Seeger W. & Grimminger F. (1999). – Role of *Listeria monocytogenes* exotoxins listerolysin and phosphatidylinositol-specific phospholipase C in activation of human neutrophils. *Infect. Immunol.*, **67**, 1125-1130.

47. Skovgaard N. & Morgen C.A. (1988). – Detection of *Listeria* spp. in faeces from animals, in feeds, and in raw foods of animal origin. *Int. J. Food Microbiol.*, **6**, 229-242.

48. Stephan R., Senczek D., Müller Ch. & Feusi Ch. (2000). – Isolierung von *Listeria* spp. und *Aspergillus fumigatus* – zwei Fallberichte aus der Mastitisdiagnostik. *Schweizer Arch. Tierheilkd.*, **142**, 387-390.

49. Stephan R. & Bühler K. (2002). – Prävalenz von *Campylobacter* spp., *Salmonella* spp. und *Listeria monocytogenes* in Bestandesmilchproben aus der Nordostschweiz. *Arch. Lebensmittelhyg.*, **53**, 62-65.

50. Tasara T. & Stephan R. (2006). – Cold stress tolerance of *Listeria monocytogenes*: a review of molecular adaptive mechanisms and food safety implications. *J. Food. Protec.*, **69** (6), 1473-1484.

51. United Sates Department of Agriculture (USDA) (2002). – New Jersey firm expands recall of poultry products for possible *Listeria* contamination. Food Safety and Inspection Service, USDA, Washington, DC. Available at: http://www.fsis.usda.gov/oa/recalls/prelease/pr098-2002.htm (accessed on 12 March 2006).

52. Uyttendaele M., De Troy P. & Debevere J. (1999). – Incidence of *Listeria monocytogenes* in different types of meat products on the Belgian retail market. *Int. J. Food Microbiol.*, **53**, 75-80.

53. Van Kessel J.S., Karns J.S., Gorski L., McCluskey B.J. & Perdue M.L. (2004). – Prevalence of Salmonellae, *Listeria monocytogenes*, and fecal coliforms in bulk tank milk on US dairies. *J. Dairy Sci.*, **87**, 2822-2830.

54. Vazquez-Boland J.-A., Kocks C., Dramsi S., Ohayon H., Geoffroy C., Mengaud J. & Cossart P. (1992). – Nucleotide sequence of the lecithinase operon of *Listeria monocytogenes* and possible role of lecithinase in cell-to-cell spread. *Infect. Immunol.*, **60**, 219-230.

55. Waak E., Tham W. & Danielsson-Tham M.L. (2002). – Prevalence and fingerprinting of *Listeria monocytogenes* strains isolated from raw whole milk in farm bulk tanks and in dairy plant receiving tanks. *Appl. environ. Microbiol.*, **68**, 3366-3370.

56. Wagner M., Melzner D., Bago Z., Winter P., Egerbacher M., Schilcher F., Zangana A. & Schoder D. (2005). – Outbreak of clinical listeriosis in sheep: evaluation from possible contamination routes from feed to raw produce and humans. *J. vet. Med. B, infect. Dis. vet. public Health.*, **52**, 278-283.

57. Walker S.J., Archer P. & Banks J.G. (1990). – Growth of *Listeria monocytogenes* at refrigeration temperatures. *J. appl. Bacteriol.*, **68**, 157-162.

58. Wemekamp-Kamphuis H.H., Sleator R.D., Wouters J.A., Hill C. & Abee T. (2004). – Molecular and physiological analysis of the role of osmolyte transporters BetL, Gbu, and OpuC in growth of *Listeria monocytogenes* at low temperatures. *Appl. environ. Microbiol.*, **70**, 2912-2918.

59. Wiedmann M. (2002). – Molecular subtyping methods for *Listeria monocytogenes*. *J. AOAC int.*, **85**, 524-531.

60. Wong A.C. (1998). – Biofilms in food processing environments. *J. Dairy Sci.*, **81**, 2765-2770.

61. World Organisation for Animal Health (OIE) (2004). – *Listeria monocytogenes*. *In* Manual of Diagnostic Tests and Vaccines for Terrestrial Animals, 5th Ed. OIE, Paris, 1138-1152.

62. Wouters J.A., Rombouts F.M., Kuipers O.P., de Vos W.M. & Abee T. (2000). – The role of cold-shock proteins in low-temperature adaptation of food-related bacteria. *Syst. appl. Microbiol.*, **23**, 165-173.

Rev. sci. tech. Off. int. Epiz., 2006, **25** (2), 581-594

Campylobacter in primary animal production and control strategies to reduce the burden of human campylobacteriosis

J.A. Wagenaar [1, 2, 5], D.J. Mevius [3] & A.H. Havelaar [4]

(1) Department of Infectious Diseases and Immunology, Faculty of Veterinary Medicine, Utrecht University, P.O. Box 80165, 3508 TD Utrecht, the Netherlands (email: j.a.wagenaar@vet.uu.nl)
(2) Animal Sciences Group, Division of Infectious Diseases, P.O. Box 65, 8200 AB Lelystad, the Netherlands
(3) Central Institute for Disease Control (CIDC), P.O. Box 2004, 8203 AA Lelystad, the Netherlands
(4) National Institute for Public Health and the Environment (RIVM), P.O. Box 1, 3720 BA Bilthoven, the Netherlands
(5) World Organisation for Animal Health (OIE) Reference Laboratory for Campylobacteriosis, Animal Sciences Group, Lelystad, P.O. Box 65, 8200 AB Lelystad, the Netherlands and Utrecht University, P.O. Box 80165, 3508 TD Utrecht, the Netherlands

Summary

Campylobacteriosis is one of the most important bacterial food-borne illnesses in humans. One significant source of infection is the handling and consumption of poultry meat, although other sources also contribute considerably. Controlling *Campylobacter* in broilers reduces the human burden of illness.

Broilers can easily become colonised with *Campylobacter* and preventive measures in primary production have a limited and unpredictable effect. Vaccination, competitive exclusion, bacteriophage therapy and the use of bacteriocins are not yet commercially available. However, measures in the slaughterhouse can reduce contamination in the final product. At present, the most promising control strategy is to keep colonised and non-colonised flocks separate during slaughter ('scheduled processing'). The virtually *Campylobacter*-free meat can supply the fresh poultry meat market, while the meat from infected flocks can be treated to reduce the *Campylobacter* concentration. Meat from infected flocks can be treated by freezing but chemical decontamination appears to be more cost effective. A variant of this scenario is to treat only highly contaminated meat.

The authors conclude that, until new techniques become commercially available, scheduled processing is the most cost-effective approach. Finally, the authors describe trends in antimicrobial resistance in *Campylobacter*.

Keywords

Antimicrobial resistance – Campylobacter – Campylobacteriosis – Food safety – Intervention strategy – Poultry – Poultry meat – Public health – Scheduled processing – Slaughter – Zoonoses.

Introduction

Campylobacteriosis and *Campylobacter*

Campylobacter species are identified as a major cause of bacterial gastroenteritis in humans worldwide (4). Depending on the country, either *Campylobacter* or *Salmonella* is the most frequently isolated bacterial pathogen from cases of diarrhoea (58). During the last decade of the 20th Century, the incidence of human campylobacteriosis increased exponentially in many countries but the reason for this remains unknown (69).

Campylobacteriosis in humans is characterised by watery or bloody diarrhoea, abdominal cramps and nausea (54). The infection is self-limiting but, in a fraction of the

Rev. sci. tech. Off. int. Epiz., 25 (2)

patients, serious sequelae occur, such as Guillain-Barré syndrome and reactive arthritis (26, 32).

In the Netherlands, which has a population of 16 million, it is estimated that, each year, 80,000 cases of *Campylobacter* gastroenteritis result in 18,000 patients visiting their general practitioner, 600 hospitalisations and approximately 30 deaths, mainly among the elderly. The economic costs of campylobacteriosis in the Netherlands are estimated at 21 million euros per year (42), while the yearly disease burden is estimated at 1,200 disability-adjusted life years. In the Netherlands, this figure is comparable to those for tuberculosis and bacterial meningitis (28).

Campylobacteriosis in humans is principally caused by *Campylobacter jejuni* and, to a lesser extent, *C. coli*. Other *Campylobacter* species are also reported to cause disease in humans but their importance differs from geographical region to geographical region. The reported number of non-*C. jejuni* or non-*C. coli* infections is only a small fraction of all *Campylobacter* infections worldwide; thus this paper focuses on *C. jejuni* and *C. coli*.

Campylobacter jejuni and *C. coli* are Gram-negative bacteria which are sensitive to many external physical conditions, including:

– dessication

– heat

– ultra-violet (UV) radiation

– salt.

Campylobacter are much more fragile than *Salmonella* or Gram-positive bacteria, like *Enterococcus*. In contrast to *Salmonella*, *Campylobacter* does not multiply on meat samples in the absence of micro-aerobic conditions.

The highest concentration of *Campylobacter* is found on meat directly after processing. In all subsequent steps in the food chain (for example, transportation to retail, refrigerator storage), the concentration may stabilise but is more likely to decrease, due to die-off of the bacteria.

Campylobacter and animal diseases

Both *C. jejuni* and *C. coli* have a high incidence in companion and production animals, where both species are a commensal gut inhabitant. *Campylobacter jejuni* can cause sporadic cases of abortion in cattle but is not of great economic importance. Sporadic cases of vibrionic hepatitis in poultry have been described, supposedly caused by *Campylobacter*. However, this causative role is suggested only (10); there is little evidence. *Campylobacter jejuni* may cause illness in ostriches (55) and has been associated with diarrhoea in dogs. However, it is not clear whether this

species really causes disease in canines or just shows an increased shedding in watery stools, secondary to other causes of diarrhoea. No animal diseases caused by *C. coli* have been described in production or companion animals.

Campylobacter in the environment

Warm-blooded animals are the amplification vessel and thus reservoir for *Campylobacter*. *Campylobacter* does not replicate in surface water, due to the absence of a micro-aerobic atmosphere, the low temperature and lack of nutrients, but it can survive when it is protected from dryness (one of the major threats for *Campylobacter*). Most surface water sources are contaminated by animal manure containing *Campylobacter*. In slurries and in dirty water, *Campylobacter* can survive for up to three months (48).

Sources of human campylobacteriosis

Epidemiological and exposure assessment studies have identified the consumption and handling of poultry meat, and direct contact with animals, as the most important sources of human campylobacteriosis (21, 57). The role of protective immunity in humans is not well documented but it is most likely that immunity may lead to temporary protection against re-infection or disease, especially in people who are frequently exposed to *Campylobacter*, for example, through their work. It is likely that this immunity also confounds the results of case-control studies. This may explain why, in rare cases, poultry meat is identified as a protective factor (2, 22). Other risk factors for human campylobacteriosis include:

– direct contact with animals

– contaminated drinking water

– foreign travel

– the consumption of raw food products, including milk.

Quantitative attribution to the different sources is difficult to establish. From a Dutch case-control study on human gastroenteritis, it was estimated that 20% to 40% of campylobacteriosis is attributable to the consumption of contaminated poultry meat (W. Van Pelt, personal communication). The upper limit of this attribution is derived from a Belgian study. During the dioxin crisis of 1999, sales of chicken meat were prohibited for a four-week period. Over this period, the incidence of campylobacteriosis was 40% lower than expected, based on previous years, but returned to the normal level after the ban on chicken sales was lifted (65). In the Netherlands, as a result of the avian influenza outbreak in poultry in 2003, a considerable decrease in human *Campylobacter* infections was observed. This decrease seemed to correlate to the reduced consumption of poultry (64).

Rev. sci. tech. Off. int. Epiz., **25** (2)

583

Campylobacter and techniques to trace infection pathways

For several food-borne pathogens, such as *Salmonella*, serotyping and phage typing of isolates are important tools to trace infections and perform epidemiological studies. Many typing methods have been described for *Campylobacter*, both phenotypic (serotyping and phagetyping) and molecular based (68). Genotyping is more commonly used than phenotyping, due to the advantages of molecular methods (which are fast, less labour-intensive and fewer strains are untypable, in comparison to serotyping), and the limited availability of antisera. When investigating outbreaks, any typing method is suitable.

It should be noted that the current typing methods for *Campylobacter* can only be used for tracing infections that are restricted in time and geographical area. Although further typing of strains is often requested for epidemiological reasons, the biology of *Campylobacter* (a natural competent species with DNA-uptake and frequent rearrangements of the genome) hampers the use of large-scale typing. In the past, large-scale typing studies did not result in clear epidemiological conclusions about specific sources. New developments in typing may overcome these old problems. As an example, multi-locus sequence typing (MLST), which has been introduced relatively recently, is a molecular method that is highly reproducible. This method provides results that can easily be exchanged between laboratories and stored in one central database. Preliminary MLST data show that there is a certain correlation between the presence of a specific allele in *C. coli* associated with strains isolated from cattle and the strong association of specific *C. jejuni* sequence types and cattle (19, 44).

In addition, origin-specific markers for strains of *C. jejuni* were suggested by Champion *et al.* (11). If these findings continue to prove true, after further typing of isolates from different continents and sources, both MLST and specific markers could become useful tools for approximate attributions of human illness to different sources.

Poultry and *Campylobacter*

All types of poultry (broilers, layers, turkeys, ducks, fowl, quail, ostriches) can become colonised with *Campylobacter*. Wild birds are also frequently colonised (46, 67). In contrast with *Salmonella*, eggs do not contribute to the human campylobacteriosis problem as *Campylobacter* is not vertically transmissible (20). The most important vehicle of transmission of *Campylobacter* to humans is poultry meat that becomes contaminated during processing. Although turkey meat may also be a source of human campylobacteriosis (7), most research has been conducted on chicken production. Since most data come from this area, this section will deal with *Campylobacter* in broilers.

Day-old chicks and older animals can easily become colonised with *Campylobacter* when they are experimentally infected. Even with low doses (10 to 100 bacterial cells), the birds become colonised and start shedding in about two to three days. The colonisation reaches > 10^6 colony-forming units (CFU) per gram of caecal contents. Infections spread rapidly between animals under experimental conditions. Colonisation with *Campylobacter* does not lead to any clinical signs in poultry.

Broilers are free of *Campylobacter* on the day of hatching, so each cycle of broilers starts with a flock which tests negative for *Campylobacter* infection. In many studies, there is a delay of one to two weeks (the 'lag phase') before *Campylobacter* is detected in a flock. Several biological explanations have been given for this lag phase. However, mathematical modelling of the spread of infection within a large flock shows that, even without factors delaying the spread, an infected flock can only be detected as positive seven days after the introduction of the infection (63, 37). Until seven days have passed, only a small fraction of the flock sheds *Campylobacter* and it is not likely that these few animals will be detected in routine surveillance programmes.

The incidence in positive flocks may vary, depending on the country (i.e. continent and climate zone), and there is strong seasonality in the infection rate. The dynamics of the seasonality are also strongly dependent on the country. Northern European countries have much sharper peaks of incidence compared to more southern countries (49).

Most flocks are infected with multiple strains (34). These mixed infections may lead to even more variety in *Campylobacter* strains as they can exchange DNA, leading to chimera strains and increasing diversity (13). Broilers may become colonised with *C. jejuni* and with *C. coli*. However, at about six weeks, the species most commonly isolated from broilers is *C. jejuni*. In older animals, for example, in organic production, there is a shift towards *C. coli* (15).

Monitoring programmes

Monitoring programmes are implemented to identify trends in *Campylobacter* infections and evaluate the feasibility of control programmes. They can also aid in linking the poultry data to human *Campylobacter* data, to assess the contribution of poultry to the human burden of illness. A good example is the obligatory monitoring of *Campylobacter* in broilers in the European Union (EU), as required by Directive 2003/99/EC (18). This directive

Rev. sci. tech. Off. int. Epiz., **25** (2)

implemented the monitoring of broiler flocks from 1 January 2005, with the European Food Safety Authority (EFSA) as the agency responsible for compiling and reporting data collected by the EU Member States. At this time (June 2006), the EU is unique in instituting this monitoring programme (http://www.efsa.eu.int/science/monitoring_zoonoses/reports/catindex_en.html).

Risk factors and sources of infection for poultry

Since *Campylobacter* is horizontally transmitted into broiler flocks, primary control measures should be implemented at the farm level. However, before targeted intervention strategies can be implemented, the sources and routes of infection for broiler flocks must be identified (47). In many different studies, several common risk factors were identified for the introduction of *Campylobacter* into a broiler flock. Contamination of flocks increases with the following:

– the age of the animals

– the number of broiler houses on a farm

– the presence of other animals on the farm or in the direct vicinity (8, 35, 61).

In a Dutch study on ten broiler farms that were screened for the presence of *Campylobacter* for ten subsequent cycles, the risk for a flock to become positive increased when a former cycle tested positive (37). Recently, a systematic review on risk factors, based on United Kingdom data, and comprising 159 research papers, was published (3). Depopulation schedules (thinning) and multiple broiler houses on farms were identified as factors associated with increased risk. Disease prevention and hygiene measures, the presence of more than one generation of chicks (i.e. broilers and their parents) and certain seasons of hatching were all associated with decreasing risk.

Strategies to prevent the introduction of *Campylobacter* into a flock

The control of *Campylobacter* along the food chain is most effective when the colonisation of living animals can be prevented. Reducing the prevalence of *Campylobacter* infection in the primary production phase decreases high numbers of *Campylobacter* in the following steps. This may result in a low concentration or absence of *Campylobacter* on the final product.

Identifying risk factors for the introduction of *Campylobacter* means that specific intervention strategies can be implemented. In the following sections, the authors discuss the possibilities and effects of biosecurity,

multispecies farming and thinning, as well as competitive exclusion, vaccination and genetic resistance.

Biosecurity

Theoretically, a high level of biosecurity on the farm should protect against *Campylobacter*. Some correlation has been found (62), but even an extremely high level of biosecurity does not guarantee a *Campylobacter*-free flock at the time of slaughter (W.F. Jacobs-Reitsma, personal communication). Educating farmers on improved disease prevention measures and hygiene may lead to a lower prevalence of *Campylobacter*. However, conflicting reports come from two Scandinavian countries: Norway reports a positive effect from its education programme but Iceland has not observed any effect (31, 50).

The effects of improved hygiene are hard to quantify. As part of the *Campylobacter* Risk Management and Assessment project (CARMA, available at: htt://www.rivm.nl/carma/index_eng.html) in the Netherlands, a mathematical model was developed to describe *Campylobacter* dynamics in the primary production phase. Improving biosecurity was evaluated as an intervention strategy and identified as a potentially effective approach. However, this could only be established in theory as there is a lack of knowledge on methods that are effective in practice. No researcher can recommend to a farmer how to improve their biosecurity and indicate a specific percentage of anticipated reduction of *Campylobacter*. As increased biosecurity cannot be broken down into specific control measures, it is not clear what investments are needed. *Campylobacter* strains are continuously present around broiler houses and even if biosecurity measures (such as anterooms, disinfection facilities for boots and separate clothing and utensils for each house/worker) are in place, they must be consistently applied to prevent colonisation. Thus, apart from the technical aspects of disease prevention, there is also a behavioural aspect involved, which has not been studied so far.

Research has been conducted on the role of flies in transmitting *Campylobacter*. Flies can act as vectors for *Campylobacter* and the fly 'traffic' in and out of broiler houses is huge, so flies are a clear risk factor (24, 53). Controlling flies leads to both delayed and reduced *Campylobacter* infection in poultry flocks (25).

Multispecies farming

As multispecies farming is a risk factor for *Campylobacter*, recommending that farmers farm only one species sounds reasonable. However, economic analysis has shown that stopping multispecies farming is not an effective approach. For economic reasons, farmers will then increase their numbers of chickens and broiler houses. Banning other livestock may lead to a reduction in *Campylobacter* infection but, by increasing the number of broiler houses on the farm, one risk factor will simply be replaced by another, and the net result is estimated to be neutral (37).

Thinning

'Thinning' is the process of partially depopulating broiler houses to give more space to the remaining birds for ethical and economic reasons. Although the definition of thinning is the same, the practical approach may vary from country to country. For this reason, there are different opinions on whether thinning is a risk factor. The period of time between thinning and final depopulation of the flock is crucial. Differences in this interval, as well as varying flock sizes, probably account for the range of opinions on thinning as a risk factor.

There is a common perception that thinning causes an increased risk of introducing *Campylobacter* into a flock through inadequate disinfection of machinery and workers. Mathematical modelling shows that, one week after infection (the start of disease spread), the prevalence of infected broilers in flocks (size 30,000) is low (< 1%) (37). Even when up to 100 broilers become infected at thinning, the prevalence of infected broilers remains at < 10% after one week. If the final depopulation of a flock takes place one week after thinning, the infection still may not be detected by common surveillance systems. However, when the interval between thinning and final depopulation increases, the number of animals testing positive in the flock also increases and so does the chance that the infection will be found. In some cases, however, the increased risk of thinning can be entirely attributed to the increased age of the broilers (52).

Competitive exclusion

Competitive exclusion has been shown to be successful in *Salmonella* control programmes in poultry. Several studies on the use of competitive exclusion to control *Campylobacter* have been published but the results are variable. As yet, there is no commercial product that claims good results against *Campylobacter*.

One recent development is the use of a bacteriocin added to feed to control *C. jejuni* in chickens (56). This approach claims to be effective in preventing colonisation but it is not yet commercially available.

Vaccination

There are no commercially available vaccines against *Campylobacter* in poultry. The development of these vaccines is hampered by three main problems:

– the antigenic variety of strains

– the lack of knowledge of antigens which induce a protective immune response

– the requirement to provide protection in the very early life stages of the bird.

Several scientific studies show a (partial) protective effect of the humoral response under experimental conditions. A vaccine against *Campylobacter* in broilers must be effective in the very early life stages of the bird, requiring either protective maternal immunity or an innovative approach to induce protective immunity in the young chick.

Genetic resistance

Differences between genetic lines for susceptibility to *Campylobacter* infection are suggested but the data are limited and the molecular background is not yet clear (9).

Strategies to eliminate *Campylobacter* infections from flocks

Once an infection is established in a flock, close to 100% of the birds become colonised and shed high numbers of *Campylobacter* (> 10^6 CFU per gram of faeces).

Over an extended time period, there is a slight reduction in shedding, suggesting that immunity plays a role. However, in the normal lifespan of a commercially housed chicken, this may be limited to approximately one log reduction of *Campylobacter* concentration in the faeces (unpublished data).

A few approaches are reported to reduce shedding in a well-colonised flock. The first is phage therapy. This method uses lytic phages that specifically attach themselves to and lyse *Campylobacter* cells. Under experimental settings, this approach has been shown to reduce *Campylobacter* shedding by two to three logs (38, 66).

Risk assessment models predict a significant reduction of risk for the consumer, with a two-to-three log reduction in the caecal level of *Campylobacter* in poultry (29). However, since the large-scale practical implementation of this method involves several problems (e.g. its application, resistance), phage therapy is not expected to be commercially available within the next few years. Although bacteriophages already exist wherever *Campylobacter* is present, including in poultry, and these phages are safe for human health, using a virus to control *Campylobacter* may not meet with public acceptance unless it is capably and comprehensively presented (6).

A second approach may be the already mentioned use of bacteriocins. Bacteriocins have been proposed as a curative treatment but the results have not yet been published (56).

Conclusion on interventions to eliminate *Campylobacter* infections in primary production

In conclusion, the only currently available and (partially) effective intervention in primary production is to introduce a higher level of biosecurity. Although some practical steps can be suggested in this direction, the biosecurity approach is yet to be developed into a full programme of specific control measures with a defined quantitative effect. Therefore, the balance between costs and benefits can only be defined theoretically. Since other potential interventions and therapeutic strategies are not yet commercially available, a major decrease of infections on broiler farms is not likely in the short term.

Contamination during transportation from farm to slaughterhouse

Several studies have shown that transport crates, during transportation from the farm to the slaughterhouse, are a source of contamination for poultry which previously tested negative for *Campylobacter* (27). However, crates only cause external contamination of the birds, not significant colonisation in the gut. The few animals that do become colonised will have only very low numbers in the intestines.

It should be noted that the people, machinery and crates introduced into broiler houses to catch and transport the birds may well be the source of contamination for the remaining animals during thinning (see 'Thinning', above).

Preventing cross-contamination in the slaughterhouse

Owing to the high concentration of *Campylobacter* in the intestines, in particular, the caeca, the outside surfaces of chicken carcasses also become contaminated during processing. Carcasses from *Campylobacter*-negative broilers can be contaminated by machinery when they are processed after a positive flock. However, this contamination results in a lower concentration of bacteria at the surface when compared to carcasses from colonised chickens. Thus, such contamination has a negligible effect on the final product (51).

Improving the slaughtering process

It is technically possible to make slight changes to the slaughtering process to prevent and reduce cross-

contamination. The most serious constraint is that a high number of birds must be slaughtered per hour and cleaning and disinfecting the machinery between every two carcasses is not possible.

There are two potential approaches in the slaughterhouse:
– to prevent cross-contamination
– to decontaminate meat by chemical or physical means.

One powerful method appears to be the newly developed and patented equipment that forces a small amount of faeces out of the cloaca, through pressure on the abdomen, and subsequently removes the faeces with a pulse of water. The aim is to limit faecal leakage during scalding and defeathering. Mathematical modelling predicts that the number of CFUs on a chicken carcass after cooling would decline by a factor of three to ten. However, this method needs to be validated in practice (29).

For decontamination, five methods may be useful. First, irradiation of the meat virtually eliminates the public health risk. However, the costs of this method are relatively high and there is a good deal of public resistance. The second method may be to treat carcasses with, for example, a lactic acid solution (2.5%). This leads to a decrease in the average count of *Campylobacter* on the carcass after cooling, by one to two log units. A third method is crust-freezing of the carcasses with a stream of cold air. This is effective but relatively costly.

A fourth method has been used in a number of Scandinavian countries (Norway, Iceland, Denmark). Carcasses or parts of carcasses from flocks which test positive for *Campylobacter* infection are frozen for several weeks. According to laboratory experiments, the numbers of *Campylobacter* may be reduced by a factor of between ten and 100. The costs are high but risk assessment models predict that this method will reduce the burden of illness considerably (45, 51).

Finally, the fifth method is to heat treat the meat.

Measures for reducing *Campylobacter* can be applied to all flocks. Alternatively, one can decide to process only those flocks which test positive for *Campylobacter* infection in this way. This approach is called 'scheduled processing'.

Scheduled processing to control *Campylobacter*

An effective approach may be to separate positive and negative flocks, followed by decontaminating the meat from the positive flocks. Theoretically, this approach will

Rev. sci. tech. Off. int. Epiz., **25** (2)

587

work but, in practical terms, it is quite complicated to separate *Campylobacter*-positive and -negative flocks. Positive flocks can be identified at different points along the production chain.

Knowing the infection status of a flock when it leaves the farm means that *Campylobacter*-positive flocks can be sent to a 'positive-only' slaughterhouse, whereas negative flocks will be transported and processed in slaughterhouses for 'negative flocks only'. Where only one slaughterhouse is available, the negative flocks would be processed first, followed by the positive flocks.

A negative flock that is misidentified as positive will not result in any problem except for a possible economic one. However, a positive flock that is misidentified as negative will be treated as 'safe meat' throughout the process, may cross-contaminate truly negative flocks and will be sold without *Campylobacter* reduction treatment.

Flocks can be tested for the presence of *Campylobacter* by conventional bacteriological culture techniques. However, *Campylobacter* die off easily during transportation from the farm to the laboratory. In addition, isolating *Campylobacter* requires at least two days (as well as the time needed to mail samples). False negative results (i.e. *Campylobacter* could not be isolated from the farm samples but the flock tested positive on arrival at the slaughterhouse) are reported frequently, due mainly to flocks that became positive between sampling and slaughter (30). There are two alternatives: either the farmer can use a rapid on-site test just before the flocks are transported to the slaughterhouse or the flocks can be tested by polymerase chain reaction (PCR) when they arrive at the slaughterhouse. The on-site test is currently under evaluation in the Netherlands, whereas the PCR technique is routinely used in Denmark (39).

The efficacy of scheduled treatment was assessed using the mathematical model (37). The reliability of negative test results, which is crucial in this approach, depends strongly on the length of time between testing and slaughter. The sensitivity and specificity of the test appeared to be of minor importance (37).

Is there an acceptable level of contamination?

Dose-response models used in microbiological risk assessment are based on the 'single-hit' principle, i.e. a single CFU of *Campylobacter* can colonise a host and potentially cause illness, albeit with a relatively low probability (23, 59). If the ingested dose increases, the likelihood that one of the pathogens establishes infection will also increase. This implies that there is no 'safe' level of

Campylobacter on broiler meat since any level may potentially cause disease in the human population. However, the risk of illness at low exposure levels is considerably less than the risk at higher levels. The concentration of *Campylobacter* on chicken meat, and the fraction of these bacteria that is ultimately ingested, vary over several orders of magnitude. Risk assessment models typically show that most cases of illness are predicted to result from high ingested doses, which occur relatively rarely (45). Thus, reducing average exposure or the probability of peak exposure is expected to result in significant reductions of risk to the consumer. For example, Rosenquist *et al.* (51) predicted that reducing the concentration of *Campylobacter* on broiler meat 100-fold may reduce disease incidence 30-fold. So, from a public health perspective, low numbers of *Campylobacter* on broiler meat may be tolerable, as they are not expected to result in a significant incidence of illness. This is also related to the fact that (in contrast to, for example, *Salmonella*) *Campylobacter* cannot multiply outside a warm-blooded host.

Other sources for human campylobacteriosis and intervention strategies

Food

Poultry meat is known to be one of the most important sources of *Campylobacter* for humans. However, *Campylobacter* colonisation in the gut is described for all production animals. *Campylobacter* is mainly a contamination of the surface of the carcass and bovine, ovine and porcine carcasses can also test positive for *Campylobacter* immediately after slaughter. Storage (cooling down) of the carcasses under dry air conditions results in the death of *Campylobacter* and reduced *Campylobacter* counts after a prolonged time. At retail level, the *Campylobacter* contamination levels of non-poultry meat are clearly less than the levels in poultry. It is to be expected that red meat contributes to human campylobacteriosis to a much lesser degree than poultry, but the quantitative contributions of various meats are unknown.

Preventing *Campylobacter* colonisation in cattle and sheep is unlikely to be achievable as farming under increased biosecurity is impossible, due to the type of husbandry. In pork production, there are practical examples of farms with high biosecurity levels. However, poultry production has demonstrated that it is hard to keep a flock free of *Campylobacter* for six weeks. For the much longer production cycle of fattening pigs, it may be a huge challenge to keep the animals free of *Campylobacter*.

Seafood may be contaminated with *Campylobacter* but it is more likely that this will be *C. lari* instead of *C. jejuni* or *C. coli*. *Campylobacter lari* is also a human pathogen but the incidence in the human population is clearly less than that of *C. jejuni* or *C. coli* infections. The only intervention is heating the product. For raw fish products (such as oysters) there are no specific intervention strategies other than depuration of the water or UV irradiation.

Other raw food items may contribute to human campylobacteriosis. Produce may be contaminated through irrigating systems or the use of contaminated manure (36). As much produce is not heated, even a low concentration may be a risk for humans.

Direct animal contact

Direct contact with production animals may be a source of human campylobacteriosis. People working with these animals on a daily basis, for instance, farmers, may be protected against the disease by acquired immunity. This protection is not very well studied and the level of protection and cross-protection will be one of the most challenging topics in better understanding *Campylobacter* epidemiology over the next few decades. People who are incidentally exposed to *Campylobacter*, e.g. visitors to a petting zoo, may contract campylobacteriosis. As companion animals like dogs and cats are often asymptomatic carriers of *Campylobacter*, these animals may also be a source for human campylobacteriosis. Epidemiological studies describe an increased risk of campylobacteriosis for owners of cats and dogs, and case studies describe the disease in humans, due to direct contact with companion animals.

Intervention strategies are solely based on hygiene. At petting zoos, people should be made aware that they should wash their hands after touching animals. However, children are mainly at risk as they do not recognise the risk. For companion animals, the situation is more complicated and there is no other option than to 'live with it'.

Antimicrobial resistance in *Campylobacter* species

Until recently it was difficult to obtain comparable susceptibility data on *Campylobacter* spp. isolated from food animals at slaughter. The primary reason was that there was no standardised methodology to determine the susceptibility of *Campylobacter* spp. (1). In 2004, the agar dilution method was validated for quantitative susceptibility testing of *Campylobacter* spp. by McDermott

et al. (41). Acceptable limits for the quality control strain *C. jejuni* ATCC 33560, determined by the broth microdilution test, are provided by the Clinical and Laboratory Standards Institute in its most recent guidance documents (M100-S16) (12). This greatly aids in determining quality controlled minimum inhibitory concentration (MIC) data.

An external quality assurance system was co-ordinated by the Danish Institute for Food and Veterinary Research within the EU Fair project (ARBAO-II, QLRT-2001-01146) (5). In this project, ring trials were organised to harmonise the results of susceptibility tests of *Campylobacter* spp. in European countries. Subsequently, MIC data of harmonised quality were reported from different European countries (Tables I and II).

Resistance percentages vary greatly from country to country, based on differences in policies on antibiotic use. In *C. coli*, resistance levels are higher than in *C. jejuni*. The antibiotics of first choice for treating campylobacteriosis in humans are macrolides and fluoroquinolones. Resistance to erythromycin is commonly present in *C. coli* from pigs and resistance to fluoroquinolones is commonly present in both *C. jejuni* from poultry and *C. coli* from pigs.

Trends in resistance to fluoroquinolones in the primary sector have been reported in the Netherlands (43) (Fig. 1). However, macrolide resistance has decreased substantially in pigs. This is potentially related to the ban of tylosine as a growth promoter in 1999, whereas resistance to ciprofloxacin has shown a slow tendency to increase in pigs after its licensing for these animals in the mid-1990s. The first occurrence of fluoroquinolone resistance in *C. jejuni* in 1988, one year after the introduction of quinolones into the poultry industry in the Netherlands, was described by Endtz *et al.* in 1991 (16). Endtz demonstrated the link between the introduction of fluoroquinolones and the simultaneous increase in ciprofloxacin resistance in *C. jejuni* from poultry and human cases of campylobacteriosis. From the 1990s until 2004, a further increase in ciprofloxacin resistance was observed to a level of approximately 40% in veterinary isolates (33, 43).

More recently, several authors have demonstrated that fluoroquinolones rapidly select for resistant mutations during the treatment of poultry and pigs (14, 33, 40, 60). This phenomenon is the basis for the discussion of the public health risks of fluoroquinolones in poultry. Fluoroquinolones are used to treat, for example, colibacillosis and *Mycoplasma* infections in poultry and, as a side effect, the *Campylobacter* spp. present in the intestines of the bird become resistant. Since poultry is considered one of the major sources for *Campylobacter* infection in humans, using fluoroquinolones in poultry indirectly selects for fluoroquinolone-resistant

Rev. sci. tech. Off. int. Epiz., 25 (2)

589

Table I
Occurrence of antimicrobial resistance among *Campylobacter coli* isolates from pigs, isolated from faeces at slaughter, in European countries in 2002

Antibiotic	Country, number of isolates and resistance percentages					
	Switzerland 251	Denmark 92	United Kingdom 706 [a]	France 317 [b]	Netherlands 64	Sweden 100
Ampicillin	–	0	16	12	13	7
Chloramphenicol	0	0	3	–	0	–
Fluoroquinolones	25	8	10	12	12	16
Erythromycin	21	32	85	65	55	0
Gentamicin	0	0	–	0	0	0
Kanamycin	1	–	2	–	–	–
Nalidixic acid	26	8	17	20	11	18
Neomycin	–	1	–	–	1.6	–
Streptomycin	80	52	–	–	88	–
Tetracycline	9	1	79	83	70	1

a) 1999-2000
b) 2000

Table II
Occurrence of antimicrobial resistance among *Campylobacter jejuni* isolates, isolated from chickens, in European countries in 2002

Antibiotic	Country, number of isolates and resistance percentages						
	Denmark 53	France 43	Germany 82	Netherlands 44	Norway 161	Sweden 84	Switzerland 180
Ampicillin	8	28	0	23	3	10	7
Chloramphenicol	0	–	–	0	–	–	0
Fluoroquinolones	0	30	9	41	< 1	0	12
Erythromycin	0	7	0	0	1	0	< 1
Gentamicin	0	2	0	0	0	0	0
Kanamycin	–	–	–	–	–	–	–
Nalidixic acid	0	36	9	39	0	0	–
Neomycin	0	–	–	5	–	–	–
Streptomycin	0	–	–	0	–	–	6
Tetracycline	2	67	33	32	0	1	4

Source: (5)

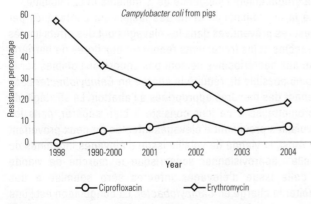
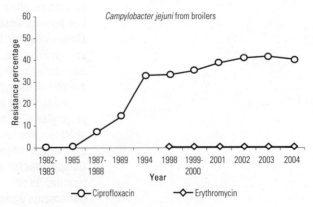

Fig. 1
Trends in resistance to erythromycin and ciprofloxacin in *Campylobacter* spp. isolated from pigs and broilers in the Netherlands from 1998 to 2004 (and since 1982 for ciprofloxacin resistance in *C. jejuni*)

Campylobacter strains in human infection, and may contribute to problems in human therapy.

Similar trends in fluoroquinolone resistance in *Campylobacter* spp. have been described for human clinical isolates by Engberg *et al.*, (17), following the introduction of fluoroquinolones into animal and human treatment. As a result of increased fluoroquinolone resistance in human *Campylobacter* isolates, the United States Food and Drug Administration banned the use of fluoroquinolones in poultry from September 2005 (http://www.fda.gov/oc/antimicrobial/baytril.pdf).

In the EU, from January 2005, a new zoonoses Directive (2003/99) was implemented, prescribing not only the annual monitoring of *Campylobacter* spp. in food animals, but also the annual surveillance of antimicrobial resistance in *Campylobacter* strains isolated from the major food animal species: cattle, pigs and poultry (18). As a result of Directive 2003/99/EC, new Community Reference Laboratories (CRLs) have been designated to monitor antimicrobial resistance (in general) and *Campylobacter*. Specific tasks will be to standardise and control the analytical methods for isolation, species identification and susceptibility testing. An important source of variation in susceptibility test results is the sampling strategy used. The CRL, in co-operation with EFSA, must develop adequate guidance documents so that existing control programmes in the Member States can be successfully harmonised.

■

La présence de *Campylobacter* dans les élevages et les stratégies de prophylaxie visant à réduire l'incidence de la campylobactériose chez l'homme

J.A. Wagenaar, D.J. Mevius & A.H. Havelaar

Résumé
La campylobactériose est l'une des maladies d'origine bactérienne les plus importantes chez l'être humain. La transmission de l'infection à *Campylobacter* se fait principalement par contact direct avec les volailles et par ingestion de viande de volaille contaminée, mais d'autres sources existent et jouent un rôle parfois considérable. La prophylaxie de l'infection à *Campylobacter* chez les poulets de chair réduit efficacement l'incidence de la maladie chez l'homme.
Les poulets destinés à la consommation étant très facilement contaminés par *Campylobacter*, les mesures préventives dans les élevages ont des effets limités et imprévisibles. Les vaccins et les traitements recourant aux flores de barrière, aux bactériophages ou aux bactériocines ne sont pas encore disponibles sur le marché. Il est néanmoins possible de réduire la charge en *Campylobacter* dans le produit final en prenant des mesures appropriées à l'abattoir. La stratégie de prophylaxie la plus prometteuse à ce jour consiste à bien séparer, dans les abattoirs, les lots de volailles provenant d'élevages infectés de ceux provenant d'élevages indemnes. Ainsi, la viande de volaille issue d'élevages indemnes de *Campylobacter* peut-elle approvisionner sans risque le marché de viande fraîche, tandis que celle issue d'élevages infectés sera soumise à des traitements visant à limiter la charge en *Campylobacter*. La congélation est l'une des méthodes possibles, mais la décontamination chimique reste la méthode la plus rentable. Il est également possible de ne traiter que les viandes fortement contaminées.

Rev. sci. tech. Off. int. Epiz., **25** (2)

591

La conclusion des auteurs est que, tant que de nouvelles méthodes ne seront pas disponibles, la gestion des lots à l'abattoir (autrement dit la stricte séparation des lots suivant le statut sanitaire de l'élevage d'origine) est la plus intéressante du point de vue économique. L'article s'achève sur une description de l'évolution de la résistance des *Campylobacter* aux antibiotiques.

Mots-clés
Abattage – Campylobacter – Gestion des lots à l'abattoir – Résistance aux antibiotiques – Santé publique – Sécurité sanitaire des aliments – Stratégie – Viande de volaille – Volaille – Zoonose.

■

El agente *Campylobacter* en la producción animal y las estrategias de control para reducir la incidencia de la campilobacteriosis humana

J.A. Wagenaar, D.J. Mevius & A.H. Havelaar

Resumen
La campilobacteriosis es una de las enfermedades bacterianas de mayor importancia transmitidas por los alimentos a los seres humanos. Si bien las principales fuentes de infección por *Campylobacter* son la manipulación y el consumo de aves de corral, también hay otras de considerable magnitud. El control del agente patógeno *Campylobacter* en los pollos de engorde reduce la incidencia de la campilobacteriosis humana.

El *Campylobacter* coloniza fácilmente los pollos para consumo y las medidas preventivas en la producción tienen efectos limitados e imprevisibles. Aún no se comercializan vacunas, productos para exclusión competitiva ni tratamientos con bacteriófagos o bacteriocinas. Pero, puede reducirse la contaminación del producto final mediante la aplicación de medidas de control en los mataderos. La estrategia de control más prometedora existente en la actualidad consiste en la matanza separada de las bandadas infectadas y sanas. La carne virtualmente libre de *Campylobacter* puede utilizarse para abastecer el mercado de productos avícolas frescos y la procedente de bandadas infectadas puede tratarse para reducir la concentración del agente patógeno. La carne de las bandadas infectadas puede tratarse por congelación, pero la descontaminación química parece más rentable. De igual modo es posible que se traten únicamente las carnes altamente contaminadas.

Los autores concluyen que mientras no se comercialicen técnicas nuevas, el procesamiento separado de las aves es el método de control más rentable. Por último, los autores describen la evolución de la resistencia antimicrobiana del género *Campylobacter*.

Palabras clave
Ave de corral – Campylobacter – Carne de pollo – Estrategia de intervención – Inocuidad de los alimentos – Matanza – Procesamiento separado – Resistencia antimicrobiana – Salud pública – Zoonosis.

■

References

1. Aarestrup F.M. & Engberg J. (2001). – Antimicrobial resistance of thermophilic *Campylobacter*. *Vet. Res.*, **32** (3-4), 311-321.

2. Adak G.K., Cowden J.M., Nicholas S. & Evans H.S. (1995). – The Public Health Laboratory Service national case-control study of primary indigenous sporadic cases of campylobacter infection. *Epidemiol. Infect.*, **115** (1), 15-22.

3. Adkin A., Hartnett E., Jordan L., Newell D. & Davison H. (2006). – Use of a systematic review to assist the development of *Campylobacter* control strategies in broilers. *J. appl. Microbiol.*, **100** (2), 306-315.

4. Altekruse S.F., Stern N.J., Fields P.I. & Swerdlow D.L. (1999). – *Campylobacter jejuni* – an emerging foodborne pathogen. *Emerg. infect. Dis.*, **5** (1), 28-35.

5. Antimicrobial Resistance in Bacteria of Animal Origin (ARBAO) (2002). – ARBAO II: Summary of annual data 2002: *Campylobacter*. ARBAO/FAIR: European Union Project, Copenhagen. Available at: http://www.dfvf.dk/Files/Filer/ARBAO/ARBAO_monitoring_summary__draft.pdf (accessed on 28 July 2006).

6. Atterbury R.J., Connerton P.L., Dodd C.E., Rees C.E. & Connerton I.F. (2003). – Isolation and characterization of *Campylobacter* bacteriophages from retail poultry. *Appl. environ. Microbiol.*, **69** (8), 4511-4518.

7. Borck B. & Pedersen K. (2005). – Pulsed-field gel electrophoresis types of *Campylobacter* spp. in Danish turkeys before and after slaughter. *Int. J. Food Microbiol.*, **101** (1), 63-72. Epub.: 5 January 2005.

8. Bouwknegt M., van de Giessen A.W., Dam-Deisz W.D.C., Havelaar A.H., Nagelkerke N.J.D. & Henken A.M. (2004). – Risk factors for the presence of *Campylobacter* spp. in Dutch broiler flocks. *Prev. vet. Med.*, **62** (1), 35-49.

9. Boyd Y., Herbert E.G., Marston K.L., Jones M.A. & Barrow P.A. (2005). – Host genes affect intestinal colonisation of newly hatched chickens by *Campylobacter jejuni*. *Immunogenetics*, **57** (3-4), 248-253. Epub.: 15 April 2005.

10. Burch D. (2005). – Avian vibrionic hepatitis in laying hens. *Vet. Rec.*, **157** (17), 528.

11. Champion O.L., Gaunt M.W., Gundogdu O., Elmi A., Witney A.A., Hinds J., Dorrell N. & Wren B.W. (2005). – Comparative phylogenomics of the food-borne pathogen *Campylobacter jejuni* reveals genetic markers predictive of infection source. *Proc. natl Acad. Sci. USA*, **102** (44), 16043-16048. Epub.: 17 October 2005.

12. Clinical and Laboratory Standards Institute (CLSI) (2006). – M100–S16, performance standards for antimicrobial susceptibility testing: 16th informational supplement. CLSI, Wayne, Pennsylvania, United States of America.

13. De Boer P., Wagenaar J.A., Achterberg R.P., van Putten J.P.M., Schouls L.M. & Duim B. (2002). – Generation of *Campylobacter jejuni* genetic diversity in vivo. *Molec. Microbiol.*, **44** (2), 351-359.

14. Delsol A.A., Sunderland J., Woodward M.J., Pumbwe L., Piddock L.J. & Roe J.M. (2004). – Emergence of fluoroquinolone resistance in the native *Campylobacter coli* population of pigs exposed to enrofloxacin. *J. antimicrob. Chemother.*, **53** (5), 872-874. Epub.: 17 March 2004.

15. El-Shibiny A., Connerton P.L. & Connerton I.F. (2005). – Enumeration and diversity of campylobacters and bacteriophages isolated during the rearing cycles of free-range and organic chickens. *Appl. environ. Microbiol.*, **71** (3), 1259-1266.

16. Endtz H.P., Ruijs G.J., van Klingeren B., Jansen W.H., van der Reyden T. & Mouton R.P. (1991). – Quinolone resistance in *Campylobacter* isolated from man and poultry following the introduction of fluoroquinolones in veterinary medicine. *J. antimicrob. Chemother.*, **27** (2), 199-208.

17. Engberg J., Aarestrup F.M., Taylor D.E., Gerner-Schmidt P. & Nachamkin I. (2001). – Quinolone and macrolide resistance in *Campylobacter jejuni* and *C. coli*: resistance mechanisms and trends in human isolates. *Emerg. infect. Dis.*, **7** (1), 24-34. Erratum: *Emerg. infect. Dis.*, **7** (3), 491.

18. European Union (2003). – Directive 2003/99/EC of the European Parliament and of the Council of 17 November 2003 on the monitoring of zoonoses and zoonotic agents, amending Council Decision 90/424/EEC and repealing Council Directive 92/117/EEC. *Off. J. Eur. Union*, **L 325** of 12.12.2003, 31-40.

19. French N.P., Barrigas M., Leatherbarrow A.J.H., Carter P., Gilpin B.J. & Fox A.J. (2005). – Epidemiology and public health importance of *Campylobacter jejuni* multilocus sequence type ST-61: the ruminant-associated strains. *In* 13th Int. Workshop on *Campylobacter, Helicobacter* and related organisms (V. Korolik, A. Lee, H. Mitchell, G. Mendz, B. Fry & P. Coloe, eds), Gold Coast, Queensland, Australia, 4-8 September. Griffith University Publications, Gold Coast, Australia.

20. Fridriksdottir V., Gunnarsson E., Jonsdottir G., Astradsdottir K., Birgisdottir K., Bjarnadottir S., Hjartardottir S., Reiersen J., Lowman R., Hiett K., Callicott K., Stern N.J. & the Campy-on-Ice Consortium (2005). – Campylobacteriosis in chicken in Iceland – is vertical transmission of infection taking place? *In* 13th Int. Workshop on *Campylobacter, Helicobacter* and related organisms (V. Korolik, A. Lee, H. Mitchell, G. Mendz, B. Fry & P. Coloe, eds), Gold Coast, Queensland, Australia, 4-8 September. Griffith University Publications, Gold Coast, Australia.

21. Friedman C.R., Neimann J., Wegener H.C. & Tauxe R.V. (2000). – Epidemiology of *Campylobacter jejuni* infections in the United States and other industrialized nations. *In Campylobacter* (I. Nachamkin & M.J. Blaser, eds), 2nd Ed. ASM Press, Washington, DC, 121-139.

Rev. sci. tech. Off. int. Epiz., **25** (2)

593

22. Friedman C.R., Hoekstra R.M., Samuel M., Marcus R., Bender J., Shiferaw B., Reddy S., Ahuja S.D., Helfrick D.L., Hardnett F., Carter M., Anderson B. & Tauxe R.V. (2004). – Risk factors for sporadic *Campylobacter* infection in the United States: a case-control study in FoodNet sites. Emerging Infections Program FoodNet Working Group. *Clin. infect. Dis.*, **38** (Suppl. 3), S285-S296.

23. Haas C.N. (1983). – Estimation of risk due to low doses of microorganisms: a comparison of alternative methodologies. *Am. J. Epidemiol.*, **118** (4), 573-582.

24. Hald B., Skovgård H., Bang D.D., Pedersen K., Dybdahl J., Jespersen J.B. & Madsen M. (2004). – Flies and *Campylobacter* infection of broiler flocks. *Emerg. infect. Dis.*, **10** (8), 1490-1492.

25. Hald B., Skovgård H., Pedersen K., Bunkenborg H. & Madsen M. (2005). – Insect screen against *Campylobacter*, an intervention study in Danish broiler houses. *In* 13th Int. Workshop on *Campylobacter*, *Helicobacter* and related organisms (V. Korolik, A. Lee, H. Mitchell, G. Mendz, B. Fry & P. Coloe, eds), Gold Coast, Queensland, Australia, 4-8 September. Griffith University Publications, Gold Coast, Australia.

26. Hannu T., Mattila L., Rautelin H., Pelkonen P., Lahdenne P., Siitonen A. & Leirisalo-Repo M. (2002). – *Campylobacter*-triggered reactive arthritis: a population-based study. *Rheumatology (Oxford)*, **41** (3), 312-318.

27. Hansson I., Ederoth M., Andersson L., Vagsholm I. & Olsson Engvall E. (2005). – Transmission of *Campylobacter* spp. to chickens during transport to slaughter. *J. appl. Microbiol.*, **99** (5), 1149-1157.

28. Havelaar A.H., de Wit M.A., van Koningsveld R. & van Kempen E. (2000). – Health burden in the Netherlands due to infection with thermophilic *Campylobacter* spp. *Epidemiol. Infect.*, **125** (3), 505-522.

29. Havelaar A.H., Mangen M.-J.J., Nauta M.J., de Koeijer A.A., Bogaardt M.-J., Evers E.G., Jacobs-Reitsma W.F., van Pelt W., Wagenaar J.A., de Wit G.A. & van der Zee H. (2006/7). – Effectiveness and efficiency of controlling *Campylobacter* on broiler chicken meat. *Risk Analysis* (in press).

30. Hofshagen M. & Bruheim T. (2004). – The surveillance and control program for *Campylobacter* in broiler flocks in Norway: annual report 2004. Available at: http://www.vetinst.no/Arkiv/Pdf-filer/NOK-2004/19Campylobacter_in_broiler_flocks.pdf (accessed on 28 July 2006).

31. Hofshagen M. & Kruse H. (2005). – Learning from experiences: the Norwegian action plan against *Campylobacter* spp. in broilers. *In* 13th Int. Workshop on *Campylobacter*, *Helicobacter* and related organisms (V. Korolik, A. Lee, H. Mitchell, G. Mendz, B. Fry & P. Coloe, eds), Gold Coast, Queensland, Australia, 4-8 September. Griffith University Publications, Gold Coast, Australia.

32. Hughes R.A. & Cornblath D.R. (2005). – Guillain-Barré syndrome. *Lancet*, **366** (9497), 1653-1666.

33. Jacobs-Reitsma W.F., Koenraad P.M., Bolder N.M. & Mulder R.W. (1994). – *In vitro* susceptibility of *Campylobacter* and *Salmonella* isolates from broilers to quinolones, ampicillin, tetracycline, and erythromycin. *Vet. Q.*, **16** (4), 206-208.

34. Jacobs-Reitsma W.F., van de Giessen A.W., Bolder N.M. & Mulder R.W. (1995). – Epidemiology of *Campylobacter* spp. at two Dutch broiler farms. *Epidemiol. Infect.*, **114** (3), 413-421.

35. Kapperud G., Skjerve E., Vik L., Hauge K., Lysaker A., Aalmen I., Ostroff S.M. & Potter M. (1993). – Epidemiological investigation of risk factors for campylobacter colonization in Norwegian broiler flocks. *Epidemiol. Infect.*, **111** (2), 245-255.

36. Karenlampi R. & Hanninen M.L. (2004). – Survival of *Campylobacter jejuni* on various fresh produce. *Int. J. Food Microbiol.*, **97** (2), 187-195.

37. Katsma W.E.A., de Koeijer A.A., Jacobs-Reitsma W.F., Mangen M.-J.J. & Wagenaar J.A. (2006/7). – Assessing interventions to reduce the risk of *Campylobacter* prevalence in broilers. *Risk Analysis* (in press).

38. Loc Carrillo C., Atterbury R.J., El-Shibiny A., Connerton P.L., Dillon E., Scott A. & Connerton I.F. (2005). – Bacteriophage therapy to reduce *Campylobacter jejuni* colonization of broiler chickens. *Appl. environ. Microbiol.*, **71** (11), 6554-6563.

39. Lund M., Wedderkopp A., Waino M., Nordentoft S., Bang D.D., Pedersen K. & Madsen M. (2003). – Evaluation of PCR for detection of *Campylobacter* in a national broiler surveillance programme in Denmark. *J. appl. Microbiol.*, **94** (5), 929-935.

40. McDermott P.F., Bodeis S.M., English L.L., White D.G., Walker R.D., Zhao S., Simjee S. & Wagner D.D. (2002). – Ciprofloxacin resistance in *Campylobacter jejuni* evolves rapidly in chickens treated with fluoroquinolones. *J. infect. Dis.*, **185** (6), 837-840. Epub.: 8 February 2002.

41. McDermott P.F., Bodeis S.M., Aarestrup F.M., Brown S., Traczewski M., Fedorka-Cray P., Wallace M., Critchley I.A., Thornsberry C. *et al.* (2004). – Development of a standardized susceptibility test for campylobacter with quality-control ranges for ciprofloxacin, doxycycline, erythromycin, gentamicin, and meropenem. *Microb. Drug Resist.*, 10 (2), 124-131.

42. Mangen M.-J.J., Havelaar A.H., Bernsen R.A.J.A.M., van Koningsveld R. & de Wit G.A. (2005). – The costs of human *Campylobacter* infections and sequelae in the Netherlands: a DALY and cost-of-illness approach. *Acta agric. scand.*, **2**, 35-51.

43. Mevius D., van Pelt W. & Pellicaan C. (eds) (2004). – MARAN: monitoring of antimicrobial resistance and antibiotic usage in animals in the Netherlands in 2004. Veterinary Antibiotic Usage and Resistance Surveillance Working Group (VANTURES), Lelystad, the Netherlands. Available at: www.cidc-lelystad.nl (accessed on 8 July 2006).

44. Miller W.G., Englen M.D., Kathariou S., Wesley I.V., Wang G., Pittenger-Alley L., Siletz R.M., Muraoka W., Fedorka-Cray P.J. & Mandrell R.E. (2006). – Identification of host-associated alleles by multilocus sequence typing of *Campylobacter coli* strains from food animals. *Microbiology*, **152** (Pt 1), 245-255.

45. Nauta M.J., Jacobs-Reitsma W.F. & Havelaar A.H. (2006/7). – A risk assessment model for *Campylobacter* in broiler meat. *Risk Analysis* (in press).

46. Newell D.G. & Wagenaar J.A. (2000). – Poultry infections and their control at the farm level. *In Campylobacter* (I. Nachamkin & M.J. Blaser, eds), 2nd Ed. ASM Press, Washington, DC, 497-509.

47. Newell D.G. & Fearnley C. (2003). – Sources of *Campylobacter* colonization in broiler chickens. *Appl. environ. Microbiol.*, **69** (8), 4343-4351.

48. Nicholson F.A., Groves S.J. & Chambers B.J. (2005). – Pathogen survival during livestock manure storage and following land application. *Bioresour. Technol.*, **96** (2), 135-143.

49. Nylen G., Dunstan F., Palmer S.R., Andersson Y., Bager F., Cowden J., Feierl G., Galloway Y., Kapperud G., Mégraud F., Molbak K., Petersen L.R. & Ruutu P. (2002). – The seasonal distribution of campylobacter infection in nine European countries and New Zealand. *Epidemiol. Infect.*, **128** (3), 383-390.

50. Reiersen J., Hardardottir H., Gunnarsson E., Fridriksdottir V., Sigmundsdottir G. & Kristinsson K. (2005). – Surveillance of campylobacteriosis in poultry and humans in Iceland. *In* 13th International Workshop on *Campylobacter, Helicobacter* and related organisms (V. Korolik, A. Lee, H. Mitchell, G. Mendz, B. Fry & P. Coloe, eds), Gold Coast, Queensland, Australia, 4-8 September. Griffith University Publications, Gold Coast, Australia.

51. Rosenquist H., Nielsen N.L., Sommer H.M., Norrung B. & Christensen B.B. (2003). – Quantitative risk assessment of human campylobacteriosis associated with thermophilic *Campylobacter* species in chickens. *Int. J. Food Microbiol.*, **83** (1), 87-103.

52. Russa A.D., Bouma A., Vernooij J.C.M., Jacobs-Reitsma W. & Stegeman J.A. (2005). – No association between partial depopulation and *Campylobacter* spp. colonization of Dutch broiler flocks. *Lett. appl. Microbiol.*, **41** (3), 280-285.

53. Shane S.M., Montrose M.S. & Harrington K.S. (1985). – Transmission of *Campylobacter jejuni* by the housefly *(Musca domestica)*. *Avian Dis.*, **29** (2), 384-391.

54. Skirrow M.B. & Blaser M.J. (2000). – Clinical aspects of *Campylobacter* infection. *In Campylobacter* (I. Nachamkin & M.J. Blaser, eds), 2nd Ed. ASM Press, Washington, DC, 69-88.

55. Stephens C.P., On S.L. & Gibson J.A. (1998). – An outbreak of infectious hepatitis in commercially reared ostriches associated with *Campylobacter coli* and *Campylobacter jejuni*. *Vet. Microbiol.*, **61** (3), 183-190.

56. Stern N.J., Svetoch E.A., Eruslanov B.V., Kovalev Y.N., Volodina L.I., Perelygin V.V., Mitsevich E.V., Mitsevich I.P. & Levchuk V.P. (2005). – *Paenibacillus polymyxa* purified bacteriocin to control *Campylobacter jejuni* in chickens. *J. Food Protec.*, **68** (7), 1450-1453.

57. Studahl A. & Andersson Y. (2000). – Risk factors for indigenous campylobacter infection: a Swedish case-control study. *Epidemiol. Infect.*, **125** (2), 269-275.

58. Tauxe R.V. (2002). – Emerging foodborne pathogens. *Int. J. Food Microbiol.*, **78** (1-2), 31-41.

59. Teunis P.F.M. & Havelaar A.H. (2000). – The Beta Poisson dose-response model is not a single-hit model. *Risk Analysis*, **20** (4), 513-520.

60. Van Boven M., Veldman K.T., de Jong M.C. & Mevius D.J. (2003). – Rapid selection of quinolone resistance in *Campylobacter jejuni* but not in *Escherichia coli* in individually housed broilers. *J. antimicrob. Chemother.*, **52** (4), 719-723. Epub.: 1 September 2003.

61. Van de Giessen A.W., Bloemberg B.P., Ritmeester W.S. & Tilburg J.J. (1996). – Epidemiological study on risk factors and risk reducing measures for campylobacter infections in Dutch broiler flocks. *Epidemiol. Infect.*, **117** (2), 245-250.

62. Van de Giessen A.W., Tilburg J.J., Ritmeester W.S. & van der Plas J. (1998). – Reduction of campylobacter infections in broiler flocks by application of hygiene measures. *Epidemiol. Infect.*, **121** (1), 57-66.

63. Van Gerwe T.J.W.M., Bouma A., Jacobs-Reitsma W.F., van den Broek J., Klinkenberg D., Stegeman J.A. & Heesterbeek J.A.P. (2005). – Quantifying transmission of *Campylobacter* spp. among broilers. *Appl. environ. Microbiol.*, **71** (10), 5765-5770.

64. Van Pelt W., Wannet W.J.B., van de Giessen A.W., Mevius D.J. & van Duynhoven Y.T.H.P. (2004). – Trends in gastroenteritis (GE) in the Netherlands, 1996-2003 [in Dutch]. *Infectieziekten Bull.*, **15**, 335-341.

65. Vellinga A. & Van Loock F. (2002). – The dioxin crisis as experiment to determine poultry-related *Campylobacter* enteritis. *Emerg. infect. Dis.*, **8** (1), 19-22.

66. Wagenaar J.A., Van Bergen M.A.P., Mueller M.A., Wassenaar T.M. & Carlton R.M. (2005). – Phage therapy reduces *Campylobacter jejuni* colonization in broilers. *Vet. Microbiol.*, **109** (3-4), 275-283.

67. Waldenstrom J., Broman T., Carlsson I., Hasselquist D., Achterberg R.P., Wagenaar J.A. & Olsen B. (2002). – Prevalence of *Campylobacter jejuni, Campylobacter lari*, and *Campylobacter coli* in different ecological guilds and taxa of migrating birds. *Appl. environ. Microbiol.*, **68** (12), 5911-5917.

68. Wassenaar T.M. & Newell D.G. (2000). – Genotyping of *Campylobacter* spp. *Appl. environ. Microbiol.*, **66** (1), 1-9.

69. World Health Organization (WHO) (2000). – The increasing incidence of human campylobacteriosis: report and proc. of a WHO Consultation of Experts, Copenhagen, 21-25 November. WHO/CDS/CSR/APH/2001.7. WHO, Geneva.

Rev. sci. tech. Off. int. Epiz., 2006, **25** (2), 595-606

Overview of food- and water-borne zoonotic parasites at the farm level

A.A. Gajadhar, W.B. Scandrett & L.B. Forbes

Centre for Foodborne & Animal Parasitology, Canadian Food Inspection Agency, Saskatoon Laboratory, Saskatchewan S7N 2R3, Canada

Summary
Zoonotic parasites found in food animals include a wide variety of protozoa, nematodes, trematodes, and cestodes. Many of these parasites are emerging or already occur globally due to changes in farming practices and the increased movement of animals, food, and people. Some of the emerging or ubiquitous parasites, including *Toxoplasma, Cryptosporidium, Trichinella*, and *Taenia*, present enormous risks to global food production and consumer health. The parasite life cycle stages, such as eggs, oocysts, and cysts, typically resist adverse temperatures, desiccation, natural irradiation, chemicals, and disinfectants that are commonly used for controlling bacteria and viruses. Other important parasites include trematodes such as *Clonorchis* and *Paragonimus*, which are transmitted via fish or crustaceans and cause serious human disease in specific regions of the world. The potential for global occurrence of these parasites is increasing. Control of zoonotic parasites at the producer level requires education and the development and implementation of effective measures to eliminate the contamination of agricultural water and feed with viable stages of parasites. Standardisation, implementation, and documentation of control measures should increase confidence in global food trade.

Keywords
Control – Cysticercosis – Food safety – Parasites – Taenia saginata – Taenia solium – Toxoplasma gondii –Trichinella – Zoonosis.

Introduction

Recent shifts in farming practices, increased transportation of animals, food and people, and global warming have created environments that facilitate the rapid and widespread dissemination of water- and food-borne zoonotic pathogens. Parasites are one group of pathogens that thrive under such environmental conditions, and they continue unabated to exploit the behavioural patterns of their hosts to further transmission among animals and to humans. However, awareness of these pathogens is generally lacking among producers, regulators, and consumers. Zoonotic parasites negatively impact human health and animal production. The globalised food market has raised issues regarding food- and water-borne parasites relevant to producers and consumers around the world. Research, education, and standardised control measures are required to provide consistently safe food for global trade. This paper provides an introduction to food- and

water-borne zoonotic parasites and the unique features of these pathogens that contribute to on-farm survival and contamination of food animals. The transmission dynamics and control of toxoplasmosis, trichinellosis, and cysticercosis are reviewed, as examples of a protozoon, a nematode, and a cestode, respectively.

The parasite group

Parasites belong to a large and diverse group of eukaryotic organisms and range in complexity and size from single cells to multi-segmented organisms. The major groups of zoonotic parasites include protozoa, nematodes (roundworms), trematodes or flukes (non-segmented flatworms), and cestodes or tapeworms (segmented flatworms). In addition to establishing habitats within and deriving nutritional support from animal and/or human hosts, parasites have a variety of transmission stages that allow them to withstand external conditions and survive in animal excreta, carrion, soil, water, feed, and invertebrate intermediate (for development) or transport hosts. Adaptive features of these stages enable a wide variety of transmission modes and facilitate contamination of food animals. The detection, identification, and destruction of these transmission stages in the environment present major obstacles to the development and execution of control programmes.

Parasite features adapted for transmission and survival

Micro-environments on animal farms are usually ideal for the long-term survival of parasite stages, such as eggs and oocysts, that are excreted by infected hosts. The protective structure of the parasite in the exogenous stages (i.e. stages outside of the host) allows many parasites to resist temperature extremes, desiccation, and irradiation, as well as chemical elements and disinfectants that are commonly used for controlling bacteria and viruses (17).

In many of the exogenous stages parasites are able to withstand freezing temperatures and are capable of over-wintering, and in some of these stages parasites are even capable of surviving freeze-thaw cycles. Transmission forms of protozoa remain viable under mild weather conditions for periods of 24 days (*Giardia* cysts) to more than six months (*Cryptosporidium* oocysts). In tropical regions, thermal death points of parasites typically occur above 40°C depending upon the period of exposure, the parasite species, and the transmission stage. Tapeworm eggs, for example, survive temperatures between – 50°C and 70°C but are destroyed when exposed to – 70°C or 100°C for brief periods of time (10). In warm weather, particularly in hot arid regions, many transmission stages of parasites are susceptible to desiccation and natural sources of irradiation. Direct sunlight can kill oocysts in 4 h to 8 h and ozone and ultraviolet-irradiation can be used to control various parasite stages, such as cysts, spores, oocysts, and eggs contaminating feed and water on farms (11, 36).

The transmission stages of most parasites are disseminated within the host's faeces. Spores and cysts are infective immediately on being excreted, while most eggs and oocysts require a period of time under suitable moisture and temperature conditions to develop and become infective.

The regular removal and proper disposal of faeces from animal pens are recommended for the control of parasites, particularly in intensive farming practices. Steps should also be taken to ensure that indirect faecal route transmission, such as via contaminated water and feed, does not occur. These aspects of food animal husbandry are particularly important since the types and concentrations of disinfectants commonly used for control of other microorganisms are rarely effective against parasites. Eggs of nematodes remain viable in 10% formalin and copper sulphate, and spores survive for brief periods of time in 70% ethanol, 0.1 N HCl, or 0.1 N NaOH (39). However, parasites in manure are eventually destroyed by heat, desiccation, or irradiation.

Free-ranging animals on farms are also susceptible to incursions of parasitic infections transmitted from wildlife. Such parasites are often zoonotic and have a broad host range, such as *Toxoplasma gondii* and *Cryptosporidium parvum*. In addition to serving as reservoir hosts, some wildlife species act as transport hosts. For example, migrating waterfowl have been shown to facilitate the distribution of zoonotic eggs, oocysts, and spores. Terrestrial insects and annelids, molluscs, shellfish, and other aquatic invertebrates have been implicated or suggested as important transport hosts for the bio-magnification and dispersal of zoonotic parasites among intermediate and final hosts (11, 18).

Parasitic infections of food animals at the farm level rely on a variety of host feeding behaviours, including garbage feeding, scavenging, and cannibalism. Specific examples of these are described below in the review of toxoplasmosis, cysticercosis, and trichinellosis.

Toxoplasmosis

Among food-borne pathogens, *Cryptosporidium, Cyclospora, Giardia*, and *Toxoplasma* are of great concern in global food production (5). These parasites are spread by water and contamination of ready-to-eat foods with oocysts or cysts, while *T. gondii* has additional transmission modes and vehicles involving food of animal origin (6).

Life cycle

Toxoplasma gondii is an intracellular coccidian parasite belonging to the phylum Apicomplexa (6, 7). A wide variety of terrestrial and aquatic vertebrate intermediate hosts become infected by ingesting oocysts excreted in the faeces of definitive hosts (felids) or by eating infected intermediate and definitive hosts containing tachyzoites and tissue cysts with bradyzoites (Fig. 1). Following ingestion of any of these stages, numerous tachyzoites are formed by repeated asexual multiplication (binary fission) within the host cells of most body tissues and fluids. Several days later, tachyzoites differentiate into tissue cysts, each of which mature and contain numerous bradyzoites.

Rev. sci. tech. Off. int. Epiz., **25** (2)

597

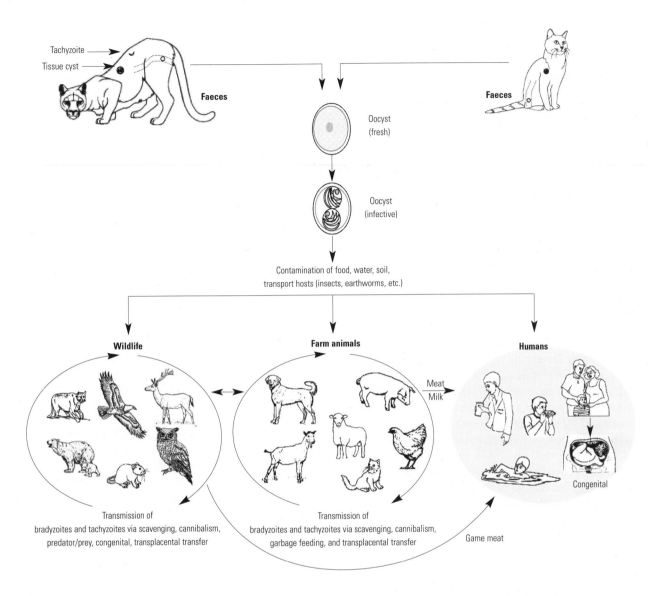

Fig. 1
Life cycle of *Toxoplasma gondii* showing transmission involving oocysts, tachyzoites, and bradyzoites (within tissue cysts) among feline definitive hosts, farm animals, wildlife, and humans

Three to ten days after ingesting tissue cysts (bradyzoites), > 13 days after ingesting tachyzoites, and > 18 days after ingesting oocysts (7) wild or domestic cats are capable of excreting millions of *T. gondii* oocysts daily. The oocysts are formed in the intestinal epithelial cells of cats following several generations of asexual multiplication (merogony) and a final phase of sexual replication (gametogony). Freshly passed oocysts require about one to five days of warmth and humidity to mature (sporulate) and become infective. Sporulated oocysts measure 11 µm by 13 µm and contain two sporocysts, each enclosing four sporozoites. Both mammals and birds serve as intermediate hosts and become infected by ingesting food contaminated with oocysts, bradyzoites in tissue cysts, or tachyzoites in animal organs and secretions, such as milk. Transplacental infection is an important mode of transmission in livestock and humans.

Disease and occurrence

Toxoplasmosis is an economically and medically important disease and is one of the most widespread of all zoonoses (1). Infection with *T. gondii* is common in both animals and humans and often remains latent, but infective, until the death of the host. Serious clinical disease is uncommon. When infection occurs in immunocompetent individuals it is self-limiting, and symptoms may include flu-like illness, swollen lymph nodes, fatigue, and joint and muscle pain. However, infection in immunosuppressed individuals is life threatening. Infection of naïve pregnant women or animals shortly before or after conception often results in congenital toxoplasmosis with consequences ranging from gross foetal abnormalities and spontaneous abortion to neonates being asymptomatic at birth but manifesting problems such as mental retardation and ocular disease much later in life.

598

Rev. sci. tech. Off. int. Epiz., **25** (2)

Toxoplasma gondii is considered the most common cause of retinochoroiditis worldwide, and it has been shown that 24% of people with ocular disease due to infection with *Toxoplasma* eventually become legally blind (2).

The prevalence of *T. gondii* infection among humans and animals varies greatly in different regions of the world. The parasite even occurs in harsh environments, such as the Arctic, but the prevalence of infection is lower than in regions with a cold but humid climate (42). Seroprevalence of human toxoplasmosis varies between 16% and 40% in North America and the United Kingdom and 50% to 80% in continental Europe and Latin America (1). Over the last three decades the prevalence of *T. gondii* infection in humans in many countries has declined markedly. However, the decline in infection and the corresponding rise in naïve populations have led to concerns about increased risks of human congenital toxoplasmosis (4). The prevalence of *T. gondii* infection differs between wildlife and farm animals. Among wild carnivores, the prevalence of infection is driven primarily by predator-prey behaviour and scavenging; whereas, husbandry practices influence the rate of infection among farmed animals. Pigs, sheep, and goats are more commonly infected than other livestock and represent a significant source of *T. gondii* for humans and other animals. Evidence of *T. gondii* infection in cattle and buffalo has been found only rarely (42). Cats and wild small mammals on farms have a high prevalence of infection and probably contribute to *T. gondii* infections in food animals raised outdoors. The increasing use of intensive indoor management practices has lowered the prevalence of *T. gondii* infection in pigs from 75% to < 10% in many countries and to < 1% in a few European countries (42).

Source and transmission

Transmission of *T. gondii* to animals occurs via ingestion of feed or water contaminated with sporulated oocysts and the consumption of meat, viscera, blood, milk, and other animal products containing tachyzoites and/or bradyzoites in tissue cysts. Wild and domestic cats play a central role in the epidemiology of *T. gondii* infections. Following primary infection, felines contaminate the environment with millions of oocysts, each of which is capable of infecting a new host. Infections in wildlife and farm animals can be established via cannibalism, scavenging, and garbage feeding. Although bradyzoites within tissue cysts are less resistant to environmental conditions than oocysts, they remain viable over a wide range of temperatures, including mild freezing conditions. Bradyzoites survive in carcasses or minced meat at 1°C to 4°C for three weeks but are usually killed at temperatures of − 12°C or lower (8). Heat also kills bradyzoites when the tissue cysts are subjected to temperatures of 67°C or higher. Transplacental infection occurs in animals, and although *Toxoplasma*-induced abortions in sheep are

common, the proportion of *T. gondii* infections in food animals due to vertical transmission is not known. Likewise, the role of rodents and other small mammals in maintaining *T. gondii* on farms is unclear. Nevertheless, wildlife remains a significant source of infection for food animals and humans (Fig. 1).

Diagnosis and control

In recognition of the public health importance of *T. gondii*, public health organisations, including the World Health Organization, encourage the collection of epidemiological data for use in developing comprehensive programmes to control *T. gondii* infections in food animals and humans. However, few countries have implemented active surveillance programmes for toxoplasmosis in humans, and food animals are rarely monitored (42). Differences in farming practices, animal populations and interactions, ecosystems and climates, as well as the epidemiological versatility and complexity of *T. gondii*, make it difficult to develop an effective global control strategy. For example, *T. gondii* infections in some livestock species can be prevented by the elimination of cats from the environment; although this is possible in controlled biosecure operations, it is not feasible in most parts of the world. Furthermore, the increasing practice of outdoor housing of livestock in Europe and North America is an added challenge for the control of *T. gondii* on farms. Outdoor housing has been shown to be associated with an increase in the rate of *T. gondii* infections in animals (26). Organic farming practices present additional difficulties in the control of *T. gondii* by limiting the use of several control methods. The availability of resources and technology in many developing countries also limits the relevance of a single global control strategy.

Numerous methods have been developed for the detection of *T. gondii* in the environment and animals, but the reliability of many of these techniques is unclear. Diagnostic approaches include serology, parasite isolation and identification by traditional parasitological methods, bioassays, polymerase chain reaction (PCR) and other molecular assays (7). Selection of the appropriate direct or indirect method of detection is important in specific situations, such as surveillance, disease outbreak investigations, and routine diagnostics. The use of properly validated assays in laboratories operating as part of a recognised quality assurance system for testing parasites is essential for producing reliable data for use in control systems (16).

Trichinellosis

Trichinellosis is a disease that affects animals and humans and is caused by small intramuscular larval nematodes of the genus *Trichinella*. Eleven genotypes (T1-T11) are currently recognised, eight of which have species status (Table I). Infective larvae are transferred from host to host by the consumption of raw or undercooked meat. Historically, human trichinellosis has been associated with the consumption of meat from *Trichinella*-infected swine, and regulations to detect and control trichinellosis in pigs have been in place in many countries for over 100 years. Consequently, human trichinellosis associated with pork slaughtered in abattoirs operating under modern inspection systems is rare. However, *Trichinella* infection in livestock and wildlife remains common in different regions of the world and the potential for transmission to humans makes this disease a significant human zoonosis (9, 15).

Life cycle

Trichinella have a simple direct life cycle with all stages occurring within one host. Following ingestion of infected raw or undercooked meat, larvae are released by digestion of the meat in the stomach and mature in the small intestine within a few days. Adult female worms survive and shed larvae for about two to three weeks. The newborn larvae enter the blood circulatory system and invade skeletal muscle where most of the genotypes become encapsulated (except T4, T10 and T11) and survive for three to five years or, in some cases, for longer periods of time until the infected meat is consumed by a new host. The tongue, diaphragm, and masseter muscles of the host often harbour higher numbers of larvae than other muscle sites, but these predilection locations may vary according to the host species (25). Clinical disease is rarely observed in naturally infected animals. The severity of human trichinellosis is dependent upon the number of infective larvae ingested, the genotype of *Trichinella*, and the immune status of the host. Small numbers of larvae usually result in asymptomatic infections. Clinical signs are specific to the stage of infection and may include diarrhoea and/or gastrointestinal upset, periorbital and facial oedema, myalgia, fever, conjunctivitis, photophobia, headache, and skin rash. Myocarditis, endocarditis, encephalitis or meningitis, if these symptoms occur, are serious and may be life-threatening (28).

Occurrence

Members of the genus *Trichinella* have a worldwide distribution, except for the Antarctic (Table I). Domestic animals are infected by deliberate or unintentional feeding of raw tissues containing the parasite or by scavenging infected carcasses of domestic or wild animals. In poorly managed farm operations, domestic cycles involving pigs and rats can readily be established. Human disease associated with the ingestion of horsemeat, dog meat, and farmed wild boar meat is frequently reported, particularly in Europe and Asia (34). In addition, trichinellosis is common in many carnivorous and omnivorous mammalian wildlife populations worldwide, and animals such as bears, foxes, and walruses are frequently the source of disease in humans (13). It has been estimated that as many as 11 million people are infected worldwide, and it is recognised that significant underreporting occurs for reasons relating to test methodology and health care infrastructure (9). The recently recognised non-encapsulated species of *Trichinella* that infects pigs and humans could be missed by traditional tissue compression techniques that rely on capsule formation for detection.

Table I
Genotype, biological characteristics and geographical distribution of *Trichinella* species

Genotype and species	Host	Capsule	Freeze tolerance	Geographical distribution
T1 – *Trichinella spiralis*	Mammal	Yes	None	Worldwide
T2 – *Trichinella nativa*	Mammal	Yes	High	Worldwide
T3 – *Trichinella britovi*	Mammal	Yes	Moderate	Europe, Asia, west Africa
T4 – *Trichinella pseudospiralis*	Mammal, bird	No	None	Worldwide
T5 – *Trichinella murrelli*	Mammal	Yes	Moderate	North America
T6 [a]	Mammal	Yes	High	North America
T7 – *Trichinella nelsoni*	Mammal	Yes	None	East Africa
T8 [b]	Mammal	Yes	Unknown	South Africa, Namibia
T9 [b]	Mammal	Yes	Unknown	Japan
T10 – *Trichinella papuae*	Mammal, reptile	No	Unknown	New Guinea
T11 – *Trichinella zimbabwensis*	Mammal, reptile	No	Unknown	Zimbabwe

a) T6 is closely related to *Trichinella nativa*
b) T8 and T9 are closely related to *Trichinella britovi*

600

Rev. sci. tech. Off. int. Epiz., **25** (2)

Diagnosis and control

Methods for the detection of trichinellosis include artificial digestion of muscle tissue to release larvae, compression techniques to visualise cysts in muscle (trichinoscopy), serology, PCR, histology, and bioassay. The digestion assay allows the intensity of infection to be quantified and is the most sensitive technique for testing individual animal carcasses (19). Single animals may also be tested using muscle biopsies examined by either digestion assay or trichinoscopy, but quantification of parasite load is not reliable due to the small sample size. The identity of recovered larvae can be confirmed by molecular genotyping (PCR). Although generally reliable for herd testing, serological tests may not detect all infected animals, particularly animals in the early stages of infection, and are therefore not recommended for use in testing individual carcasses for food safety purposes.

Control measures for trichinellosis can be instituted at the producer, abattoir (slaughter and processing), or consumer level. Appropriate identification of animals and products during transport (farm-abattoir, abattoir-marketplace) is necessary for trace-back purposes and is an important component of on-farm certification programmes for producing *Trichinella*-free pigs.

On-farm control at the producer level requires preventing access of domestic animals to any source of raw muscle tissues. Uncooked animal parts may be fed intentionally as a high protein finishing ration prior to slaughter or unintentionally as a cheap food source in the form of household or commercial (restaurant or food processing) garbage. Human trichinellosis has frequently been associated with pork and horsemeat produced using such practices. Poorly managed or primitive farming conditions may create opportunities for cannibalism, predation, and the scavenging of carrion. Lack of rodent control can result in the carcasses of infected small mammals, such as rats, becoming accidentally incorporated into mixed feed. A swine-rat cycle of infection is well known. Prevention of garbage feeding, rodent control, and enhanced management practices are required to break the chain of infection at the producer level (19). Although many countries have legislation regulating some aspects of on-farm control, such as garbage feeding, strict regulations, and enforcement, procedures are required to achieve and maintain an effective integrated system at the producer level. A detailed list of good production practices for use in an on-farm certification programme for pork has been described (35). The programme includes guidelines for animal source, food source, food storage, rodent control, wildlife control, garbage feeding, carcass disposal, general hygiene and sanitation (solid waste, spilled feed, etc.), animal arrival/departure documentation, and detailed and updated record keeping. Additionally, regular audits are conducted and an official non-industry regulatory body to govern the programme exists. Appropriate quality assured laboratory programmes are recommended for testing and surveillance to monitor and verify control programmes (14).

Abattoir control involving digestion testing of individual carcasses for food safety purposes is recommended in endemic areas (19). Freezing for food safety purposes should be used with caution in areas where freeze-tolerant genotypes exist (Table I). A certified and actively monitored *Trichinella*-free herd or region could reduce or eliminate control procedures at the abattoir level. Regular sero-surveys and digestion testing of a representative proportion of slaughtered animals for surveillance purposes is required in support of the control programmes (45).

Consumer control includes thoroughly heating meat or meat products to 71°C before consumption. In the case of traditional preparations that are consumed raw or undercooked, the source meat should be acquired from an assured safe supplier. Consumer education and a high degree of consumer responsibility are required for meat obtained from wildlife and farm animals that are slaughtered privately.

Cysticercosis

Cysticercosis is a parasitic disease characterised by infection of the muscle with larvae of the cestodes *Taenia solium*, *T. saginata*, and *T. saginata asiatica*. Historically, the adult tapeworms, found in the intestine of humans, were assigned to the genus *Taenia* and the larvae (cysticerci), found in pigs or cattle, to the genus *Cysticercus*. Consequently, *T. solium* cysticerci became known as *Cysticercus cellulosae* and *T. saginata* cysticerci as *C. bovis*. *Taenia saginata asiatica*, described more recently, has the same name for both the larval and adult stages. Both bovine and porcine cysticercoses are recognised worldwide as the cause of human taeniosis (taeniasis). *Taenia solium* also causes human neurological disease (neurocysticercosis). Due to the public health implications of taeniosis and neurocysticercosis, and the negative aesthetics of infested meat, cysticercosis of cattle and swine causes significant economic loss through condemnation of infected meat and offal and trade restrictions for endemic regions.

Life cycle

Taenia tapeworms have an indirect life cycle and are relatively host specific. Humans are the only natural hosts of the adult tapeworms. The tapeworms measure up to several metres in length and consist of an anterior scolex

Rev. sci. tech. Off. int. Epiz., **25** (2)

601

for attachment to the intestinal mucosa and a chain of progressively maturing hermaphroditic reproductive segments, or proglottids. Thick walled eggs released from mature gravid proglottids are approximately 30 μm to 45 μm in diameter and morphologically indistinguishable among species. The eggs are discharged from infected humans spontaneously or in the faeces. Upon ingestion by a suitable intermediate host, an oncosphere hatches from the egg and eventually develops in the muscle of the host into a cysticercus, which can remain viable for up to several years. The cysticercus consists of a larval tapeworm (with a fluid-filled bladder and invaginated scolex) contained within a connective tissue capsule (cyst) which is oval in shape, and up to 1 cm long. The intermediate hosts for *T. saginata* and *T. saginata asiatica* cysticerci are domestic cattle and swine, respectively. Reindeer have also proven to be suitable intermediate hosts for *T. saginata* (27). In cattle, *T. saginata* cysticerci are found mostly in the tissues of the cardiac and skeletal musculature, whereas *T. saginata asiatica* cysticerci localise on the serosal surface and within the parenchyma of the liver of pigs. The normal intermediate host of *T. solium* is domestic swine, although humans, and occasionally dogs, can serve as intermediate hosts. *Taenia solium* cysticerci localise in the tissues of the tongue, skeletal muscle, subcutis, and central nervous system of pigs. Human consumption of infected pork or beef completes the cycle.

Disease and occurrence

Cysticercosis in cattle does not typically cause detectable disease, but swine with heavy infections can manifest clinically. Human taeniosis is often asymptomatic or manifests as mild non-specific gastrointestinal illness. However, *T. solium* human cysticercosis can result in potentially fatal neurocysticercosis and is the most common cause of acquired epilepsy.

There are no accurate prevalence data on a global scale for any *Taenia* species. Both *T. saginata* and *T. solium* occur worldwide, with the highest occurrence in developing regions where poor sanitation and animal husbandry, as well as some cultural practices, facilitate parasite transmission among hosts. Only sporadic cases of *T. saginata* taeniosis and epizootic outbreaks of bovine cysticercosis occur in North America and other non-endemic areas. *Taenia solium* taeniosis and neurocysticercosis 'imported' from endemic regions are increasingly recognised, and endemic foci resulting from immigration are now established in the United States of America, with approximately 1,000 cases reported annually (44). Neurocysticercosis is an emerging global disease causing an estimated 50,000 deaths annually (37).

Distribution of *T. saginata asiatica* is believed to be limited mostly to South-East Asia and Korea. Prevalence estimates

for this species must be interpreted with caution, however, as the distinction between *T. saginata* and *T. saginata asiatica* has only been recently recognised.

Source and transmission

A person harbouring a single tapeworm can contaminate the environment with up to half a million eggs per day over the course of an infection, which, if left untreated, can persist for years. Eggs can be further disseminated by water, wind, scavenging birds (e.g. gulls feeding on raw sewage), oribatid mites, earthworms, or inanimate objects, such as boots or farm machinery. Infective eggs can persist under a variety of environmental conditions. As with most parasite environmental stages, cool and moist conditions favour long-term survival. *Taenia saginata* eggs can over-winter on pasture and can survive for several months in sewage and sludge, as well as in fresh, brackish, or salt water. The eggs are also resistant to most conventional chemical disinfecting agents (33).

Transmission to livestock occurs via ingestion of food or water contaminated with infective eggs. Scavenged human faeces are a major source of infection in pigs. Parasite transmission from humans to pigs is facilitated by the common practice in many endemic rural regions of allowing pigs to roam free in areas without human latrines. Since cattle do not intentionally consume human faeces, bovine cysticercosis occurs via inadvertent ingestion of contaminated feedstuffs or water, including pasture fertilised with human sewage.

Diagnosis and control

Globalisation poses an increasing threat of incursions of cysticercoses and taenioses via the immigration of people and importation of animals and animal products and potentially contaminated produce or other fomites from endemic regions. Eradication of these infections in humans and livestock is possible, as pigs and cattle are the only significant reservoir of cysticercosis, humans can be easily and inexpensively treated with anthelmintics, and education about the parasite life cycle and mitigating measures (such as proper hygiene and latrine use, preventing access of livestock to human faeces, and thorough cooking or freezing of meat) will reduce overall parasite transmission (12).

Detection of cysticercosis in cattle and pigs usually occurs *post mortem*, although pigs with heavy infections may be presumptively diagnosed *ante mortem* by observation and/or palpation of cysts in the tongue. Many countries regulate *post mortem* screening for cysticercosis, requiring examination of the so-called 'predilection sites'. Affected carcasses are condemned or treated by cooking or freezing

602

Rev. sci. tech. Off. int. Epiz., **25** (2)

to kill the parasite. Such screening is insensitive, particularly for lightly infected carcasses (38). Dead or dying cysticerci elicit inflammatory lesions that are easier to detect than viable parasites. Since carcasses can harbour both viable (infective) and degenerated cysticerci, detection of degenerated cysts is still significant. However, definitive diagnosis of degenerated lesions using gross examination or histology is often difficult. A recently developed immunohistochemical assay for bovine cysticercus excretory-secretory antigen will help in this regard (32). Molecular methods have been adapted for detecting cysticerci but require further validation (23). Although commercially available enzyme-linked immunosorbent (ELISA) and enzyme-linked immuno-transfer blot (EITB) assays have high sensitivity and specificity when used on human serum or cerebrospinal fluid samples, reliability has been low for samples collected from naturally infected animals (41, 43). Such assays have value as epidemiological tools for screening herds for cysticercosis but not for assessing individual animals.

Reliable methods for recovering *Taenia* eggs from various environmental matrices are not available. In most sporadic outbreaks of bovine cysticercosis in low prevalence regions, such as North America, a definitive source of the infection is not identified. Even if a particular feed or water source is suspected, processing of relatively large volumes of test samples with low level contamination is problematic. Modified flotation methods have been attempted, but the high specific gravity of *Taenia* eggs and confounding debris in the assayed matrix decreases the sensitivity of detection (40). Eggs of the taeniid family cannot be speciated based on morphology, and there are no baseline data available for levels of environmental contamination with taeniid species from other infected domestic animals or wildlife species. Reliable molecular methods for detecting low numbers of *Taenia* eggs are still being developed (20, 31). Since *Taenia* eggs are resistant to many environmental conditions and most practical and conventional chemical treatments, efforts should be aimed at preventing environmental contamination. If sewage must be used as fertiliser, measures should be taken to reduce the number of viable eggs in the applied sludge (3).

Anthelmintic treatment of livestock is effective but does not quickly or reliably eliminate cysticerci and is not economically feasible for cattle (21). Vaccines hold more promise but are not yet commercially available. Recombinant subunit vaccines based on oncosphere antigens have proven highly effective in protecting cattle and pigs from experimental challenge with *T. saginata* and

T. solium eggs, respectively (29, 22). A synthetic peptide vaccine against *T. solium* cysticercosis has been shown to significantly reduce the prevalence and intensity of natural infections in pigs (24).

Other parasites

Other zoonotic parasites also infect domestic or wild animals, particularly animals in aquatic environments. Among the nematodes, *Anisakis simplex*, *Pseudoterranova decipiens*, and *Gnathostoma* species are fish-borne, while *Angiostrongylus cantonensis* is transmitted by fresh water molluscs, crab, and shrimp (1). Although humans are not normal hosts for these parasites, infection can result in serious disease. Many species of fresh water fish in Asia and elsewhere serve as intermediate hosts for several trematodes that use humans and other mammals as primary definitive hosts (30). These parasites, which include *Clonorchis sinensis* (Chinese liver fluke), *Heterophyes heterophyes, Metagonimus yokogawi*, and *Opistorchis* spp., develop in the intestine or bile duct of humans. *Paragonimus westermani*, another trematode that infects humans, causes pulmonary disease following the ingestion of freshwater crab and crayfish containing the infective stage (metacercaria). Since specific aquatic invertebrates on fish farms serve as intermediate hosts, control of these hosts may be a useful strategy for reducing trematode zoonoses.

Many zoonotic parasites use water as a vehicle for transmission to their definitive or intermediate hosts, either directly or via aquatic plants, invertebrates, and/or fish. For example, large numbers of animals become infected with *T. gondii* and *Taenia* spp. when they consume common-source water infected with oocysts and eggs, respectively. Implementation of on-farm control measures to eliminate the contamination of agricultural water with human faeces is a key factor in the control of many zoonotic parasitic infections.

Acknowledgements

Dr Murray Lankester reviewed a draft of the manuscript and provided many valuable suggestions, and Ms Doreen Kyler provided excellent support services for several aspects of the manual preparation, including the illustration for Figure 1.

■

Rev. sci. tech. Off. int. Epiz., **25** (2)

603

Un aperçu des parasitoses zoonotiques d'origine alimentaire ou hydrique présentes dans les élevages

A.A. Gajadhar, W.B. Scandrett & L.B. Forbes

Résumé
Parmi les parasites présents dans les denrées alimentaires d'origine animale, on retrouve une grande variété de protozoaires, de nématodes, de trématodes et de cestodes. L'émergence ou la distribution mondiale de la plupart de ces parasites sont liées à la transformation des pratiques d'élevage et à la mobilité croissante des animaux, des personnes et des produits alimentaires. Certains de ces parasites émergents ou ubiquistes, notamment *Toxoplasma, Cryptosporidium, Trichinella* et *Taenia* représentent une menace considérable pour la production alimentaire et la santé des consommateurs au niveau mondial. À chacun des stades du cycle parasitaire (œufs, oocystes, kystes), la plupart des parasites résistent aux traitements thermiques, par dessiccation, par radiation, ainsi qu'aux produits chimiques et aux désinfectants habituellement utilisés pour inactiver les bactéries et les virus. Autres parasites importants, les trématodes du genre *Clonorchis* et *Paragonimus* sont présents dans les poissons et les fruits de mer et occasionnent chez l'homme des maladies graves bien que circonscrites à certaines régions du globe. Le risque d'extension de l'aire de répartition de ces parasites au niveau mondial va en augmentant. La maîtrise des parasitoses zoonotiques au niveau des élevages passe par une meilleure formation des éleveurs et par la conception et la mise en place de mesures efficaces visant à empêcher que l'eau et les aliments distribués aux animaux dans les exploitations ne soient contaminés par des parasites parvenus à un stade viable. La normalisation, la mise en œuvre et la diffusion d'informations sur les mesures de prophylaxie devraient améliorer la confiance dans le commerce mondial de denrées alimentaires.

Mots-clés
Cysticercose – Parasites – Prophylaxie – Sécurité sanitaire des aliments – Taenia saginata – Taenia solium – Toxoplasma gondii – Trichinella – Zoonose.

■

Parásitos zoonóticos transmitidos por los alimentos y el agua en las granjas

A.A. Gajadhar, W.B. Scandrett & L.B. Forbes

Resumen
Los parásitos zoonóticos que se encuentran en animales para consumo incluyen una amplia variedad de protozoarios, nematodos, trematodos y céstodes. Muchos de estos son parásitos emergentes, o que aparecen en todas partes del mundo debido al incremento de los movimientos de animales, alimentos y personas, así como a la evolución de las prácticas pecuarias. Algunos de los parásitos emergentes o ubicuos, incluidos *Toxoplasma, Cryptosporidium, Trichinella* y *Taenia*, representan enormes amenazas para la producción de

alimentos y la salud de los consumidores mundiales. Habitualmente, las distintas etapas del ciclo biológico de los parásitos – huevo, ooquiste y quiste – resisten a las temperaturas elevadas, la desecación, la radiación natural, los productos químicos y los desinfectantes que suelen utilizarse para controlar bacterias y virus. Otros importantes parásitos incluyen los trematodos, como *Clonorchis* y *Paragonimus*, transmitidos por los peces y crustáceos y que provocan enfermedades graves a los seres humanos de determinadas regiones. La posibilidad de que se extiendan por todo el mundo es cada vez mayor. Para controlar los parásitos zoonóticos en el nivel de la producción es preciso formar a sus responsables y, también, formular y aplicar medidas eficaces para eliminar sus etapas viables del agua y los alimentos destinados a los animales. La estandarización, implementación y documentación de medidas de control, debería aumentar la confianza en el comercio mundial de alimentos.

Palabras clave

Cisticercosis – Control – Inocuidad de los alimentos – Parásito – Taenia saginata – Taenia solium – Toxoplasma gondii – Trichinella – Zoonosis.

■

References

1. Acha P.N. & Szyfres B. (2003). – Zoonoses and communicable diseases common to man and animals, 3rd Ed., Vol. 3, Parasitoses. Pan American Health Organization, Washington, DC.

2. Bosch-Driessen L.E., Berendschot T.T., Ongkosuwito J.V. & Rothova A. (2002). – Ocular toxoplasmosis: clinical features and prognosis of 154 patients. *Ophthalmology*, **109**, 869-878.

3. Cabaret J., Geerts S., Madeline M., Ballandonne C. & Barbier D. (2002). – The use of urban sewage sludge on pastures: the cysticercosis threat. *Vet. Res.*, **33** (5), 575-597.

4. Cook A.J., Gilbert R.E., Buffolano W., Zufferey J., Petersen E., Jenum P.A., Foulon W., Semprini A.E. & Dunn D.T. (2000). – Sources of *Toxoplasma* infection in pregnant women: European multicentre case-control study. European Research Network on Congenital Toxoplasmosis. *BJM*, **321**, 142-147.

5. Dawson D. (2005). – Foodborne protozoan parasites. *Int. J. Food Microbiol.*, **103**, 207-227.

6. Dubey J.P. (1993). – *Toxoplasma, Neospora, Sarcocystis*, and other tissue cyst-forming coccidia of humans and animals. *In* Parasitic protozoa (J.P. Kreier, ed.), 2nd Ed., Vol. 6. Academic Press, London, 1-158.

7. Dubey J.P. (2004). – Toxoplasmosis – a waterborne zoonosis. *In* Waterborne zoonotic parasites (A.A. Gajadhar, ed.). *Vet. Parasitol.*, **126** (special issue), 57-71.

8. Dubey J.P., Kotula A.W., Sharar A., Andrews C.D. & Lindsay D.S. (1990). – Effect of high temperature on infectivity of *Toxoplasma gondii* tissue cysts in pork. *J. Parasitol.*, **76**, 201-204.

9. Dupouy-Camet J. (2000). – Trichinellosis: a worldwide zoonosis. *In Trichinella* and trichinellosis (A.A. Gajadhar & H.R. Gamble, eds). *Vet. Parasitol.*, **93** (special issue), 191-200.

10. Eckert J., Gottstein B., Heath D. & Liu F.J. (2001). – Prevention of echinococcosis in humans and safety precautions. *In* WHO-OIE Manual on echinococcosis in humans and animals: a public health problem of global concern. OIE, Paris, 238-247.

11. Fayer R. (2004). – *Cryptosporidium*: a waterborne zoonotic parasite. *In* Waterborne zoonotic parasites (A.A. Gajadhar, ed.). *Vet. Parasitol.*, **126** (special issue), 37-56.

12. Flisser A., Sarti E., Lightowlers M. & Schantz P. (2003). – Neurocysticercosis: regional status, epidemiology, impact and control measures in the Americas. *Acta trop.*, **87** (1), 43-51.

13. Forbes L.B. (2000). – The occurrence and ecology of *Trichinella* in marine mammals. *In Trichinella* and trichinellosis (A.A. Gajadhar & H.R. Gamble, eds). *Vet. Parasitol.*, **93** (special issue), 321-334.

Rev. sci. tech. Off. int. Epiz., **25** (2)

605

14. Forbes L.B., Scandrett W.B. & Gajadhar A.A. (2005). – A program to accredit laboratories for reliable testing of pork and horsemeat for *Trichinella. Vet. Parasitol.*, **132**, 173-177.

15. Gajadhar A.A. & Gamble H.R. (2000). – Historical perspectives and current global challenges of *Trichinella* and trichinellosis. *In Trichinella* and trichinellosis (A.A. Gajadhar & H.R. Gamble, eds). *Vet. Parasitol.*, **93** (special issue), 181-189.

16. Gajadhar A.A. & Forbes L.B. (2002). – An internationally recognized quality assurance system for diagnostic parasitology in animal health and food safety, with example data on trichinellosis. *Vet. Parasitol.*, **103**, 133-140.

17. Gajadhar A.A. & Allen J.R. (2004). – Factors contributing to the public health and economic importance of waterborne zoonotic parasites. *In* Waterborne zoonotic parasites (A.A. Gajadhar, ed.). *Vet. Parasitol.*, **126** (special issue), 3-14.

18. Gajadhar A.A., Measures L., Forbes L., Kapel C. & Dubey J.P. (2004). – Experimental *Toxoplasma gondii* infection in grey seals (*Halichoerus grypus*). *J. Parasitol.*, **90**, 255-259.

19. Gamble H.R., Bessonov A.S., Cuperlovic K., Gajadhar A.A., van Knapen F., Noeckler K., Schenone H. & Zhu X. (2000). – International Commission on trichinellosis: recommendations on methods for the control of *Trichinella* in domestic and wild animals intended for human consumption. *In Trichinella* and trichinellosis (A.A. Gajadhar & H.R. Gamble, eds). *Vet. Parasitol.*, **93** (special issue), 393-408.

20. Gonzalez L.M., Montero E., Harrison L.J.S., Parkhouse R.M.E. & Garate T. (2000). – Differential diagnosis of *Taenia saginata* and *Taenia solium* infection by PCR. *Clin. Microbiol.*, **38** (2), 737-744.

21. Gonzalez A.E., Gavidia C., Falcon N., Bernal T., Verastegui M., Garcia H.H., Gilman R.H. & Tsang V.C.W. (2001). – Protection of pigs with cysticercosis from further infections after treatment with oxfendazole. *Am. J. trop. Med. Hyg.*, **65** (1), 15-18.

22. Gonzalez A.E., Gauci C.G., Barber D., Gilman R.H., Tsang V.C.W., Garcia H.H., Verastegui M. & Lightowlers M.W. (2005). – Vaccination of pigs to control human neurocysticercosis. *Am. J. trop. Med. Hyg.*, **72** (6), 837-839.

23. Harrison L.J.S., Garate T., Bryce D.M., Gonzalez L.M., Foster-Cuevas M., Wamae L.W., Onyango-Abuje J.A. & Parkhouse R.M.E. (2005). – Ag-ELISA and PCR for monitoring the vaccination of cattle against *Taenia saginata* cysticercosis using an oncospheral adhesion protein (HP6) with surface and secreted localization. *Trop. anim. Hlth Prod.*, **37** (2), 103-120.

24. Huerta M., De Aluga A.S., Fragoso G., Toledo A., Villalobos N., Hernandez M., Gevorkian G., Acero G., Diaz A., Alvarez I., Avila R., Beltran C., Garcia G., Martinez J.J., Larralde C. & Sciutto E. (2002). – Synthetic peptide vaccine against *Taenia solium* pig cysticercosis: successful vaccination in a controlled field trial in rural Mexico. *Vaccine*, **20**, 262-266.

25. Kapel C.M.O. (2000). – Host diversity and biological characteristics of the *Trichinella* genotypes and their effect on transmisson. *In Trichinella* and trichinellosis (A.A. Gajadhar & H.R. Gamble, eds). *Vet. Parasitol.*, **93** (special issue), 263-278.

26. Kijlstra A., Eissen O., Cornelissen J., Munniksma K., Eijck I. & Kortbeek T. (2004). – *Toxoplasma gondii* infection in animal-friendly pig production systems. *Investigative Ophthalmol. visual Sci.*, **45** (9), 3165-3169.

27. Kirichek V.S. (1985). – Peculiarities of the biology of *Taenia saginata* and of the disease that it causes. *Veterinariya (Kiev) or (Moscow)*, **2**, 50-52.

28. Kociecka W. (2000). – Trichinellosis: human disease, diagnosis and treatment. *In Trichinella* and trichinellosis (A.A. Gajadhar & H.R. Gamble, eds). *Vet. Parasitol.*, **93** (special issue), 365-383.

29. Lightowlers M.W., Rolfe R. & Gauci C.G. (1996). – *Taenia saginata*: vaccination against cysticercosis in cattle with recombinant oncosphere antigens. *Experim. Parasitol.*, **84**, 330-338.

30. Nithiuthai S., Anantaphruti M.T., Waikagul J. & Gajadhar A. (2004). – Waterborne zoonotic helminthiases. *In* Waterborne zoonotic parasites (A.A. Gajadhar, ed.). *Vet. Parasitol.*, **126** (special issue), 167-193.

31. Nunes C.M., Dias A.K.K., Dias F.E.F., Aoki S.M., De Paula H.B., Lima L.G.F. & Garcia J.F. (2005). – *Taenia saginata*: differential diagnosis of human taeniasis by polymerase chain reaction-restriction fragment length polymorphism assay. *Experim. Parasitol.*, **110** (4), 412-415.

32. Ogunremi O., Macdonald G., Geerts S. & Brandt J. (2004). – Diagnosis of *Taenia saginata* cysticercosis by immunohistochemical test on formalin-fixed and paraffin-embedded bovine lesions. *J. vet. diagn. Invest.*, **16** (5), 438-441.

33. Pawlowski Z.S. (1994). – *Taeniasis and cysticercosis. In* Foodborne disease handbook (Y.H. Hiu, J.R. Gorham, K.D. Murrel & D.O. Cliver, eds), Vol. 2. Marcel Dekker, Inc., New York, 199-254.

34. Pozio E. (2005). – The broad spectrum of *Trichinella* hosts: from cold to warm-blooded animals. *Vet. Parasitol.*, **132**, 3-11.

35. Pyburn D.G., Gamble H.R., Wagstrom E.A., Anderson L.A. & Miller L.E. (2005). – Trichinae certification in the United States pork industry. *Vet. Parasitol.*, **132**, 179-183.

36. Quintero-Betancourt W. & Rose J.B. (2004). – Drinking water processes for removal of *Cryptosporidium* and *Giardia. In* Waterborne zoonotic parasites (A.A. Gajadhar, ed.). *Vet. Parasitol.*, **126** (special issue), 219-234.

606

Rev. sci. tech. Off. int. Epiz., **25** (2)

37. Roman G., Sotelo J., Brutto O.D., Flisser A., Dumas M., Wadia N., Botero D., Cruz M., Garcia H., De Bittencourt P.R.M., Trelles L., Arriagada C., Lorenzana P., Nash T.E. & Spina-Franca A. (2000). – A proposal to declare neurocysticercosis an international reportable disease. *Bull. WHO*, **78** (3), 399-406.

38. Saini P.K., Webert D.W. & McCaskey P.C. (1997). – Food safety and regulatory aspects of cattle and swine cysticercosis. *J. Food Protec.*, **60** (4), 447-453.

39. Santillana-Hayat M., Sarfati C., Fournier S., Chau F., Porcher R., Molina J.-M. & Derouin F. (2002). – Effects of chemical and physical agents on viability and infectivity of *Encephalitozoon intestinalis* determined by cell culture and flow cytometry. *Antimicrob. Agents Chemother.*, **46** (6), 2049-2051.

40. Scandrett W.B. & Gajadhar A.A. (2004). – Recovery of putative taeniid eggs from silt in water associated with an outbreak of bovine cysticercosis. *Can. Vet. J.*, **45**, 758-760.

41. Sciutto E., Martinez J.J., Villalobos N.M., Hernandez M., Jose M.V., Beltran C., Rodarte F., Flores I., Bobadilla J.R., Fragoso G., Parkhouse M.E., Harrison L.J.S. & De Aluja A.S. (1998). – Limitations of current diagnostic procedures for the diagnosis of *Taenia solium* cysticercosis in rural pigs. *Vet. Parasitol.*, **79**, 299-313.

42. Tenter A., Heckeroth A. & Weiss L. (2000). – *Toxoplasma gondii*: from animals to humans. *Int. J. Parasitol.*, **30**, 1217-1258.

43. Van Kerckhoven I., Vansteenkiste W., Claes M., Geerts S. & Brandt J. (1998). – Improved detection of circulating antigen in cattle infected with *Taenia saginata* metacestodes. *Vet. Parasitol.*, **76**, 269-274.

44. White A.C. (2000). – Neurocysticercosis: updates on epidemiology, pathogenesis, diagnosis, and management. *Annu. Rev. Med.*, **51**, 187-206.

45. World Organisation for Animal Health (OIE) (2004) – Terrestrial Animal Health Code, 14 Ed. OIE, Paris, 110-111.

Rev. sci. tech. Off. int. Epiz., 2006, **25** (2), 607-625

Food safety hazards that occur during the production stage: challenges for fish farming and the fishing industry

T. Håstein [1], B. Hjeltnes [1], A. Lillehaug [1], J. Utne Skåre [1], M. Berntssen [2] & A.K. Lundebye [2]

(1) National Veterinary Institute, P.O. Box 8156 Dep., N-0033 Oslo, Norway
(2) National Institute of Nutrition and Seafood Research (NIFES), P.O. Box 2029, 5817 Bergen, Norway

Summary
Seafood derived from wild fish as well as farmed fish has always been an important source of protein in the human diet. On a global scale, fish and fish products are the most important source of protein and it is estimated that more than 30% of fish for human consumption comes from aquaculture.
The first part of this paper outlines the hazards and challenges associated with handling fish during farming and capture. The authors describe infectious agents that cause disease in fish as well as humans, zoonotic agents, intoxications due to bacteria and allergies caused by the consumption of fish.
Although only a few infectious agents in fish are able to infect humans, some exceptions exist that may result in fatalities. However, the greatest risk to human health is due to the consumption of raw or insufficiently processed fish and fish products.
The second part of the paper considers environmental contaminants in seafood that may pose a risk to human health, such as medicinal products and residues associated with aquaculture, persistent lipophilic organic compounds and metals (methyl-mercury, organotin).
The authors include an updated overview of the various factors associated with farmed and captured fish that may cause risks to human health after consumption. Moreover, they discuss the challenges (in the widest sense) associated with handling fish during capture and farming, as well as those encountered during processing.

Keywords
Allergy – Aquaculture – Capture fishery – Contaminant – Fish – Fish farming – Fish handling – Fish processing – Food safety – Metal – Persistent lipophilic organic compounds – Residue – Seafood – Wild fish – Zoonotic agent.

Introduction

Over the past three decades, aquaculture has developed to become the fastest growing food-producing sector in the world. A large proportion of fish products come from small-scale producers in developing countries or low-income-deficit countries. More than 80% of global aquaculture products are produced in fresh water. From its early development in Asia, aquaculture has undergone huge development and is today highly diversified.

Aquaculture consists of a broad spectrum of systems, from small ponds to large-scale, highly intensified commercial systems. The production of Atlantic salmon (*Salmo salar*) in marine net pens is one example of an intensified commercial system that has developed during the last 20 to 30 years.

The main aquaculture products are finfish, crustaceans, molluscs and aquatic plants. The Food and Agriculture Organization (FAO) of the United Nations has estimated

Rev. sci. tech. Off. int. Epiz., **25** (2)

that more than 30% of all fish used for human consumption originates from aquaculture. These fish comprise primarily herbivorous species, such as tilapia and carp. In export value, finfish (Atlantic salmon) and crustaceans (shrimps) are the most important products. In 2004, the total global production in aquaculture was 17.3 million tonnes of carp (*Cyprinius carpio*), 1.2 million tonnes of tilapia (*Tilapia* spp.), 1.1 million tonnes of salmon, 0.5 million tonnes of rainbow trout (*Oncorhynchus mykiss*), 0.5 million tonnes of shrimp and more than 10 million tonnes of molluscs (55). The production of algae is estimated to be more than 12 million tonnes. The People's Republic of China is, by far, still the largest producer of aquaculture products in the world.

Current conditions and practices in aquatic animal production

Food safety hazards in aquaculture include fish disease agents and hygienic aspects (microbiological agents), and contaminants such as environmental pollutants. However, in a broader sense, these risks also include those related to the handling of fish during catching, farming, slaughter and processing for human consumption.

Zoonotic agents in fish

In general, true zoonotic agents associated with fish, crustaceans and molluscs are few. Many commensal and pathogenic bacteria, viruses, fungi and parasites associated with fish have temperature growth limits that will not support their development in humans.

However, there are some exceptions. In the following section, bacterial and parasitic agents which can cause disease in both fish and humans are discussed.

Fish pathogenic bacteria as potential causal agents for disease in humans

Viruses, bacteria, fungi and parasites in fish may cause disease or food-borne infections in humans. Under normal conditions, practically no infectious agents which cause disease in fish also infect humans. Nevertheless, under certain conditions, bacteria which cause fish diseases may also infect humans, without necessarily being regarded as a major human health problem.

Bacteria

Bacteria represent a major and important group of micro-organisms because of their frequent occurrence and activities that may have a negative impact on fish quality. Generally, seafood from cold waters harbours lower numbers of potentially pathogenic micro-organisms than seafood from warmer waters. The presence of human pathogenic bacteria in fish and fish products may also be attributed to contamination during processing.

Several bacteria are, however, reported to cause infection and mortality in both fish and humans (6) and these represent a particular hazard, caused either by handling infected fish on fish farms or in grocery stores (12, 28) or by the ingestion of raw or inadequately processed infected fish and/or contaminated fish products.

Vibrio species

To date, some 12 species of the *Vibrio* family, which have marine and estuary environments as their main habitat, have been shown to cause disease in humans (6). Human pathogenic *Vibrio* species can be detected in temperate waters, especially during the summer months, but at lower frequencies than in tropical waters.

The most important *Vibrio* species associated with disease problems in humans, due to ingestion or other routes of exposure, are *V. cholerae, V. parahaemolyticus* and *V. vulnificus* (25, 54, 92, 106). The last has been associated with wound infection and septicaemia, while the first two mainly cause gastro-intestinal symptoms.

In the United States of America (USA), *V. vulnificus* has been reported to have caused deaths, not by food poisoning after the consumption of seafood, but because of its ability to cause wound infection, especially in soft tissues, either with penetrating injuries or through contamination of existing wounds (18, 90, 91).

Amaro and Biosca (3) reported that Biotype 2 of *V. vulnificus*, which is considered an obligate pathogen causing skin lesions, septicaemia and mortality in eels (*Anguilla* spp.), may also be an opportunistic pathogen in humans (3, 66). Skin-penetrating scratches received while handling fish have been reported to cause necrotising dermo-hypodermatitis in fish workers (26), as well as local cellulitis and even life-threatening disease due to fish-spine injuries (18). As a consequence, appropriate care must be taken by consumers at risk, as well as by fishfarmers handling diseased eels (3). Both the infected fish and the water may be sources of infection (3).

In Israel, *Vibrio* infections caused by *V. alginolyticus, V. parahaemolyticus, V. vulnificus* and non-typable

Vibrio spp. were reported in humans, due to changes in the way that pond-raised fish were being packed (12). In most cases, these infections were initiated by exposure to the fins of the fish. An epidemiological study showed that the reason for this was a change in trade patterns. The producers had changed their delivery practice from packing fish in ice to packing live fish in containers. When producers changed back to selling the fish on ice, no further infections were recorded.

In Japan, *V. parahaemolyticus* has been reported as the most common cause of food poisoning (86).

Photobacterium damselae (previously *Listonella damsela*, *V. damsela*), which causes skin ulcers in several fish species, in particular, damselfish (*Chromis punctipinnis*), has also been considered an important pathogen in humans, as several cases of progressive necrotising wounds have been reported (1, 83). Infection in humans has usually been caused either by injuries from fins or by contamination of wounds exposed to water (23, 86, 97). Before 1993, all cases in humans had originated from wound infections but Perez-Tirse *et al.* (97) described a septicaemic condition in a patient caused by a knife injury when filleting blue fish (*Pomatus saltatrix*).

Hafnia alvei

Hafnia alvei, a Gram-negative, facultative anaerobic bacterium of the family Enterobacteriaceae, is found in natural environments, such as sewage, soil and water, but is also a gastro-intestinal commensal. This bacterium is not usually considered pathogenic but has occasionally been reported to cause disease in fish as well as terrestrial animals and humans (93).

Hafnia alvei has been associated with epizootic haemorrhagic septicaemia in rainbow trout (56); kidney pathology in cherry salmon (*O. masou*) (107); and mortalities in brown trout (*S. trutta* L.) in freshwater aquaculture (101), but not in marine aquaculture (93). In humans, *H. alvei* has been associated with several disease conditions, such as:

– septicaemia

– gastroenteritis

– meningitis

– pneumonia

– wound infections (51, 117).

However, so far, there have been no reports of the bacterium transferring from fish to humans. Nevertheless, in some regions there may be a combination of marine fish farming and human activities, such as disposal of sewage in areas where people swim, which may lead to the transfer

of *H. alvei* between humans and fish and vice versa. Based on challenge experiments with *H. alvei* in gilthead seabream (*Sparus aurata* L.), Padilla *et al.* (93) concluded that, although the gilthead seabream seemed to have a considerable resistance to experimental infections, the bacterium could remain viable in the fish without clinical signs for some three months. This means that aquaculture and human activities should take place in separate areas as farmed fish may represent a risk for the transfer of *H. alvei* to humans.

Streptococcus iniae

The genus *Streptococcus* includes many species that can cause disease in different hosts, including fish in sea, brackish and fresh water as well as in mammals and humans (79). *Streptococcus iniae* has been described as a cause of disease in both fish ('mad fish disease') and people (49, 58). It is a Gram-positive, beta-haemolytic bacterium that was first isolated from diseased Amazon freshwater dolphins (*Inia geoffrensis*) (99), but was later described in cultured fish species, such as rainbow trout (*O. mykiss*), tilapia, channel catfish (*Ictalurus nebulosus*), Japanese flounder (*Paralichthys olivaceus*) and yellowtail (*Seriola quinqueradiata*) (32, 79).

In fish, infection with *S. iniae*, previously described as *S. shiloi* and *S. difficile* (32, 33), is characterised as a septicaemic disease which may become chronic. In humans, disease caused by *S. iniae* was not described until 1995 to 1996, when the bacterium was isolated from a group of patients in Canada who had handled fresh whole tilapia from infected farms (116, 125). This was despite the fact that the bacterium had been identified as early as 1991 (21, 49). The disease condition in humans, characterised principally by septicaemia, cellulitis, endocarditis, meningitis and pneumonia, has been particularly associated with people of Asian ethnicity, caused by their handling live and freshly killed fish (mainly tilapia) contaminated with *S. iniae* during food preparation (49, 80, 89, 116, 125). The bacterium is most often introduced through wounds and abrasions in the skin. In the reported cases from Canada, the affected patients were elderly and many had poor health and compromised immune systems. The risk of healthy humans acquiring disease is minimal (125).

Mycobacterium species

Several *Mycobacterium* spp., such as *M. marinum*, *M. chelonei* and *M. fortuitum*, have been reported in both fish and humans. Fish with mycobacteriosis pose a particularly significant threat of transmitting the infection to humans and thus may well become hazardous to human health (89). Mycobacteriosis is a chronic disease reported

Rev. sci. tech. Off. int. Epiz., **25** (2)

in seawater, brackish water and freshwater fish species, in aquaculture and aquariums as well as from the wild (89). Human infection with *M. marinum* has been reported in many countries since 1951, yet it is still considered rare. It is mainly associated with granulomatous skin lesions, especially lesions acquired by aquarists when cleaning fish tanks. The infection usually enters through open wounds or abrasions exposed to contaminated water in which infected fish have been kept or while processing fish (20, 22, 78, 110). In the USA, rockfish infected with *M. marinum* are believed to cause skin problems in humans (95).

Contaminating bacteria as potential agents for disease in humans

Erysipelothrix rhusiopathiae

Infection with *Erysipelothrix rhusiopathiae* (erysipeloid) is also known as 'fish handler's disease', 'fish hand', 'blubber finger', etc., in humans, since it is most commonly characterised by swollen fingers (65). The bacterium is reported to occur on fish, and the infection is most often introduced to humans through skin wounds. Thus, the disease must be considered as occupational in humans, due to handling fish and fish products contaminated with *E. rhusiopathiae*. The disease is usually benign, but may be fatal in some cases. Fatal endocarditis has been described following the gutting of eels (65).

Listeria

Listeria monocytogenes has been isolated on a regular basis from a wide variety of seafood products, including fresh, frozen, fermented, cold smoked and salted fish derived from aquaculture as well as captive fisheries. It is a problem often associated with fish and fish products from temperate climates (17, 24, 53). The organism is ubiquitous in nature and regarded as a zoonotic agent, causing meningitis and abortions in sheep and septicaemia in lambs, as well as food-borne illness in humans (17). The occurrence of *L. monocytogenes* in seafood is reported to range from 0% to 75% (8).

'Ready-to-eat' products, such as refrigerated, vacuum-packed products with a long shelf life, are of particular concern for *L. monocytogenes*, especially when they are inadequately heated before consumption (17, 53). Table I gives an overview of outbreaks of listeriosis caused by marine sources (103).

It has been shown that bacterial growth occurs during the fermentation process at 8°C and storage at 4°C. The ability

Table I

An overview of outbreaks of listeriosis from marine sources (103)

Country	Year	Number of outbreaks	Source
United States of America	1989	2	Shrimps
New Zealand	1991	4	Smoked shellfish
Australia	1991	2	Smoked shellfish
Sweden	1994	6	Smoked/brine-cured fish
Canada	1996	2	Crabsticks
Finland	1999	5	Smoked trout

to grow at low temperatures, together with halotolerance, enables bacteria to reproduce in salted products (24, 103). *Listeria monocytogenes* has also occasionally been found in smoked salmon and it is thought that the bacterium is introduced through water during the production process (102). Cold smoking does not eliminate *L. monocytogenes* (31) and, although bacterial counts are reduced by hot smoking, the bacterium is not completely eliminated from smoked products (62). The isolation of different strains of *L. monocytogenes* from raw fish and final products indicates that contamination may take place at several stages in the production chain between harvesting and production for consumption (53).

Outbreaks of listeriosis in humans due to contaminated seafood have been reported from many parts of the world, particularly from industrialised countries (53, 103). Outbreaks have been related to different types of food items, including products such as shrimps, vacuum-packed smoked salmon and fermented fish. Most cases of listeriosis in humans occur in immunocompromised people, the elderly and pregnant women, and the disease is characterised by septicaemia, intra-uterine infection and meningitis. It may also cause abortions (stillbirths). However, more recently, *Listeria* has been associated with mild gastro-intestinal symptoms (53). Disease caused by *L. monocytogenes* is rare and a high infectious dose is required. The zero tolerance policy established in many countries for *Listeria* in fish products may be over-protective from a public health point of view (53).

Other bacteria

Aeromonad bacteria are ubiquitous in the environment and several *Aeromonas* species have been reported to cause disease in fish, as well as being potential food-borne pathogens that may cause disease in humans (89).

Although *Salmonella* spp. may be harboured and survive in fish, seafoods seldom harbour *Salmonella*. Fish may be exposed to *Salmonella* through consumption of contaminated feed or living in contaminated water. The

Rev. sci. tech. Off. int. Epiz., **25** (2)

611

occurrence of *Salmonella* in feed has, for a long time, been a well-recognised problem worldwide. However, research has shown that the level of *Salmonella* contamination in the feed must be extremely high if the bacteria are to persist in the fish for more than a few days (87). If *Salmonella* is present in freshwater or marine fish species, this is mainly due to faecal contamination (124).

Food-borne pathogenic bacteria such as *Campylobacter, Shigella* and *Yersinia* are seldom associated with fish. Nevertheless, the fish pathogenic bacteria *Y. ruckeri* has been reported to occur in humans (50).

Edwardsiella tarda, which causes 'red disease' in eels as well as enteritis in penguins, is also sporadically reported as causing gastroenteritis and septicaemia in humans (72).

Parasites in fish as potential agents for disease in humans

A great majority of freshwater and seawater fish species harbour parasites. These are more common in wild fish than in farmed fish. Most of these parasites are harmless to humans but some may make the fish products unsuitable for human consumption, either due to quality deterioration ('milky flesh') or because humans may be an aberrant or final host of the parasites.

The use of raw, inadequately cooked, salted or smoked fish, common in many countries, has zoonotic potential and has been reported to have caused serious disease conditions in humans. To avoid disease problems caused by parasites, fish that is going to be used for sashimi, sushi or other raw fish dishes should be frozen before use.

Trematodes

The number of food-borne infections caused by trematodes has increased dramatically in Eastern Europe in recent years, where millions of people are affected by *Opisthorcis* spp. (119).

In Asia, cyprinids are the most important group of fish species used in aquaculture and species belonging to this group are the principal hosts of trematodes, such as *Clonorchis sinensis, Opisthorcis felinus* and *O. viverrini*. If infected fish and their products are inadequately prepared before consumption, the risk of human infection is obvious. The consumption of 'hot rice congee' in the People's Republic of China and raw fish in the Republic of Korea is reported to cause infection with *Clonorchis* spp. in humans, while the dish 'koi-pla' in Thailand has been reported to cause infection with *Opisthorcis* spp.

The trematode *Heterophyes heterophyes* is another parasite that is reported to cause problems in the Middle East and Asia, but other heterophyides are also of importance (61, 94).

Pain and discomfort are the most common effects of acute trematode infection. More chronic infections, i.e. with *Clonorchis* spp. and *Opisthorcis* spp., can result in cholangio-carcinoma, chronic diarrhoea and hepatic cancer (119).

If, however, the contamination of aquaculture premises with untreated human and reservoir-animal excreta can be avoided, such problems may be diminished considerably (119).

Cestodes

The pseudophyllean cestode *Diphyllobothrium latum* is reported from many regions throughout the world. Several fish species act as intermediate hosts in which plerocercoids occur in the muscular tissues or on the viscera (85). Consuming raw or lightly cooked fish may result in infection in humans as the parasite establishes itself in the gut.

Nematodes

Anisakis

Anisakiasis is usually associated with the consumption of raw, wild, caught fish as *Anisakis* spp. are seldom a problem in farmed fish. The parasite has a complex life cycle involving passage through a number of hosts, including fish and mammals. The stage that infects fish is found as a distinct 'watch-spring coiled shape'. When uncoiled, the parasite is approximately 2 cm long. Usually, *Anisakis* is localised on the outside of internal organs but may occasionally be found in the flesh or beneath the skin. If infected fish are eaten by a marine mammal, the life cycle is completed.

However, *Anisakis* is also able to infect humans if raw, fermented or inadequately cooked fish is eaten. In such cases, humans will act as aberrant hosts.

This parasite is one of the most significant factors in reducing the quality of seafood and may thus harm human health, either through infection with *Anisakis* or allergic reaction (81). Several cases of gastro-intestinal problems caused by anisakiasis have been reported from the Netherlands and Japan (115, 127). Most of these cases have been associated with the intake of raw fish, in particular, herring. In the Netherlands especially, the dish 'groene herring' has played a role.

612

Rev. sci. tech. Off. int. Epiz., **25** (2)

Gnathostoma

Spirurid nematodes, such as *Gnathostoma* spp., normally found in the stomachs of carnivorous animals, such as dogs, have also been reported to occur in humans if the larvae of the parasites are ingested. Humans are an aberrant host to the parasite. When larvae are ingested, they migrate from the intestine to the skin and musculature, causing the so-called 'larvae migrans' syndrome. However, they may also invade other organs, causing serious problems (100).

Intoxications caused by fish consumption

Clostridium botulinum

Clostridium botulinum type E is a strict anaerobic bacterium that may occasionally be present in fish. This bacterium is a recognised commensal in fish in fresh water, as well as in sea water. Under optimal growth conditions, the bacterium may produce a potent neurotoxin in processed fish (63, 67, 69). To avoid problems, it is important to control the factors that can prevent the growth of this organism in fish and fish products, such as temperature and salt concentration.

The anaerobic bacterium *C. botulinum* has been reported to cause intoxication in farmed fish, as well as terrestrial animals and humans (19, 30, 68, 109). Thus, *C. botulinum* may become an important hazard to the food safety of aquaculture products. The condition in pond-cultured fish is usually called botulism or 'bankruptcy disease' and, as in humans, it is due to the potent neurotoxin produced by the bacterium. In countries where fermented fish (both farmed and wild salmonids) is a speciality, unhygienic production conditions may result in intoxication and death in humans.

Histamine fish poisoning

Scombrotoxic fish poisoning, also known as scombroid or histamine fish poisoning, is caused by bacterial spoilage of a limited number of fish species. These comprise mainly:

– mackerel (*Scomber scombrus*)

– bonito (*Sarda* spp.)

– various tuna species (*Thunnus* spp.)

– swordfish (*Xiphias gladius*)

– common dolphinfish (mahi-mahi) (*Coryphaena* spp.).

As bacteria break down fish proteins, by-products, such as histamine and substances blocking histamine breakdown, may build up in fish. The human tolerance limit for histamine is 10 mg per 100 g. In general, there is no risk of histamine poisoning in well-iced fish.

Allergies to fish and seafood

Eating fish may produce severe allergic reactions. Allergies to fish, shellfish and mussels are among the most common food allergies triggered by immunoglobulin-E antibodies, and allergic reactions to seafood antigens may produce severe symptoms, including angio-oedema and anaphylaxis. These symptoms do not differ from allergic reactions to any other type of food (82).

Even though allergens are more or less species-specific, there is a high degree of cross-reactivity among different fish species. This means that a patient who is allergic to one fish species is at a high risk of being allergic to other species.

There are no specific symptoms for allergic reactions to food. Consequently, after ingesting seafood, the clinical manifestations of an allergic reaction do not differ from allergic reactions to any other type of food (82).

An allergy to fish and shellfish often becomes evident during the first year of life but, in general, presents later than an allergy to eggs and milk (96). While many children outgrow their allergies to eggs, cows' milk, wheat and soy, they may continue to be hypersensitive to fish and shellfish in later life (14, 29, 64, 104).

There is no evidence supporting the contention that the prevalence of fish allergy has anything to do with the level of fish intake, despite comments made in the literature. Studies on fish allergy in Reykjavik (high consumption) and Uppsala (low consumption) showed that, although the population in Reykjavik ate two to three times as much fish as that of Uppsala, there were no significant differences in prevalence between these two populations (57).

Fish consumption in Norway is among the highest in Europe; the median value being about 65 g per day. Of this, approximately two-thirds is lean white fish and about one-third is fatty fish (H. Meltzer, personal communication). However, the prevalence of seafood allergy in the Norwegian population is low (< 1%). The importance of seafood allergy to the health of the Norwegian population is marginal.

The first isolated allergen from fish is the calcium-binding protein, parvalbumin. Since patients usually react to both raw and cooked fish, it is assumed that the allergen is heat resistant. However, recent data indicate that some individuals react only to raw fish, while others react only to cooked, suggesting the existence of additional allergens. The lowest dose of fish reported to produce an allergic reaction is 5 mg.

Rev. sci. tech. Off. int. Epiz., **25** (2)

613

Established thresholds for food allergens are important tools for food production and labelling. However, at present there are insufficient data available to establish such thresholds. Consequently, no values have been established for food allergens in European Union (EU) legislation.

Residues in fish

Residues of antibiotics and chemotherapeutics in fish

In aquaculture, particularly in fish-farming, various types of antimicrobials have always been needed to combat or prevent disease (126). In some countries, antibiotics were even used as growth promoters. Before the 1990s, the use of medicinal products was high in countries with a large aquaculture industry. The use of drugs for 'fire-fighting' (i.e. solving an immediate problem) was markedly reduced in many countries (60) during the 1990s, reflecting the introduction of widely available and effective vaccines against some of the most serious fish diseases in aquaculture.

However, some medicinal products are still in use, giving rise to several public health aspects, such as toxicity, drug hypersensitivity and the development of antibiotic resistance in fish pathogenic bacteria, as well as in environmental bacteria and human pathogens. The risk of transfer of antibiotic resistance to human microflora is probably low in countries where the use of antimicrobials is limited. However, in countries with less restrictive legislation, the risk of contaminating fish and fish products with resistant bacteria is greater (2).

So-called 'integrated farming', which combines intensive animal husbandry (in particular, of pigs and poultry) and aquaculture, may represent a route of transmission of bacterial resistance genes from fish to humans (98). Wastes from the animals are a source of feed for the fish in such production systems.

Malachite green

Malachite green is an industrial dye that has effectively been used to treat fungal infections in fish. However, it has not been authorised as a veterinary drug, and its application in aquaculture is not permitted. Although malachite green has been abandoned for use in food-producing animals for many years, the active substance and its metabolite, leuco-malachite green, are still being detected in fish and fish products. In eels, the related crystal violet (also known as gentian violet) dye has been found. The EU has set the minimum required performance limit for malachite green to be two parts per billion of the analytical method used to detect the substance (48).

The EU (52) has reported that residues of leuco-malachite green and malachite green have been detected in fillets of pangassius (*Pangassius hypothalamus*), eel and Pacific salmon (*Oncorhynchus* spp.), respectively. Despite the fact that malachite green has been banned on the Chinese mainland since 2002, this chemical was found in freshwater fish in local markets in Hong Kong, leading the Hong Kong Government to take measures to safeguard food safety in fish (5).

Environmental contaminants in fish

A wide variety of chemical contaminants may be present in the environment, including persistent lipophilic organic compounds, as well as metals (e.g. methyl-mercury and organotin). In particular, there are numerous lipophilic organochlorine contaminants, including: – poly chlorinated dibenzo-p-dioxins (PCDDs) and furans (PCDFs) (collectively, PCDD/Fs)

– polychlorinated biphenyls (PCBs)

– camphechlor

– hexachlorcyclohexane

– dichlorodiphenyltrichloroethane and its metabolites

– aldrin

– chlordane

– dieldrin

– endrin

– heptachlor

– hexachlorbenzene.

Most of these compounds are, however, no longer produced and levels in the environment are generally decreasing.

In contrast, the environmental levels of another group of chemicals, brominated flame retardants (BFRs), some of which are still in use, seem to be increasing (27, 107). This group includes, for example:

– polybrominated diphenyl ethers (PBDEs)

– tetrabromobisphenyl A (TBBPA)

– hexabromododecane.

Lipophilic, persistent organic compounds have a strong tendency to bio-accumulate in fatty tissues and will also biomagnify in food chains. The highest levels are found in the fatty tissues of species at the end of the food chain.

Organometals, such as methyl-mercury, also have the potential to bio-accumulate in the food chain, and the

614

Rev. sci. tech. Off. int. Epiz., **25** (2)

concentrations increase with the age and size of the individual. Persistent organic pollutants (POPs) in fish are predominantly derived from their diet. Owing to their lipophilic nature, POPs are particularly likely to be present in fatty, predatory fish, such as:

– wild herring

– mackerel

– tuna

– salmon.

In contrast, methyl-mercury does not accumulate in fatty tissue, but becomes concentrated with age and as it progresses along the food chain. The highest concentration of methyl-mercury is found in older, predatory fish at the top of the food chain (e.g. tuna, trout).

The diet of wild fish cannot be controlled and the only way to reduce the exposure of these fish to contaminants is to reduce the spread of contaminants into the environment.

Potential risks associated with contaminants throughout the food chain

Contaminants in fish farming

Feed is the main source of POPs and metals in farmed fish (34). Since the safe production of farmed fish starts with fish feed, the development of feed products with low levels of undesirable substances has become pivotal (34). The concentration of several POPs (e.g. dioxins and BFRs) and metals (e.g. methyl-mercury) in fillets of farmed fish has been reported to correlate with their concentration in feed (10, 70, 77, 84).

These POPs are highly persistent, fat-soluble environmental pollutants that are ubiquitous in the marine ecosystem and are readily biomagnified in the food chain. Fish oils, extracted from marine pelagic fish species, such as capelin (*Mallotus villosus*), sand eel (*Amodytes* spp.) and blue whiting (*Micromesistius* spp.), used in high-energy fish feeds, are considered to be the main source of POPs in farmed salmon (34, 120).

The potential threat of POPs to human health is not related to a single chemical component, but to a mixture of several related congeners of different basic chemical structures. For dioxins and dioxin-like PCBs, there are 29 different chemical forms that share a similar toxic mechanism (114). The profile of these 29 congeners, and hence the total World Health Organization (WHO) toxic equivalency (TEQ) in feed (the WHO-TEQ), is often not reflected in the

fish. Some congeners (such as dioxin-like PCBs) are more predominant in feed than in fish, when compared to other congeners (such as dioxins) (11, 70). The different 'carry-over' or transfer of the chemical forms shows the complexity of aiming for a 'feed-to-fork' approach to controlling undesirable substances along the food chain. When selecting new feed resources to 'tailor' a fish product that is low in certain contaminants, differences in feed-fish transfer dynamics for each contaminant congener must be taken into consideration.

Several strategies are being developed on how to produce fish low in undesirables by designing specific diets and optimising feeding strategies, taking into account both cost efficiency and fish welfare.

There are three main approaches that, alone or in combination, may reduce the levels of PCDD/Fs and dioxin-like PCBs in fish feed and farmed fish. There is a large variation in the levels of PCDD/Fs and dioxin-like PCBs found in fish oil, depending on such factors as seasonal variation, fish species, age or geographical origin (34, 88). Thus, it is possible to select marine ingredients with relatively low background levels of POPs for use in fish feeds (71, 84).

Another strategy is to replace fish oil with alternative terrestrial feed ingredients that contain lower levels of dioxins. Plant oils have lower PCDD/F and dioxin-like PCB levels than most commonly used fish oils, and thus have great potential to reduce the level of dioxins in farmed salmon (7, 11). Moreover, several techniques are available that remove POPs from fish oils without affecting the nutritional status of the oil (16, 26). As a result, the POP levels in fish fillets can be reduced considerably.

The toxicity of mercury depends on the chemical form. The organic, methylated form of mercury is considerably more toxic than inorganic forms (9). Inorganic mercury is methylated to organic mercury through microbial, predominantly anoxic processes in aquatic ecosystems (73, 118). Methyl-mercury is the dominant form of mercury in fish, and fish meal is the main source for methyl-mercury in fish feeds. Methyl-mercury is efficiently accumulated in fish muscle, which is one of the main organs for methyl-mercury deposition (13, 15, 59, 75). Methyl-mercury has a higher assimilation level (41% to 23%) than dietary inorganic mercury (6% to 4%) (10). In the terrestrial system, inorganic mercury is the dominant form. Mercury uptake by plants from the soil is low; therefore the concentration of mercury in plant feedstuffs is limited.

The use of novel feedstuffs in fish feeds may remove current problems caused by POPs and metals, but may also introduce new challenges to food safety. Higher levels of pesticides, such as endosulfan, have been found in some plant oils, compared to fish oils. The use of alternative

Rev. sci. tech. Off. int. Epiz., **25** (2)

615

marine feed ingredients, such as krill, will introduce high levels of fluorine to the feed. That may limit the use of this resource, due to current legislation on maximum permitted levels of fluorine in feed.

Hazard identification and hazard characterisation of contaminants

The ability of a chemical to cause adverse health effects and thus its tolerable daily intakes (TDI) and/or tolerable weekly intakes (TWI) are established by risk assessments performed by international bodies (123). The TDI of a chemical represents the amount of the chemical that can be safely consumed throughout life with no risk of any significant adverse health effect.

Some chemicals are carcinogenic. For genotoxic carcinogens, it is not possible to establish a dose threshold below which there is no effect. Several methods are used for quantitative risk assessment of such chemicals. Recently, the European Food Safety Authority (EFSA) has recommended using the 'margin of exposure' (MOE) as a harmonised approach for assessing the risks posed by substances which are both genotoxic and carcinogenic (46).

Toxicity of important contaminants in fish

The most important contaminants in fish for consumer health are methyl-mercury and POPs, since fish may contribute significantly to dietary exposure to these compounds. It is, however, important to differentiate the generic term 'fish', since there are great variations in both nutritional values and levels of contaminants. These variations may depend on such factors as:

- the origin of the fish and the species in question

- the season of harvest

- the type of fish tissue consumed

- the content of contaminants in the feed of farmed fish.

Mercury

Methyl-mercury, which is the most toxic mercury compound, is the predominant form of mercury in fish. The percentage of methyl-mercury to total mercury ranges between 65% and 100%, depending on the fish species (74, 75, 105). The primary target of methyl-mercury toxicity is the nervous system. Based on a number of intoxication incidents (Minamata and Niigata in Japan,

rural Iraq), the Joint FAO/WHO Expert Committee on Food Additives (JECFA) derived a provisional TWI (PTWI) for methyl-mercury of 3.3 µg per kg of body weight (bw) per week.

This PTWI was maintained over several re-evaluations, but JECFA noted that pregnant women and nursing mothers may be at greater risk than the general population (121). In 2003, JECFA (122) revised the PTWI to 1.6 µg per kg of bw per week, to protect the developing foetus. *In utero* exposure is the most sensitive period, and an effect on neurodevelopment was considered to be the most sensitive health outcome. This evaluation took into account new data from large epidemiological studies performed in the Seychelles and the Faroe Islands, as well as additional epidemiological data. Moreover, EFSA supported the decision by JECFA to reduce the PTWI for methyl-mercury, since it was based on the most susceptible stage of life (i.e. the developing foetus and intake of the mother during pregnancy), rather than on the risk to the general adult population (44).

Dioxins and dioxin-like compounds

There are, in total, 210 different congeners of PCDD/Fs which are not intentionally produced, but formed as by-products or impurities from most combustion and several industrial processes. Moreover, PCDD/Fs are also found in soil and sediment, and these may act as secondary sources of dioxins in the environment.

Among the 210 congeners, the 17 PCDD/Fs with chlorine substitution in positions 2, 3, 7 and 8 are the most toxic. All 17 congeners, as well as 12 dioxin-like PCBs (sometimes collectively called 'dioxins'), have the same mode of action binding to the Ah receptor and show comparable qualitative effects, but with different potencies. These differences in potency are expressed in toxic equivalency factors (TEFs) (126). Consensus on the TEFs for PCDD/Fs and dioxin-like PCBs for human risk assessment (WHO-TEFs) was obtained at a WHO meeting in 1997 (114). Long-term exposure leads to increased dioxin levels in fatty tissues and may result in developmental effects in children, as well as cancer and several other diseases.

The EU Scientific Committee for Food (SCF) and JECFA established tolerable intake levels for 'dioxins' in 2001 (37, 45, 122). Both committees concluded that the risk assessment should be based on the effects of 2,3,7,8-tetrachlordibenzo-p-dioxins (TCDDs), the most toxic congener, on the developing male reproductive system, resulting from the maternal body burden. A threshold approach was used to derive a TDI of 2 picograms (pg) TCDDs per kg of bw. This was extended to include other PCDDs, PCDFs and dioxin-like PCBs and, because of their

Rev. sci. tech. Off. int. Epiz., **25** (2)

long half-lives in the human body, this TDI was expressed over a longer time period (a week or month). The SCF established a group PTWI intake of 14 pg WHO-TEQ per kg of bw (37). In addition, JECFA established a group provisional tolerable monthly intake of 70 pg WHO-TEQ per kg of bw (122). There are some differences in the approaches used by other authorities to assess the risks of dioxins and dioxin-like compounds to human health.

Polychlorinated biphenyls

Theoretically, there are 209 different congeners of PCBs, in total. They are all lipophilic, and the lipophilicity increases with the increasing degree of chlorination. Polychlorinated biphenyls are highly persistent and accumulate within food chains. The type and potency of the toxicity of the congeners vary with the number of chlorines substituted and the placement of the chlorine on the phenyl rings.

Owing to their unique physical and chemical properties, PCBs have been widely used commercially since the 1920s, as dielectric and heat exchange fluids and in a variety of other industrial applications. Since the 1970s, there have been restrictions on the use of PCBs in several EU countries, and today PCBs are banned in most countries. However, entry into the environment, due to improper disposal practices of PCB-containing materials or leakage from transformers and hydraulic systems still in use, cannot be excluded. The PCBs are listed in Annex A of the Stockholm Convention (4) on POPs. This Convention seeks the global elimination of the production and use of all intentionally produced POPs listed in annexes A, B and C of the Convention (http://www.pops.int).

For technical purposes, PCBs have never been used as single compounds, but always as complex technical mixtures. Dioxin-like PCBs exhibit toxicological effects on the liver, thyroid, immune function, reproduction and behaviour, similar to those caused by TCDD/Fs. The dioxin-like PCBs are included in the tolerable intake levels established for PCDDs and PCDFs.

The other group of PCBs, non-dioxin-like PCBs, constitutes a major part of the PCB congeners found in human tissues and food. These PCBs do not bind to the Ah receptor and do not show dioxin-like toxicity, but exhibit a different toxicological profile, affecting, in particular, the developing nervous system and neurotransmitter function. Mixtures used to study the toxicity of PCBs contain both non-dioxin-like and dioxin-like PCBs. It is therefore difficult, if not impossible, to differentiate between the toxic effects of dioxins and non-dioxin-like and dioxin-like PCBs.

Currently, there is no reliable, health-based guidance value for non-dioxin-like PCBs to use in human risk assessment.

Dietary intake is considered the main pathway of exposure to non-dioxin as well as dioxin-like PCBs. Fish, particularly fatty fish, is considered an important source for these chemicals.

Brominated flame retardants

The brominated bisphenols, diphenyl ethers, cyclododecanes, phenols and phthalic acid derivatives are the five major classes of BFRs; the first three classes representing the highest production volumes. At present, five major BFRs (TBBPA, hexabromocyclododecane [HBCD] and three commercial mixtures of PBDEs) constitute the overwhelming majority, but the situation changes as new substances are introduced and older ones discontinued.

Some of these substances are persistent organic contaminants in the environment, with the potential to contaminate the food chain long after production has ceased. Risk assessment is difficult, since databases on toxicology and exposure to humans from different sources are very limited. Risk assessment reports and scientific opinions of the European Commission Scientific Committee on Toxicity, Ecotoxicity and the Environment and the Scientific Committee on Health and Environmental Risks are available for pentabromodiphenyl ether, octabromodiphenyl ether, decabromodiphenyl ether, HBCD and tetrabromobisphenol (35, 36, 38, 39, 40, 41, 42, 43).

Polybrominated diphenyl ethers

Theoretically, there are, in total, 209 different congeners of PBDEs. These congeners are lipophilic and the lipophilicity increases with the increasing degree of bromination. Tri- to hexa-BDEs are easily absorbed, slowly eliminated (persistent) and bio-accumulated, and are more bioactive than deca-BDE. Deca-BDE may be transformed to lower brominated BDEs.

There are three principal commercial PBDE flame retardants produced:

– PentaBDE

– OctaBDE

– DecaBDE.

These mixtures have different compositions of congeners and purity. DecaBDE is, however, mainly composed of deca-BDE. PentaBDE and OctaBDE were banned in the EU in August 2004. Several toxic endpoints have been identified. However, in general, the toxicological databases are poor. The liver is the target organ for PBDEs. Penta-BDE is the most toxic congener and deca-BDE the least. As

Rev. sci. tech. Off. int. Epiz., **25** (2)

617

a result of the limited toxicological data, any basic characterisation of the health risk from human exposure to PBDEs is extremely uncertain.

Hexabromocyclododecane and tetrabromobisphenol A

Toxicological knowledge on these BFRs is very limited. The BFR HBCD is commercially available in the EU as a mixture of three stereo-isomers: α, β and γ. The α-isomer predominates in food. All toxicological studies on HBCD were conducted with the commercial mixture. The extent of metabolism of the commercial HBCD is unknown. Hexabromocyclododecane is also hepatotoxic, with a lowest-observed-adverse-effect level (LOAEL) of 100 mg/kg bw/day. It has not been shown to cause developmental toxicity, but neuro-developmental effects have been observed after administration to neonatal mice, using a protocol similar to that with PBDEs (with a LOAEL for HBCD of 0.9 mg/kg bw/day) (111).

In the United Kingdom (UK), following a similar approach to that taken for PBDEs, the Committee on Toxicity of Chemicals in Food, Consumer Products and the Environment (COT) considered that a target MOE of 3,000 to 10,000 was required for HBCD. Comparison with the LOAEL of 100 mg/kg bw/day indicates that exposures below 10 mg/kg bw/day would not be a concern (111).

Since TBBPA is a single compound, the database is relatively more complete than it is for PBDEs and HBCD. Furthermore, COT evaluated TBBPA in 2004 (112).

Repeat-dose studies revealed that there were no toxicologically significant effects at doses up to 10,000 mg/kg bw/day, after administration for 90 days. No long-term carcinogenicity study is available. However, TBBPA is not mutagenic and there is no indication of relevant carcinogenicity in humans. That is, TBBPA has weak oestrogenic effects in *in vitro* studies, but no effects were revealed in a recent two-generation study in rats, with doses of up to 1,000 mg/kg bw/day. There are conflicting results from two neurotoxicity studies in rats. No adverse effects were found in the two-generation study, but a study where rats were administered TBBPA during pregnancy showed some behavioural effects. The Committee on Toxicity of Chemicals judged these effects to be random and derived a TDI of 1 mg/kg bw/day from a no-observed-adverse-effect level (NOAEL) of 1,000 mg/kg bw by use of an uncertainty factor of 1,000.

Polybrominated biphenyls

The toxicological profiles of polybrominated biphenyls are expected to resemble those of the PCBs. However, TEFs have not been allocated for the co-planar congeners, and relevant toxicological evaluations have not been conducted.

Risk characterisation

Assessments of fish consumption that have recently been performed in the UK and the EU (113) indicate that methyl-mercury, the PCDD/Fs and the dioxin-like PCBs are the principal contaminants of concern. That is, consumption of specific fish species could result in the consumers exceeding their respective PTWIs for these contaminants. High-level consumers of predator fish species that accumulate methyl-mercury with age (e.g. tuna and old freshwater trout) may exceed the PTWI of 1.6 µg/kg bw/week. The PCDD/F levels in certain oily fish species may lead some high-level consumers to exceed the TWI of 14 pg toxic equivalents/kg bw/week, even without taking into account other sources of dietary exposure.

It is, however, important to note that the PTWIs for methyl-mercury and dioxin-like contaminants were set to protect the most susceptible life stage, i.e. the developing foetus exposed as a result of the body burden (i.e. concentration of the contaminant in the body) of the mother. Thus, the subgroup of special consideration for methyl-mercury is women who are pregnant or may become pregnant, while, for dioxins, girls and women of reproductive age are the subgroup of concern, due to the very long half-life of dioxins in the human body. The body burden during pregnancy is determined by the total previous intake over many years. Life stages other than the foetal stage are likely to be less susceptible.

Intakes of fish containing other chemical contaminants mentioned above are not a health concern, because they result in intakes below the available toxicological comparator (e.g. TDI) or contribute only minimally to overall human dietary exposure.

Risks and benefits of consuming wild and farmed fish

It is well known that fish, particularly oily fish, are an important source of long chain fatty acids (LC n-3 polyunsaturated fatty acid or PUFA), reducing the risk of cardiovascular diseases, as well as having beneficial effects on foetal development. Seafood is also a valuable source of certain minerals, vitamins and protein. However, balanced against this are the possible detrimental effects of contaminants found in certain fish species.

618

Rev. sci. tech. Off. int. Epiz., **25** (2)

Scientific publications, as well as the national and international press, have questioned if the presence of certain contaminants and residues represents a health risk to fish consumers. In these discussions, the main emphasis has been on the chemical assessment and possible health risk of consuming wild or farmed fish, while little or no consideration has been given to the nutritional value. In an effort to bring together the nutritional and toxicological considerations, food safety authorities in several countries have requested their relevant scientific committees to weigh the nutritional benefits against the possible risks of fish consumption, and such benefit-risk assessments have recently been performed in the UK and EU (113). In Norway, a similar assessment is being completed by the Norwegian Committee on Food Safety.

It is important to understand the mechanisms and interactions between nutrients and contaminants in seafood if researchers are to give sound scientific advice on the amount and type of seafood that should be recommended to promote health and maximise safety in different groups of the population. At present, there is no agreed methodology for taking both the risks and benefits of seafood into account in a quantitative way. The organisation EFSA advised that a framework should be developed which allows such a quantitative comparison, based on a common scale of measurement (47).

To protect animal and human health, internationally agreed maximum permitted levels have been set for several chemical contaminants in both feed and food. National and international monitoring programmes exist to ensure that the levels present are acceptable. In addition, aquaculture industries are using hazard analysis critical control point principles to ensure the acceptable quality of their products.

If fish and fish products contain values of environmental contaminants above the accepted international levels, this will almost certainly have a significant impact on international trade. Importing countries will introduce bans on fish and fish products. They have already done so due to contaminants such as cadmium, dioxins and malachite green.

Dangers pour la sécurité sanitaire des aliments en phase de production : les enjeux pour l'aquaculture et le secteur de la pêche

T. Håstein, B. Hjeltnes, A. Lillehaug, J. Utne Skåre, M. Berntssen & A.K. Lundebye

Résumé
Les aliments provenant de poissons sauvages et élevés constituent depuis toujours une source importante de protéines pour l'alimentation humaine. À l'échelle mondiale, les poissons et leurs dérivés représentent la première source de protéines et l'on estime que plus de 30 % du poisson consommé provient de l'aquaculture.
La première partie de cet article décrit les dangers et les défis associés à la manipulation du poisson dans les élevages et lors des prises en mer. Les auteurs décrivent les agents pathogènes affectant les poissons et l'homme, les agents de zoonoses, les bactéries responsables de toxi-infections alimentaires et les allergies associées à la consommation de poisson.
Bien que peu d'agents infectieux des poissons soient capables d'infecter l'homme, il existe quelques exceptions, qui s'avèrent parfois fatales pour l'homme. Les plus grands dangers pour la santé publique résident néanmoins dans la consommation de poisson cru ou insuffisamment cuit.
La deuxième partie de l'article traite des polluants environnementaux affectant les poissons et les fruits de mer et dangereux pour la santé publique, tels que les

médicaments vétérinaires et les résidus de produits utilisés dans les élevages, les polluants persistants tels que les composés organiques lipophiles et les métaux (méthyl-mercure, organotine).

Les auteurs font l'inventaire actualisé des divers facteurs de risque associés aux produits de la pêche et de l'aquaculture pouvant menacer la santé des consommateurs. En outre, ils abordent les divers enjeux, au sens large, associés à la manipulation du poisson pendant la prise et en phase de production, ainsi que ceux résultant de la transformation du poisson.

Mots-clés

Agent de zoonose – Allergie – Aquaculture – Composé organique lipophile persistant – Contaminant – Manipulation du poisson – Métal – Pêche en mer – Poisson – Poisson d'élevage – Poisson et fruit de mer – Poisson sauvage – Résidu – Sécurité sanitaire des aliments – Transformation du poisson.

■

Peligros para la inocuidad de los alimentos que surgen durante la fase de producción: problemas de la piscicultura y la industria piscícola

T. Håstein, B. Hjeltnes, A. Lillehaug, J. Utne Skåre, M. Berntssen & A.K. Lundebye

Resumen

Los alimentos derivados de los peces, tanto salvajes como de vivero, siempre han sido una fuente importante de proteínas para el ser humano. A escala mundial, el pescado y sus derivados constituyen la principal fuente de proteínas, y se calcula que más del 30% del pescado para consumo humano proviene de la acuicultura.

En la primera parte del artículo los autores destacan los peligros y problemas asociados a la manipulación de peces en las actividades de cría o captura. Asimismo, describen a los agentes infecciosos que provocan enfermedades en los peces y el ser humano, agentes zoonóticos, intoxicaciones de origen bacteriano y alergias causadas por el consumo de pescado.

Aunque son muy pocos los agentes infecciosos de los peces capaces de infectar al hombre, hay ciertas excepciones a esta regla que pueden dar lugar a casos mortales. Con todo, el mayor riesgo para la salud humana radica en el consumo de pescado o productos a base de pescado crudos o insuficientemente cocinados.

En la segunda parte los autores examinan los contaminantes ambientales presentes en los alimentos de origen marino que pueden resultar peligrosos para la salud humana, tales como productos medicinales y residuos asociados a la acuicultura, compuestos orgánicos lipofílicos persistentes o metales (metilmercurio, organotina).

Rev. sci. tech. Off. int. Epiz., **25** (2)

Los autores ofrecen información actualizada sobre los diversos factores relacionados con los peces de vivero o capturados que pueden entrañar riesgo para la salud humana una vez consumidos. Además, examinan los problemas (en su sentido más amplio) vinculados a la manipulación de peces durante su captura o cría y en el curso de su procesamiento.

Palabras clave

Acuicultura – Agente zoonótico – Alergia – Alimento de origen marino – Compuesto orgánico lipofílico persistente – Contaminante – Inocuidad de los alimentos – Manipulación del pescado – Metal – Pez – Pez de vivero – Pez salvaje – Piscicultura – Procesamiento del pescado – Residuo.

References

1. Actis L.A., Tolmasky M.E. & Crosa J.H. (1999). – Vibriosis. *In* Fish diseases and disorders, Vol. 3. Viral, bacterial and fungal infections (P.T.K. Woo & D.W. Bruno, eds). CABI Publishing, Wallingford, Oxfordshire, United Kingdom, 523-557.

2. Alderman D.J. & Hastings T.S. (1998). – Antibiotic use in aquaculture: development of antibiotic resistance – potential for consumer health risks. *Int. J. Food Sci. Technol.*, **33**, 139-155.

3. Amaro C. & Biosca E.G. (1996). – *Vibrio vulnificus* biotype 2, pathogenic for eels, is also an opportunistic pathogen for humans. *Appl. environ. Microbiol.*, **62** (4), 1454-1457.

4. Anon. (2001). – Stockholm Convention on Persistent Organic Pollutants, prepared under the auspices of the United Nations (UN) Environment Programme Chemical Division. Treaty adopted at the Conference of Plenipotentiaries, Stockholm, 24 May, open for signature at UN Headquarters, New York, until 22 May.

5. Anon. (2005). – Asian response to malachite green residues in fish. AquaVetMed, 3 September. Available at: http://news.xinhuanet.com/english/200508/22/content_3389085.htm.

6. Austin B., Austin D., Sutherland R., Thompson F. & Swings J. (2005). – Pathogenicity of vibrios to rainbow trout (*Oncorhynchus mykiss*, Walbaum) and *Artemia nauplii. Environ. Microbiol.*, **7** (9), 1488-1495.

7. Bell J.G., McGhee F., Dick J.R. & Tocher D.R. (2005). – Dioxin and dioxin-like polychlorinated biphenyls (PCBs) in Scottish farmed salmon (*Salmo salar*): effects of replacement of dietary marine fish oil with vegetable oils. *Aquaculture*, **243** (1-4), 305-314.

8. Ben Embarek P.K. (1994). – Microbial safety and spoilage of *sous vide* fish products. Thesis/dissertation. Technological Laboratory of the Danish Ministry of Agriculture and Fisheries/Royal Veterinary and Agricultural University, Frederiksberg, Copenhagen.

9. Berlin M. (1986). – Mercury. *In* Handbook on the toxicology of metals (L. Friberg, G.F. Nordberg & V.B. Vouk, eds), Vol. 2. Elsevier, Amsterdam, 387-445.

10. Berntssen M.H.G., Hylland K., Julshamn K., Lundebye A.-K. & Waagbø R. (2004). – Maximum limits of organic and inorganic mercury in fish feed. *Aquacult. Nutr.*, **10** (2), 83-97.

11. Berntssen M.H.G., Lundebye A.-K. & Torstensen B.E. (2005). – Reducing the levels of dioxins and dioxin-like PCBs in farmed Atlantic salmon by substitution of fish oil with vegetable oil in the feed. *Aquacult. Nutr.*, **11** (3), 219-231.

12. Bisharat N. & Raz R. (1996). – *Vibrio* infection in Israel due to changes in fish marketing. *Lancet*, **348** (9041), 1585-1586.

13. Bloom N.S. (1992). – On the chemical form of mercury in edible fish and marine invertebrate tissue. *Can. J. Fish. aquat. Sci.*, **49** (5), 1010-1017.

14. Bock S.A. (1982). – The natural history of food sensitivity. *J. Allergy clin. Immunol.*, **69** (2), 173-177.

15. Boudou A. & Ribeyre F. (1985). – Experimental study of trophic contamination of *Salmo gairdneri*: two mercury compounds – $HgCl_2$ and $CH_3 HgCl$ – analysis at the organism and organ levels. *Water Air Soil Pollut.*, **26**, 137-148.

Rev. sci. tech. Off. int. Epiz., **25** (2)

621

16. Breivik H. & Thorstad O. (2004). – Removal of organic environmental pollutants from fish oil by short path distillation: the effect of a working fluid. *In* Proc. EuroFed Lipid Conference, Edinburgh, 5-8 September. Eurofed, Edinburgh.

17. Bremer P.J., Fletcher G.C. & Osborne C. (2003). – *Listeria monocytogenes* in seafood. *NZ Crop & Food Res.*, May, 1-15. Available at: www.crop.cri.nz/home/research/marine/pathogens, *Listeria* (accessed on 24 May 2006).

18. Calif E., Kaufman B. & Stahl S. (2003). – *Vibrio vulnificus* infection of the lower limb after fish spine injuries. *Clin. Orthopaedics related Res.*, **411**, 274-279.

19. Cann D.C. & Taylor L.Y. (1982). – An outbreak of botulism in rainbow trout, *Salmo gairdnerii* Richardson, farmed in Britain. *J. Fish Dis.*, **5** (5), 393-399.

20. Cassetty C.T. & Sanchez M. (2004). – *Mycobacterium marinum* infection. *Dermatol. online J.*, **10** (3), 21.

21. Centers for Disease Control and Prevention (CDC) (1996). – Invasive infection with *Streptococcus iniae* – Ontario, 1995-1996. *JAMA*, **276** (11), 866-867; *MMWR*, **45** (30), 650-653. Available at: www.cdg.gov/mmwr (accessed on 17 July 2006).

22. Chinabut S. (1999). – Mycobacteriosis and nocardiosis. *In* Fish diseases and disorders, Vol. 3. Viral, bacterial and fungal infections (P.T.K. Woo & D.W. Bruno, eds). CABI Publishing, Wallingford, Oxfordshire, United Kingdom, 319-340.

23. Coffey J.A. Jr, Harris R.L., Rutledge M.L., Bradshaw M.W. & Williams T.W. Jr (1986). – *Vibrio damsela*: another potentially virulent marine vibrio. *J. infect. Dis.*, **153** (4), 800-802.

24. Dabrowski W., Różcka-Kasztelan K., Kur J. & Kotlowski R. (2000). – *Listeria monocytogenes* in salted herring. *Electronic J. Polish Agricult. Univ., Series Food Sci. Technol.*, **3** (2), 8.

25. Dalsgaard A. (1998). – The occurrence of human pathogenic *Vibrio* spp. and *Salmonella* in aquaculture. *Int. J. Food Sci. Technol.*, **33**, 127-138.

26. De Kock J., De Gryt W., Ayala V., Vanheerswynghels P. & Kellens M. (2004). – Removal of dioxins and PCB's from marine oils: current status and future developments. *In* Proc. 11th International Symposium on nutrition and feeding in fish, Phuket Island, Thailand, 2-7 May.

27. De Wit C.A., Alaee M. & Muir D. (2004). – Brominated flame retardants in the Arctic – an overview of spatial and temporal trends. *Organohalogen Compounds*, **66**, 3811-3816.

28. Dieng M.T., Niang S.O., Ly F., Bathily T. & Ndiaye B. (2001). – Necrotizing dermo-hypodermatitis due to *Vibrio vulnificus*. *Ann. Dermatol. Venerol.*, **128** (5), 653-655.

29. Eigenmann P.A., Sicherer S.H., Borkowski T.A., Cohen B.A. & Sampson H.A. (1998). – Prevalence of IgE-mediated food allergy among children with atopic dermatitis. *Pediatrics*, **101** (3), E8. Available at: http://www.pediatrics.org/cgi/content/full/101/3/e8 (accessed on 17 July 2006).

30. Eklund M.W., Peterson M.E., Poysky F.T., Peck L.W. & Conrad J.F. (1982). – Botulism in juvenile coho salmon (*Oncorhynchus kisutch*) in the United States. *Aquaculture*, **27**, 1-11.

31. Eklund M.W., Poysky F.T., Paranjpye R.N., Lashbrook L.C., Peterson M.E. & Pelroy G.A. (1995). – Incidence and sources of *Listeria monocytogenes* in cold-smoked fishery products and processing plants. *J. Food Protec.*, **58** (5), 502-508.

32. Eldar A., Bejerano Y. & Bercovier H. (1994). – *Streptococcus shiloi* and *Streptococcus difficile*: two new streptococcal species causing a meningoencephalitis in fish. *Curr. Microbiol.*, **28**, 139-143.

33. Eldar A., Frelier P.F., Assenta L., Varner P.W., Lawhon S. & Bercovier H. (1995). – *Streptococcus shiloi*, the name of an agent causing septicemic infection in fish, is a junior synonym of *Streptococcus iniae*. *Int. J. syst. Bacteriol.*, **45** (4), 840-842.

34. European Commission (EC) (2000). – Opinion of the Scientific Committee on Animal Nutrition (SCAN) on the dioxin contamination of feedingstuffs and their contribution to the contamination of food of animal origin. EC, Brussels. Available at: http://europa.eu.int/comm/food/fs/sc/scan/outcome.en.html.

35. European Commission (EC) (2000). – Opinion of the Scientific Committee on Toxicity, Ecotoxicity and the Environment (CSTEE) on the results of the environmental risk assessment of: decabromodiphenyl ether. CAS No. 1163-19-5. EINECS No. 214-604-9. Opinion expressed at the 16th CSTEE plenary meeting, Brussels, 19 June. EC, Brussels. Available at: http://europa.eu.int/comm/health/ph_risk/committees/sct/docshtml/sct_out67_en.htm.

36. European Commission (EC) (2000). – Opinion of the Scientific Committee on Toxicity, Ecotoxicity and the Environment (CSTEE) on the results of the human risk assessment of: pentabromodiphenyl ether. CAS No. 32534-81-9. Opinion expressed at the 16th CSTEE plenary meeting, Brussels, 19 June. EC, Brussels. Available at: http://europa.eu.int/comm/health/ph_risk/committees/sct/docshtml/sct_out64_en.htm.

37. European Commission (EC) (2001). – Opinion of the Scientific Committee on Food (SCF) on the risk assessment of dioxins and dioxin-like PCBs in food (update based on the new scientific information available since the adoption of the SCF opinion of 22 November 2000). EC, Brussels. Available at: http://europa.eu.int/comm/food/fs/sc/scf/outcome_en. html.

38. European Commission (EC) (2005). – Scientific Committee on Health and Environmental Risks (SCHER) opinion on: update of the risk assessment of bis (pentabromophenyl) ether (decabromodiphenyl ether). CAS No. 1163-19-5. EINECS No. 214-604-9. Adopted by SCHER on the 4th plenary meeting of 18 March. Available at: http://europa.eu.int/comm/health/ph_risk/committees/04_scher/docs/scher_o_012.pdf.

39. European Commission (EC) Joint Research Centre (JRC) (2001). – European Union risk assessment report on pentabromodiphenyl ether (diphenyl ether, pentabromo deriv.). CAS No. 32534-81-9. EC, Brussels. Available at: http://ecb.jrc.it/DOCUMENTS/Existing-Chemicals/RISK_ASSESSMENT/REPORT/penta_bdpereport 015.pdf.

40. European Commission (EC) Joint Research Centre (JRC) (2002). – European Union risk assessment report on decabromodiphenyl ether (bis [pentabromophenyl] ether). CAS No. 1163-19-5. EC, Brussels. Available at: http://ecb.jrc.it/DOCUMENTS/Existing-Chemicals/RISK _ASSESSMENT/REPORT/decabromodiphenyletherreport 013.pdf.

41. European Commission (EC) Joint Research Centre (JRC) (2002). – European Union risk assessment report on hexabromocyclododecane. Draft report, August 2003. EC, Brussels.

42. European Commission (EC) Joint Research Centre (JRC) (2003). – European Union risk assessment report on octabromodiphenyl ether (diphenyl ether, octabromo deriv.). CAS No. 32536-52-0. EC, Brussels. Available at: http://ecb.jrc.it/DOCUMENTS/Existing-Chemicals/RISK_ASSESSMENT/REPORT/octareport014.pdf.

43. European Commission (EC) Joint Research Centre (JRC) (2004). – European Union risk assessment report on decabromodiphenyl ether (bis [pentabromophenyl] ether). CAS No. 1163-19-5. Final environmental draft. EC, Brussels. Available at: http://ecb.jrc.it/DOCUMENTS/Existing-Chemicals/RISK_ASSESSMENT/ADDENDUM/decabromo diphenylether_add_013.pdf.

44. European Food Safety Authority (EFSA) (2004). – Opinion of the Scientific Panel on Contaminants in the Food Chain on a request from the Commission related to mercury and methylmercury in food (EFSA-Q-2003-030). EFSA, Parma, Italy. Available at: http://www.efsa.eu.int/science/contam/contam_opinions/259/opinion_contam_01_en1.pdf.

45. European Food Safety Authority (EFSA) (2004). – The 1st Scientific Colloquium on methodologies and principles for setting tolerable intake levels for dioxins, furans and dioxin-like PCB's. Scientific Colloquium 1 – Summary report and presentations. EFSA, Parma, Italy. Available at: http://www.efsa.eu.int/science/colloquium_series/no1_dioxin s/599_en.html.

46. European Food Safety Authority (EFSA) (2005). – Opinion of the Scientific Committee on a request from EFSA related to a harmonized approach for risk assessment of compounds which are both genotoxic and carcinogenic. Request No. EFSA-Q-2004-020. *EFSA J.*, **282**, 1-31.

47. European Food Safety Authority (EFSA) (2005). – Opinion of the Scientific Panel on Contaminants in the Food Chain on a request from the Commission related to the presence of non-dioxin-like polychlorinated biphenyls (PCBs) in feed and food. Adapted on 8 November, Question No. EFSA-Q-2003-114. EFSA, Parma, Italy.

48. European Union (EU) (2003). – EC Commission Decision of 22 December 2003 amending Decision 2002/657/EC as regards the setting of minimum required performance limits (MRPLs) for certain residues in food of animal origin. *Off. J. Eur. Union*, **L 006** of 10.01.2004, 38-39.

49. Facklam R., Elliott J., Shewmaker L. & Reingold A. (2005). – Identification and characterization of sporadic isolates of *Streptococcus iniae* isolated from humans. *J. clin. Microbiol.*, **43** (2), 933-937.

50. Farmer J.J. III, Davis B.R., Hickman-Brenner F.W., McWhorter A., Huntley-Carter G.P., Asbury M.A., Riddle C., Wathen-Grady H.G., Elias C., Fanning E.G.R., Steigerwalt A.G., O'Hara C.M., Morris K.G., Smith P.B. & Brenner D.J. (1985). – Biochemical identification of new species and biogroups of Enterobacteriaceae isolated from clinical specimens. *J. clin. Microbiol.*, **21** (1), 46-76.

51. Fazal B.A., Justman J.E., Turett G.S. & Telzak E.E. (1997). – Community-acquired *Hafnia alvei* infection. *Clin. infect. Dis.*, **24** (3), 527-528.

52. FishUpdate.com (2005). – Malachite green found in frozen eel. 21 July. Special Publications, Edinburgh.

53. Food and Agriculture Organization of the United Nations (FAO) (1999). – Report of the FAO Expert Consultation on the trade impact of *Listeria* in fish products. Amherst, Massachusetts, 17-20 May. *FAO Fish. Rep.*, **604**, 1-34.

54. Food and Agriculture Organization of the United Nations (FAO) (2001). – Hazard identification, exposure assessment and hazard characterization of *Campylobacter* spp. in broiler chickens and *Vibrio* spp. in seafood. Joint FAO/World Health Organization (WHO) Expert Consultations on risk assessment of microbiological hazards in food, Geneva, 23-27 July. WHO, Geneva.

55. Food and Agriculture Organization of the United Nations (FAO) (2005). – The state of world fisheries and aquaculture (SOFIA), Part 1: world review of fisheries and aquaculture. FAO, Rome. Available at: www.fao.org/fi/statist/FISOFT/FISHPLUS.asp.

56. Gelev I., Gelev E., Steigerwalt A.G., Carter G.P. & Brenner D.J. (1990). – Identification of the bacterium associated with haemorrhagic septicaemia in rainbow trout as *Hafnia alvei*. *Res. Microbiol.*, **141** (5), 573-576.

57. Gislason D., Björnsson E., Gislason T., Janson C., Sjöberg O., Elfman L. & Boman G. (1999). – Sensitization to airborne and food allergens in Reykjavik (Iceland) and Uppsala (Sweden) – a comparative study. *Allergy*, **54** (11), 1160-1167.

58. Goh S.H., Driedger D., Gillett S., Low D.E., Hemmingsen S.M., Amos M., Chan D., Lovgren M., Willey B.M., Shaw B. & Smith J.A. (1998). – *Streptococcus iniae*, a human and animal pathogen: specific identification by the chaperonin 60 gene identification method. *J. clin. Microbiol.*, **36** (7), 2164-2166.

Rev. sci. tech. Off. int. Epiz., **25** (2)

623

59. Handy R.D. & Penrice W.S. (1993). – The influence of high oral doses of mercuric chloride on organ toxicant concentrations and histopathology in rainbow trout, *Oncorhynchus mykiss. Comp. Biochem. Physiol.,* **106 C**, 717-724.

60. Håstein T., Gudding R. & Evensen Ø. (2005). – Bacterial vaccines for fish – an update of the current situation worldwide. *In* Progress in fish vaccinology (P.J. Midtlyng, ed.). *Dev. Biol.,* **121**, 55-74.

61. Healy G.R. (1970). – Trematodes transmitted to man by fish, frogs, and crustacea. *J. Wildl. Dis.,* **6** (4), 255-261.

62. Heinitz M.L. & Johnson J.M. (1998). – The incidence of *Listeria* spp., *Salmonella* spp., and *Clostridium botulinum* in smoked fish and shellfish. *J. Food Protec.,* **61** (3), 318-323.

63. Hielm S., Hyytiä E., Andersen A.B. & Korkeala H. (1998). – A high prevalence of *Clostridium botulinum* type E in Finnish freshwater and Baltic Sea sediment samples. *J. appl. Microbiol.,* **84** (1), 133-137.

64. Hill D.J., Firer M.A., Ball G. & Hosking C.S. (1989). – Recovery from milk allergy in early childhood: antibody studies. *J. Pediatr.,* **114** (5), 761-766.

65. Hjetland R., Søgnen E. & Våge V. (1995). – *Erysipelothrix rhusiopathiae* – a cause of erysipeloid and endocarditis [in Norwegian]. *Tidsskr. Nor. Lægeforen.,* **115** (22), 2780-2782.

66. Hsueh P.R., Lin C.Y., Tang H.J., Lee H.C., Liu J.W., Liu Y.C. & Chuang Y.C. (2004). – *Vibrio vulnificus* in Taiwan. *Emerg. infect. Dis.,* **10** (8), 11. Available at: http://www.cdc.gov/ncidod/EID/vol10no8/04-0047.htm (accessed on 17 July 2006).

67. Huss H.H. (1980). – Distribution of *Clostridium botulinum. Appl. environ. Microbiol.,* **39** (4), 764-769.

68. Huss H.H. & Eskildsen U. (1974). – Botulism in farmed trout caused by *Clostridium botulinum* type E: a preliminary report. *Nord. vet. Med.,* **26** (12), 733-738.

69. Huss H.H. & Pedersen A. (1979). – *Clostridium botulinum* in fish. *Nord. vet. Med.,* **31** (5), 214-221.

70. Isosaari P., Kiviranta H., Lie Ø., Lundebye A.-K., Ritchie G. & Vartiainen T. (2004). – Accumulation and distribution of polychlorinated dibenzo-p-dioxin, dibenzofuran, and polychlorinated biphenyl congeners in Atlantic salmon (*Salmo salar*). *Environ. Toxicol. Chem.,* **23** (7), 1672-1679.

71. Isosaari P., Lundebye A.-K., Ritchie G., Lie Ø., Kiviranta H. & Vartiainen T. (2005). – Dietary accumulation efficiencies and biotransformation of polybrominated diphenyl ethers in farmed Atlantic salmon (*Salmo salar*). *Food Addit. Contam.,* **22** (9), 829-837.

72. Janda J.M., Abbott S.L., Kroske-Bystrom S., Cheung W.K., Powers C., Koka R.P. & Tamura K. (1991). – Pathogenic properties of *Edwardsiella* species. *J. clin. Microbiol.,* **29** (9), 1997-2001.

73. Jensen S. & Jernelov A. (1969). – Biological methylation of mercury in aquatic organisms. *Nature,* **223** (207), 753-754.

74. Joiris C.R., Holsbeek L. & Moatemri N.L. (1999). – Total and methyl-mercury in sardines *Sardinella aurita* and *Sardina pilchardus* from Tunisia. *Mar. Pollut. Bull.,* **38** (3), 188-192.

75. Julshamn K., Ringdal O. & Brækkan O.R. (1982). – Mercury concentrations in liver and muscle of cod (*Gadus morhua*) as an evidence of migration between waters with different levels of mercury. *Bull. environ. Contam. Toxicol.,* **29**, 544.

76. Kamps L.R. & Miller H. (1972). – Total mercury-monomethyl-mercury content of several species of fish. *Bull. environ. Contam. Toxicol.,* **8**, 273.

77. Karl H., Kuhlmann H. & Ruoff U. (2003). – Transfer of PCDDs and PCDFs into the edible parts of farmed rainbow trout, *Oncorhynchus mykiss* (Walbaum), via feed. *Aquacult. Res.,* **34** (12), 1009-1014.

78. Kullavanijaya P., Sirimachan S. & Bhuddhavudhikrai P. (1993). – *Mycobacterium marinum* cutaneous infections acquired from occupations and hobbies. *Int. J. Dermatol.,* **32** (7), 504-507.

79. Kusuda R. & Salati F. (1999). – *Enterococcus seriolicida* and *Streptococcus iniae. In* Fish diseases and disorders, Vol. 3. Viral, bacterial and fungal infections (P.T.K. Woo & D.W. Bruno, eds). CABI Publishing, Wallingford, Oxfordshire, United Kingdom, 303-317.

80. Lau S.K.P., Woo P.C.Y., Tse H., Leung K.W., Wong S.S.Y. & Yuen K.Y. (2003). – Invasive *Streptococcus iniae* infections outside North America. *J. clin. Microbiol.,* **41** (3), 1004-1009.

81. Levsen A. (2005). – Zoonotiske parasitter fra fisk og sjømat. [Zoonotic parasites from fish and seafood]. *In* Fisk og sjømat – smitterisiko for mennesker [Fish and seafood – disease risk for humans] [in Norwegian]. Seminar 3, Bergen, Norway, November.

82. Lopata A.L. & Jeebhay M.F. (2001). – Seafood allergy in South Africa – studies in the domestic and occupational setting. *Allergy clin. Immunol. Int.: J. World Allergy Org.,* **13** (5), 204-210.

83. Love M., Teebken-Fisher D., Hose J.E., Farmer J.J. III, Hickman F.W. & Fanning G.R. (1981). – *Vibrio damsela,* a marine bacterium, causes skin ulcers on the damselfish, *Chromis punctipinnis. Science,* **214**, 1139-1140.

84. Lundebye A.-K., Berntssen M.H.G., Lie Ø., Ritchie G., Isosaari P., Kiviranta H. & Vartiainen T. (2004). – Dietary uptake of dioxins (PCDD/PCDFs) and dioxin-like PCBs in Atlantic salmon (*Salmo salar*). *Aquacult. Nutr.,* **10** (3), 199-207.

85. Meyer M.C. (1970). – Cestode zoonoses of aquatic animals. *J. Wildl. Dis.,* **6** (4), 249-254.

86. Morris J.G. Jr, Miller H.G., Wilson R., Tacket C.O., Hollis D.G., Hickman F.W., Weaver R.E. & Blake P.A. (1982). – Illness caused by *Vibrio damsela* and *Vibrio hollisae*. *Lancet*, **1** (8284), 1294-1297.

87. Nesse L.L., Løvold T., Bergsjø B., Nordby K., Wallace C. & Holstad G. (2005). – Persistence of orally administered *Salmonella enterica* serovars Agona and Montevideo in Atlantic salmon (*Salmo salar* L.). *J. Food Protec.*, **68** (7), 1336-1339.

88. Nordisk Atlantsamarbejde (NORA), Icelandic Association of Fishmeal Manufacturers and Havsbrún Faroe Islands (2003). – Dioxins and PCBs in four commercially important pelagic fish stocks in the North East Atlantic. Nordisk Atlanterhavssamarbejde (NORA), together with the Icelandic Association of Fishmeal Manufacturers and p/f Havsbrún Faero Islands, Thorshavn, Faero Islands. Available at: http://www.nora.fo/docs/Dioxin_Final_report.pdf (accessed on 18 July 2006).

89. Novotny L., Dvorska L., Lorencova A., Beran V. & Pavlik I. (2004). – Fish: a potential source of bacterial pathogens for human beings. *Vet. Med. (Praha)*, **49** (9), 343-358.

90. Oliver J.D. (1989). – *Vibrio vulnificus*. *In* Foodborne bacterial pathogens (M.P. Doyle, ed.). Marcel Dekker, New York, 569-599.

91. Oliver J.D. & Bockian R. (1995). – *In vivo* resuscitation, and virulence towards mice, of viable but nonculturable cells of *Vibrio vulnificus*. *J. Appl. environ. Microbiol.*, **61** (7), 2620-2623.

92. Oliver J.D. & Kaper J.B. (2001). – *Vibrio* species. *In* Food microbiology: fundamentals and frontiers (M.P. Doyle, ed.), 2nd Ed. ASM Press, Washington, DC, 263-300.

93. Padilla D., Real F., Gómez V., Sierra E., Acosta B., Déniz S. & Acosta F. (2005). – Virulence factors and pathogenicity of *Hafnia alvei* for gilthead seabream, *Sparus aurata* L. *J. Fish Dis.*, **28** (7), 411-417.

94. Paperna I. (1975). – Parasites and diseases of grey mullet (Mugilidae) with special reference to the seas of the near East. *Aquaculture*, **5**, 65-80.

95. Parker G. (2004). – Fish handler's disease on rise in Chesapeake Bay. Associated Press, 27 April. Available at: http://espn.go.com/outdoors/conservation/news/2004 (accessed on 23 May 2006).

96. Pascual C.Y., Martin Esteban M. & Crespo J.F. (1992). – Fish allergy: evaluation of the importance of cross-reactivity. *J. Pediatr.* **121** (5 Pt 2), S29-S34.

97. Perez-Tirse J., Levine J.F. & Mecca M. (1993). – *Vibrio damsella*: a cause of fulminant septicemia. *Arch. internal Med.*, **153** (15), 1838-1840.

98. Petersen A. & Dalsgaard A. (2003). – Antimicrobial resistance of intestinal *Aeromonas* spp. and *Enterococcus* spp. in fish cultured in integrated broiler-fish farms in Thailand. *Aquaculture*, **219**, 71-82.

99. Pier G.B. & Madin S.H. (1976). – *Streptococcus iniae* sp. nov., a beta-hemolytic streptococcus isolated from an Amazon freshwater dolphin, *Inia geoffrensis*. *Int. J. syst. Bacteriol.*, **26**, 545-553.

100. Roberts R.J. (2001). – Fish pathology. W.B. Saunders, London.

101. Rodriguez L.A., Gallardo C.S., Acosta F., Nieto T.P., Acosta B. & Real F. (1998). – *Hafnia alvei* as an opportunistic pathogen causing mortality in brown trout, *Salmo trutta* L. *J. Fish Dis.*, **21** (5), 365-370.

102. Rørvik L.M. (1991). – *Listeria monocytogenes* in foods; occurrence and characterization. Thesis for the degree of Doctor Scientiarum, Norwegian School of Veterinary Science, Oslo.

103. Rørvik L.M. (2005). – *Listeria* i fisk og sjømat [*Listeria* in fish and seafood]. *In* Fisk og sjømat – smitterisiko for mennesker [Fish and seafood – disease risk for humans] [in Norwegian]. Seminar 3, Bergen, Norway, November.

104. Sampson H.A. & Scanlon S.M. (1989). – Natural history of food hypersensitivity in children with atopic dermatitis. *J. Pediatr.*, **115** (1), 23-27.

105. Storelli M.M., Giacominelli Stuffler R. & Marcotrigiano G.O. (2001). – Total mercury and methylmercury in *Auxis rochei, Prionacee glauca* and *Squalus acanthias* from the South Adriatic Sea. *Ital. J. Food Sci.*, **13**, 103-108.

106. Tacket C.O., Barrett T.J., Mann J.M., Roberts M.A. & Blake P.A. (1984). – Wound infections caused by *Vibrio vulnificus*, a marine vibrio, in inland areas of the United States. *J. clin. Microbiol.*, **19** (2), 197-199.

107. Teshima C., Kudo S., Ohtani Y. & Saito A. (1992). – Kidney pathology from the bacterium *Hafnia alvei*: experimental evidence. *Trans. Am. Fish. Soc.*, **121**, 599-607.

108. Thomsen C., Lundanes E. & Becher G. (2002). – Brominated flame retardants in archived serum samples from Norway: a study on temporal trends and the role of age. *Environ. Sci. Technol.*, **36** (7), 1414-1418.

109. Tjaberg T.B. & Håstein T. (1975). – Utbredelse av *Clostridium botulinum* i norske fiskeoppdrettsanlegg [*Clostridium botulinum* in Norwegian fish farms]. *Norsk Vet. Tidsskr.*, **87**, 718-720.

110. Ucko M. & Colorni A. (2005). – *Mycobacterium marinum* infections in fish and humans in Israel. *J. clin. Microbiol.*, **43** (2), 892-895.

111. United Kingdom Committee on Toxicity in Food, Consumer Products and the Environment (COT) (2004). – COT statement on brominated flame retardants in fish from the Skerne-Tees rivers system. Statement agreed December 2003. The Stationery Office (TSO), London. Available at: http://www.food.gov.uk/science/ouradvisors/toxicity/statem ents/cotstatements2004branch/cotstatementbfrfish2004 (accessed on 17 July 2006).

Rev. sci. tech. Off. int. Epiz., **25** (2)

625

112. United Kingdom Committee on Toxicity in Food, Consumer Products and the Environment (COT) (2004). – COT statement on tetrabromobisphenol A – review of toxicological data. The Stationery Office (TSO), London. Available at: http://www.food.gov.uk/science/ouradvisors/ toxicity/statements/cotstatements2004branch/cotstatements 2004tbbpa (accessed on 17 July 2006).

113. United Kingdom Food Standards Agency (2004). – Advice on fish consumption: benefits and risks. Scientific Advisory Committee on Nutrition (SACN) and Committee on Toxicity (COT). The Stationery Office (TSO), London. Available at: http://www.food.gov.uk/multimedia/pdfs/fishreport2004full .pdf (accessed on 17 July 2006).

114. Van den Berg M., Birnbaum L., Bosveld A.T.C., Brunström B., Cook P., Feeley M., Giesy J.P., Hanberg A., Hasegawa R., Kennedy S.W., Kubiak T., Larsen J.C., van Leeuwen F.X.R., Liem A.K.D., Nolt C., Peterson R.E., Poellinger L., Safe S., Schrenk D., Tillitt D., Tysklind M., Younes M., Waern F. & Zacharewski T. (1998). – Toxic equivalency factors (TEFs) for PCBs, PCDDs, PCDFs for humans and wildlife. *Environ. Hlth Perspect.*, **106** (12), 775-792.

115. Van Thiel P.H., Kuipers F.C. & Roskam R.Th. (1960). – A nematode parasitic to herring causing acute abdominal syndromes in man. *Trop. geogr. Med.*, **12**, 97-113.

116. Weinstein M.R., Litt M., Kertesz D.A., Wyper P., Rose D., Coulter M., McGeer A., Facklam R., Ostach C., Willey B.M., Borczyk A. & Low D.E. (1997). – Invasive infections due to a fish pathogen, *Streptococcus iniae. N. Engl. J. Med.*, **337** (9), 589-594.

117. Westblom T.U. & Milligan T.W. (1992). – Acute bacterial gastroenteritis caused by *Hafnia alvei. Clin. infect. Dis.*, **14** (6), 1271-1272.

118. Wood J.M. (1974). – Biological cycles for toxic elements in the environment. *Science*, **183** (129), 1049-1052.

119. World Health Organization (WHO) (1995). – Control of foodborne trematode infections. Report of a WHO Study Group. WHO Technical Report Series 849. WHO, Geneva.

120. World Health Organization (WHO) (1999). – Food safety issues associated with products from aquaculture. Report of a Joint FAO/ Network of Aquaculture Centres in Asia-Pacific (NACA)/WHO Study Group. WHO Technical Report Series 883. WHO, Geneva.

121. World Health Organization (WHO) (2000). – Safety evaluation of certain food additives and contaminants. Joint FAO/WHO Expert Committee on Food Additives (JECFA). WHO Food Additives Series No. 44. WHO, Geneva.

122. World Health Organization (WHO) (2001). – Polychlorinated dibenzodioxins, polychlorinated dibenzofurans, and coplanar polychlorinated biphenyls. *In* Safety evaluation of certain food additives and contaminants. Joint FAO/WHO Expert Committee on Food Additives (JECFA). WHO Food Additives Series No. 48. WHO, Geneva. Available at: http://www.inchem.org/ documents/ jecfa/jecmono/v48je20.htm (accessed on 17 July 2006).

123. World Health Organization (WHO) (2004). – Safety evaluation of certain food additives and contaminants. Joint FAO/WHO Expert Committee on Food Additives (JECFA). WHO Food Additives Series No. 52. WHO, Geneva.

124. Wyatt L.E., Nickelson R. & Vanderzant C. (1979). – Occurrence and control of *Salmonella* in freshwater catfish. *J. Food Sci.*, **44** (4), 1067-1073.

125. Yanong R.P.E. & Francis-Floyd R. (2002). – Streptococcal infections of fish. University of Florida Extension, Circular 57. University of Florida, Ruskin, Florida.

126. Yndestad M. (1992). – Public health aspects of residues in animal products: fundamental considerations. *In* Chemotherapy in aquaculture: from theory to reality (C.M. Michel & D.J. Alderman, eds). Office International des Epizooties (OIE) Symposium, Paris, 12-15 March 1991. OIE, Paris, 494-510.

127. Yokogawa M. & Yoshimura H. (1965). – *Anisakis*-like larvae causing eosinophilic granulomata in stomach of man. *Am. J. trop. Med. Hyg.*, **14** (5), 770-773.

Rev. sci. tech. Off. int. Epiz., 2006, **25** (2), 627-635

Problems associated with shellfish farming

S. Chinabut [1], T. Somsiri [1], C. Limsuwan [2] & S. Lewis [1]

(1) Department of Fisheries, Jatujak, Bangkok 10900, Thailand
(2) Faculty of Fisheries, Kasetsart University, Jatujak, Bangkok 10900, Thailand

Summary
Shellfish culture is a major sector of aquaculture production worldwide, and zoonoses and drug residues associated with shellfish farm practice are of concern to public health. This paper focuses on three of the most important shellfish species: molluscs, crabs and shrimp. Although many diseases can affect shellfish, they do not appear to be transmittable to humans. Rather, the main hazards are associated with the methods used to farm the different species. The risk to human health from shellfish most commonly relates to contamination by biotoxins produced by marine algae. Another well-recognised problem associated with shellfish culture is the contamination of shellfish with domestic sewage that contains human pathogenic bacteria and viruses, which causes diseases such as typhoid fever and hepatitis. In shrimp farming, the main potential food safety hazards are zoonoses, chemical contamination and veterinary drug residues. Untreated effluent from shrimp farms is a major concern to the environmental sector as it is known to promote plankton blooms if directly discharged into natural water sources.

Keywords
Amnesic shellfish poisoning – Crab – Diarrhetic shellfish poisoning – Dinoflagellate – Food safety – Mollusc – Neurotoxic shellfish poisoning – Paralytic shellfish poisoning – Red tide – Shellfish farming – Shrimp – Toxic algae bloom – Vibrio cholerae.

Introduction

Shellfish aquaculture has continued to expand, with an ever-increasing consumer demand for shellfish-derived products worldwide, and a wide variety of different species of shellfish are cultured in various systems around the world. Increased population and human activity in the world's coastal regions continue to harm the environmental quality of near-shore waters. This increasing anthropogenic degradation of the coastal environment also has a negative effect on the quality and quantity of coastal shellfish culture. The use of intensive or super-intensive culture systems in the production of some shellfish species, involving factors such as heavy stocking densities and the use of feed, chemicals and drugs, can easily have a detrimental impact on the local environment. Such intensive methods of culture can also be responsible for the production of potentially unsafe shellfish products for the consumer market. The issue of food safety and quality is of paramount concern to the consumers of both importing and exporting countries, and particularly important for the shellfish industry, which needs to maintain consumer confidence in its products. Food safety hazards associated with shellfish farming generally vary according to the species and the type of culture system. This paper will therefore provide information on hazards that may occur during the production stages and can affect the safety of shellfish food. The paper will focus on the three main groups of shellfish farmed around the world: molluscs, crabs and shrimp.

Mollusc farming

The molluscs are among the most successfully cultured and commercially important types of shellfish, and a large variety of different mollusc species are cultured throughout the world. Some, such as oysters and abalones, have a very high market value. Molluscs are generally cultivated in inshore coastal areas, using bottom and hanging/pole-culturing systems. The main species cultured are clams, mussels, oysters and abalones.

Clams

Canada is one of the major producers of the Manila clam (*Tapes philippinarum*), which is one of the most commonly cultured species. The clam culture system involves three principal stages of production: seed production, nursery rearing and the grow-out stage. All three stages can be undertaken by large-scale clam farmers, but clams are usually cultured in separate specialised farms at each of the three stages. Hatcheries maintain the broodstock for seed production, which is sold to growers or nursery units. The seed can be raised to the specific sizes that growers prefer, as larger seed normally has a higher survival rate, thus making production more predictable. After the seeds have been removed from the nursery area, they will be spread on prepared sub-tidal plots where they will grow to a marketable size.

Mussels

Two mussel species (*Mytilus edulis* and *M. galloprovincialis*) are the principle types of cultured mussel on the coasts of the Netherlands, France and Spain. In New Zealand the green-lip mussel (*Perna canaliculus*) is the main cultured species of choice. In most Asian countries, mussel seed stock is collected from the wild, whereas in Western countries such as Canada the seed stock is supplied by hatcheries. The seed stock may be nursed on suitable surface materials or set on framed screens. After three months of nursing, the mussels are ready to be hung or 'socked' in the grow-out systems. A variety of systems are utilised for the grow-out in order to reduce losses of stock from predation. Both off-bottom systems, such as the suspended long-line and raft methods, and bottom culture techniques are used.

Oysters

The most commonly cultured species of oyster is the Pacific oyster (*Crassostrea gigas*). Other species that are grown to a lesser extent include the Pacific Kumamoto oyster (*C. sikamea*), European oyster (*Ostrea edulis*) and Eastern oyster (*C. virginica*) (6). Oyster culture methods vary widely, because many different factors – including substrate type, current velocity, tidal range and phytoplankton productivity – are important for culturing a specific species. Bottom culture is primarily practised by spreading the spat over the selected area in the bay and growing the young oysters to marketable size. However, to overcome predation problems, the off-bottom technique has been developed to give a variety of different methods, such as the hanging and rack systems. Another advantage of the off-bottom system is that the oysters are suspended in the water column, and less silt therefore accumulates on the oyster.

Abalones

Abalone (*Haliotis kamtschatkana*) is a high-value species for the Japanese market. The culture cycle consists of a hatchery phase, a juvenile phase, and a grow-out phase. Culture systems include the land-based tank system and suspended system (34). The land-based tank system with a seawater pumping unit is the most common type, but a suspended system in seawater has also been used with various types of containers, including plastic cages, plastic barrels and mesh pouches.

A significant biological barrier in the culture of abalone is the slow growth rate, which currently makes it one of the most expensive shellfish to culture. The culture technique requires a fully supplemented specific feeding regime for each of the various stages of abalone culture. For the hatchery stage, the young larvae must be fed on benthic algae and diatoms which have been coated onto a selected surface. The water-flow system and aeration must be regulated to adequately replenish the algal film for the larvae until they reach the juvenile stage. The young abalone is subsequently fed with macro-algae or feed pellets in the grow-out system.

Hazards to human health

Bivalves are filter-feeders and feed on a wide range of phytoplankton species in the marine environment. Filter-feeders are particularly susceptible to sudden blooms of phytoplankton organisms, which can occur in nutrient-enriched coastal areas and may contain biotoxins that are hazardous to human health. These toxic algae blooms are frequently referred to as 'red tides' in the popular literature. Paralytic shellfish poisoning (PSP) is one of the most serious diseases associated with red tides, and consumption of shellfish exposed to red tide blooms can result in high human mortality. In the Philippines consumption of shellfish exposed to an algal bloom of *Pyrodinium*, a toxic dinoflagellate, resulted in the deaths of at least 21 people and the hospitalisation of over 200 others in June to August 1983 (22). Bivalves affected by red tides do not generally

Rev. sci. tech. Off. int. Epiz., **25** (2)

629

die, but tend to accumulate toxins within their flesh. Depuration studies have shown that bivalves can be depurated, but a long time is required to make contaminated shellfish safe for human consumption, and this option is therefore uneconomical at present.

Another problem associated with filter-feeding bivalves is their susceptibility in estuarine and coastal areas to contamination with domestic sewage, which is known to contain bacteria and viruses that are pathogenic to humans. Again it is known that these pathogens can accumulate in the flesh of bivalves. Major disease risks from this source are typhoid and paratyphoid fever, salmonellosis, *Vibrio parahaemolyticus* infection, cholera, viral hepatitis type A and viral gastroenteritis. Contaminated bivalves can be made edible by:

a) re-laying, or transferring the shellfish to pollution-free waters

b) depuration.

These processes are expensive and require large inputs of time and labour.

Diarrhetic shellfish poisoning (DSP) is a food-borne illness caused by the consumption of shellfish that contain biotoxins produced by dinoflagellates belonging to the genera *Dinophysis* and *Prorocentrum* (37, 38). It is a gastrointestinal disease with no neurological symptoms. The first reported cases occurred in the Netherlands in the 1960s (1), and since then outbreaks have been described in Japan, Europe, South America, and the Far East. In Antwerp, Belgium, 403 cases of DSP were reported in February 2002 after consumption of blue mussels that contained biotoxins specific to dinoflagellates. The mussels were imported from Denmark and were part of a batch presenting high concentrations of okadaic acid above the regulatory limits (9).

The cause of DSP is a group of polyethers, including okadaic acid, dinophysis toxins, pectenotoxins and yessotoxin (5). Poisoning caused by these toxins is probably under-diagnosed and under-reported in many parts of the world because of the non-specific symptoms and because the disease itself is often limited and mild.

The much more serious PSP is due to a toxin produced by single-celled dinoflagellate algae of the genus *Alexandrium* which causes neurological symptoms that include paralysis, numbness and disorientation (25). The toxicity of PSP is estimated to be 1,000 times greater than cyanide and all cases require immediate medical attention.

Apart from PSP, algal biotoxins can also cause amnesic shellfish poisoning (ASP) and neurotoxic shellfish poisoning (NSP) in people who consume contaminated shellfish. These toxins can also have adverse effects on fish, shore birds and marine mammals. The cause of ASP is domoic acid, found in marine algae and some species of diatoms. It is accumulated in a number of filter-feeding bivalve molluscs, including mussels, clams, scallops and oysters. The symptoms of ASP may vary from nausea, vomiting and diarrhoea to muscle weakness, disorientation and memory loss (4). Although ASP is relatively uncommon, cases have occurred in eastern Canada, North America, Spain, Ireland and Scotland, causing illness and death.

The alga *Karenia brevis*, which produces brevetoxin, causes the gastrointestinal and neurological symptoms of NSP. Affected people can recover completely in a few days and no deaths due to the syndrome have been reported. Another algal toxin hazard is azaspiracid poisoning (AZP), produced by a dinoflagellate species, *Protoperidinium* sp., which also causes vomiting, diarrhoea, abdominal pain and headache. In addition, AZP may have serious long-term impacts, such as the development of pneumonia and lung tumours.

In Spain, cases of *V. parahaemolyticus* infections are now more common in hospitals than previously. The organism has been isolated from patients with gastroenteritis in the areas where most Spanish shellfish are produced. Before 2004, most Spanish clinical isolates were serotype 04:K11, which was shown to be a unique clone distinct from Asian and American clinical strains. By mid-2004, however, all isolates of *V. parahaemolyticus* from the patients were 03:K6, which exhibited a pattern indistinguishable from those of pandemic strains from Asia. The pandemic 03:K6 clone of *V. parahaemolyticus* appeared in Asia around 1996. It spread to the United States in 1998 and more recently to Chile, where it has caused hundreds of infections, resulting in the first *V. parahaemolyticus* pandemic in history. The emergence of this virulent serotype in Europe is a serious public health concern that demonstrates the need to include *V. parahaemolyticus* in microbiological surveillance and re-examine control programmes in Europe for shellfish-harvesting areas and ready-to-eat seafood (24).

The way forward

A programme for the comprehensive monitoring and regular analysis of molluscs should be implemented to provide an early warning to the public of the appearance of biotoxins in molluscs. Samples of molluscs in growing areas should be regularly collected and tested for shellfish poisons. When the toxin level exceeds the regulatory limit, the growing area should be quarantined and sale prohibited, and the public health authorities should be informed. The programme should include a routine assessment of coastal resources for the presence of marine biotoxins and toxic phytoplankton blooming before public health is threatened. Some biotoxins may be associated with certain seasons. For instance, although azaspiracid-contaminated shellfish can occur in all seasons, the prevalence is much higher in the summer months (18). Therefore, the biotoxin distribution of each area, which may vary with the seasons, should be well documented in each country to support provision of public health measures.

Crab farming

Crab aquaculture has been practised for many years in Southeast Asia and is an important source of income among fish farmers. Crab culture operations have not expanded to the level of shrimp or prawn culture, and stocking densities are comparatively low.

Aquaculture of mud crabs has been conducted for at least a century in the People's Republic of China (36) and for the past 30 years throughout Asia (19). Crab farming is a relatively simple aquaculture practice. Traditionally, mud crab culture was based on stocking wild-caught juveniles and adults for grow-out culture and fattening. Although hatchery production of megalopae is now feasible, the initial source of spawners and broodstock is mostly wild stock. Four species of mud crabs (*Scylla* sp.) are distributed in the Indo-Pacific region: *S. serrata, S. olivacea, S. tranquebarica,* and *S. paramamosain*. They are all currently recognised for culture purposes. *Scylla serrata* is the most commonly farmed species in many Southeast Asian countries and Australia (7), while *S. olivacea* and *S. paramamosain* are the two common species farmed in the lower Mekong Delta (23).

There are two types of land-based mud crab aquacultures; one involves fattening crabs with low flesh content, and the other is grow-out of juveniles to a marketable size. Mangrove ponds/pens are used to operate two kinds of system: an intensive system with high stocking rates and supplementary feeding, and an extensive system where the stocking rate is low and there is no supplementary feeding (19). Various chemicals are used to control or treat disease, including malachite green, copper sulphate and zinc sulphate (20).

Hazards to human health

Vibrio cholerae is a natural bacteria occurring in brackish and estuarine waters, which can cause diarrhoea in humans. *Vibrio cholerae* O1 was isolated from blue crabs in Malaysia in 2003 (11). A case of cholera occurred in a patient in Maryland, who had eaten crab harvested commercially along the Texas coast in October 1984 (21). Findings of *V. cholerae* in the hindgut of crabs are considered to be correlated with the epidemiology and transmission of cholera in the aquatic environment (16).

The way forward

Crab or crab meat is normally cooked before consumption, so the health risk is low. However, contamination with bacteria that can cause human diseases may occur during the processing of crab meat, and food safety regulations should therefore be strictly applied.

Shrimp farming

The shrimp industry has grown very rapidly in the last two decades, with a wide variety of different shrimp and prawn species being cultured in many parts of the world. The two predominant areas for large-scale culture today are Asia and South America. The giant freshwater prawn, *Macrobrachium rosenbergii*, has been cultured in many Southeast Asian countries for more than four decades (27). Pacific white shrimp (*Litopenaeus vannamei*) is widespread along the eastern coast of the Pacific Ocean from Mexico to northern Peru (15, 28). More recently, culture of the black tiger shrimp, *Penaeus monodon*, has been booming in many regions.

Most Latin American countries, such as Brazil, Ecuador, Panama, Peru and Mexico, use a semi-intensive system for culturing white shrimp (2). However, since the outbreak of white spot syndrome virus in Latin American countries in 1999, some farms have changed to an intensive culture system with smaller pond sizes. In Asia, the black tiger shrimp is currently the most widely cultured type, particularly in Thailand, Indonesia, India, Vietnam, Sri Lanka, the Philippines and Malaysia. These countries together contribute about 60% of the world's total cultured shrimp production (10). Most countries in Asia use semi-intensive culture systems, but Thailand, the leading shrimp exporter for over ten years, uses an intensive culture system.

Currently, shrimp farming in Asia is undergoing a dramatic transformation. The white shrimp (*L. vannamei*) is rapidly replacing the giant or black tiger shrimp as the main farmed species. This change began in Taipei China in the late 1990s with the importation of specific-pathogen-free (SPF) broodstock of *L. vannamei* from Hawaii. The People's Republic of China then began to import this broodstock, followed by Thailand, Indonesia and Vietnam, and the white shrimp is now being cultured on a very large scale. The main reason for this change is that *L. vannamei* has a faster growth, higher yield and lower production costs than *P. monodon*. The biological basis of this advantage is the SPF and domestication status of imported *L. vannamei*. In contrast, *P. monodon* post-larvae are produced from wild-caught broodstock and are both non-domesticated and contaminated with pathogens.

Rev. sci. tech. Off. int. Epiz., **25** (2)

631

The impacts of shrimp farming can be categorised into two groups, environmental impact and hazards to human health.

Impact of shrimp farming on the environment

In the past, most shrimp farms in Southeast Asia were located in mangrove forests and used extensive culture systems. Shrimp seed was typically obtained from the wild as post-larvae, either passively in water that was pumped into the ponds, or through the collection from one location of post-larvae which were then transferred into ponds at other locations. This type of shrimp culture destroyed large areas of mangrove forests, which are the spawning ground for many species of aquatic animals, including shrimp. Mangrove forests can also protect land from waves and storms, and even offer considerable protection from such catastrophic events as tsunami. In the future, no aquaculture farming – including shrimp culture – should exploit these important areas.

There is growing concern about environmental pollution from the rapid expansion of shrimp farm areas. In the intensive shrimp culture system, pollution from shrimp farms is directly related to excessive use of feed. The effluents from the ponds are flushed out into the surrounding water resources during the culture period or after harvest. The major components of the wastes are dissolved nutrients such as ammonia, nitrogen, carbon dioxide and phosphorus; suspended organic solids such as faeces and phytoplankton; and inorganic suspended solids such as clay particles. These wastes often exceed the natural biological capacity to degrade such materials, leading to widespread eutrophication and degradation of the environment in many areas.

The way forward

In order to stop the harm caused to surrounding areas by waste from shrimp farms, shrimp culture practice should be based on a recirculation system. In such a system, wastewater from shrimp culture is reused after it has been treated in various ways. The treatment processes ensure water quality, make better use of the water, and at the same time protect the environment by reducing the waste discharge. The treatment units are described in the following sections.

Sedimentation pond

This first treatment involves storing wastewater in a pond to remove by sedimentation any settable solids that are present. Aeration of the pond water can be used to enhance the sedimentation process and help oxidise waste organic material. The aeration process also facilitates the oxidisation of toxic gases such as ammonia, nitrite and hydrogen sulphide into other more harmless compounds.

For small shrimp farms, water from cultured ponds should be kept in the sedimentation pond for an appropriate period of time (until the water quality parameters meet national requirements or regulations) before it is discharged outside the farm into surrounding water.

Fish or other filter-feeding organisms

These organisms are involved with the secondary treatment pond. Filter-feeding fish such as tilapia or mullet are the most common species recommended. These fish species remove any waste organic material that remains suspended in the water after the sedimentation process. Water from these ponds will then be reused for shrimp ponds during the different cycles.

Hazards to human health

Potential food safety risks associated with shrimp aquaculture will vary according to the system that is used. Hazards may include biological contaminants such as pathogenic bacteria, or chemical contamination by agro-chemicals, veterinary drug residues and heavy metals. The reasons for these food safety hazards are very diverse, ranging from poor aquacultural practices to cultural habits of food preparation and consumption.

Improper management by shrimp culturists in many countries during the grow-out period can cause human health problems. Organic fertilisers are widely used to promote phytoplankton blooms as a food source for the shrimp in the first stage of shrimp culture. Materials used to promote these blooms have included animal manures, grass, by-products from the harvesting or processing of agricultural products, waste from fisheries and aquaculture processing plants, and discarded fish. In some instances discarded fish and processing wastes have been used not only as fertiliser but as feed. Most of these bloom-creating materials clearly have the potential to introduce serious contamination hazards into the shrimp under culture conditions.

The use of uncooked organisms and their by-products as feed in shrimp ponds can also promote the spread of shrimp diseases. Such raw food has a high oxygen demand that can degrade pond-water quality and so affect the health of the shrimp.

Shrimp producers do not intentionally dispose of human sewage in ponds, but some farms draw water from rivers or estuaries that receive untreated human waste in the immediate vicinity of the farm. Wastes of human and animal origin are a source of pathogenic organisms that may be transmitted to humans via the products of aquaculture. Disease transmission associated with aquaculture use of excreta and wastewater has been reported by the International Reference Centre of Waste Disposal (17). There are potential health hazards for humans who consume inadequately cooked shrimp grown in ponds that receive human waste, untreated animal manure or organic fertilisers containing salmonella or other food-poisoning organisms.

Most countries culture shrimp for export. The greatest problem affecting the export of frozen shrimp is contamination by microorganisms that are pathogenic to humans, especially *Salmonella* and pathogenic *Vibrio* spp. Environmental sources of these organisms include water, soil, insects, animal faeces, raw meats, raw poultry and raw seafood. *Salmonella typhi* and the paratyphoid bacteria cause acute disease, normally septicaemia, and produce typhoid or typhoid-like fever in humans. Other forms of salmonellosis generally produce milder, gastrointestinal symptoms and have led to public health problems in various countries. *Salmonella* has been detected in samples of the water supply, pond water (3, 31), feed materials, fresh shrimp at farms (29, 31) and from wholesale markets, and frozen shrimp destined for export (32, 33, 35).

Both *V. cholerae* O1 and *V. cholerae* non-O1 have been isolated from water of shrimp cultured in brackish water in Southeast Asia, with *V. cholerae* O1 present in 2% and *V. cholerae* non-O1 in 33% of samples (8, 31). In similar studies, *V. cholerae* non-O1 was isolated from shrimp culture environment in India (26).

Antibiotics

Current knowledge of the health and environmental impact of antibiotics used in aquaculture is poor, particularly in tropical regions. Improper use of antibiotics in hatcheries and grow-out ponds will result in antibiotic residues in cultured shrimp. Most importing countries have prohibited the use of chloramphenicol and nitrofurans in aquaculture.

The Food and Drug Administration in the United States of America (USA) banned the powerful and potentially toxic chloramphenicol (one of the phenicols) in 1989 because of the risks of antibiotic resistance developing in human pathogens and a link with a rare and often fatal disease, aplastic anaemia (13). Chloramphenicol is highly toxic to humans, but the antibiotics are used to treat humans in life-threatening situations when no other drug is effective. Europe, Japan and many other countries also banned the antibiotic in feed, but it is still permitted for specific veterinary treatments.

Nitrofurans are also dangerous because of their potential carcinogenic properties, and so their use in animals produced for human consumption is similarly banned in the European Union and the USA (12, 14). The USA is comparatively strict in this respect, limiting the use of antibiotics in aquaculture to three drugs: oxytetracycline, sulphamerazine, and a drug combination containing sulphadimethozine and ormethoprime. The occurrence of antibiotic residues in cultured shrimp from several exporting countries from Asia has led to rejection of the product in export markets.

The way forward

The use of chemical fertilisers, properly treated organic manure and pellet feed in ponds should be encouraged. Some uncooked food organisms may be allowed in broodstock ponds where special diets are needed for gonadal maturation, but this is an exceptional circumstance. Certified farms should not use any untreated manure or uncooked organisms in grow-out ponds.

Human waste and untreated animal manure must be prevented from entering grow-out ponds. Domestic sewage should always be treated to prevent the contamination of the surrounding areas, and raw sewage should never be discharged into shrimp ponds from canals or natural water sources under any circumstances. Septic runoff from human and animal sources should also be avoided. Waste treatment systems should be maintained adequately to ensure that they do not leak into ponds or farm canals, and toilets should not be located near farm canals, farm reservoirs or shrimp ponds. Shrimp farms should have a reservoir as part of their farming system to act as a holding facility for water or as a pre-treatment pond. Water from rivers or canals should be pumped into this pond to allow organic matter and suspended solids to settle out. This practice can reduce much of the bacteria in cultured ponds.

Hatcheries should pay particular attention to the use of natural organic foods and unadulterated artificial feed to produce good-quality post-larvae. The use of drugs such as chloramphenicol and nitrofurans at any stage of production should be prohibited. When antibiotics are used according to the regulations of each country and recommended safety guidelines, foods from the aquatic food chain are unlikely to pose any serious public health risks from antibiotic residues. Antibiotic use should be curtailed as much as possible to prevent the development of antibiotic-resistant bacteria in the food chain. Food safety hazards associated with products from aquaculture and the proposed application of principles of the hazard analysis and critical control point (HACCP) system have been reviewed in order to develop a general strategy to control the hazards identified (30).

Record keeping is an essential part of good aquacultural practice and is important for HACCP implementation. The preparation of the HACCP plan, including updating and implementation, must be fully documented. Generally, records should be kept for a period of two years and be available for inspection by a regulatory authority.

Rev. sci. tech. Off. int. Epiz., **25** (2)

633

Les problèmes liés à l'élevage des mollusques et des crustacés

S. Chinabut, T. Somsiri, C. Limsuwan & S. Lewis

Résumé
L'élevage des mollusques et des crustacés représente un sous-secteur important de l'aquaculture dans le monde. Les risques de zoonoses et de résidus de médicaments associés aux pratiques d'élevage de ces espèces posent de véritables problèmes de santé publique. Les auteurs abordent trois des principales espèces concernées : les mollusques, les crabes et les crevettes. Ces espèces sont sensibles à de nombreuses maladies qui ne semblent toutefois pas transmissibles à l'homme. Le principal danger réside plutôt dans les méthodes d'élevage pratiquées. Les risques associés aux fruits de mer et pouvant menacer la santé publique sont le plus souvent liés à la contamination par les bio-toxines produites par les algues marines. Un autre problème connu affectant les élevages de mollusques et de crustacés est celui de la pollution par les eaux usées, qui contiennent des bactéries et des virus pathogènes pour l'homme et responsables d'infections telles que la fièvre typhoïde et l'hépatite. Concernant l'élevage de crevettes, les principaux dangers potentiels menaçant la sécurité sanitaire des aliments sont les agents zoonotiques, la contamination par des polluants chimiques et les résidus de médicaments vétérinaires. Le problème des effluents non traités rejetés par les fermes de crevettes représente un enjeu fondamental pour l'environnement, dans la mesure où il a été démontré que le déversement de l'effluent non traité dans les eaux naturelles favorise la prolifération de plancton.

Mots-clés
Crabe – Crevette – Dinoflagellé – Efflorescence toxique des algues – Élevage de mollusques et de crustacés – Intoxication avec effet d'amnésie – Intoxication diarrhéique – Intoxication neurotoxique – Intoxication paralysante – Marée rouge – Mollusque – Sécurité sanitaire des aliments – Vibrio cholerae.

Problemas ligados a la conchilicultura

S. Chinabut, T. Somsiri, C. Limsuwan & S. Lewis

Resumen
En términos de producción, las actividades conchilícolas (cría de mariscos) representa en todo el mundo una parte importante de la acuicultura, razón por la cual las zoonosis y los residuos de medicamentos asociados a esas actividades constituyen un motivo de preocupación en el terreno de la salud pública. Los autores se centran en tres de los más importantes grupos de animales conchilícolas: moluscos, cangrejos y camarones. Todos ellos pueden verse afectados por numerosas enfermedades, aunque éstas no parecen transmisibles al ser humano. Los aspectos más peligrosos de la conchilicultura derivan más bien de los métodos utilizados para criar a las distintas especies. El riesgo que presentan estos animales para el ser humano proviene generalmente de su contaminación por toxinas biológicas generadas por algas marinas. Otro problema bien conocido es el de la contaminación de los animales por aguas

residuales domésticas que contengan bacterias y virus patógenos para el hombre, origen de enfermedades como la fiebre tifoidea o la hepatitis. En la cría de camarones, los principales peligros en cuanto a la inocuidad alimentaria radican en las zoonosis, la contaminación química y los residuos de medicamentos veterinarios. Los efluentes no tratados de los viveros de camarones suscitan gran preocupación en los círculos ligados al medio ambiente, pues se sabe que su vertido directo en aguas naturales promueve floraciones planctónicas.

Palabras clave

Camarón – Cangrejo – Conchilicultura – Dinoflagelado – Envenenamiento amnésico por mariscos – Envenenamiento diarreico por mariscos – Envenenamiento neurotóxico por mariscos – Envenenamiento paralítico por mariscos – Floración de algas tóxicas – Inocuidad de los alimentos – Marea roja – Molusco – Vibrio cholerae.

■

References

1. Anue T. & Ynstadt M. (1993). – Diarrhetic shellfish poisoning. *In* Algal toxins in seafood and drinking water (I.R. Falconer, ed.). Academic Press, London, 87-104.

2. Arrignon J.V.C., Huner J.V., Laurent P.J., Griessinger J.M., Lacroix D., Gonduin P. & Autrand M. (1994). – Warm-water crustaceans. Macmillan, London and Basingstoke.

3. Bhaskar N., Setty T.M.R., Reddy G.V.S., Manoj Y.B., Anantha C.S., Raghunath B.S. & Joseph M.A. (1995). – Incidence of *Salmonella* in cultured shrimp *Penaeus monodon. Aquaculture*, **138**, 257-266.

4. Canadian Food Inspection Agency (CFIA) (2001). – Food safety facts on amnesic shellfish poisoning (ASP). CFIA, Ottawa. Available at: http://www.inspection.gc.ca/english/corpaffr/foodfacts/aspdae.shtml (accessed on 7 December 2005).

5. Center for Food Safety and Applied Nutrition (CFSAN) (1993). – Various shellfish-associated toxins. *In* Foodborne pathogenic microorganisms and natural toxins handbook. CFSAN, College Park, Maryland. Available at: http://www.cfsan.fda.gov/~mow/chap37.html (accessed on 7 December 2005).

6. Conte F., Harbell S. & RaLonde R. (1996). – Oyster culture: fundamentals and technology of the West Coast industry. Western Regional Aquaculture Consortium (WRAC) Publication No. 94-101. WRAC, Seattle.

7. Cowan L. (1984). – Crab farming in Japan, Taiwan and the Philippines. *In* Australia Information series, Q 184009. Queensland Department of Primary Industries, Brisbane, 43-61.

8. Dalsgaard A., Huss H.H., H-Kittikun A. & Larsen J.L. (1995). – Prevalence of *Vibrio cholerae* and *Salmonella* in a major shrimp production area in Thailand. *Int. J. Food Microbiol.*, **28**, 101-113.

9. De Schrijver K., Maes I., De Man L. & Michele J. (2002). – An outbreak of diarrhoeic shellfish poisoning in Antwerp, Belgium. *Eurosurveillance*, **7** (10), 138-141.

10. Dey V.K. (1995). – World shrimp market: changing trends. *Seafood Export J.*, **26**, 17-27.

11. Elhadi N. & Radu S. (2003). – Determination of survival and growth of *Vibrio cholerae* O1 in food. Available at: http://www.e-imj.com/Vol2-No2/Vol2-No2-B10.htm (accessed on 29 July 2005).

12. Food and Agriculture Organization (FAO) (1997). – Towards safe and effective use of chemicals in coastal aquaculture. Reports and studies, GESAMP, No. 65. FAO, Rome.

13. Food and Drug Administration (FDA) (1998). – Prescription and over-the-counter drug product list, 18th Ed., Cumulative Supplement No. 3, March. Available at: http://www.fda.gov/cder/ rxotcdpl/pdpl_398.htm (accessed on 29 July 2005).

14. Food and Drug Administration (FDA) (2002). – FDA prohibits nitrofuran drug use in food-producing animals. Available at: http://www.fda.gov/cvm/CVM_Updates/nitroup.htm (accessed on 29 July 2005).

15. Holthuis L.B. (1980). – Shrimps and prawns of the world. Food and Agriculture Organization (FAO) species catalogue, Vol. 1. FAO, Rome.

Rev. sci. tech. Off. int. Epiz., **25** (2)

635

16. Huq A., Huq S.A., Grimes D.J., O'Brien M., Chu K.H., Capuzzo J.M. & Colwell R.R. (1986). – Colonization of the gut of the blue crab (*Callinectes sapidus*) by *Vibrio cholerae*. *Appl. environ. Microbiol.*, **52** (3), 586-588.

17. International Reference Centre of Waste Disposal (IRCWD) (1985). – Health aspects of wastewater and excreta use in agriculture and aquaculture: the Engelberg Report. *ICRWD News*, **23**, 11-18.

18. James K.J., Saez M.J.F., Furey A. & Lehane M. (2004). – Azaspiracid poisoning, the food-borne illness associated with shellfish consumption. *Food Addit. Contam.*, **21** (9), 879-892.

19. Keenan C.P. (1999). – Aquaculture of the mud crab, genus *Scylla* – past, present and future. *In* Mud crab aquaculture and biology (C.P. Keenan & A. Blackshaw, eds). ACIAR [Australian Centre for International Agricultural Research] Proceedings No. 78, Canberra, 9-13.

20. Lavilla-Pitogo C.R. & de la Peña L.D. (2004). – Diseases in farmed mud crabs *Scylla* spp.: diagnosis, prevention, and control. Aquaculture Department, Southeast Asian Fisheries Development Center, Iloilo, Philippines.

21. Lin F.Y., Morris J.G. Jr, Kaper J.B., Gross T., Michalski J., Morrisson C., Libonati J.P. & Israel E. (1986). – Persistence of cholera in the United States: isolation of *Vibrio cholerae* O1 from a patient with diarrhea in Maryland. *J. clin. Microbiol.*, **23** (3), 624-626.

22. Lovatelli A. (1988). – Status of oyster culture in selected Asian countries. FAO/UNDP, NACA [Network of Aquaculture Centres in Asia], Regional sea farming development and demonstration project RAS/86/024. Working Paper NACA-SF/WP/88/2. FAO, Rome.

23. Macintosh D.J., Overton J.L. & Thu H.V.T. (2002). – Confirmation of two common mud crab species (genus: *Scylla*) in the mangrove ecosystem of the Mekong Delta. *J. Shellfish Res.*, **21**, 259-265.

24. Martinez-Urtaza J., Simental L., Velasco D., DePaola A., Ishibashi M., Nakaguchi Y., Nishibuchi M., Carrera-Flores D., Rey-Alvarez C. & Pousa A. (2005). – Pandemic *Vibrio parahaemolyticus* 03:K6, Europe. *Emerg. infect. Dis.*, **11** (8), 1319-1320.

25. Mosher H.S., Fuhrman F.A., Buchwald H.S. & Fischer H.G. (1964). – Tarichatoxin-tetrodotoxin: a potent neurotoxin. *Science*, **144**, 1100.

26. Nair G.B., Oku Y., Takeda Y., Ghosh A., Ghosh R.K., Chattopadhyay S., Pal S.C., Kaper J.B. & Takeda T. (1988). – Toxin profiles of *Vibrio cholerae* non-O1 from environmental sources in Calcutta, India. *Appl. environ. Microbiol.*, **54** (12), 3180-3182.

27. New M.B. (2002). – Farming freshwater prawns: a manual for the culture of the giant river prawn (*Macrobrachium rosenbergii*). Fisheries Technical Paper No. 428. FAO, Rome.

28. Perez Farfante I. & Kensley B. (1997). – Penaeoid and sergesteoid shrimps and prawns of the world: keys and diagnoses for the families and genera. Mémoires du Muséum national d'histoire naturelle, Paris.

29. Rattagool P. (1991). – Microbiology of farmed shrimp. *In* Quality assurance in the fish industry (H.H. Huss, M. Jakobsen & J. Liston, eds). Elsevier, Amsterdam, 180-194.

30. Reilly A. & Kaferstein F. (1997). – Food safety hazards and the application of the principles of the hazard analysis and critical control point (HACCP) system for their control in aquaculture productions. *Aquacult. Res.*, **28**, 735-752.

31. Reilly P.J.A. & Twiddy D.R. (1992). – *Salmonella* and *Vibrio cholerae* in brackishwater tropical prawns. *Int. J. Food Microbiol.*, **16**, 293-301.

32. Sajjapala T., Solprom A., Srisomwong P., Juengmanukul P. & Wilaipan P. (1987). – Study on *Salmonella* incidence in frozen fishery products. Report of the 5th National Seminar on Epidemiology. Ministry of Public Health, Bangkok.

33. Suwanrangsi S., Srimanobhas K. & Keerativiriyaporn S. (1999). – Incidence of *Salmonella* in fishery products. *Fish Technol. Res. and Inspect.*, **3**, 14-21.

34. Viana M.T. (2002). – Abalone aquaculture, an overview. *World Aquacult.*, **33** (1), 34-39.

35. Wongchinda N., Sirimanuyutt S., Piromrak R. & Rachniyom S. (2005). – Determination of profiles of *Salmonella* and pathogenic *Vibrio* spp. in black tiger shrimp for export by introduction of quality assured microbiological assays. *In* Determination of human pathogen profiles in food by quality assured microbial assays. Proc. Final Research Coordination Meeting, 22-26 July 2002, Mexico City. International Atomic Energy Agency (IAEA), Vienna, Austria, 121-129.

36. Yalin S. & Qingsheng L. (1994). – Present status of mangrove crab (*Scylla serrata* Forsskål) culture in China. *NACA, ICLARM Q.*, **17** (1), 28-29.

37. Yasumoto T., Oshima Y. & Yamaguchi M. (1979). – Occurrence of a new type shellfish poisoning in Japan and chemical properties of the toxin. *In* Toxic dinoflagellate blooms (D.L. Taylor & H.H. Seliger, eds). Elsevier, Amsterdam, 495-502.

38. Yasumoto T., Murata M., Oshima Y., Matsumoto G.K. & Clardy J. (1984). – Diarrhetic shellfish poisoning. *In* Seafood toxins (E.P. Ragelis, ed.). AOAC International, Washington, DC, 214-217.

Rev. sci. tech. Off. int. Epiz., 2006, **25** (2), 637-653

Residues from veterinary medicinal products, growth promoters and performance enhancers in food-producing animals: a European Union perspective

J. Serratosa [1], A. Blass [2], B. Rigau [3], B. Mongrell [3], T. Rigau [4],
M. Tortadès [3], E. Tolosa [3], C. Aguilar [3], O. Ribó [5] & J. Balagué [4]

(1) Scientific Co-ordinator of the Panel on Animal Health and Welfare, European Food Safety Authority, Largo Natale Palli 5/A I, 43100 Parma, Italy
(2) European Commission, DG Health and Consumer Protection, B-1049 Brussels, Belgium
(3) Bellesguard, n° 28, 08755 Castellbisbal, Barcelona, Spain
(4) Veterinary Faculty of the UAB, 08193 Bellaterra, Barcelona, Spain
(5) Scientific Assistant of the Panel on Animal Health and Welfare, European Food Safety Authority, Largo Natale Palli 5/A I, 43100 Parma, Italy

Summary
The authors present an overview of the presence of residues from veterinary medicinal products, growth-promoting agents and performance enhancers in food-producing animals, as a result of administering these substances – legally or illegally – on farms. The current situation in the European Union (EU) is represented by an analysis of the 2004 results from the national residue monitoring plans of EU Member States. Aspects of ante-mortem and post-mortem inspection are also considered, as well as the practical challenges facing veterinary inspectors attempting to uncover illegal uses and prevent public health risks. Substances which are considered illegal because their risks have not yet been assessed, such as those employed in minority species or for minor uses, are also discussed.

Keywords
Antibiotics – Beta-agonists – Bovine somatotrophin – European Union – Feed additives – Food safety – Growth promoters – Legislation – Monitoring – Performance enhancers – Prohibited substances – Residues – SPS Agreement – Veterinary legislation – Veterinary medicinal products.

Residues from growth promoters, performance enhancers and veterinary medicinal products: the legal framework

The definition of residues in European Union (EU) legislation includes substances having a pharmacological action, their metabolites and other substances transmitted to animal products that are likely to be harmful to human health.

Safe levels of residues in food of animal origin result from the participation of all parties involved in the food chain – 'from stable to table'. Toxicological evaluations are developed into agreed limits that determine, with other measures, the level of protection. This occurs through a political decision-making process. Farmers, veterinarians and all those parties involved in the food business have primary responsibility for the quality and safety of food on the market. They need to be sure which substances can safely be used in agricultural production. Regulators must adopt food control measures, taking international trade obligations into account. In cases of non-compliance, inspectors and laboratory analysts must provide evidence and know what can be enforced. Judges decide on penalties for the illegal use of pharmacologically active substances. Finally, the consumer decides the success of these food products at the shop counter.

Trade in foods of animal origin can be significantly affected by differences in food safety requirements between countries, such as those for veterinary medicine residues. The availability of different analytical methods and differences in performance between laboratories, especially when detecting substances for which no permitted limit has been established, can also lead to technical barriers to trade.

Background to the Agreement on Sanitary and Phytosanitary Measures

The Agreement on the Application of Sanitary and Phytosanitary Measures (the 'SPS Agreement') was signed at the end of the General Agreement of Tariffs and Trade Uruguay Round (1986-1994). This led to the foundation of the World Trade Organization (WTO) to regulate international trade. The SPS Agreement was signed by 132 Member Governments (34) in Marrakesh on 15 April 1994 and entered into force, with the establishment of the WTO, on 1 January 1995. The Agreement deals with the application of food safety and animal and plant health regulations.

The SPS Agreement allows countries to set their own biosecurity standards but encourages governments to 'harmonise' these, i.e. base their national measures on the international standards, guidelines and recommendations developed by:

– the joint Food and Agriculture Organization (FAO)/World Health Organization (WHO) Codex Alimentarius Commission (the Codex) for food safety

– the World Organisation for Animal Health (OIE)

– the FAO International Plant Protection Convention for plant health (23).

The SPS Agreement establishes rules based on scientific measures, which aim to reduce uncertainty in trade. Thus, the Agreement facilitates trade while still enabling each Member State to take the necessary measures to: 'protect human, animal and plant health, subject to the requirement that these measures are not applied in a manner which would constitute a means of arbitrary or unjustifiable discrimination between Members where the same conditions prevail or a disguised restriction on international trade'.

These rules apply to:

– foodstuffs for human consumption

– feed intended for animal consumption

– plants and animals, and any products derived from them.

The basic aim of the SPS Agreement is to ensure that, if a Member State wishes to: 'maintain, introduce or amend a technical regulation or standard, or procedures for conformance, it must be able to justify its actions by verifiable scientific and technical information'.

The Agreement is an 'international obligation', which requires governments to abide by the rules affecting their trade in an: 'open, non-discriminatory and science-based fashion'.

European Union legislation on residue control

As a member of the WTO, the EU must comply with the SPS Agreement (Article 2.3) and attempt to prevent countries from using SPS measures to restrict international trade.

European Union legislation should guarantee to EU consumers that the food available on the EU market is safe, regardless of whether it was produced in the EU or a third country.

In 1996, following a proposal from the European Commission, the European Council published two Directives, Directive 96/22/EC (17) and 96/23/EC (16), which repealed earlier directives and constitute the present legal framework for controlling residues in foods of animal origin. Directive 96/22/EC prohibits the use of beta-agonists and certain substances which have a hormonal or thyrostatic action in livestock farming. Directive 96/23/EC establishes the measures that EU Member States should take to monitor substances and their residues in both live animals and animal products. (See Table I for a list of these substances and residues, as detailed in Annex I of the Directive.)

Together, these Directives describe how to investigate and detect substances in animals, feedingstuffs and animal products.

In addition, Commission Decision 97/747/EC (4) establishes the levels and frequencies of sampling required to monitor such substances and their residues in certain animal products. For instance, this Decision extends residue control from red meat to include poultry, rabbit and game meats, eggs, milk, honey and fish. Decision 97/747/EC also makes substantial changes to the criteria for selecting samples, moving from random to target sampling.

To conform with Annex II of Directive 96/23/EC, all Member States should draw up a plan for the detection of

Rev. sci. tech. Off. int. Epiz., **25** (2)

639

Table I

Substances and their residues which should be monitored in both live animals and animal products in Member States of the European Union

These substances are listed in Annex I of Directive 96/23/EC, organised by sub-group (A1 – A6) (16, 28)

Groups of substances which have an anabolic effect or are unauthorised	Principal substances in this group
A1– Stilbenes, stilbene derivatives and their salts and esters	Diethylstilboestrol, dienoestrol, hexoestrol
A2 – Antithyroid agents	Thiouracil, methylthiouracil, propylthiouracil, phenylthiouracil
A3 – Steroids	Trenbolone 17-alpha and -beta, 19 nortestosterone 17-alpha and -beta, testosterone, oestradiol and esters, medroxyprogesterone, nandrolone, methyltestosterone, melengestrol, megestrol, ethylestrenol, boldenone, cortisone, dexamethasone/prednisolone, chlormadione, stanozolol, chlortestosterone, 16 OH-stanozonol, norgestrel, methandriol, fluoxymesterone, flumethasone, flugestone, chloroandostedione, caproxyprogesterone, acetoxyprogesterone
A4 – Resorcyclic acid lactones, including zeranol	Taleranol, zearalenol, ethinylestradiol, estradiol benzoate
A5 – Beta-agonists	Clenbuterol, salbutamol, cimaterol, mabuterol, ractopamine, terbutaline, brombuterol, isoxsuprine, methyl-clenbuterol, hydroxymethyl-clenbuterol, clenproperol
A6 – Compounds included in Annex IV to Council Regulation (EEC) No. 2377/90 of 26 June 1990 (13)	Chloramphenicol, nitrofurans, chlorpromazine, dimetridazole, ronidazole, metronidazole, phenylbutazone, dapsone, ipronidazole

groups of residues or substances, according to the type of animal. Since 1998, monitoring programmes have been based on this Directive, which takes a different approach from the previous Directive, 86/469/EEC (10). While Directive 86/469/EEC established purely random sampling criteria, Directive 96/23/EC sets targeted sampling criteria (16), effectively meaning that the results obtained from monitoring programmes before 1997 cannot be compared with those obtained after 1998.

Applying targeted criteria means that the selection of samples is oriented towards detecting the maximum number of positive results, based on such factors as:

– previous results

– the current situation in the region

– knowledge of the possible abuse of certain substances in this area, etc.

European Community legislation on the use of growth promoters

Since 1981, Community legislation (Council Directive 81/602/EEC) has banned certain hormones (diethylstilboestrol and other stilbenes and thyrostatics) (9), but Member States were free to ban or authorise the use of hormonal growth promoters. However, melengestrol acetate (MGA) was never authorised by any Member State.

In 1988, the European Community (EC) prohibited the use of six hormones for animal growth promotion:

– 17-beta oestradiol

– testosterone

– progesterone

– zeranol

– trenbolone acetate

– MGA.

This ban applied internally and to imports from third countries, without discrimination, from 1 January 1989 (12). As a result, third countries that want to export bovine meat and meat products to the EC must either have equivalent legislation or operate a hormone-free cattle programme.

Directive 96/22/EC, concerning the prohibition of certain substances with a hormonal or thyrostatic action and beta-agonists, does, however, allow the use of EC-approved veterinary medicines containing hormones (e.g. 17-beta oestradiol, testosterone, progesterone and derivatives) for therapeutic use and reproductive purposes (17). The veterinary medicine must be administered by a veterinarian and treatment of food-producing animals is prohibited.

In the United States of America (USA), according to the Code of Federal Regulations (CFR), Title 21, Parts 522, 556, and 558, such hormones are authorised as growth promoters for food production animals (30). For instance, estradiol, MGA, progesterone, testosterone, trenbolone acetate and zeranol are all authorised for bovines. The Joint FAO/WHO Expert Committee on Food Additives conducted risk evaluations on these hormones in 1988, 1999 and 2000 (31, 32, 33).

The EU approval procedure for certain substances may lead to the same substance being evaluated through two parallel processes for two different purposes. For example, a hormone may be evaluated for:

a) therapeutic use, based on independent scientific advice from the Committee for Veterinary Medicinal Products (CVMP) (www.emea.eu.int)

b) use as a growth promotant, based on advice from the Scientific Committee on Veterinary Measures Relating to Public Health (SCVPH) and, since 2003, the European Food Safety Authority (EFSA) (www.efsa.eu.int).

Residues of veterinary medicinal products

Article 6 of Directive 2004/28/EC (amending Directive 2001/82/EC) requires the inclusion of a pharmacologically active substance in Annex I, II or III of Regulation 2377/90 (13) as a pre-condition for obtaining marketing authorisation for veterinary medicinal products for food-producing animals in the EU (22).

Administering veterinary medicinal products containing pharmacologically active substances included in Annex IV (such as chloramphenicol and nitrofurans) to food-producing animals is prohibited within the EU. Malachite green is an example of a pharmacologically active substance which has never been evaluated, according to Regulation 2377/90 (13). Therefore, this substance is not authorised for use in food-producing animals in the EU.

Veterinary medicinal products can be authorised and should be used according to the specific marketing authorisation granted. Other substances are authorised for use in some species but cannot be legally used in all food-producing animals.

Since its creation, the European Medicines Evaluation Agency (EMEA) (www.emea.eu.int) has managed the technical aspects of this process, notably through the CVMP. No marketing authorisation may be granted for a veterinary medicinal product unless a maximum residue level (MRL) for the active substance has been established by the Commission. This is essentially a food safety measure.

Once an MRL has been set for an active substance, companies may apply for marketing authorisation for veterinary medicines containing this active substance, through either the 'centralised' or 'decentralised' procedure. In the centralised procedure, authorisation is granted by the Commission on the basis of an opinion from the CVMP. In the decentralised procedure, marketing authorisations are granted by Member State authorities. There is also a process for mutually recognising the decision taken by another Member State. In cases of disagreement, the dossier is referred to the CVMP for an opinion, which is then forwarded to the Commission for adoption.

An MRL is set for each relevant food product (i.e. eggs, milk, meat, liver, etc.) for each relevant species. This is because the MRL is linked to the level of the active substance which remains in the animal tissue at the end of medical treatment, and also to the amount of this particular food which is consumed by the population on a daily basis.

The time period required for the level of the active substance to decrease to the MRL differs, depending on the particular animal product and the formulation of the active substance. This so-called 'withdrawal period' is determined through depletion studies for all substances with MRLs. As defined in Article 1, Point 9, of Directive 2001/82/EC (20), it is the period necessary between the last administration of a veterinary medicinal product to animals, and the production of foodstuffs from such animals, to protect public health. The withdrawal period ensures that these foodstuffs do not contain residues in quantities over the MRLs for active substances laid down under Regulation (EEC) No. 2377/90 (13).

The EU legislation (Directive 96/23/EC) (16) requires that a routine analytical method for the active substance be developed and validated by the pharmaceutical company. This is a sensitive issue, as developing a validated method is time-consuming, costly and benefits the testing laboratories rather than the company.

Thus, the pharmaceutical industry is not willing to invest in studies on species for which the market is limited (for instance, horses, rabbits, goats, fish and bees, or in the case of a disease which occurs only rarely). From the industry perspective, the lack of commercial interest means that the costs outweigh the benefits. As a result, many veterinary products previously used in these species have no MRL and their use has become illegal. This has led to 'the lack of availability of medicines for minor uses and minor species'. In the human domain, these types of products are called 'orphan medicines' and receive special support programmes (for instance, government subsidies, tax exemptions, research funding).

Mutual recognition of MRL procedures between Members of the WTO and the exchange of appropriate risk assessments could help to avoid trade problems due to non-harmonised MRLs.

Rev. sci. tech. Off. int. Epiz., **25** (2)

641

As in marketing authorisations, MRLs do not include any provisions covering the misuse of a substance or product and, of course, the pharmaceutical companies which submit applications to the EMEA do not support or promote the illegal use of their products. Nevertheless, their products may be bought for misuse, a problem which – unless official institutions develop their own validated analytical methods – will remain undetected. It is considered that the appropriate way to avoid misuse is for each Member State to implement its own adequate risk management measures.

Medicines which are authorised for some food-producing animals may not have been granted marketing authorisation for minor uses and minor species (e.g. honey, rabbit meat, game meat, etc.). In addition, some veterinary medicines which were commonly used for food-producing animals may now be banned, due to a lack of MRLs (e.g. sulphonamides), despite the fact that their safety risk assessment is well known. In such cases, an international position should be agreed upon to avoid trade barriers.

Feed additives and performance enhancers

Feed additives are intended to improve feed quality, nutritional aspects, animal health and animal performance. According to Regulation (EC) No. 1831/2003 (21), there is a wide range of substances considered feed additives that may be classified as technological, organoleptic, nutritional and zootechnical (i.e. increasing animal production or performance).

Feed additives cannot be placed on the market in the EU unless they are authorised, based on scientific evaluation of their:
– efficacy
– effect on animal health
– effect on human health
– effect on the environment.

As noted above, zootechnical feed additives (performance enhancers) are substances that have a positive impact on the production of healthy animals, affecting particularly their gastro-intestinal flora, the digestibility of their diet and the environment. (Some current food additives may damage the environment. In this context, an additive which has 'zero impact' on the environment is considered positive. Other additives may be designed to, for example, reduce levels of phosphates and other contaminants when the manure containing them is spread as slurry.)

For instance, due to the demonstrated increase of antimicrobial resistance, the use of antibiotics as a feed additive was banned from 1 January 2006, except those authorised as coccidiostats or histomonostats. The fact that antibiotics have been widely used as feed additives, with possible detrimental effects on animal and public health, is something to be considered when evaluating the risk of substances with pharmacological activity. In the USA (http://www.fda.gov/cvm/animalfeed_info.htm# ingredients), feed containing antibiotics as growth promoters is considered as medicated feed for control purposes, even if it contains sub-therapeutic doses according to authorised use.

The code of good practice for animal feeding in the Codex, published in 2004 (2), does not include the concept of improving animal production in the definition of feed additives. However, the code does not explicitly exclude the use of antibiotics to improve animal growth, provided that there has been a previous risk assessment on their safety for public health.

In the USA, food products are regulated by the provisions of the Federal Food, Drug and Cosmetic Act (FFDCA), and the regulations issued under its authority (29). These regulations are published in the CFR (30). The FFDCA defines food as: 'articles used for food or drink for man or other animals'. Therefore, any product that is intended to be used as an animal feed ingredient, become part of an ingredient or feed, or be added to the drinking water of an animal is considered 'food' and thus subject to regulation.

The Food and Drug Administration (FDA) Center for Food Safety and Applied Nutrition is responsible for regulating human food products. In the USA, any substance intentionally added to an animal feed, including pet food, must be used in accordance with a food additive regulation, unless it is generally recognised as safe for its intended use, among qualified experts (http://www.fda.gov/cvm/prodregulation.htm).

Independent of their specific evaluations for efficacy, etc., feed additives can be considered part of the food chain. Therefore, from the point of view of safety evaluation for residues, the same toxicological approach should be taken towards feed additives as towards contaminants and food additives.

In general, the evaluation criteria for performance enhancers or zootechnical products that have no benefit for the animal or the consumer but are used to reduce production costs should respond to new safety standards. As such substances could potentially be used in all types of animal production units, the new standards for evaluating risk should consider all kinds of population groups, including particularly susceptible groups, such as pregnant women, children, the elderly and immuno-compromised, because consumers may be exposed throughout the whole of their lifetime.

642

Rev. sci. tech. Off. int. Epiz., **25** (2)

Beta-adrenoceptor agonists

Beta-adrenoceptor agonists (β-agonists) bind to β-receptors on cardiac and smooth muscle tissues. They also have important functions in other tissues, especially in:

– bronchial smooth muscle (in relaxation)

– the liver (in stimulating glycogenolysis)

– kidneys (in stimulating the release of renin).

Overall, the effects of the β-agonists are cardiac stimulation (increased heart rate, contractility, conduction velocity, relaxation) and systemic vasodilatation.

Beta-agonists can be used for a number of purposes, including promoting growth. At doses several times higher than therapeutic doses, they induce muscular hypertrophy by decreasing muscular degradation and fat synthesis. As a result, the ratio of muscle to fat is modified (the proportion of muscle in the carcass is increased), with an overall improvement in growth performance.

In the EU, placing β-agonists on the market for use in farm animals intended for human consumption is forbidden under Council Directive 96/22/EC (17). The exception is when they are used for therapeutic treatment, under direct veterinary supervision, in calving cows, foaling horses and companion animals. The Directive prohibits the importation from third countries of farm animals, or their meat, to which β-agonists have been administered (except for the therapeutic uses outlined above) and irrespective of any guarantee that the meat is free from residues. As a category, β-agonists are banned for growth promotion.

Clenbuterol

Clenbuterol is an authorised β-agonist for specific therapeutic uses in the EU (horses and cows) (3), USA (horses) (http://www.fda.gov/cvm/CVM_Updates/clenbut. htm), and Canada. In Australia, some β-agonists, including clenbuterol, are authorised and their MRLs have been established.

Ractopamine

On 22 December 1999, the US FDA authorised (29) the use of ractopamine as a growth promoter for pigs during the finishing period, with zero days of withdrawal time. The drug is sold in the form of a medicated feed preparation to be added to pig feed without any veterinary supervision. The high potential exposure of all kinds of at-risk population groups to ractopamine residues must be clearly analysed when evaluating its risk. Ractopamine has not yet been authorised for use in the EU.

Bovine somatotrophin

Bovine somatotrophin (BST) is a bovine growth hormone produced by the pituitary gland of the cow. This hormone is a protein, like insulin, not a steroid hormone, such as sex hormones or cortisone. During lactation, BST mobilises body fat for use as energy and diverts feed energy towards milk production rather than tissue synthesis. In fact, BST increases efficiency in milk production by 10% to 15%.

Council Decision 90/218/EEC (14) banned the placing of BST on the market and its administration to dairy cows by any means whatsoever. Council Decision 94/936/EC (15) extended the moratorium on marketing and using BST in the EU until 31 December 1999.

The Treaty of Amsterdam (1), in force since 1 May 1999, defines new ground rules on animal welfare in the EU in a special 'Protocol on the Protection and Welfare of Animals'. This protocol recognises that animals are sentient beings and obliges European institutions to pay full regard to the welfare requirements of animals when formulating and implementing Community legislation.

Council Directive 98/58/EC on the protection of animals kept for farming purposes is motivated by the spirit expressed in the European Convention (8, 18). In point 18 of the Annex, the Directive states that: '... no other substance with the exception of those given for therapeutic or prophylactic purposes, shall be administered to an animal unless it has been demonstrated by scientific studies of animal welfare or established experience that the effect of the substance is not detrimental to the health or welfare of the animal'.

Bovine somatotrophin is not used for therapeutic purposes but only to enhance milk production. The Scientific Committee on Animal Health and Animal Welfare (SCAHAW) adopted a report on animal welfare aspects of the use of BST on 10 March 1999 (26). The report stated that BST:

– increases the risk of clinical mastitis, as well as the duration of mastitis treatment

– increases the incidence of foot and leg disorders

– can adversely affect reproduction

– can induce severe reactions at the injection site.

The SCAHAW opinion concluded that BST should not be used in dairy cows because it is not a treatment for disease (on the contrary, it can cause disease) and hence is likely to increase the use of veterinary medicines. Council Decision 1999/879/EC (19) permanently banned the marketing and use of BST in the Community from 1 January 2000, in accordance with the provisions laid down in Council

Rev. sci. tech. Off. int. Epiz., **25** (2)

643

Decision 98/58/EC on the protection of animals kept for farming purposes (18).

The Codex has not yet established maximum residue limits or an acceptable daily intake for BST. A draft standard has been retained in the last step of the Codex procedure for several years but, though proposed, has not yet been approved. In addition, BST-treated cows have been found to have much higher levels of insulin-like growth factor 1 (IGF 1) in their milk than normal cows. According to the conclusions on BST accepted by the EU SCVPH (27), further studies are needed to establish whether there is a correlation between IGF 1 and breast and prostate cancer in humans.

When a growth promoter is clearly toxic or has unambiguously negative animal welfare effects, the risk analysis may be relatively obvious but as soon as the risks are uncertain, the situation becomes difficult to assess. Bovine somatotrophin is an example of a substance which may be used in a continuous and systematic way to enhance yield. In risk terms, this is qualitatively quite different from occasional therapeutic use. Evaluating the toxicological risks associated with long-term exposure is a challenging exercise.

Controlling residues of veterinary medicines and illegal substances in the European Union: current situation

National residue monitoring plans

In the EU, Council Directive 96/23/EC (16) requires Member States to adopt and implement a national residue monitoring plan for specific groups of residues. Member States must assign the task of implementing these controls to a central public department or body. This department is responsible for:

– drawing up the national plan

– co-ordinating the activities of the central and regional departments responsible for monitoring the various residues

– collecting data

– sending the results of the surveys undertaken to the European Commission each year.

National monitoring plans should be targeted. That is, samples should be taken with the aim of detecting illegal treatment or controlling compliance with:

– the MRLs for veterinary medicinal products set out in Annexes I and III of Council Regulation (EC) 2377/90 (13)

– the maximum levels for pesticides set out in Annex II of Council Directive 86/363/EEC (11)

– the maximum levels laid down in the relevant legislation on contaminants.

This means that, in the national plan, Member States target the groups of animals and the sex/age combinations where the probability of finding residues is highest. This approach is different from random sampling, where the objective is to gather statistically significant data, for instance, to evaluate consumer exposure to a specific substance.

In addition, suspect samples are those samples in the national monitoring plans taken as a consequence of:

a) non-compliant results on samples taken in accordance with the monitoring plan

b) the possession or presence of prohibited substances at any point during manufacture, storage, distribution or sale throughout the food and feed production chain

c) suspicion or evidence of illegal treatment or non-compliance with the withdrawal period for an authorised veterinary medicinal product.

Results of residue monitoring in food of animal origin in European Union Member States in 2004

Approximately 807,000 targeted samples and 64,000 suspect samples were taken for the purpose of residue control by Member States in 2004 (6). These samples were taken from all food commodities, including bovines, pigs, horses, sheep and goats, poultry, milk, eggs, rabbit meat, game and honey. A total of 806,525 samples were taken in 2003.

For hormones (including stilbenes, steroids and zeranol derivates), in terms of absolute results, a total of 61,623 targeted samples were taken in 2004. Seventy-five non-compliant results were found for steroids and zeranol derivatives in bovines, which means 0.12% of samples were non-compliant for hormones in the EU, the same percentage as in 2003. A total of 84 targeted samples (75 in 2003) out of 27,709 (17,474 in 2003) were non-compliant for steroids and zeranol derivatives in pigs, which means that 0.3% of the results were non-compliant for hormones in pigs (mainly due to the presence of nandrolone and contamination with the metabolite zearalenone), compared to 0.43% in 2003. There were no non-compliant results for stilbenes and derivatives or for thyrostatic agents in 2004.

The number of non-compliant results for corticosteroids in bovines decreased from 73 targeted and 57 suspect samples in 2003 to 42 targeted and 22 suspect samples in 2004. Dexamethasone was the most frequently found substance for corticosteroids.

The incidence of non-compliant samples increased from 0.02% of the bovines analysed in 2003 to 0.06% in 2004. Six Member States reported findings of β-agonists (only one was a new Member State) and only two Member States had more than one case each.

In terms of absolute results, five targeted and seven suspected non-compliant samples were found in 2003 and 17 targeted and 28 suspected samples in bovines in 2004. In pigs, ten targeted and three suspected non-compliant results were found in 2003 and 11 targeted non-compliant samples in 2004. In addition, one targeted non-compliant result was found for poultry (salbutamol) and four for sheep. Apart from one sample which was non-compliant for salbutamol and one for isoxsuprine (from targeted samples in bovines), plus one non-compliant result for isoxsuprine (from suspect samples in bovines), all the remaining samples from bovines were non-compliant for clenbuterol.

For prohibited substances, the percentage of non-compliant results in bovines increased from 0.05% in 2003 to 0.11% in 2004. In pigs, the percentage of non-compliant results for the A6 group of substances (see Table I) was 0.9% (the same as in 2003). Some non-compliant results were found for chloramphenicol in different food commodities, such as in:

– bovines: 14 targeted samples and two suspected samples

– pigs: seven targeted samples and one suspected sample

– poultry: 18 targeted samples and six suspected samples

– sheep: two targeted samples

– aquaculture: two targeted samples and 40 suspected samples

– milk: five targeted samples.

In the case of nitrofurans, the following samples were non-compliant:

– in bovines: three suspected samples

– in pigs: one targeted sample and 64 suspected samples

– in sheep: seven targeted samples

– in poultry: seven targeted samples and 58 suspected samples

– in rabbits: one targeted sample.

For nitromidazoles: two targeted samples from poultry were found to be non-compliant; five targeted samples from eggs were non-compliant; and one targeted sample from rabbits did not comply.

For veterinary medicinal products, most of the non-compliant results in bovines were for anti-inflammatory drugs, such as dexamethasone, which has an MRL for meat, liver and milk but can also be used illegally as a growth-promoting agent.

Additional investigations should be conducted when detecting residues to rule out the possibility that the substance is present because of its illegal use as an anabolic substance. There were also some non-compliant results for non-steroid anti-inflammatory drugs (NSAIDs) (carprofen and phenylbutazone), and for sedatives in pigs (acepromazin, carazolol, xylazine, azaperone).

Non-compliant results for anticoccidials were reported in bovines, pigs, poultry, eggs and rabbit meat. The most commonly found substances were lasalocid, nicarbazin and salinomycin.

Antihelmintic residues were found in cattle, sheep and goats, and aquaculture. The most commonly found substance was ivermectin.

Residues of malachite green were found in aquaculture products in 14 Member States. The number of non-compliant results increased from 41 targeted and 40 suspected samples in 2003 to 58 targeted and 190 suspected samples in 2004.

In milk, most of the non-compliant results, apart from antibiotics, were for aflatoxin M1. In eggs, they were for anticoccidials, which are not authorised as feed additives for laying hens older than 16 weeks. However, residues are often found in eggs, possibly due to cross-contamination of the feed in the feed mill.

The use of antibacterials in bees is not authorised. Several non-compliant results for antibacterials were reported in honey, as well as pesticides and heavy metals.

Figure 1, shows the overall distribution of non-compliant results for bovines, sheep, goats, pigs, poultry and horses in the EU in 2004. With regard to targeted samples:

– 51% did not comply for antibacterials

– 25% did not comply for environmental contaminants

– 10% did not comply for veterinary medicinal products

– 9% did not comply for hormones

Rev. sci. tech. Off. int. Epiz., **25** (2)

645

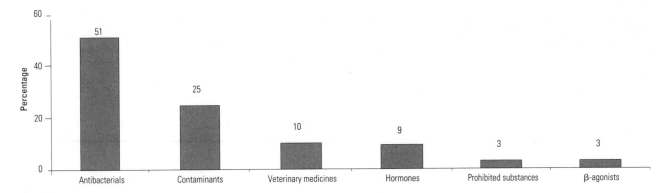

Fig. 1
Overall distribution of non-compliant results (by targeted sampling) for bovines, sheep, goats, pigs, poultry and horses in the EU in 2004

– 3% did not comply for β-agonists

– 3% did not comply for prohibited substances.

Follow-up of non-compliant results

When non-compliant results are found, follow-up measures are of the utmost importance in residue control. Article 16 and Articles 22-28 of Directive 96/23/EC prescribe a series of actions to be taken in the case of non-compliant results or infringements (16). Some measures are aimed at investigating the origin of the infringement, such as verifying the records on the non-compliant farm. Others are to avoid products containing residues from entering the food chain. Depending on the nature of the identified substance, the animals or animal products must be held on the farm until additional tests prove that the other animals are free of residues. If illegal treatment is confirmed, animals should be slaughtered and sent to a high-risk processing plant. When non-compliant results are found at the slaughterhouse, carcasses can be impounded and the products declared unfit for human consumption.

Finally, when the person (or persons) responsible for the presence of the residue in the food has been identified, and the breach of EU legislation proved, penalties can be imposed, including:

– fines

– loss of the ability to apply for Community aid for a period of 12 months

– cancellation of the farming licence

– sanctions against the veterinarian

– criminal sanctions against the person responsible, including jail.

Aspects of ante-mortem and post-mortem inspection

Slaughterhouse findings on bovine animals suspected of having potentially harmful residues

All animals arriving at a slaughterhouse are submitted to an ante- and post-mortem inspection by a competent and qualified authority (i.e. veterinarian) to identify any risk to public health.

In terms of identifying the use of illegal substances or the misuse of legal ones, it is possible to distinguish between:

a) animals with clinical signs of disease

b) animals showing signs of the possible use of substances (legal or illegal) for growth promotion.

Animals showing clinical signs or lesions

Suspect animals showing clinical signs or lesions may have been treated with different pharmacological products, such as antibiotics or anti-inflammatory substances, without following the recommended withdrawal times. In any case, those animals will be submitted to a very careful post-mortem inspection (Table II) to try to establish a correlation between clinical and post-mortem findings.

Animals showing signs of the possible use of legal or illegal growth promoters

Suspect animals showing signs of the possible use of legal or illegal substances for growth promotion (i.e. hormones, β-agonists, thiouracils, etc.) may have appropriate samples taken and analysed for confirmation. However, these animals are usually in good health, so identifying such

Table II

Typical signs indicating probable residues of veterinary medicinal products in animals identified during ante-mortem and post-mortem inspection at the slaughterhouse

Necessary withdrawal times are established by Regulation EEC No. 2377/90 (13)

Type of inspection	Clinical signs or lesions
Ante-mortem	Signs of disease, including coughing, mucus, breathing difficulties, lameness, dehydration and/or trauma
	Weak animals, animals which are smaller than usual for their age and breed, apathetic animals, very excited animals
	Animals showing skin disorders (raised hair, dry skin, alopecia, etc.)
Post-mortem	Lesions in vital organs (e.g. lungs, liver, kidney) or joints
	Signs of affected lymph nodes
	Other general signs: possible oedemas, abnormal colours in meat (too bright), unusually dry meat
	Visible injection sites

Table III

Typical signs indicating probable residues of growth-promoting substances identified during ante-mortem and post-mortem inspections of animals at the slaughterhouse

Type of inspection	Signs or lesions shown by animals treated with growth promoters		
	Corticosteroids	Hormones	Beta-agonists
Ante-mortem	Animals usually show a large abdominal volume (pendulous abdomen)	Heifers showing over-developed mammary glands, with leaking milk or milk in the lairage pens	Animals showing above-average muscular development for their breed, sex and age
	Abnormal skin appearance, alopecia	Males with abnormally small testicles for their breed and age	
	Oedemas detected in the extremities		
	An increase in water retention		
	Abnormal amounts of urine in the lairage pens		
	Animals are usually well fattened for their breed and sex		
Post-mortem	Bladders full of urine in several animals from the same production unit, sometimes also containing sand and calculus	Highly developed mammary glands (galactophorous conducts with or without serum and/or milk)	Unusually improved carcass conformation for their breed, sex and age
	Kidney lesions	Increased perirenal and pelvic fat in both males and females	Carcasses with an abnormally low fat level, especially in the intercostal and diaphragmatic muscles, and in perirenal and dorsal subcutaneous fat
	Abnormal vascular permeability which results in formation of oedemas	Males with unusually small testicles for their age and breed	
		Injection sites or implants, liquids or pellets	

signs (Table III) and consequent intervention by the inspection services is very difficult.

Owing to the difficulties in detecting specific signs (Table III), additional information may be useful, such as recent findings from the same herd or information provided by other inspectors in other slaughterhouses receiving animals from the same herd/farm. Data collected at the ante-mortem inspection must be correlated with the post-mortem findings, using appropriate protocols.

Two examples at slaughterhouse

Figure 2 shows a Holstein Friesian calf of 11 months, from a production unit of eight calves, from which seven showed testicular atrophy. Clinical findings: there was suspicion during the ante-mortem inspection of possible testicular atrophy (confirmed in the post-mortem inspection), and an increase in the perirenal and pelvic fat. Injection sites or implants were not detected.

Figure 3 shows the testicles of another Friesian calf of the same age, from a different herd, for comparison purposes with Figure 2. The testicles in Figure 2 show an evident testicular atrophy.

Inspectors should have technical information about the normal sizes of various organs (e.g. testicles) in regional breeds, according to age and sex, and the tools to measure them (25).

It is important to emphasise that, for some of the signs listed in Tables I and II, there could be other causes, not related to any treatment, which have the same consequences. For instance, the mammary gland in heifers may be abnormally developed if the female has been suckled by other animals on the farm. Other examples are:

– ovarian tumours (to be confirmed at the post-mortem inspection)

– animals being fed with forage which has a high content of phyto-oestrogens (clover)

– precise hormonal treatments to induce lactation, combining oestrogens and progestagens (24).

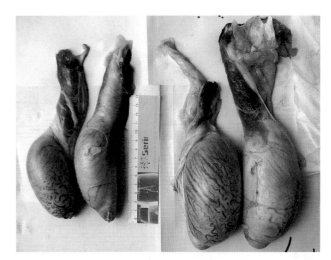

Fig. 3
Comparison between the testicles of one calf from the herd shown in Figure 2 and the testicles of another Holstein Friesian calf of the same age, from a different herd
The testicles on the left-hand picture show evident testicular atrophy

However, these are very special cases and do not involve a large number of animals.

Figures 4 and 5 show the mammary glands of two fleckvieh heifers, each 11 months old, for comparison. Nine out of 16 heifers from the same production unit showed abnormal mammary gland development. Six heifers displayed the presence of serum and three of milk. Clinical findings for Figures 4 and 5: the mammary gland (hyperplasic tissue) contained a large amount of milk (some has been collected in a glass). There was also an increase in perirenal and pelvic fat. Injection sites or implants were not detected.

It is well known that: 'Oestrogenic substances induce the galactophorous conduct of the heifer from the beginning of puberty in bovines (average nine to ten months – deviation +/– 6-18 months), while the alveolar synthesis is correlated with the synergic action of oestrogens and progestagen substances. Lactation may be induced after applying seven days of 0.1 mg/kg of 17-β estradiol + 0.25 mg/kg of progesterone; the administration of 0.03 mg/kg of dexamethasone during days 17, 18 and 19 also helps milk induction so that production may begin on day 21 of treatment' (24).

Factors to consider at inspection: suspicion and sampling

Control measures to avoid exceeding the MRLs of authorised substances, or the non-authorised use of legal substances, should be focused on the distribution of veterinary medicinal products, both at wholesale and retail level.

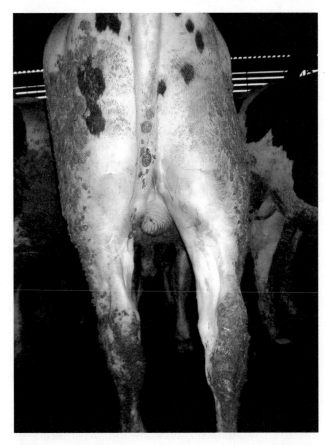

Fig. 2
A Holstein Friesian calf, aged eleven months, from a production unit of eight calves, of which seven showed testicular atrophy

Rev. sci. tech. Off. int. Epiz., **25** (2)

Fig. 4
Mammary gland and milk of a fleckvieh heifer, eleven months old

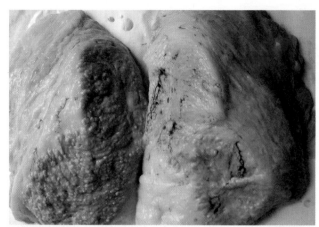

Fig. 5
Mammary gland of a fleckvieh heifer, eleven months old

In feed-mills that manufacture medicated feedingstuffs, controls should be established to avoid 'top dressing' or inadequate mixing of animal feedstuffs. Other measures should be introduced to:

– control the sale and distribution of veterinary medicines

– control the administration of veterinary medicines

– ensure that withdrawal times are followed, etc.

The most efficient measures to decrease illegal residues in food are those aimed at avoiding their use in the first place (at the farm level).

Table IV details the main factors to consider when trying to improve detection of unauthorised substances or the unauthorised use of legal substances.

Possible negative effects of undue suspicion

Inside the slaughterhouse

Investigating suspicions of infringement can have negative effects, as follows.

a) Interruptions in the production line may affect the production process. The corresponding increase in slaughter times will probably be unpopular among slaughterhouse operators, the owners of the animals and workers, due to its financial consequences;

b) Considerable time is needed to conduct tests and obtain analytical results. If those results subsequently prove negative, the consequences could be:

– depreciation in the quality of the meat and its price

– loss of confidence in the competence of the inspectors;

c) If no prosecutions are taken, the system loses credibility. Thus, an over-protective attitude simply decreases confidence in the industry and among the different stakeholders.

For these reasons, inspectors may avoid instigating any stoppages at the slaughterhouse unless the evidence of illegal treatment is very clear.

Outside the slaughterhouse

Negative effects may also occur outside the slaughterhouse, as follows.

a) National policies may be established which divide farm and slaughterhouse inspection responsibilities among several different departments or agencies, discouraging integrated approaches (i.e. the 'from farm to fork' approach). Some EU countries already divide these responsibilities between the departments of Health and Agriculture. In the USA, there are three agencies: the US Department of Agriculture, the FDA and the Environmental Protection Agency;

b) Governments may impose budget limitations on control measures and restrict general policies and strategies on residue controls.

It must be stressed that success in detecting residues of misused or illegal substances in animal carcasses is not simply the result of individual veterinarians, competent authorities or inspectors, but of team work. The process starts with government action on the food chain and effective co-ordination between the departments of agriculture (at the farm level) and public health (at the 'fork' level). Evaluating the risks of legal or illegal substances in animals should also take into consideration

Rev. sci. tech. Off. int. Epiz., **25** (2)

649

Table IV

Principal factors which should be considered when trying to improve the monitoring and policing of unauthorised substances in animals or products of animal origin

Area of improvement	Factors for consideration
Illegal trade ('black market') in illegal substances	– Food inspectors, agricultural departments, public prosecutor offices and police services should work together to improve the exchange of information and experience at European Union level – Black market networks operate in several countries. Illegal substances may be manufactured in one country, mixed with feed in another and finally illegally distributed to other Member States and third countries
Design of slaughterhouse facilities (to make ante- and post-mortem inspections easier)	Factors to be considered for identification and follow-up of any suspected carcass and its offal: – lighting – position and structure of lairage pens in relation to the position of the inspector – correct correlation of carcass with its offal – slaughterhouse facilities readily accessible to workstations for post-mortem inspections
Human resources	– Veterinary assistants are needed, to help inspectors with sampling, and identification and correlation of carcasses and offals. For instance, they can continue with the post-mortem inspection while the inspector investigates the presence of residues. – Scheduled slaughter times should be co-ordinated with inspection resources, especially during weekends and at nights – Palpation of both ears and other parts of the carcass should be conducted on every suspect animal (i.e. 100% of suspicious carcasses should be examined in this way)
Further training needed for inspectors and farmers	– Periodical update of the trends for new substances and their effects on animals and carcasses – Some farmers may become confused about the legal use of some products from well-known companies (e.g. melengestrol acetate in the United States of America) since limitations on such use may depend on the species, sex and age of the animal
Laboratory infrastructure necessary for a reliable residue control system	– Basic requirements are: accredited laboratories, appropriate analytical techniques for the various substances, recommended detection limits and validated methods – The list of available methods should be well disseminated and publicised by the competent authority – The results of the analytical methods should be consistent with the current authorised limits (e.g. a result indicating that a residue has been found at fewer than 15 parts per million (ppm) is not relevant if the maximum authorised limit is 2 ppm) – Better analytical techniques should be developed to improve the existing capacity to validate some illegal substances. Sometimes this is slower than producing and testing new substances for non-authorised use. Endogenous-like substances (such as 17-beta oestradiol) are more difficult to identify; thus, so are abnormal levels of these substances
Sampling at farm level (at production units suspected of infringement)	This is the most efficient way to follow up suspicious animals and conduct tests. Council Directive 96/23 provides that, for bovines, half the samples should be taken at farm level (16)
Legal advice should be sought at an early stage	To ensure the correct administrative process and appropriate prosecution measures are followed, there should be effective feedback among laboratories, the police, health officials and prosecutors (e.g. sometimes a prosecution cannot be conducted due to an error in the administrative procedure)
Technical facilities and communication systems should be available at the inspection point	To ensure effective communication: – telephone, e-mail, fax, digital cameras and intranet systems connecting all inspectors in all relevant regions should be available – all information should be shared with the appropriate research centres, government institutions and among slaughterhouse veterinarians

the risks arising from the misuse of these substances and the difficulties of controlling such abuse.

Analytical methods

Analytical methods are crucial in detecting illegal residues. To ensure reliable results, all analyses should be conducted by accredited laboratories (ISO 17025) using validated analytical methods. Commission Decision 2002/657/EC (5), concerning the performance of analytical methods and the interpretation of results, provides guidelines for the appropriate analytical methods to be used when testing official samples and specifies common criteria for interpreting the results. Variations when performing such tests mean that, in practice, results could vary when the same samples are analysed in different laboratories.

Rev. sci. tech. Off. int. Epiz., 25 (2)

Table V

Analyte testing profile for some banned substances (with no maximum residue level or established tolerance limit) in the European Union

Analytes	Analytical methods for screening	Target tissue	Detection limit: µg per kg (current recommended tested values)
Diethylstilboestrol and other steroids, hexoestrol/dienoestrol	GC/MS	Muscle Urine/liver + IS	0.5 1.0
2-Thiouracil and other thyrostatics	HPLC/MS	Urine + IS	100
Melengestrol acetate	GC	Kidney/fat Muscle	1 0.5
Trenbolone acetate and epimers/nortestosterone	GC/MS	Urine or liver + IS Muscle	2 0.5
Zeranol/taleranol	GC/MS	Urine or liver + IS	2
Clenbuterol (accepted for: parturient cows: 0.5 µg per kg in liver; equines: tocolysis and respiratory treatments: 0.5 µg per kg in liver), cimaterol, salbutamol and other beta-agonists	HPLC*/MS HPLC*/MS	Retinal tissue Liver	2 0.2

GC: gas chromatography
MS: mass spectrometry
IS: injection site on suspected animals
HPLC: high pressure liquid chromatography
HPLC*: HPLC alone or in combination with MS

For control purposes and to ensure harmonisation and transparency, Commission Decision 2004/34/EC (7) established minimum required performance limits for chloramphenicol, nitrofurans, and malachite and leuco-malachite green residues in aquaculture products. In the absence of harmonised limits for banned substances, Member States must apply available analytical methods for detecting minimum levels on the basis of other legitimate factors. Therefore, it is possible that, when trade occurs between countries with different detection limits, the exporting country may consider samples negative (according to EU rules), while the same products are classified as positive in the destination country. Table V lists the different analytical methods available for some banned substances (those which have no MRL and no established tolerance limit) and the target tissues for analysis, as well as the recommended detection limits. The current use of 'cocktails' containing mixtures of different illegal substances in lower doses may challenge the ability of the existing analytical methods to detect some residues. This may also decrease the clinical signs listed in Tables I and II above, making suspicion and identification of illegal use much more difficult for the veterinary inspector at the ante-mortem inspection.

For substances of endogenous origin, such as 17-β oestradiol, it is analytically difficult to show whether the substance is endogenously produced or has been injected for growth promotion, if the correct withdrawal time has been applied.

■

Rev. sci. tech. Off. int. Epiz., **25** (2)

651

Résidus de médicaments vétérinaires, de promoteurs de croissance et d'additifs zootechniques chez les animaux d'élevage destinés à la consommation : le point de vue de l'Union européenne

J. Serratosa, A. Blass, B. Rigau, B. Mongrell, T. Rigau, M. Tortadès, E. Tolosa, C. Aguilar, O. Ribó & J. Balagué

Résumé
Les auteurs brossent un tableau de la présence de résidus de médicaments vétérinaires, de promoteurs de croissance et d'additifs zootechniques chez les animaux d'élevage destinés à la consommation, résultant de l'administration (légale ou illégale) de ces substances dans les fermes. La situation actuelle dans l'Union européenne (UE) est décrite en analysant les résultats, pour l'année 2004, des plans de contrôle nationaux des résidus conduits par les États membres de l'UE. L'analyse aborde également les aspects relatifs à l'inspection *ante mortem* et *post mortem* ainsi que les défis concrets qui se posent aux vétérinaires soucieux de mettre en lumière les cas d'utilisation illégale et de prévenir les risques pour la santé publique. Les auteurs examinent enfin certaines substances qui, pour être peu utilisées, ou seulement chez une minorité d'espèces, sont considérées comme illégales tant qu'elles n'ont pas fait l'objet d'une évaluation des risques.

Mots-clés
Accord sur l'application des mesures sanitaires et phytosanitaires – Additif alimentaire – Additif zootechnique – Antibiotique – Béta-agoniste – Contrôle – Législation – Législation applicable à la médecine vétérinaire – Médicament vétérinaire – Promoteur de croissance – Résidu – Sécurité sanitaire des aliments – Somatotropine bovine – Substance prohibée – Union européenne.

■

Presencia de residuos de medicamentos veterinarios, promotores de crecimiento y potenciadores de rendimiento en animales destinados a la producción de alimentos en la Unión Europea

J. Serratosa, A. Blass, B. Rigau, B. Mongrell, T. Rigau, M. Tortadès, E. Tolosa, C. Aguilar, O. Ribó & J. Balagué

Resumen
Los autores presentan un panorama general de la presencia de residuos de medicamentos veterinarios, promotores de crecimiento y potenciadores de rendimiento en animales destinados a la producción de alimentos debida a la administración, legal o ilegal, de esas sustancias en las explotaciones. Ilustran la situación actual en la Unión Europea (UE) mediante el análisis de los

652

Rev. sci. tech. Off. int. Epiz., **25** (2)

resultados de los planes nacionales de vigilancia de residuos de sus Estados Miembros, realizados en 2004. También examinan distintos aspectos de la inspección *ante mortem* y *post mortem*, así como los problemas prácticos que han de enfrentar los inspectores veterinarios a la hora de descubrir la administración de sustancias ilegales y prevenir riesgos para la salud pública. Asimismo, se analizan las sustancias cuya administración se ha prohibido hasta que se hayan evaluado los riesgos que pudieran presentar, tales como las que se administran a especies minoritarias o para indicaciones poco frecuentes.

Palabras clave

Acuerdo MSF – Aditivo para alimentación animal – Antibiótico – Beta-agonistas – Inocuidad de los alimentos – Legislación – Potenciador de rendimiento – Producto medicinal veterinario – Promotor de crecimiento – Reglamentación veterinaria – Residuo – Somatotrofina bovina – Sustancia prohibida – Unión Europea – Vigilancia.

∎

References

1. Anon. (1997). – Treaty of Amsterdam amending the Treaty on European Union, the Treaties establishing the European Communities and certain related acts. Minutes of the signing of the Treaty of Amsterdam amending the Treaty on European Union, the Treaties establishing the European Communities and certain related acts. *Off. J. Eur. Union*, **C** 340 of 10.11.1997, 1-308. Available at: http://www.eurotreaties. com/amsterdamtext.html (accessed on 21 July 2006).

2. Codex Alimentarius (2004). – Recommended code of practice on good animal feeding. CAC/RCP 54-2004. Available at: http://www.codexalimentarius.net/web/standard _list.do?lang=en (accessed on 21 July 2006).

3. European Commission (1996). – Commission Regulation (EC) No. 1312/96 of 8 July 1996 amending Annex III of Council Regulation (EEC) No. 2377/90 laying down a Community procedure for the establishment of maximum residue limits of veterinary medicinal products in foodstuffs of animal origin. *Off. J. Eur. Union*, **L** 170 of 9.7.1996, 8-10.

4. European Commission (1997). – 97/747/EC: Commission Decision of 27 October 1997 fixing the levels and frequencies of sampling provided for by Council Directive 96/23/EC for the monitoring of certain substances and residues thereof in certain animal products (text with EEA relevance). *Off. J. Eur. Union*, **L** 303 of 6.11.1997, 12-15.

5. European Commission (2002). – 2002/657/EC: Commission Decision of 12 August 2002 implementing Council Directive 96/23/EC concerning the performance of analytical methods and the interpretation of results (text with EEA relevance) (notified under document number C (2002) 3044). *Off. J. Eur. Union*, **L** 221 of 17.8.2002, 8-36.

6. European Commission (2004). – Commission Staff Working Document on the implementation of national residue monitoring plans in the Member States in 2004 (Council Directive 96/23/EC). Available at: http://europa.eu.int/comm/ food/food/chemicalsafety/residues/control_en.htm (accessed on 21 July 2006).

7. European Commission (2004). – 2004/34/EC: Commission Decision of 6 January 2004 amending Decision 2003/828/EC with regards to the movements of vaccinated animals from protection zones (text with EEA relevance) (notified under document number C (2003) 5306). *Off. J. Eur. Union*, **L** 7 of 13.1.2004, 47-50.

8. European Economic Community (1978). – European Convention for the protection of animals kept for farming purposes. *Off. J. Eur. Union*, **L** 323 of 17.11.1978, 14-22.

9. European Union (1981). – Council Directive 81/602/EEC of 31 July 1981 concerning the prohibition of certain substances having a hormonal action and of any substances having a thyrostatic action. *Off. J. Eur. Union*, **L** 222 of 7.8.1981, 32-33.

10. European Union (1986). – Council Directive 86/469/EEC of 16 September 1986 concerning the examination of animals and fresh meat for the presence of residues. *Off. J. Eur. Union*, **L** 275 of 26.9.1986, 36-45.

11. European Union (1986). – Council Directive 86/363/EEC of 24 July 1986 on the fixing of maximum levels for pesticide residues in and on foodstuffs of animal origin. *Off. J. Eur. Union*, **L** 221 of 7.8.1986, 43-47.

12. European Union (1988). – Council Directive 88/299/EEC of 17 May 1988 on trade in animals treated with certain substances having a hormonal action and their meat, as referred to in Article 7 of Directive 88/146/EEC. *Off. J. Eur. Union*, **L** 128 of 21.5.1988, 36-38.

13. European Union (1990). – Council Regulation (EEC) No. 2377/90 of 26 June 1990 laying down a Community procedure for the establishment of maximum residue limits of veterinary medicinal products in foodstuffs of animal origin. *Off. J. Eur. Union*, **L** 224 of 18.8.1990, 1-8.

Rev. sci. tech. Off. int. Epiz., **25** (2)

653

14. European Union (1990). – 90/218/EEC: Council Decision of 25 April 1990 concerning the administration of bovine somatotrophin (BST). *Off. J. Eur. Union*, **L 116** of 8.5.1990, 27.

15. European Union (1994). – 94/936/EC: Council Decision of 20 December 1994 amending Decision 90/218/EEC concerning the placing on the market and administration of bovine somatotrophin (BST). *Off. J. Eur. Union*, **L 366** of 31.12.1994, 19-20.

16. European Union (1996). – Council Directive 96/23/EC of 29 April 1996 on measures to monitor certain substances and residues thereof in live animals and animal products and repealing Directives 85/358/EEC and 86/469/EEC and Decisions 89/187/EEC and 91/664/EEC. *Off. J. Eur. Union*, **L 125** of 23.5.1996, 10-32.

17. European Union (1996). – Council Directive 96/22/EC of 29 April 1996 concerning the prohibition on the use in stockfarming of certain substances having a hormonal or thyrostatic action and of β-agonists, and repealing Directives 81/602/EEC, 88/146/EEC and 88/299/EEC. *Off. J. Eur. Union*, **L 125** of 23.5.1996, 3-9.

18. European Union (1998). – Council Directive 98/58/EC of 20 July 1998 concerning the protection of animals kept for farming purposes. *Off. J. Eur. Union*, **L 221** of 8.8.1998, 23-27.

19. European Union (1998). – 1999/879/EC: Council Decision of 17 December 1999 concerning the placing on the market and administration of bovine somatotrophin (BST) and repealing Decision 90/218/EEC. *Off. J. Eur. Union*, **L 331** of 23.12.1999, 71-72.

20. European Union (2001). – Directive 2001/82/EC of the European Parliament and of the Council of 6 November 2001 on the Community code relating to veterinary medicinal products. *Off. J. Eur. Union*, **L 311** of 28.11.2001, 1-66.

21. European Union (2003). – Regulation (EC) No. 1831/2003 of the European Parliament and of the Council of 22 September 2003 on additives for use in animal nutrition (text with EEA relevance). *Off. J. Eur. Union*, **L 268** of 18.10.2003, 29-43.

22. European Union (2004). – Directive 2004/28/EC of the European Parliament and of the Council of 31 March 2004 amending Directive 2001/82/EC on the Community code relating to veterinary medicinal products (text with EEA relevance). *Off. J. Eur. Union*, **L 136** of 30.4.2004, 58-84.

23. Food and Agriculture Organization of the United Nations (FAO) (1997). – International Plant Protection Convention (new revised text). FAO, Rome. Available at: https://www.ippc.int/IPP/En/default.jsp (accessed on 30 June 2006).

24. Grünnert E. (1996). – Euterkrankheiten, Geburtshilfe und Gynäkologie, Andrologie und Besamung. *In* Buiatrik, Band I. Schaper Verlag, Hanover, Germany.

25. Rosenberger G. (1981). – Clinical examination of cattle. Editorial Hemisferio Sur, Buenos Aires.

26. Scientific Committee on Animal Health and Animal Welfare of the European Commission (1999). – Report of the Scientific Committee on Animal Health and Animal Welfare on animal welfare aspects of the use of bovine somatotrophin, 10 March. Available at: http://europa.eu.int/comm/food/committees/scientific/index_en.htm (accessed on 21 July 2006).

27. Scientific Committee on Veterinary Measures Relating to Public Health of the European Commission (1999). – Report of the Scientific Committee on Veterinary Measures Relating to Public Health on public health aspects of the use of bovine somatotrophin, 16 March. Available at: http://europa.eu.int/comm/food/committees/scientific/index_en.htm (accessed on 21 July 2006).

28. Serratosa J. (2001). – European view on illegal growth promoters: key lecture. *In* Proc. 2nd European Seminar on the fight against the illegal use of growth promoters, Maastricht, the Netherlands, 4-6 April.

29. United States Food and Drug Administration (FDA) (2004). – Federal Food, Drug, and Cosmetic Act (FFDCA), as amended through December 31, 2004. Available at: http://www.fda.gov/opacom/laws/fdcact/fdctoc.htm (accessed on 21 July 2006).

30. United States Government (2006). – The Code of Federal Regulations (CFR). Updated 2006. Available at: http://www.gpoaccess.gov/cfr/index.html (accessed on 21 July 2006).

31. World Health Organization (WHO) (1988). – Evaluation of certain veterinary drug residues in food: 32nd report of the Joint FAO/WHO Expert Committee on Food Additives (JECFA). WHO Technical Report Series No. 763. WHO, Geneva.

32. World Health Organization (WHO) (2000). – Evaluation of certain food additives and contaminants: 53rd report of the Joint FAO/WHO Expert Committee on Food Additives (JECFA). WHO Technical Report Series No. 896. WHO, Geneva.

33. World Health Organization (WHO) (2000). – Evaluation of certain veterinary drug residues in food: 52nd report of the Joint FAO/WHO Expert Committee on Food Additives (JECFA). WHO Technical Report Series No. 893. WHO, Geneva.

34. World Trade Organization (WTO) (1995). – Agreement on the application of sanitary and phytosanitary measures. *In* The results of the Uruguay Round of multilateral trade negotiations: the legal texts. WTO, Geneva. Available at: http://www.wto.org/english/tratop_e/sps_e/sps_e.htm (accessed on 21 July 2006).

Rev. sci. tech. Off. int. Epiz., 2006, **25** (2), 655-673

On-farm contamination of animals with chemical contaminants

C. Saegerman [1], L. Pussemier [2], A. Huyghebaert [3], M.-L. Scippo [4] & D. Berkvens [5]

(1) Department of Infectious and Parasitic Diseases, Epidemiology and Risk Analysis Applied to Veterinary Sciences, Faculty of Veterinary Medicine, University of Liege, Boulevard de Colonster, 20, B42, B-4000 Liege, Belgium

(2) Department of Quality and Safety, Veterinary and Agrochemical Research Centre, Leuvensesteenweg 17, B-3080 Tervuren, Belgium

(3) Department of Food Safety and Quality, Faculty of Bioscience Engineering, Ghent University, Coupure Links 653, B-9000 Ghent, Belgium

(4) Department of Food Science, Analysis of Foodstuffs of Animal Origin, Faculty of Veterinary Medicine, University of Liege, Boulevard de Colonster, 20, B43b, B-4000 Liege, Belgium

(5) Department of Animal Health, Unit of Epidemiology and Applied Statistics, Prince Leopold Institute of Tropical Medicine, Nationalestraat 155, B-2000 Antwerp, Belgium

Summary

Food products should not contain unsafe levels of chemical contaminants. However, it is not possible to monitor each and every one of the many thousands of chemicals that are used in our advanced societies. Chemical contaminants in foodstuffs of animal origin may be classified into three categories: natural contaminants (e.g. mycotoxins), environmental contaminants linked to industrialisation and/or urbanisation (e.g. dioxins and dioxin-like compounds) and authorised chemical products (e.g. residues of veterinary medical products). Chemical hazards may contaminate foodstuffs of animal origin all the way from farm to fork. Contamination may occur in any of the different production systems, and it is difficult to make comparisons between production systems (e.g. extensive versus intensive farming systems) with regard to food safety.

Even when we take into account the latest analytical methods, which can detect ever-smaller quantities of residues, the relative importance of chemical contaminants seems to have declined during recent decades due to improvements in information and prevention. Nonetheless, individual incidents can never be ruled out and may have serious economic, health or social repercussions. Particular attention must be paid to chemical hazards, in order to reduce as much as possible the risks to livestock and to the consumer. Continued monitoring and periodic reassessment of risks posed by these contaminants (at the national level) are needed to detect or anticipate new problems, so that appropriate actions can be taken in the interest of public health. More attention should be paid to the production of detailed information, especially with regard to background data (e.g. the objectives of the monitoring, sampling methods, chemicals to be analysed, analytical methods, detection limits, raw data and specified units), in order to obtain a better basis for risk assessment. Such risk assessment provides control authorities with an effective tool for the exchange of information and measures to be taken to ensure food safety.

Keywords

Animal – Chemical contaminant – Dioxin – Farm – Food safety – Foodstuffs of animal origin – Public health – Residue – Risk assessment.

656

Rev. sci. tech. Off. int. Epiz., **25** (2)

Introduction

In the vast majority of cases, food products do not contain unsafe levels of chemical contaminants (101). However, there is a potential for chemicals to contaminate foodstuffs of animal origin at any point in the continuum from farm to fork; the risk is highest during primary production, but also exists during transport from farm to slaughter, during processing, distribution, retail, and finally also when preparing a meal (13).

Foodstuffs may be divided into different groups depending on the type of agricultural production system, for example family-produced foodstuffs, conventionally produced foodstuffs, organically produced foodstuffs, integrated-pesticide-management foodstuffs, foodstuffs produced under label or with market claims, and foodstuffs produced according to technical specifications set by the distribution sector. Chemical contamination cannot be excluded in any of the production systems.

Because of inadequate sampling methods, the considerable number of parameters to be considered and the high variability of the parameters measured in most studies published in the scientific literature, a comparison between production systems with regard to food safety (in particular chemical contaminants) is currently not prudent. For example, despite the widespread popularity of organic products, it appears that in some cases they present specific risks because they are produced according to natural production modes (e.g. no clearly defined hygienic requirements, lack of professionalism of the growers). On the other hand, conventional production systems require more inputs and outputs than the average family farm (e.g. large-scale trade of cereals and feedstuffs within the organic food market, internationalisation of the exchange of animals and products of animal origin). Whatever the rules and regulations of the different animal production systems, the same problems are faced by Veterinary Services, regulatory agencies and producers when attempting to produce safe food.

Many thousands of chemicals that are used in society have to be considered when assessing food safety. It is not possible to monitor all of them. For foodstuffs of animal origin, the chemical contaminants of greatest concern include:

– residues of veterinary medicinal products

– hormone and pesticide residues

– nitrates

– bacterial toxins

– mycotoxins

– phytotoxins

– algal toxins

– marine toxins

– heavy metals

– dioxins and dioxin-like compounds

– disinfectants

– polycyclic aromatic hydrocarbons (PAHs)

– processing contaminants such as acrylamide

– chemicals migrating from packaging materials.

Moreover, some animal tissues are inherently toxic (e.g. livers of puffer fish) (116). People can be exposed to chemicals through various routes, including:

– air (volatile organic compounds such as formaldehyde, ammonia and carbon dioxide)

– skin and mucosa (e.g. pesticides)

– water (e.g. heavy metals)

– food (e.g. toxins or dioxins and dioxin-like compounds) (10, 20, 21, 76, 91, 105, 133).

The need to ensure food safety throughout the food chain is evident, but it starts with primary production (i.e. at the farm) (13).

This paper provides an overview of some chemical hazards that occur during the production phase of food of animal origin. They are described here in relation to production systems, commodities and specific contaminants. Several options to prevent, monitor and manage these hazards in order to avoid chemical contaminants in the final product are also described.

What is a chemical contaminant and what are chemical incidents?

A contaminant is a potentially harmful chemical substance, of anthropogenic or natural origin, which may be present in food following deliberate treatment or accidental contamination during the production, transformation or preservation of foodstuffs. Deliberate treatment includes the use of plant protection products, veterinary medicine products, and feed and food additives. Accidental contamination may be caused by poor control of the production system or by production factors that are not controllable; for example, climatic risk can increase the production of mycotoxins if there is excessive rainfall at certain times of the year (110, 112). Several databases

Rev. sci. tech. Off. int. Epiz., 25 (2)

657

describing chemical contaminants are available online (e.g. the food contaminants and residue information system) (54).

A chemical incident is a release from containment of a chemical of public health or environmental concern that results in actual or potential exposure to a chemical substance or its hazardous by-products, and that causes or has the potential to cause human ill-health. This includes incidents in which two or more individuals suffer from a similar illness that is due to common exposure to one or more chemicals (153). According to the International Programme on Chemical Safety (IPCS), 436 chemical incidents of international public health importance were reported in the world during the period between 1 August 2002 and 31 July 2003 (153). This figure probably underestimates the actual number of incidents, because incidents reported in English-language media were more likely to be listed. In terms of World Health Organization (WHO) regions, the largest proportion of the 436 events occurred in the Americas (45.6%), followed by Europe (27.3%), the Western Pacific (13.8%), South-East Asia (6.2%), Africa (3.7%) and the Eastern Mediterranean (3.4%). Only one incident concerning a farm was reported in this programme (153).

The actions taken to protect public health are multiple and include, for example, advising against eating seafood obtained from contaminated water (e.g. 6, 102), banning the use of contaminated drinks, and food recalls (153). There are also many regional initiatives to ensure food safety, such as the rapid alert system for food and feed (RASFF) in the European Union (EU). The RASFF was established to provide control authorities with an effective tool for the exchange of information on measures taken to ensure food safety (51). During the year 2004, more than 1,800 notifications concerning chemical contaminants were exchanged between EU Member States. These are listed according to chemical hazards in Table I, which shows that mycotoxins, residues of veterinary products and heavy metals are of particular concern as chemical hazards in the food chain.

Consumer perception: a powerful lever for policy-makers

Many examples demonstrate that public confidence in the safety of the food supply is affected by incidents involving different classes of chemical contaminants, different animal species and different links in the food chain. Examples are:

– in the past, the association of diethylstilbestrol (DES) with vaginal cancer in daughters of women treated with

Table I

Alert and information notifications based on the rapid alert system for food and feed according to chemical hazard type in the European Union (according to Regulation [EEC] No. 178/2002 [51])

Chemical hazards	Alert [a]	Information [b]	Total
Mycotoxins	44	837	881
Residues of veterinary medicinal products	41	101	142
Heavy metals	14	82	96
Pesticide residues	7	41	48
Food additives	0	11	11
Biotoxins	7	2	9
Feed additives	2	5	7
Other chemical contamination	273	363	636
Total	388	1,442	1,830

a) Alert notifications are sent when the food or feed presenting the risk is on the market and when immediate action is required
b) Information notifications concern a food or feed for which a risk has been identified, but for which the other members of the network do not have to take immediate action because the product has not reached their market

this hormone raised questions about the safety of DES as a growth promoter in animals (e.g. 117);

– in 1979, there was widespread distribution of chicken and egg-based products and fat contaminated with polychlorinated biphenyls (PCBs) across the United States of America (USA) and as far away as Canada and Japan. The contamination was traced to an accidental leakage of PCBs from a transformer stored in a pig-slaughtering plant in Montana (35). Twenty years later, a Belgian PCB incident occurred when a mixture of PCBs contaminated with dioxins was accidentally added to a stock of recycled fat used in the production of animal feeds for more than 2,500 farms (poultry, pigs and cattle). This resulted in a major food crisis, which rapidly extended to the whole country and could be resolved only by the implementation of a large PCB/dioxin food-monitoring programme (14, 15). Several studies concluded that this incident would probably not have caused adverse effects in the general Belgian population (15, 121, 141). These episodes illustrate the need for vigilance on fat recycling and for a professional risk assessment as a basis for measures to be taken;

– recently, nitrofen contamination of organic poultry meat, eggs, pork and organic feed was found in Germany (45), despite the fact that nitrofen has been banned in the EU since 1988 (1990 for the former German Democratic Republic) (49). Nitrofen is a contact herbicide that was found to be teratogenic and carcinogenic (73). This example shows that unauthorised chemicals can be found a long time after they have been banned.

– scombrotoxic or histamine fish poisoning is a common seafood-borne disease (especially of tuna, mackerel, bonito

Rev. sci. tech. Off. int. Epiz., **25** (2)

and skipjack) (60, 100, 156). Around 10% of the infectious intestinal disease outbreaks reported to the Communicable Disease Surveillance Centre were associated with fish, and about half of those were due to histamine fish poisoning (7, 61). This is the most common cause of seafood poisoning in the USA (89). A variety of factors, including misdiagnosis, result in its under-reporting (156).

All of the above incidents affect the confidence of consumers in food and may subsequently result in (excessively) severe food safety laws and regulations. In this respect, it should be noted that rapid, clear, complete, written communication (including information about uncertainties) about chemical incidents must be the rule for all producers, operators, Veterinary Services and regulatory agencies.

The need for international harmonisation and collaboration in the evolution of analytical performance

Analytical procedures for the detection of chemical contaminants in foodstuffs of animal origin need international harmonisation and collaboration because of the risks to trade and animal and public health in case of non-compliance with legal limits. The evolution of analytical procedures has improved the capacity to detect both greater numbers of chemical contaminants and smaller amounts of such contaminants (Table II). However, developing countries may not be able to obtain the expensive methodology, laboratory materials and operators required to guarantee the necessary monitoring (118). Another factor to consider when selecting methods is that several groups of chemical contaminants, such as residues of antibiotics, can be more efficiently detected with a simple method by monitoring microbial growth. We also need to distinguish between natural occurrence of antibiotics and occurrence that results from intentional treatment, and this task requires more expensive techniques, such as liquid chromatography coupled to mass spectrometric detection (143). A comparison between conventional and organic production farm systems may help explore the effects of deliberate antibiotic treatment. Zero tolerance for antimicrobials in food is still a matter of debate. However, the order of parts per billion (ng/g) as safe food levels seems, in many cases, reasonable for public health purposes (59, 62).

In Europe, in order to achieve harmonisation of analytical methods applied by Member States to monitor chemical contaminants, minimum criteria have been introduced for the performance of analytical methods (44, 47) and harmonised standards for testing for certain residues in products of animal origin imported from third countries (48, 131).

Table II

General analytical procedures for the detection of chemical contaminants in foodstuffs of animal origin

Group of chemical contaminants	Analytic method (for typical compounds of the target group)	Limit of detection (order of magnitude)
Residues of antibacterial and parasitic drugs	HPLC-DAD (UV) or HPLC-FLD, GC-MS, GC-ECD, LC-MS, bio-assays	ng/g (ppb)
Residues of hormones	GC-HRMS, GC-MS, LC-MS, bio-assays	ng/g (ppb)
Heavy metals	ICP-MS	ng/g (ppb)
Nitrates	anion exchange HPLC	µg/g (ppm)
Bacterial toxins	LC-MS, bio-assays	ng/g (ppb) ; pg/g (ppt)
Mycotoxins	LC-MS	ng/g (ppb)
Phytotoxins	HPLC-DAD, LC-MS	mg/g (ppm); ng/g (ppb)
Marine toxins	LC-MS, HPLC, bio-assays	ng/g (ppb)
Polychlorinated biphenyls	GC-ECD, GC-MS	ng/g (ppb)
Dioxins and dioxin-like compounds	HRGC-HRMS, bio-assays	pg/g (ppt)
Pesticides	GC-ECD, GC-MS, LC-MS	ng/g (ppb)
Polycyclic aromatic hydrocarbons	HPLC-DAD (UV) or FLD, GC-MS, LC-MS (in development)	ng/g (ppb)
Acrylamide	LC-MS	ng/g (ppb)
Chemicals released from packaging materials	ICP-MS, GC-MS	ng/g (ppb)

GC-ECD: gas chromatography-electron capture detector
GC-HRMS: gas chromatography-high resolution mass spectrometry
GC-MS: gas chromatography-mass spectrometry
HPLC: high performance liquid chromatography
HPLC-DAD (UV): high performance liquid chromatography-diode array detector (ultra violet)

HPLC-FLD: high performance liquid chromatography-fluorescence detector
HRGC-HRMS: high resolution gas chromatography-high resolution mass spectrometry
ICP-MS: inductively coupled plasma-mass spectrometry
LC-MS: liquid chromatography-mass spectrometry

Risk of chemical contaminants

The four elements of risk assessment are hazard identification, hazard characterisation (dose–response assessment), exposure assessment and risk characterisation. Estimating the risk associated with dietary intakes of chemical residues by the consumer is a vital and integrated part of regulatory processes. The exposure of the consumer is compared directly to the acceptable daily intake (ADI) (e.g. of pesticides, veterinary medicinal drugs), to the tolerable daily intake (TDI) (e.g. of heavy metals, mycotoxins) and the tolerable weekly (WTI) or monthly (MTI) intake (e.g. of dioxins and dioxin-like compounds). For pesticides or medicinal drugs such as antimicrobial substances, the first step is to compare the detected amounts of residues with the maximum residue level (MRL) authorised in foodstuffs. If the residue level in the food exceeds the MRL, the theoretical maximum daily intakes and the ADI have to be taken into account in order to assess the risk to the consumer. The exposure is obtained using the basic equation:

$$\text{exposure (mg/kg bw/day)} = \text{consumption (kg/kg bw/day)} \times \text{residue level (mg/kg)}$$

The establishment of the ADI and the TDI is based on the results of toxicological studies that involve the determination of the lowest no-observed-adverse-effect level divided by a safety factor (e.g. of 100), taking into account the interspecies and intraspecies variability (101). Because of the possibility that short-term excursions might give rise to acute toxicity, the concept of the acute reference dose has been developed.

Classification of chemical contaminants

Chemical contaminants may be classified into three categories:

a) natural contaminants

b) environmental contaminants linked to industrialisation and/or urbanisation

c) authorised chemical products.

Natural contaminants

A number of natural contaminants, such as various toxins produced by bacteria (bacterial toxins), fungi (mycotoxins), plant pathogens (phytotoxins) and algae (algal toxins), affect the food chain. In addition, inherently toxic animal tissues may contaminate humans.

Bacterial toxins

Foodstuffs of animal origin may be contaminated with naturally occurring bacterial toxins (e.g. botulinum neurotoxins, staphylococcal enterotoxin). Time and temperature manipulation of a food product contaminated with enterotoxigenic staphylococci can result in the formation of enterotoxin, which can produce food-borne illness when the product is ingested. The staphylococcal enterotoxins are extremely thermostable and can remain biologically active after exposure to retort temperatures (12). Botulinum toxin is regarded as the most lethal substance known (69) and has been a concern in the food industry for a long time (127). Implications for the safety of human food are important (26, 122): botulism is a deadly disease caused by ingestion of the preformed neurotoxin produced from the anaerobic spore-forming bacteria *Clostridium botulinum* (127).

Mycotoxins

Mycotoxins are natural secondary metabolites produced by fungi, which develop on agricultural crops (108, 157). While fungi are destroyed during processing, most of the mycotoxins remain in the final product (28) because of their thermal and acid stability (66). Mycotoxin-contaminated foods may be responsible for toxic effects in animals and humans (108, 115). The main route of exposure of animals and humans to mycotoxins is via foodstuffs, although aerial and dermal routes are also reported (108). The Food and Agriculture Organization estimates that 25% of all harvests are contaminated (2). Dealing with the problem is complex, because a single toxigenic fungus is able to produce different mycotoxins, and a particular toxin can be produced by more than one fungus species (25). Toxigenic fungi from the three genera *Fusarium*, *Penicillium* and *Aspergillus* are widespread in various agricultural products and considered to be economically important worldwide.

The proliferation of the fungi and the synthesis of the mycotoxins can take place before harvest or afterwards, during storage, transport or transformation of the product (53, 109). This phenomenon is very complex and depends on a combination of factors such as the temperature, humidity or oxygenation level of the substrate. Thermal stress, humidity stress (e.g. dryness) and physical stress (e.g. lesions caused by insects) enhance the contamination by fungi and the synthesis of mycotoxins (33, 66, 118, 157). Human disorders are usually the result of chronic exposure to low mycotoxin doses (25, 108). Mycotoxins, such as aflatoxins produced by some *Aspergillus* species, have been found in a large number of agricultural products, including foodstuffs of animal origin (34, 128). They are classified as carcinogenic (74). In order to minimise human and animal exposure to mycotoxins, most industrialised countries carry out regular analyses of

Rev. sci. tech. Off. int. Epiz., **25** (2)

food and feed supplies (19). These products may be exported to developing countries, which are less restrictive (17).

The synthesis, degradation, dilution or concentration of mycotoxins during the treatment of meat and transformation and conservation of milk and its by-products are poorly documented (90).

Phytotoxins

Phytotoxins are products of plant pathogens or host–pathogen interactions that directly injure plant cells and influence the course of disease development or symptoms (blights, leaf spots and galls). Both fungal and bacterial pathogens produce a number of secondary metabolites that are toxic to plant cells, although these metabolites may not be important in plant disease (11). Both neurotoxic poisonous alkaloids and hepatotoxic peptides have been isolated in toxic algae inflorescences (e.g. *Microcystis, Anabena* or *Aphanizomenon*). Usually, the intoxication only occurs if the bloom is dense (warm weather, sunny, eutrophic waters). Algal intoxications affect animals and humans (56).

Marine (algal) toxins

A number of algae can produce heat-resistant toxins which are not destroyed when the algae are eaten by a predator (150). Marine poisoning results from the ingestion of crabs, fish and shellfish that contain toxic substances, and causes substantial illness in coastal regions (neurological symptoms: ciguatera, tetrodotoxin poisoning and paralytic shellfish poisoning) (76). In parts of the Pacific, the number of cases of marine poisoning exceeds 1,200 per 100,000 people per year (146).

Inherently toxic animal tissue

Natural examples of this phenomenon include the bio-accumulation of vitamin A in the livers of some arctic animals in such amounts that a single meal of such tissue can be acutely toxic for a human (116).

Environmental contaminants linked to industrialisation and/or urbanisation

Environmental contaminants are linked to atmospheric deposition, pollution of the soil and pollution of water. Heavy metals, dioxins and dioxin-like compounds, and PAHs are some of the most important chemicals that are found in the environment, especially in the most densely inhabited and/or industrialised countries.

Heavy metals

The level of heavy metals reflects the level of industrial pollution of the local environment. Plants that are contaminated by atmospheric deposition absorb only limited quantities of heavy metals, and the relative importance of heavy metals and metalloids is tending to decline due to improved information and prevention. Nonetheless, individual incidents can never be ruled out and may have serious economic, medical or social repercussions. Particular attention must be given to this problem, in order to minimise the risk to livestock and to the consumer (122). Heavy metals such as mercury tend to bio-accumulate in fish and shellfish due to the remarkable capacity of these animals to turn inorganic mercury into organic compounds that are more easily transferable throughout the aquatic food chain (36).

Dioxins and dioxin-like compounds

Polychlorinated dibenzo-*p*-dioxins (PCDDs) and polychlorinated dibenzofurans (PCDFs) are cyclic aromatic compounds. Their dispersion in the atmosphere is likely to occur mainly in particulate aerosols (152). These compounds are not produced intentionally but frequently occur as unwanted by-products in chemical processes such as the synthesis of pesticides or of PCBs (136). Combustion processes are recognised as the major sources of PCDDs and PCDFs. Most thermal reactions which involve the burning of chlorinated organic or inorganic compounds appear to result in the formation of these substances. Both PCDDs and PCDFs have been detected in emissions from the incineration of various types of wastes, particularly municipal, medical and hazardous wastes; from the production of iron, steel and other metals; from fossil fuel plants; and domestic coal and wood fires, especially those involving chlorine-containing materials such as polyvinyl chloride and PCBs (37).

Polychlorinated biphenyls are aromatic synthetic chemicals that were produced between 1930 and 1970 and commercialised in relatively large quantities for use as dielectrics, hydraulic fluids, plastics and paints (125). The universal distribution of PCBs throughout the world suggests that they are transported in air (151).

Dioxins (PCDDs and PCDFs) and PCBs with dioxin-like toxicity (dioxin-like compounds) are found in the environment, are persistent and, being fat-soluble, tend to accumulate in higher animals, including humans. Their resistance to degradation and low volatility means that these substances may be transported over long distances and give rise to exchanges of pollutants between countries. In addition, dioxins released into the environment many years ago continue to contribute to contemporary exposure (42).

Humans are exposed to dioxins and dioxin-like compounds predominately through their diet, with dairy

Rev. sci. tech. Off. int. Epiz., **25** (2)

661

products, eggs, meat and fish contributing roughly 90% of the exposure (57, 87, 111, 121, 134), although no single food group emerges as the principal contributor (64). A common hypothesis explaining the presence of dioxins in livestock is that animals consume feed that has been contaminated by emissions from combustion sources via atmospheric depositions. Dioxins, which have a high affinity for lipid-rich tissues (94), bio-accumulate in the fats of these animals and are passed on to the humans who consume them (58).

Various effects have been reported in animals exposed to PCDDs, PCDFs and PCBs (145). Many of the toxic effects of dioxins were high-dose effects (43). The most commonly reported pathologies are endometriosis, developmental neurobehavioral effects, developmental reproductive effects and immunotoxic effects (81, 83, 145, 149). Dioxins are carcinogenic in several animal species (93), including humans, and increased risk of cancer has been demonstrated at exposure levels more than 100 times the normal intake of the general population (129). Dioxins are classified as human carcinogenic by the International Agency for Research in Cancer (96, 130).

The concept of toxicity equivalency factors has been established for the evaluation of congeners other than 2,3,7,8-tetrachlorodibenzo-*p*-dioxin (TCDD) (the most toxic) and of mixtures of dioxins (50, 139). Using the available toxicological database on dioxins in 1998, the WHO established a TDI in humans between 1 pg and 4 pg toxic equivalents (TEQ)/kg body-weight/day (bw/d) (140). For the health risk assessment of dioxin-like compounds, the WHO consultation focused on the most sensitive effects that are considered adverse (hormonal, reproductive and developmental effects) seen at low doses in animal studies (rats and monkeys). Human daily intakes corresponding with body burdens similar to those associated with adverse effects in animals could be estimated to be in the range of 14 pg TEQ/kg bw/d to 37 pg TEQ/kg bw/d. To arrive at the TDI, a composite uncertainty factor of 10 was used (149). The upper limit of the TDI should be considered as the maximum tolerable intake on a provisional basis, with the ultimate goal being to reduce human intake levels below 1 pg TEQ/kg bw/d. More recently a WTI of 14 pg TEQ/kg bw/week (43) and a MTI of 70 pg TEQ/kg bw/month (50, 80) were also determined, to reflect the long half-life of TCDD.

The above three methodologies assume a threshold for human cancer risks. Another recent international evaluation based on a non-threshold effect (38, 39) estimates the lifetime risk for all cancers to be 1×10^{-3} risk/pg TEQ/kg bw/d. When evaluating standard diets in different parts of the world the results indicated that the estimated intakes of dioxins and dioxin-like compounds approach or exceed the monthly tolerable intake of 70 pg TEQ/kg bw/month (155).

Food incidents have occasionally been reported with dioxins and dioxin-like compounds involving different animal species and occurring at different links of the food chain. Incidents may be caused by environmental contamination (e.g. lightning on pylons with old transformers in cattle pasture) (31), feed contamination (e.g. contamination of dairy products, due to high concentrations of dioxins in citrus pellets which were added to the cattle feed) (23) or by failure in the process (e.g. leakage of PCBs from a transformer stored in a pig slaughtering plant, as was the case in Montana) (35).

Polycyclic aromatic hydrocarbons

The PAHs originate from incomplete combustion (pyrolysis) of organic materials, for instance during industrial processes (e.g. burning of fossil fuels) (30), and have carcinogenic properties (71, 72). Rapid industrialisation and/or urbanisation resulted in excessive release of PAHs into the environment (atmospheric deposition), particularly into estuaries. Exposure to these ubiquitous environmental contaminants appears practically unavoidable. Fish appear to be sensitive because the bio-concentration from water, via the gills and skin, and ingestion of contaminated food are possible routes for PAHs to accumulate in tissue (84). The route depends mainly on feeding preference, general behaviour and trophic level of the fish (52, 85, 104). The Environmental Protection Agency in the USA recommends a guideline concentration of 0.67 ng PAHs/g wet weight for fish for human consumption (39, 84).

Authorised chemical products

Residues of veterinary medicinal products, of agricultural pesticides and of biocides, and nitrates are among the most important chemicals that are regulated by MRLs. The use of hormones for growth promotion in meat animals, or for enhancement of milk production in dairy animals, remains a controversial issue; the European Union has banned such use in food animals (132, 144).

Residues of veterinary medicinal products

Most residues of veterinary products relate to antibacterial and antiparasitic drugs. Among other effects, antibacterial residues in foods of animal origin may cause problems through:

– the direct toxicity of the residues (chloramphenicol, for example, is banned for this reason in Europe) (5, 97, 126)

– involvement in allergic reactions (e.g. β-lactam antibiotics) (79)

– triggering the development of antibacterial-resistant strains of bacteria in animals and people (27)

– interference with starter cultures for fermented food products including cheese, buttermilk and yoghurt (4, 65).

Antibacterial use in on-farm animals and the development of resistant bacteria is dealt with separately in this issue (1). The use of veterinary medicinal products requires strict adherence to the recommendations given by the producer: species, type of animal (dairy versus beef), disease condition, correct dose, route of administration, and frequency and number of treatments (59).

Residues from agricultural pesticides

Pesticides are chemicals specifically developed for use in the control of agricultural and public health pests (68). According to the Federal Insecticide, Fungicide, and Rodenticide Act of the USA, pesticides include any substance or mixture of substances intended for preventing, destroying, repelling or mitigating any pest, and any substance or mixture of substances intended for use as a plant regulator, defoliant or desiccant (137).

Due to the widespread use of pesticides in agriculture and public health, and due to a high level of public concern in both developed and developing countries (because of the intrinsic toxicity of and potential exposure to these chemicals), the IPCS devotes significant resources to pesticides, primarily for their assessment, but also for management support. The inventory of pesticides (55), the inventory of evaluations and the summary of toxicological evaluations through 2002 are available electronically (154).

Most commonly used in agriculture are herbicides (residues of these have only occasionally been reported in fruits and vegetables, and occasionally in foodstuffs of animal origin) (95).

Several studies suggest that exposure to some fungicides (and other pesticides) may increase the risk of retinal degeneration among farmers who use them and may cause endocrine disruption, warranting further investigation (20, 32, 67, 77, 82, 92, 98, 106).

Some of the difficulties in dealing with pesticide residues arise because:

a) the number of chemicals to trace is very high

b) although many old products are no longer authorised, accidental or fraudulent contaminations can always occur (e.g. the recent experience with nitrofen in Germany, see above).

Moreover, despite their potential carcinogenicity several chemical compounds were still used, such as dichlorodiphenyltrichloroethane (DTT) in the fight against malaria in many developing countries (150). This use must have induced particular problems because such compounds persist in the environment, accumulate in the fatty tissues and increase in concentration as they pass up the food chain.

Residues of biocide products

Biocide products are active substances and preparations containing one or more active substance, produced in the form in which they are supplied to the user, intended to destroy, deter, render harmless, prevent the action of, or otherwise exert a controlling effect on any harmful organism by chemical or biological means (41). Insecticides and fungicides have given most concern in meat, milk and eggs (18, 103, 135, 142).

Insecticides such as organophosphates, carbamates and pyrethrins have been frequently used in veterinary practices (86, 137). These agents are used directly on animals or applied to the area where the animals are confined to control flies, mange, mites, lice, grubs and other external pests (78). They also may be acutely toxic to the people who apply them (24).

Reports of adverse effects following exposure to residues from foods that were treated with insecticides in accordance with their respective approval standards remain very rare (101). However, animals housed in pens made of treated wood, bedded on wood shavings treated with pentachlorophenol (fungicide) or fed with grain treated with fungicides may be contaminated (70, 95).

Disinfectants or sanitisers may be used in several steps of the food chain such as on the farm, in drinking water, in milk producing establishments and in processing areas for food of animal origin, including kitchen areas. In order to minimise the amount of substance applied and to avoid unnecessary residues, disinfectants or sanitisers are classified by groups of food products, and the recommendations given by the producer must be strictly followed (75, 99, 114).

Nitrates

Contamination with nitrates in foodstuffs of animal origin has not been thoroughly investigated (8), but several studies in vegetables indicate that food produced in organic production systems has significantly lower nitrate levels in food from conventional production systems (112, 148).

Rev. sci. tech. Off. int. Epiz., **25** (2)

663

Prevention of chemical contaminants

Preventing contamination by dioxin chemicals serves to minimise their impact on food safety and public health. Prevention is the basis for improvement of awareness and information, and for establishing and implementing the hazard analysis and critical control point (HACCP) system (Table III), in which critical limits are established that take food safety objectives into account (63, 158).

Table III
The seven principles of the chemical hazard analysis and critical control point (HACCP) system

HACCP principles	
1	Conduct analysis of potential chemical hazards
2	Determine critical control points for the targeted hazard or hazards
3	Establish critical limits
4	Establish routine monitoring procedures to assess these critical limits
5	Establish corrective actions to be implemented if critical limits are exceeded
6	Establish an effective record-keeping system for the programme
7	Establish a system of verification to document that the HACCP programme is being followed

A better diffusion of health and chemical hazard data obtained through on-farm surveillance (e.g. 107) is needed to improve the awareness of farmers, veterinarians and other food-chain operators. Formal educational programmes for veterinarians and farmers must be devised in order to increase understanding of rational, safe use of drugs in food animals. For most producers, a veterinarian is their first choice for information about dairy market food safety, and more than a third report that they would pay veterinarians to perform food safety assessments (138). Due to a number of food safety failures, quality assurance is becoming increasingly important in the primary livestock production sector. The use of HACCP systems must be encouraged and disseminated to all operators in the food chain, including farmers (118, 123). An HACCP system must be highly farm-specific and focused on self-management; it should require relatively few documents and not be overly labour-intensive (88). A range of farm hazard inspection checklists should be used to help in this context (e.g. 147).

Monitoring of chemical contaminants

Monitoring systems for chemical contaminants have been set up in various countries (e.g. the National Chemical Residue Monitoring Programme in Canada) (22), often after major incidents (see the section on 'Consumer

perception: a powerful lever for policy-makers'). For example, a new monitoring system for chemical contaminants was set up in Belgium after the 1999 PCB/dioxin incident (CONtaminant SUrveillance systeM) (25, 120). This national system aims to achieve better control of the production chain, and is based on a group of actions:

– a permanent monitoring of critical raw materials

– monitoring by means of surveillance and an obligation of traceability of batches of compound feedstuffs

– investigations targeted on farms presenting a particular risk

– the introduction of a statute reflecting the contamination status

– monitoring by means of surveillance of the first transformation and the distribution

– a total system of traceability in the food industry

– a scenario to be applied in the event of any report of contamination (including an emergency plan).

The authors urge all countries to install a similar system with the aim of preventing incidents as far as possible, and having in place the necessary measures to control their consequences should they occur. The programme of controls based on this monitoring must be a continuous process where all relevant information will be taken into account (Fig. 1) (e.g. 3).

Because there are many thousands of chemicals, the general approach to monitoring is based mainly on target sampling after a risk assessment of potential sources of contamination in each country (e.g. 40). However, random sampling of slaughtered animals is advisable in order to estimate the prevalence of particular chemical compounds in an individual country, as this approach allows a comparison of prevalence levels in different countries. Testing of live animals may be considered for a detection system, and may offer an opportunity for future population studies (119). In fact, more attention should be drawn to the production of detailed results, especially concerning background data (objectives of the monitoring, sampling methods, molecules to analyse, analytical methods, detection limits, raw data and specified units), in order to obtain useful risk assessments. It is also noted that milk, meat, egg and honey products do not always originate from a specific country, and the monitoring system must take this into account. The risk assessment provides control authorities with an effective tool for the exchange of information and measures taken to ensure food safety.

Most residue-monitoring programmes employ at least screening and confirmatory tests. The screening test is

664

Rev. sci. tech. Off. int. Epiz., **25** (2)

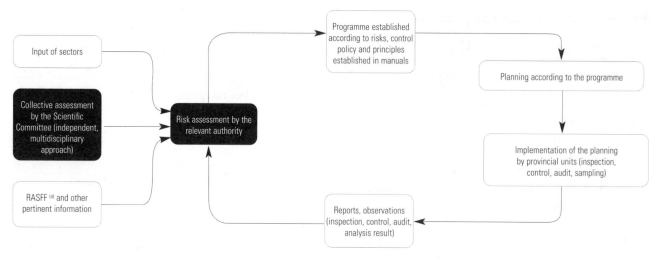

a) rapid alert system for food and feed

Fig. 1
The continued programme of chemical control (according to the Agence Fédérale belge pour la Sécurité de la Chaîne Alimentaire [3])

sensitive but somewhat lacking in specificity. The confirmatory test should have a higher degree of specificity but be at least as sensitive as the screening test (143). The very specific physico-chemical methods used for confirmation are usually expensive. In the case of deliberate treatment, one option used in several countries is to make the offending livestock producers pay for the confirmatory tests in cases where residues of authorised chemical products above the MRL or residues of an unauthorised chemical product are found.

Managing chemical contaminants

Food safety laws and regulations deal in particular with:

– identification and registration of animals, operators and products

– harmonised systems of traceability throughout the food chain

– guidelines for each sector and procedure for all operators

– rapid notification of incidents

– scientific advice

– risk analysis

– regular exchanges between regulatory authorities and consumers

– where necessary, an adequate use of the precautionary principle (9, 16, 113, 124).

Even though the newest tests are able to detect ever-smaller quantities of residues, the relative importance of chemical contaminants seems to have declined in the last decades due to improvements in information and prevention. Nonetheless, individual incidents can never be ruled out and may have serious economic, health or social repercussions. Particular attention must be paid to this problem, in order to minimise the risks to livestock and consumers. Continued monitoring and periodic reassessment of risks posed by these contaminants (at the national level) are needed to detect or anticipate new problems so that appropriate actions can be taken in the interest of public health.

Challenge for the future

The number of chemical incidents actually reported probably greatly underestimates the real number of cases. There is thus a need to accurately assess chemical hazards throughout the food chain in order to determine the real use of potentially harmful chemicals, assess their risks, and develop strategies to prevent accidents arising from their use.

Rev. sci. tech. Off. int. Epiz., **25** (2)

665

Contamination des animaux à la ferme par des contaminants chimiques

C. Saegerman, L. Pussemier, A. Huyghebaert, M.-L. Scippo & D. Berkvens

Résumé

Les denrées alimentaires ne devraient pas contenir des concentrations en contaminants chimiques qui présentent des risques pour la santé. Il n'est toutefois pas possible de surveiller chacun des milliers de composés chimiques qui sont utilisés dans nos sociétés avancées. Les contaminants chimiques qui concernent les denrées alimentaires d'origine animale peuvent être classifiés en trois catégories : les contaminants naturels (par exemple, les mycotoxines), les contaminants de l'environnement liés à l'industrialisation et/ou l'urbanisation (par exemple, les dioxines et les composés à activité dioxine) et les produits chimiques autorisés (par exemple, les résidus de médicaments vétérinaires). Les dangers chimiques peuvent contaminer les denrées alimentaires d'origine animale de la ferme à la fourchette, en particulier lors de la production primaire, mais aussi lors du transport de la ferme à l'abattoir, lors de la transformation, de la distribution, de la vente au détail et lors de la préparation du repas. Aucun système de production n'est exclu d'une possible contamination chimique et, actuellement, la comparaison entre ces systèmes (par exemple entre les systèmes d'exploitation intensive et extensive) est difficilement réalisable du point de vue de la sécurité alimentaire.

Bien que la capacité des nouveaux tests à détecter de plus faibles quantités de résidus augmente, la relative importance des contaminants chimiques tend à décroître dans les dernières décades en raison de l'amélioration de l'information et de la prévention. Malgré tout, des incidents individuels ne peuvent jamais être écartés et peuvent avoir de sérieuses répercussions économiques, sanitaires et sociales. Une attention particulière doit être accordée à ce problème en vue d'atténuer le risque pour le cheptel animal et le consommateur. En outre, une surveillance continue et une réévaluation périodique des risques posés par ces contaminants (au niveau national) sont nécessaires pour détecter ou anticiper les nouveaux problèmes de sorte qu'une action appropriée puisse être prise dans l'intérêt de la santé publique. En vue d'obtenir une meilleure information pour réaliser des évaluations de risque, plus d'attention devrait être consacrée pour mettre à disposition des résultats détaillés, en particulier pour obtenir des données relatives aux niveaux de fond (par exemple, les objectifs de la surveillance, les méthodes d'échantillonnage, les molécules recherchées, les méthodes analytiques, les limites de détection, les valeurs brutes et les unités de mesures spécifiées). Cette évaluation de risque offre aux autorités de contrôle un outil effectif pour l'échange d'information et de mesures à prendre pour garantir la sécurité sanitaire des aliments.

Mots-clés

Animal – Contaminant chimique – Dioxine – Exploitation agricole – Sécurité sanitaire des aliments – Denrées alimentaires d'origine animale – Santé publique – Résidus – Evaluation de risque.

∎

666

Rev. sci. tech. Off. int. Epiz., **25** (2)

Contaminación de animales con sustancias químicas en las explotaciones

C. Saegerman, L. Pussemier, A. Huyghebaert, M.-L. Scippo & D. Berkvens

Resumen

Los productos alimenticios no deben contener concentraciones peligrosas de contaminantes químicos. Pero es imposible vigilar a todas y cada una de los miles de sustancias químicas que se utilizan en nuestras sociedades avanzadas. Los contaminantes químicos presentes en los productos alimenticios de origen animal pueden clasificarse en tres categorías: contaminantes naturales (por ejemplo, las micotoxinas); contaminantes ambientales, consecuencia de la industrialización y la urbanización (por ejemplo, las dioxinas y compuestos similares), y los productos químicos autorizados (por ejemplo, los residuos de medicamentos veterinarios). Los productos alimenticios pueden contaminarse con sustancias químicas en cualquier etapa de la cadena alimentaria, en particular durante la producción primaria pero también durante el transporte de la explotación al matadero, la transformación, la distribución, la venta al por menor y la preparación de la comida. Asimismo, todos los sistemas de producción pueden sufrir contaminaciones. Además, estos últimos (por ejemplo, los sistemas de cría intensiva y extensiva) son difíciles de comparar en relación con la seguridad sanitaria de los alimentos.

Según los resultados obtenidos incluso con los métodos de análisis más recientes, que permiten detectar cantidades cada vez más pequeñas de residuos, la importancia relativa de los contaminantes químicos parece haber disminuido en las últimas décadas gracias a la mejora de la información y la prevención. No obstante, no puede descartarse la posibilidad de que se produzcan incidentes aislados, que pueden tener consecuencias económicas, sanitarias o sociales de gravedad. Debe prestarse una especial atención a los peligros químicos para reducir al máximo los riesgos que amenazan al ganado y a los consumidores. La vigilancia ha de ser permanente y los riesgos que presentan esos contaminantes deben reevaluarse periódicamente en todo el territorio nacional para detectar los problemas existentes y prever los que podrían aparecer, de modo que se puedan tomar medidas adecuadas para proteger la salud pública. Debe darse una mayor importancia a la publicación de información detallada, en particular la relativa a las finalidades perseguidas (por ejemplo, los objetivos de la vigilancia, los métodos de muestreo, las sustancias químicas que deben analizarse, los métodos de análisis, las concentraciones a detectar, los datos brutos y las unidades a utilizar) para disponer de datos más completos en los que basar los análisis de riesgos. Gracias a estos últimos, que constituyen una eficiente herramienta, las autoridades responsables de los controles pueden intercambiar información y tomar medidas adecuadas para asegurar la inocuidad de los alimentos.

Palabras clave

Animal – Contaminante químico – Dioxina – Evaluación de riesgos – Explotación – Producto alimenticio de origen animal – Residuo – Salud pública – Seguridad sanitaria de los alimentos.

∎

References

1. Acar J. (2006). – Antimicrobial resistance at farm level. *In* Animal production food safety challenges in global markets. *Rev. sci. tech. Off. int. Epiz.*, **25** (2), 775-792.

2. Adams M. & Matarjemi Y. (1999). – Basic food safety for health workers. Document WHO/SDE/FOS/99.1. World Health Organization, Geneva.

3. Agence Fédérale belge pour la Sécurité de la Chaîne Alimentaire (2005). – Business plan pour l'Agence Alimentaire (P. Vanthemsche, ed.). Agence Fédérale pour la Sécurité de la Chaîne Alimentaire, Brussels.

4. Allison J.R. (1985). – Antibiotic residues in milk. *Br. vet. J.*, **141**, 9-16.

5. Anadon A. (1985). – Standard residue regulations for chloramphenicol in Spain. *Ann. Rech. vet.*, **16**, 149-153.

6. Arctic Monitoring and Assessment Programme (AMAP) (2004). – Persistent toxic substances. Food security and indigenous peoples of the Russian North. Final report, Oslo, AMAP Report 2004:2. AMAP, Oslo. Available at: http://www.amap.no/ (accessed on 15 August 2005).

7. Attaran R.R. & Probst F. (2002). – Histamine fish poisoning: a common but frequently misdiagnosed condition. *Emerg. Med. J.*, **19**, 474-475.

8. Baranova M., Mala P., Pleva J. & Jackova A. (1994). – Cumulation NOx in foodstuffs and raw materials of animal origin. *Arch. vet. pol.*, **34** (1-2), 63-68.

9. Barcos L.O. (2004). – Animal identification and traceability. *In* 72nd General Session of the International Committee, World Organisation for Animal Health (OIE), 23-28 May, Paris. OIE, Paris.

10. Barton H. (2005). – Predicted intake of trace elements and minerals via household drinking water by 6-year-old children from Krakow, Poland. Part 2: Cadmium, 1997-2001. *Food Addit. Contam.*, **22** (9), 816-828.

11. Bender C.L., Alarcón-Chaidez F. & Gross D.C. (1999). – *Pseudomonas syringae* phytotoxins: mode of action, regulation, and biosynthesis by peptide and polyketide synthetases. *Microbiol. molec. Biol. Rev.*, **63** (2), 266-292.

12. Bennett R.W. (2005). – Staphylococcal enterotoxin and its rapid identification in foods by enzyme-linked immunosorbent assay-based methodology. *J. Food Protec.*, **68** (6), 1264-1270.

13. Beran G.W. & Baum D.H. (1997). – Food safety begins at the farm. Iowa State University (ISU), Swine research report on health, document ASL-R1512. ISU, Ames.

14. Bernard A., Hermans C., Broeckaert F., De Poorter G., De Cock A. & Houins G. (1999). – Food contamination by PCBs and dioxins. *Nature*, **401**, 231-232.

15. Bernard A., Broeckaert F., De Poorter G., De Cock A., Hermans C., Saegerman C. & Houins G. (2002). – The Belgian PCB/Dioxin incident: analysis of the food chain contamination and health risk evaluation. *Environ. Res.*, **88**, 1-18.

16. Beulens A., Broens D., Folstar P. & Hofstede G. (2005). – Food safety and transparency in food chains and networks. Relationships and challenges. *Food Control*, **16**, 481-486.

17. Bhat R.V. & Vasanthi S. (1999). – Contamination de l'alimentation humaine et animale par les mycotoxines. *In* Troisième conférence internationale mixte FAO/OMS/PNUE sur les mycotoxines, 3-6 March, Tunis. Food and Agriculture Organization, Rome, 22.

18. Black W.D. (1994). – Pesticide residues in foods of animal origin. *In* Animal drugs and human health (L.M. Crawford & D.A. Franco, eds). Technomic, Lancaster, Pennsylvania and Basel, 63-80.

19. Blanc M. (2001). – Nouvelles exigences en matière de sécurité sanitaire dans le commerce international des produits agricoles et agroalimentaires : incidence pour les pays d'Afrique exportateurs de produits oléagineux. *Ol. Corps gras Lipides*, **8**, 246-250.

20. Boyes W.K., Tandon P., Barone S. & Padilla S. (1994). – Effects of organophosphates on the visual system of rats. *J. appl. Toxicol.*, **13**, 135-143.

21. Bradberry S.M., Cage S.A., Proudfoot A.T. & Vale J.A. (2005). – Poisoning due to pyrethroids. *Toxicol. Rev.*, **24** (2), 93-106.

22. Canadian Food Inspection Agency (2005). – The national chemical residue monitoring program. Available at: http://www.inspection.gc.ca/english/fssa/microchem/resid/2001-2002/fooali_indexe.shtml#1 (accessed on 15 August 2005).

23. Carvalhaes G.K., Brooks P., Marques C.G., Azevedo J.A., Machado M.C. & Azevedo G.C. (2002). – Lime as the source of PCDD/F contamination in citrus pulp pellets from Brazil and status of the monitoring program. *Chemosphere*, **46** (9-10), 1413-1416.

24. Center for Disease Control and Prevention (1988). – Organophosphate toxicity associated with flea-dip products – California. *MMWR*, **37**, 329-336.

25. Chandelier A., Michelet J.Y., Tangni E.K., Baert K., Moons E. & Vinkx C. (2004). – Mycotoxins survey in Belgium and toxigenic fusarium in Belgian wheat. *In* An overview on toxigenic fungi and mycotoxins in Europe (A. Logrieco & A. Visconti, eds). Kluwer Academic Publishers, Dordrecht, Netherlands, 11-32.

26. Cobb S.P., Hogg R.A., Challoner D.J., Brett M.M., Livesey R.T., Sharpe R.T. & Jones T.O. (2002). – Suspected botulism in dairy cows and its implications for the safety of human food. *Vet. Rec.*, **150**, 5-8.

27. Corpet D.E. & Lumeau S. (1989). – Effect of low levels of antimicrobials on drug resistant populations of intestinal bacteria in gnotobiotic mice. *In* Rational view of antimicrobials residues: an assessment of human safety (J.P. Raynaud, ed.). Paul Parey, Berlin, 75.

28. Creppy E.E. (2002). – Update of survey, regulation and toxic effects of mycotoxins in Europe. *Toxicol. Lett.*, **127**, 19-28.

30. De Kok T.M.C.M. & van Maanen J.M.S. (2000). – Evaluation of fecal mutagenicity and colorectal cancer risk. *Mutat. Res.*, **463**, 53-101.

31. Debongnie P., Hallaux B., Etienne F. & Pussemier L. (2000). – Environmental PCB contaminations. *In* Proc. 8th Annual Meeting of the Flemish Society for Veterinary Epidemiology and Economics, 26 October, Brussels. VEE, Brussels, 72-73.

32. Dementi B. (1994). – Ocular effects of organophosphates: a historical perspective of Saku disease. *J. appl. Toxicol.*, **14**, 119-129.

33. Dowd P.F. (1998). – Involvement of arthropods in the establishment of mycotoxigenic fungi under field conditions. *In* Mycotoxins in agriculture and food safety (K.K. Sinha & D. Bhatnagar, eds). Marcel Dekker, New York, 1307-1350.

34. Dragacci S., Grosso F., Pfauwathel-Marchond N., Fremy J.-M., Venant A. & Lombard B. (2002). – Proficiency testing for the evaluation of the ability of European Union-National Reference laboratories to determine aflatoxin M1 in milk at levels corresponding to the new European Union legislation. *Food Addit. Contam.*, **18** (5), 405-415.

35. Drotman D.P., Baxter P.J., Liddle J.A., Brokopp C.D. & Skinner M.D. (1983). – Contamination of the food chain by polychlorinated biphenyls from a broker transformer. *Am. J. public Hlth*, **73**, 290-292.

36. Dudka S. & Miller W.P. (1999). – Accumulation of potentially toxic elements in plants and their transfer to human food chain. *J. environ. Sci. Hlth B*, **34** (4), 681-708.

37. Environmental Protection Agency (1999). – The inventory of sources of dioxin in the United States. Exposure analysis and risk characterization group, National Center for Environment Assessment, Office of Research and Development, United States Environmental Protection Agency, Washington, DC. Available at: http://www.epa.gov/ncea/diox.htm (accessed on 15 August 2005).

38. Environmental Protection Agency (2000). – Guidance for assessing chemical contaminant data for use in fish advisories, Vol. 1. Fish sampling and analysis, 3rd Ed. EPA 823-R-95-007. Office of Water, Washington, DC.

39. Environmental Protection Agency (2000). – Guidance for assessing chemical contaminant data for use in fish advisories, Vol. 2. Risk assessment and fish consumption limits. United States Environmental Protection Agency, Washington, DC, 3rd Ed. Available at: http://www.epa.gov/ost/fishadvice/volume2/index.html (accessed on 15 August 2005).

40. European Commission (1996). – Council Directive 96/23/EC of 29 April on measures to monitor certain substances and residues thereof in live animals and animal products and repealing Directives 85/358/EEC and 86/469/EEC and Decisions 89/187/EEC and 91/664/EEC. *Off. J. Eur. Communities*, **L125**, 10-32.

41. European Commission (1998). – Directive 98/8/EC of the European Parliament and of the Council of 16 February concerning the placing of biocidal products on the market. *Off. J. Eur. Communities*, **L123**, 1-63.

42. European Commission (1999). – Compilation of EU dioxin exposure and health data, summary report. European Commission and United Kingdom (Department of the Environment, Transport and Regions). Available at: http://europa.eu.int/comm/environment/dioxin/pdf/summary.pdf (accessed on 15 August 2005).

43. European Commission (2001). – Opinion of the Scientific Committee on Food on the risk assessment of dioxins and dioxin-like PCBs in food adopted on 30 May. Update based on new scientific information available since the adoption of the SCF opinion of 22 November 2000. European Commission, Health and Consumer Protection Directorate-General, Brussels. Available at: http://europa.eu.int/comm/food/fs/sc/scf/out90_en.pdf (accessed on 15 August 2005).

44. European Commission (2002). – Decision (CE) No. 2002/657 of 12 August implementing Council Directive 96/23/EC concerning the performance of analytical methods and the interpretation of results. *Off. J. Eur. Communities*, **L221**, 8-36.

45. European Commission (2002). – Final report of a mission carried out in Germany from 19 to 23 August in order to evaluate the relevant control systems in place, in the light of the recent findings of nitrofen in food and feedingstuffs. Document DG(SANCO)/8686/2002 – MR Final. Health and Consumer Protection Directorate-General, Brussels.

46. European Commission (2004). – Rapid alert system for food and feed. Annual report on the functioning of the RASFF 2004. Health and Consumer Protection Directorate-General, European Commission, Brussels.

47. European Commission (2004). – Regulation (EC) No. 882/2004 of the European Parliament and of the Council of 29 April on official controls performed to ensure the verification of compliance with feed and food law, animal health and animal welfare rules. *Off. J. Eur. Communities*, **L165**, 1-141.

48. European Commission (2005). – Decision (EEC) No. 34/2005 of 11 January laying down harmonised standards for the testing for certain residues in products of animal origin imported from third countries. *Off. J. Eur. Communities*, **L16**, 61-63.

49. European Council (1987). – Directive (EEC) No. 87/181 of 9 March amending the Annex to Directive 79/117/EEC prohibiting the placing on the market and use of plant protection products containing certain active substances. *Off. J. Eur. Communities*, **L71**, 33.

50. European Food Safety Authority (EFSA) (2004). – Methodologies and principles for setting tolerable intake levels for dioxins, furans and dioxin-like PCBs. Summary report of the EFSA scientific colloquium, 28-29 June, Brussels. EFSA, Parma.

51. European Parliament and Council (2002). – Regulation (EC) No. 178/2002 of 28 January laying down the general principles and requirements of food law, establishing the European Food Safety Authority and laying down procedures in matters of food safety. *Off. J. Eur. Communities*, **L31**, 1-24.

52. Fisher S.W. (1995). – Mechanisms of bioaccumulation in aquatic systems. *In* Reviews of environmental contamination and toxicology (G.W. Ware, ed.), Vol. 142. Springer, New York, 87-118.

53. Food and Agriculture Organization (FAO) (1997). – Agriculture food and nutrition for Africa: a resource book for teachers of agriculture. FAO, Rome.

54. Food and Agriculture Organization (2005). – Food contaminants and residue information system. Joint FAO/IAEA Programme, nuclear techniques in food and agriculture, infocrisis. Available at: http://infocris.iaea.org/en/default.htm (accessed on 15 August 2005).

55. Food and Agriculture Organization (2005). – List of pesticides residues in food: maximum residue limits. Available at: http://faostat.fao.org/faostat/pestdes/jsp/pest_q-f.jsp (accessed on 15 August 2005).

56. Fraser C.M., Bergeron J.A., Mays A. & Aiello S.E. (eds) (1996). – Toxicologie. *In* Manuel vétérinaire Merck, 1st Ed. Editions d'Après, Paris, 486-541.

57. Fries G.F. (1995). – A review of the significance of animal food products as potential pathways of human exposures to dioxins. *J. Anim. Sci.*, **73** (6), 1639-1650.

58. Fries G.F. & Paustenbach D.J. (1990). – Evaluation of potential transmission of 2,3,7,8-tetrachlorodibenzo-*p*-dioxin-contaminated incinerator emissions to humans via foods. *J. Toxicol. environ. Hlth*, **29** (1), 1-43.

59. Fuhrmann T. (1991). – Overview of residue concerns of the dairy industry. *J. Am. vet. med. Assoc.*, **198**, 836-837.

60. Gilbert R.J., Hobbs G., Murray C.K., Cruickshank J.G. & Young S.E. (1980). – Scombrotoxic fish poisoning: features of the first 50 incidents to be reported in Britain (1976-1979). *Br. med. J.*, **281**, 71-72.

61. Gillespie I.A., Adak G.K., O'Brien S.J., Brett M.M. & Bolton F.J. (2001). – General outbreaks of infectious intestinal disease associated with fish and shellfish, England and Wales, 1992-1999. *Communic. Dis. public Hlth*, **4**, 117-123.

62. Gloyd J.S. (1990). – Safe levels of antimicrobial residues in milk announced by FDA. *J. Am. vet. med. Assoc.*, **197**, 815.

63. Gorris L. (2005). – Food safety objective: an integral part of food chain management. *Food Control*, **16**, 801-809.

64. Guo X., Longnecker M.P. & Michalek J.E. (2001). – Relation of serum tetrachlorodibenzo-*p*-dioxin concentration to diet among veterans in the Air Force Health Study with background-level exposure. *J. Toxicol. environ. Hlth*, **63**, 159-172.

65. Hamann J., Tolle A. & Heeschen W. (1979). – Antibiotics and sulphonamides: residues in milk of treated cows and its products. *Doc. Int. Dairy Fed., Brussels*, **113**, 43-56.

66. Harris B. & Staples C.R. (1992). – The problems of mycotoxins in dairy cattle rations. Institute of Food and Agricultural Sciences, Florida. Available at: http://edis.ifas.ufl.edu/BODY_DS152 (accessed on 15 August 2005).

67. Hellman B. & Laryea D. (1990). – Inhibitory action of benzimidazole fungicides on the *in vivo* incorporation of [3H]thymidine in various organs of the mouse. *Food chem. Toxicol.*, **28**, 701-706.

68. Hodgson E., Mailman R.B. & Chambers J.E. (1988). – Dictionary of toxicology, 1st Ed. Macmillan, London.

69. Horowitz B.Z. (2005). – Botulinum toxin. *Crit. Care Clin.*, **21** (4), 825-839.

70. Huwe J.K., Davison K., Feil V.J., Larsen G., Lorentzen M., Zaylskie R. & Tiernan T.O. (2004). – Levels of polychlorinated dibenzo-*p*-dioxins and dibenzofurans in cattle raised at agricultural research facilities across the USA and the influence of pentachlorophenol-treated wood. *Food Addit. Contam.*, **21** (2), 182-194.

71. International Agency for Research on Cancer (IARC) (1983). – Polynuclear aromatic compounds. Part 1. Chemical environment and experimental data. IARC Monograph, Vol. 32. IARC, Lyons. Available at: http://monographs.iarc.fr/ (accessed on 15 August 2005).

72. International Agency for Research on Cancer (IARC) (1984). – Polynuclear aromatic compounds. Part 3. Industrial exposures in aluminium products, coal gasification, coke production, and iron and steel founding. IARC Monograph, Vol. 34. IARC, Lyons. Available at: http://monographs.iarc.fr/ (accessed on 15 August 2005).

73. International Agency for Research on Cancer (IARC) (1987). – Working Group on the evaluation of carcinogenic risks to humans, overall evaluations of carcinogenicity: an updating of IARC monographs volumes 1-42. IARC monographs on the evaluation of carcinogenic risks to humans, Supplement 7. IARC, Lyons. Available at: http://monographs.iarc.fr/ (accessed on 15 August 2005).

670

Rev. sci. tech. Off. int. Epiz., 25 (2)

74. International Agency for Research on Cancer (IARC) (2002). – Aflatoxins. IARC Monograph, Vol. 82. IARC, Lyons.

75. International Programme on Chemical Safety (2005). – Disinfectants and disinfectant by-products. World Health Organization, Geneva.

76. Isbister G.K. & Kiernan M.C. (2005). – Neurotoxic marine poisoning. *Lancet Neurol.*, **4** (4), 219-228.

77. Ishikawa S. (1973). – Chronic optico-neuropathy due to environmental exposure of organophosphate pesticides (Saku disease): clinical and experimental study. *Nippon Ganka Gakkai Zasshi*, **77**, 1835-1886.

78. Jeyaretnam J. & Jones H. (2000). – Physical, chemical and biological hazards in veterinary practice. *Aust. vet. J.*, **78** (1), 751-758.

79. Joint Food and Agriculture Organization/World Health Organization (WHO) Expert Committee on Food Additives (1991). – Toxicological evaluation of certain veterinary drug residues in food. International Programme on Chemical Safety/WHO. WHO Food Additives Series 27. WHO, Geneva.

80. Joint Food and Agriculture Organization/World Health Organization (WHO) Expert Committee on Food Additives (2002). – Polychlorinated dibenzodioxins, polychlorinated dibenzofurans, and coplanar polychlorinated biphenyls. WHO Food Additives Series 48. WHO, Geneva. Available at: http://www.inchem.org/documents/jecfa/jecmono/v48je20.htm (accessed on 15 August 2005).

81. Kavlock R.J., Daston G.P., De Rosa C., Fenner-Crisp P., Gray L.E., Kaattari S., Lucier G., Luster M., Mac M.J., Maczka C., Miller R., Moore J., Rolland R., Scott G., Sheehan D.M., Sinks T. & Tilson H.A. (1996). – Research needs for the risk assessment of health and environmental effects of endocrine disruptors: a report of the US EPA-sponsored workshop. *Environ. Hlth Perspect.*, **104**, 715-810.

82. Kirrane E., Hoppin J.A., Kamel F., Umbach D.M., Boyes W.K., DeRoos A.J., Alavanja M. & Sandler D.P. (2005). – Retinal degeneration and other eye disorders in wives of farmer pesticide applicators enrolled in the agricultural health study. *Am. J. Epidemiol.*, **161**, 1020-1029.

83. Kogevinas M. (2001). – Human health effects of dioxins: cancer, reproductive and endocrine system effects. *Hum. Reprod.*, **7** (3), 331-339.

84. Kong K.Y., Cheung K.C., Wong C.K.C. & Wong M.H. (2005). – The residual dynamic of polycyclic aromatic hydrocarbons and organochlorine pesticides in fishponds of the Pearl River delta, South China. *Water Res. (Oxford)*, **39**, 1831-1843.

85. Lake J.-L., Mckinney R., Lake C.A., Osterman F.A. & Heltshe J. (1995). – Comparisons of patterns of polychlorinated biphenyl congeners in water, sediment and indigenous organisms from New Bedford Harbour, Massachusetts. *Arch. environ. Contam. Toxicol.*, **29**, 207-220.

86. Langley R., Pryor W. & O'Brian K. (1995). – Health hazards among veterinarians: a survey and review of the literature. *J. Agromed.*, **2**, 23-52.

87. Liem A.K., Furst P. & Rappe C. (2000). – Exposure of populations to dioxins and related compounds. *Food Addit. Contam.*, **17** (4), 241-259.

88. Lievaart J.J., Noordhuizen J.P.T.M., van Beek E., van der Beek C., van Risp A., Schenkel J. & van Veersen J. (2005). – The hazard analysis critical control point's (HACCP) concept as applied to some chemical, physical and microbiological contaminants of milk on dairy farms. A prototype. *Vet. Q.*, **27** (1), 21-29.

89. Lipp E.K. & Rose J.B. (1997). – The role of seafood in foodborne diseases in the United States of America. *In* Contamination of animal products: prevention and risks for public health. *Rev. sci. tech. Off. int. Epiz.*, **16** (2), 620-640.

90. Lopez C.E., Ramos L.L., Ramadan S.S. & Bulacio L.C. (2003). – Presence of aflatoxin M1 in milk for human consumption in Argentina. *Food Control*, **14**, 31-34.

91. Maghuin-Rogister G., Delaunois A., De Pauw E. & Gustin P. (1999). – La pollution de la chaîne alimentaire par la dioxine. *Ann. Méd. vét.*, **143**, 379-392.

92. Maita K., Tsuda S. & Shirasu Y. (1991). – Chronic toxicity studies with thiram in Wistar rats and beagle dogs. *Fundament. appl. Toxicol.*, **16**, 667-686.

93. Mann P.C. (1997). – Selected lesions of dioxins in laboratory rodents. *Toxicol. Pathol.*, **25**, 72-79.

94. Matthews H.B. & Dedrick R.L. (1984). – Pharmacokinetics of PCBs. *Annu. Rev. Pharmacol. Toxicol.*, **24**, 85-103.

95. McEwen S.A. & McNab W.B. (1997). – Contaminants of non-biological origin in foods from animals. *In* Contamination of animal products: prevention and risks for public health. *Rev. sci. tech. Off. int. Epiz.*, **16** (2), 684-693.

96. McGregor D.B., Partensky C., Wilbourn J. & Rice J.M. (1998). – An IARC evaluation of polychlorinated dibenzo-*p*-dioxins and polychlorinated dibenzofurans as risk factors in human carcinogenesis. *Environ. Hlth Perspect.*, **106**, 755-760.

97. Milhaud G. (1985). – Chloramphenicol residues and their toxicity. *Ann. Rech. vét.*, **16** (2), 133-148.

98. Misra U.K., Nag D., Misra N.K., Melra M.K. & Ray P.K. (1985). – Some observations on the macula of pesticides workers. *Hum. Toxicol.*, **4**, 135-145.

99. Moreau F. & Saegerman C. (1990). – La pratique de la désinfection en élevage bovin (première et deuxième parties). *Probio-Revue*, **13** (3), 257-273.

100. Murray C.K. & Hobbs G. (1982). – Scombrotoxin and scombrotoxin-like poisoning from canned fish. *J. Hyg. (Camb.)*, **88**, 215-220.

Rev. sci. tech. Off. int. Epiz., **25** (2)

671

101. Nasreddine L. & Parent-Massin D. (2002). – Food contamination by metals and pesticides in the European Union. Should we worry? *Toxicol. Lett.*, **127**, 29-41.

102. National Food Agency Finland (2005). – Varying species of fish twice a week. Available at: http://www.palvelu.fi/evi/files/55_519_349.pdf (accessed on 15 August 2005).

103. Neidert E., Trotman R.B. & Saschenbrecker P.W. (1994). – Levels and incidence of pesticide residues in selected agricultural food commodities available in Canada. *J. Assoc. off. anal. Chem.*, **77**, 18-24.

104. Oliver B.G. & Niimi A.J. (1988). – Trophodynamic analysis of polychlorinated biphenyl congeners and other chlorinated hydrocarbons in the Lake Ontario ecosystem. *Environ. Sci. Technol.*, **22**, 388-397.

105. Paoliello M.M. & De Capitani E.M. (2005). – Environmental contamination and human exposure to lead in Brazil. *Rev. environ. Contam. Toxicol.*, *184*, 59-96.

106. Paris F., Jeandel C., Servant N. & Sultan C. (2006). – Increased serum estrogenic bioactivity in three male newborns with ambiguous genitalia: a potential consequence of prenatal exposure to environmental endocrine disruptors. *Environ. Res.*, **100** (1), 39-43.

107. Pedersen D.H., Wilkins III J.R., Bean T.L., Mitchell G.L., Crawford J.M. & Jones L.A. (1999). – Agricultural hazard data from a population-based survey of cash grain farms: Ohio observations. *Appl. occupat. environ. Hyg.*, **14**, 299-305.

108. Peraica M., Radic B., Lucic A. & Pavlovic M. (1999). – Toxic effects of mycotoxins in humans. *Bull. WHO*, **77**, 754-766.

109. Pfohl-Leszkawicz A. (1999). – Les mycotoxines dans l'alimentation : évaluation et gestion du risque. Lavoisier, Collection Rec&Doc, Paris.

110. Pussemier L. (2003). – Les contaminations chimiques dans les systèmes de production « bio » et conventionnel. *In* La sécurité alimentaire. Une approche scientifique. Institut Danone, Brussels, 35-56.

111. Pussemier L., Mohimont L., Huyghebaert A. & Goeyens L. (2004). – Enhanced levels of dioxins in eggs from free range hens; a fast evaluation approach. *Talanta (Oxford)*, **63**, 1274-1276.

112. Pussemier L., Larondelle Y., van Peteghem C. & Huyghebaert A. (2006). – Chemical safety of conventionally and organically produced foodstuffs: a tentative comparison under Belgian conditions. *Food Control*, **17**, 14-21.

113. Renwick A.G., Barlow S.M., Hertz-Picciotto I, Boobis A.R., Dybing E., Edler L., Eisenbrand G., Greig J.B., Kleiner J., Lambe J., Müller D.J.G., Smith M.R., Tritscher A., Tuijtelaars S., van den Brandt P.A., Walker R. & Kroes R. (2003). – Risk characterisation of chemicals in food and diet. *Food chem. Toxicol.*, **41**, 1211-1271.

114. Reuter G. (1989). – Requirements for the effectiveness of disinfectants for the food-processing industry. *Zentralbl. Bakteriol. Mikrobiol. Hyg.*, **187**, 564-577.

115. Riley R.T. (1998). – Mechanistic interactions of mycotoxins: theoretical consideration. *In* Mycotoxins in agriculture and food safety (K.K. Sinha & D. Bhatnagar, eds). Marcel Dekker Inc., New York and Basle, 227-253.

116. Rodahl K. (1949). – Toxicity of polar bear liver. *Nature*, **164**, 530-531.

117. Rodricks J.V. (1986). – FDA's ban on the use of DES in meat production: a case study. *In* Agriculture and human values. Kluwer Academic Publishers B.V., Dordrecht, Boston, New York, London, 10-25.

118. Ruppol P., Delfosse Ph. & Hornick J.-L. (2004). – La contamination de la filière laitière par les mycotoxines : un risque pour la santé publique en Afrique subsaharienne. *Ann. Méd. vét.*, **148**, 141-146.

119. Saegerman C. (2004). – Epidémiosurveillance des événements rares chez les bovins en Belgique. Thèse de doctorat en Sciences vétérinaires, orientation Médecine vétérinaire, Université de Liège.

120. Saegerman C., Boelaert F., Van Vlanderen I., Lomba M., Berkvens D., Ermens A., Biron P., Broeckaert F., Bernard A., De Cock A., Demont S., De Poorter G., Torfs B., Robijns J.-M., Monfort V., Vermeersch J.-P. & Lengelé L. (2001). – Monitoring des animaux vivants: exemple d'un échantillonnage pour la détection des PCBs et des dioxines chez les bovins de boucherie en Belgique. *Epidémiol. Santé anim.*, **38**, 39-49.

121. Saegerman C., Berkvens D., Boelaert F., Speybroeck N., Van Vlanderen I., Lomba M., Biront P., Broeckaert F., De Cock A., Mohimont L., Demont S., De Poorter G., Torfs B., Robijns J.-M., Monfort V., Vermeersch J.-P., Lengelé L. & Bernard A. (2002). – Detection of polychlorinated biphenyls and dioxins in Belgian cattle and estimation of the maximal potential exposure in humans through diets of bovine origin. *J. Toxicol. environ. Hlth*, **65**, 1289-1305.

122. Saegerman C., Claes L., Dewaele A., Desmecht D., Rollin F., Hamoir J., Gustin P., Czaplicki G., Bughin J., Wullepit J., Laureyns J., Roels S., Berkvens D., Vanopdenbosch E. & Thiry E. (2003). – Differential diagnosis of neurologically expressed disorders in Western European cattle. *In* Risk analysis of prion diseases in animals. *Rev. sci. tech. Off. int. Epiz.*, **22** (1), 83-102.

123. Schillhorn van Veen T. (2005). – International trade and food safety in developing countries. *Food Control*, **16**, 491-496.

124. Schwägele F. (2005). – Traceability from a European perspective. *Meat Sci.*, **71**, 164-173.

125. Seawright A.A. (1982). – Chemical residues in foods of animal origin. *In* Animal health in Australia, Vol. 2. Chemical and plant poisons. Australian Government Publishing Service, Canberra, 235-244.

672

Rev. sci. tech. Off. int. Epiz., **25** (2)

126. Settepani J.A. (1984). – The hazard of using chloramphenicol in food animals. *J. Am. vet. med. Assoc.,* **184** (8), 930-931.

127. Sharma S.K. & Whiting R.C. (2005). – Methods for detection of *Clostridium botulinum* toxin in foods. *J. Food Protec.,* **68** (6), 1256-1263.

128. Smith J.E., Lewis C.W., Anderson J.G. & Solomos G.L. (1994). – Mycotoxins, occurrence and toxicity. *In* Mycotoxins in human nutrition and health. European Commission, Directorate-General XII, Science, Research and Development, Agro-Industrial Research Division, Brussels, 1-55.

129. Steenland K., Piacitelli L., Deddens J., Fingerhut M. & Chang L. (1999). – Cancer, heart disease, and diabetes in workers exposed to 2, 3, 7, 8-tetrachlorodibenzo-*p*-dioxin. *J. natl Cancer Inst.,* **91** (9), 779-786.

130. Steenland K., Bertazzi P., Baccarelli A. & Kogevinas M. (2004). – Dioxin revisited: developments since the 1997 IARC classification of dioxin as a human carcinogen. *Environ. Hlth Perspect.,* **112** (13), 1265-1268.

131. Stolker A. & Brinkman U. (2005). – Analytical strategies for residue analysis of veterinary drugs and growth-promoting agents in food-producing animals: a review. *J. Chromatogr.,* **1067**, 15-53.

132. Sudlof S.F., Riviere J.E. & Graigmill A.L. (1990). – Food animal residue avoidance databank: trade name file. A comprehensive compendium of dairy cattle drugs, 5th Ed. University of Florida, Gainesville.

133. Sunesson A.L., Gullberg J. & Blomquist G. (2001). – Airborne chemical compounds on dairy farms. *J. environ. Monit.,* **3** (2), 210-216.

134. Travis C.C. & Hattemer-Frey H.A. (1991). – Human exposure to dioxin. *Sci. total Environ.,* **104** (1-2), 97-127.

135. Trotter W.J. & Dickerson R. (1993). – Pesticide residues in composited milk collected through the US pasteurized milk network. *J. Assoc. off. anal. Chem.,* **76** (6), 1220-1225.

136. United Nations Environment Programmes (1999). – Dioxin and furan inventories: national and regional emissions of PCDD/PCDF. Available at: http://www.chem.unep.ch/pops/pdf/dioxinfuran/difurpt.pdf (accessed on 15 August 2005).

137. United States Department of Agriculture (2002). – Agricultural chemical usage 2001: dairy cattle and dairy facilities summary. National Agricultural Statistics Service, Washington, DC.

138. Van Baale M.J., Galland J.C., Hyatt D.R. & Milliken G.A. (2003). – A survey of dairy producer practices and attitudes pertaining to dairy market beef food safety. *Food Protec. Trends,* **23** (6), 466-473.

139. Van den Berg M., Birnbaum L., Bosveld A., Brunstrom B., Cook P., Feeley M., Giesy J.P., Hanberg A., Hasegawa R., Kennedy S., Kubiak T., Larsen J.C., van Leeuwen F., Liem K., Nolt C., Peterson R., Poellinger L., Safe S., Schrenk D., Tillitt D., Tysklind M., Younes M., Waern F. & Zacharewski T. (1998). – Toxic equivalency factors (TEFs) for PCBs, PCDDs, PCDFs for humans and wildlife. *Environ. Hlth Perspect.,* **106** (12), 775.

140. Van Leeuwen F.X., Feeley M., Schrenk D., Larsen J.C., Farland W. & Younes M. (2000). – Dioxins: WHO's tolerable daily intake (TDI) revisited. *Chemosphere,* **40** (9-11), 1095-1101.

141. Vrijens B., De Henauw S., Dewettinck K., Talloen W., Goeyens L., De Backer G. & Willems J.L. (2002). – Probabilistic intake assessment and body burden estimation of dioxin-like substances in background conditions and during a short food contamination episode. *Food Addit. Contam.,* **19** (7), 687-700.

142. Waltner-Toews D. & McEwen S.A. (1994). – Insecticide residues in foods of animal origin: a risk assessment. *Prev. vet. Med.,* **20**, 179-200.

143. Waltner-Toews D. & McEwen S.A. (1994). – Residues of antibacterial and antiparasitic drugs in foods of animal origin: a risk assessment. *Prev. vet. Med.,* **20**, 219-234.

144. Waltner-Toews D. & McEwen S.A. (1994). – Residues of hormonal substances in foods of animal origin: a risk assessment. *Prev. vet. Med.,* **20**, 235-247.

145. Weber L.W. & Greim H. (1997). – The toxicity of brominated and mixed-halogenated dibenzo-*p*-dioxins and dibenzofurans: an overview. *J. Toxicol. environ. Hlth,* **50** (3), 195-215.

146. White J., Warrell D., Eddleston M., Currie B.J., White I.M. & Isbister G.K. (2003). – Clinical toxicology: where are we now? *J. Toxicol. clin. Toxicol.,* **41**, 263-276.

147. Wilkinson T.L., Purschwitz M.A., Schuler R.T. & Skjolaas C.A. (1998). – Farm hazard inspection checklist. University of Wisconsin-Madison Extension, Madison.

148. Woese K., Lange D., Boess C. & Bögl K.W. (1997). – A comparison of organically and conventionally grown foods: results of a review of the relevant literature. *J. Sci. Food Agric.,* **74**, 281-293.

149. World Health Organization (1998). – Executive summary. *In* Assessment of health risk of dioxins: re-evaluation of the tolerable daily intake. WHO, Geneva, 1-19.

150. World Health Organization (WHO) (1999). – Basic food safety for health workers. WHO, Geneva.

151. World Health Organization (WHO) (2000). – Polychlorinated biphenyls (PCBs). *In* Air quality guidelines, second edition, Chapter 5.10. WHO Regional Office for Europe, Copenhagen, 22. Available at: http://www.euro.who.int/document/aiq/5_10pcb.pdf (accessed on 15 August 2005).

152. World Health Organization (WHO) (2000). – Polychlorinated dibenzodioxins and dibenzofurans. *In* Air quality guidelines, second edition, Chapter 5.11. WHO Regional Office for Europe, Copenhagen, 21. Available at: http://www.euro.who.int/document/aiq/5_11pcddpcdf.pdf (accessed on 15 August 2005).

153. World Health Organization (WHO) (2004). – Database of public health chemical incidents: first year pilot phase report. *Weekly epidemiol. Rec.*, **7**, 72-76.

154. World Health Organization (WHO) (2005). – International programme on chemical safety. Chemical safety information from intergovernmental organisations. Available at: http://www.inchem.org/ (accessed on 15 August 2005).

155. World Health Organization (WHO) (2005). – PCBs and dioxins in salmon. WHO, Geneva. Available at: http://www.who.int/foodsafety/chem/pcbsalmon/en/print.html (accessed on 15 August 2005).

156. Wu M.L., Yang C.C., Yang G.Y., Ger J. & Deng J.F. (1997). – Scombroid fish poisoning: an overlooked marine food poisoning. *Vet. hum. Toxicol.*, **39**, 236-241.

157. Yiannikouris A. & Jouany J.-P. (2002). – Les mycotoxines dans les aliments des ruminants, leur devenir et leurs effets chez l'animal. *Prod. anim.*, **15**, 3-16.

158. Zwietering M. (2005). – Practical considerations on food safety objectives. *Food Control*, **16**, 817-823.

Rev. sci. tech. Off. int. Epiz., 2006, **25** (2), 675-684

Conditions of transfer and quality of food

K.J. Southern, J.G. Rasekh, F.E. Hemphill & A.M. Thaler

Zoonotic Diseases and Residue Surveillance Division, United States Department of Agriculture Food Safety and Inspection Service, 1400 Independence Ave., SW Room 343 Aerospace Center, Washington, DC 20250, United States of America

The ideas in this paper represent those of the authors alone and do not represent any official position of the United States Department of Agriculture.

Summary
Many factors contribute to the production of safe foods of animal origin. Initiatives for an integrated approach to food safety recognise the importance of optimising transportation conditions to ensure on-farm interventions are preserved. Physical, microbial, and environmental hazards during the transportation process may adversely affect the safety and quality of meat, poultry, and egg products. Additionally, the stress level in animals can be raised by transportation conditions, potentially causing increased pathogen shedding in carrier animals which exposes other animals to possible contamination. The physiological effects of stress on animals can reduce the quality of meat, poultry, and egg products produced by the animals, thus decreasing the economic value of the animal. Increased globalisation of markets provides an incentive for transportation standards of food animals within a country as well as transportation standards between countries.

Keywords
Animal welfare – Food-borne disease – Lairage – Meat quality – Meat safety – Pre-slaughter handling – Stress – Transportation.

Introduction

Incidence of food-borne illness in the United States of America (USA) has declined in recent years, in part due to preventative, risk-based measures implemented in meat and poultry establishments by regulators and the food industry (3). The development of risk-based animal production principles on the farm helps to reduce the risk of food-borne pathogens amongst food animals. While the health status of animals at the time they leave the farm is important, it is crucial to recognise the importance of optimising transportation conditions. Researchers are now looking at the process of transporting food animals from farm to slaughter to determine how the positive effects of on-farm interventions aimed at controlling the spread of pathogens in live animals can be preserved during transportation.

Transporting animals to slaughter is far more demanding than the transfer of animals from one location to another (Fig. 1). Numerous microbial, physical, and/or environmental hazards during transport have the potential to negatively affect not only the health and welfare of the animals, but also the safety and quality of the resulting meat, poultry, and egg products. In addition, studies have shown that animals experience a great deal of stress during pre-slaughter handling and transportation that may impair cellular immune responses and cause physiological changes, possibly affecting the safety and quality of the resulting food products (1, 12, 21). Time in transit, distance travelled, pre-transport conditioning, environmental conditions, and lairage at the slaughterhouse are all components of transportation that may negatively affect stress levels and diminish the economic value of the animals and the food products.

This paper focuses on the various hazards that food animals face during transport to slaughter and their impact on the safety and quality of food products from these animals. The paper will briefly address global and economic considerations and consequences associated with transporting food animals.

676

Rev. sci. tech. Off. int. Epiz., **25** (2)

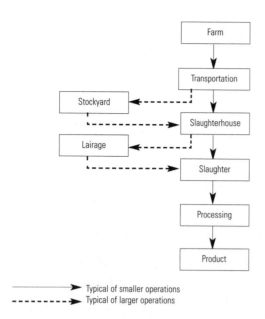

→ Typical of smaller operations
---→ Typical of larger operations

This diagram illustrates various phases of transportation. Microbial, environmental and/or physical hazards can occur at any one of these stages and directly or indirectly affect the safety and quality of meat, poultry and egg products

Fig. 1
Stages of transportation in the 'farm-to-table' continuum

Effects of stress on meat safety and quality

It is well known that mammals possess the capacity to feel pain and experience stress (4). In the case of food animals, much of this pain and stress takes place prior to slaughter, particularly involving the events associated with transportation. There are a number of factors that determine the effect that varying amounts of stress will have on a particular animal. Health status at time of transportation, state of nutrition, and the genetic makeup of certain species or breeds are just a few of the variables that can bring about dissimilar responses to various stressors (1, 21).

Shedding of pathogenic microorganisms

Many food-borne pathogens are ubiquitous in the livestock and poultry environment and may be carried by healthy, unstressed animals without shedding (22). The physiological changes associated with stress can cause continual shedding in these animals due to a disturbance in intestinal function and lowered immune resistance (15, 21). Although the mechanism of increased shedding of microorganisms during stressful situations in carrier animals is not completely understood, the stress of transportation alone cannot account for all of the increases seen in post-transportation isolation rates.

Individual animal responses to stress and meat quality

Transportation stress not only affects the safety of the meat and poultry products produced, but also the quality. The physiological effects of stress cause decreased product value. For example, some breeds of pigs are susceptible to developing what has been termed the 'porcine stress syndrome' (PSS) which has been linked to pale, soft, exudative (PSE) meat. Confusion over these two acronyms has led many to believe that they refer to the same thing, but this is not so. PSS refers to a syndrome that occurs in the live animal, while PSE is the quality of the meat commonly produced from pigs suffering from this syndrome. Other causes of PSE include rough handling, electrical prodding, and stressful environmental conditions, such as extreme heat. The resulting quality defect has been attributed to muscle glycogen and lactic acid levels which play an essential role in meat quality. After slaughter, glycogen in the muscle is converted to lactic acid and it is this lactic acid which is needed to produce tasteful, tender meat of good quality and colour (4). When an animal is stressed, the glycogen is used up and the level of lactic acid is reduced. In cases of PSS, lactic acid is produced in excess, but it is contained within the blood and not the muscle. PSE meat and meat from pigs suffering from PSS are very similar in quality because they both produce very pale, soft meat that appears exudative or 'wet' with pronounced acidity and poor flavour (4, 13) (Fig. 2). This type of meat is undesirable and may have to be discarded (4).

 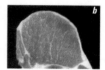 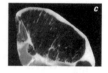

a) pale, soft, exudative (PSE)
b) normal
c) dark, firm and dry (DFD)
Fig. 2
Quality differences in pork meat
Source: Chambers and Grandin (2), courtesy of Gunter Heinz

Another meat quality problem resulting from depleted muscle glycogen and lactic acid levels is that of dark, firm and dry meat (DFD). The term DFD is generally reserved for pork meat, but when this defect is seen in beef, the term 'dark cutters' is applied (13). Previous studies have found that the incidence of dark-cutting meat is higher among cattle that became agitated and excited in the squeeze chute and during other handling and transportation associated stressors (i.e. fighting and mixing of strange animals) near the time of slaughter (9, 25). Not only is this meat darker, drier and firmer and, as a result, less desirable to the consumer, but it also has a shorter

Rev. sci. tech. Off. int. Epiz., **25** (2)

677

shelf life (4) (Fig. 2). The level of lactic acid in meat has been shown to directly influence the shelf life of the meat product. Lactic acid in the muscle could be considered as 'nature's bacteriostatic', because it retards the growth of spoilage bacteria that may contaminate carcasses during processing (4). When muscle lactic acid levels are low and the storage environment supports bacterial growth, the meat quickly develops an unpleasant odour and colour, and rancidity (4, 13).

Pre-transport preparation

Feed withdrawal

One of the first steps in preparing food animals for transfer to slaughter is feed withdrawal. Feed withdrawal is commonly performed prior to transportation with the intent of minimising the gastrointestinal contents in order to reduce faecal contamination of carcasses at slaughter (29).

In theory, the practice of feed withdrawal makes sense; if the gastrointestinal tract is empty, there should not be any faeces to cross-contaminate live animals during transportation or the facilities and equipment at processing and slaughter. However, the exact biochemical and physiological changes which will occur as a result of this practice on an individual animal cannot be predicted. Research has suggested that the stress associated with feed withdrawal may actually increase the carriage and shedding of pathogenic organisms (12, 15, 29). In poultry, it is estimated that after about four hours of feed withdrawal, birds instinctively peck at faecal-contaminated litter resulting in crop and intestinal contamination at slaughter (29). In a study by Harvey *et al.* (12), it was hypothesised that reductions in volatile fatty acid concentrations, as a consequence of emptying the gut, leads to an increase in intestinal pH. Alkaline environments tend to support the growth of pathogenic microorganisms and concurrently reduce the growth of beneficial microbes.

Animals transported from the farm to the stockyard, rather than directly to the slaughterhouse, potentially experience additional stresses from multiple episodes of transportation and handling, as well as repeated periods of feed withdrawal (19). Depending upon the number of destinations in the transportation process, food animals could be subjected to variable periods of feed and water deprivation. When planning for transportation, it is important to take into consideration feed withdrawal times in order to reduce the amount of carcass weight loss and dehydration. Carcass weight loss is most likely to occur between 9 h and 18 h after feed withdrawal has begun (8). Carcass weight loss initially results from fluid loss through the excretion of faeces and urine but longer feed withdrawal periods may contribute to a decrease in tissue substance and muscle glycogen levels (8).

Vehicle cleanliness and contamination

Proper sanitisation of trailers used for transport can contribute to a considerable reduction in the environmental levels of *Salmonella* and other pathogens (22). Non-carrier animals may be exposed to pathogenic organisms when transported in poorly cleaned vehicles or cages (22). The level of mud and faecal contamination on the hides/feathers of live animals presented to slaughter is directly associated with levels of visible contamination on dressed carcasses. It is intuitive that high levels of vehicle and cage contamination can contribute to the prevalence of pathogens on finished carcasses and processing equipment and pose a public health threat that may translate into incidences of food-borne illness (24).

Catching and loading

In preparation for transportation, catching and loading serve as immediate sources of stress for food animals. During this time, the animals are placed into unfamiliar situations that involve changes in their environment, social groups and handling. Research has shown an almost instantaneous increase in salivary cortisol (stress hormone) and heart rate during the initial stages of transportation (2, 8). Peak stress situations for pigs and animals unaccustomed to the noises and handling associated with transportation tend to occur during loading and unloading which is considered a critical stress and injury control point (8). It is especially imperative that animal handlers be proactive in the provision of humane handling and care during these stages. It is also important that these employees are properly trained on the appropriate use of behaviour modifying devices, such as electrical prods, when deemed necessary. Different methods of pre-transit preparation of livestock and poultry that may minimise stress have been examined by various sources. Table I is a summary of some of these recommendations.

Transport conditions

The concerns associated with transport conditions depend partly on the mode of transport, the type of animals being transported, and the age of the animals. Good management and well-designed equipment and facilities play vital roles in decreasing the amount of stress encountered during transportation. Poor transport conditions can have harmful effects on the welfare of the animal and can lead to considerable product loss, due to death and/or injury, and cross-contamination of pathogens among the animals.

678

Rev. sci. tech. Off. int. Epiz., 25 (2)

Table I

Pre-transport preparation and handling recommendations for minimising stress in livestock and poultry

Pre-transport activities	Recommendations
Pre-transport health check	Ensure that animals are physically fit for transportation (7). Veterinary Services should be consulted before making any final decisions if the health of an animal is questionable
Feed withdrawal	Practise appropriate pre-slaughter feeding management by providing feed and water up to a pre-determined feed withdrawal start time. This helps to ensure that the animals are not subjected to longer than necessary feed withdrawal times
Catching	Poultry should be caught in the evening or use dim lights or dark curtains. A darker environment may provide a sense of calmness to the birds and reduce strain
	If bird-catching machines are available, they may help to make catching an easier process for the handlers and less stressful for the birds
	Catching animals during cooler parts of the day and/or keeping the transport vehicles shaded helps to provide some thermal relief from the exertion of catching and decrease the incidence of heat exhaustion in some animals (8)
Loading	Load quietly and minimise yelling, unnecessary noise, harassment or force
	Make sure that untrained assistants or spectators do not impede the loading process
	Painful procedures should not be used to move animals. Electric prods should only be used by trained handlers and only when deemed necessary and there is enough room for the livestock to move forward or react instinctively
	Restraint methods should be appropriate for the situation accounting for the age, size and type of animal
	Animals can best enter transportation vehicles when they do not have to overcome differences in height (6). The heart rate has been shown to increase linearly with that of the ramp's incline. The use of a hydraulic ramp with some animals, such as pigs, allows both the heart rate and body temperature to remain at a more stable level than when these animals have to climb over a slanted ramp (6)
	Ensure that the passageways livestock must travel to reach the transport vehicles are well lit and void of obstructions

Vehicle cleanliness while in transit

As previously mentioned, the cleanliness of the crates and trailers impacts the transmission of disease and external contamination of the animals being transported. The importance of cleaning transportation equipment must be emphasised. Trailers and crates become contaminated with faecal matter during transportation which compounds pathogen levels and the associated risk. The specific transportation method directly influences susceptibility of animals to pathogens and the potential for external contamination, even if the trailers and crates are thoroughly cleaned and disinfected before loading. For instance, in the USA, most poultry are transported to processing plants in 'modules'. A typical module consists of individual cages that can hold as many as 25 birds. The cages are stacked upon each other and side-by-side to make up the module. One module may contain up to 300 birds (28). Due to the complex structure of these modules and the close proximity of the birds to one another, the potential for cross-contamination from faecal droppings or birds that die in transport is intensified. It is common for some animals to experience motion sickness and vomit when encountering unfavourable transport conditions thereby exposing the adjacent animals to bodily fluids that might transmit pathogens and result in carcass contamination during slaughter (8).

Crate density and space allowance

Crate density and space allowance can significantly affect stress levels during transport. Already stressed animals are further stressed when they are packed tightly and in uncomfortable positions. Heat stress can also occur when heavy crate densities do not allow for adequate ventilation in warmer temperatures. In addition to the physiological consequences of stress, the issue of space addresses physical consequences such as bruising, injury, and death due to fighting, trampling, or suffocation. An article by Chambers and Grandin (4) reported that fighting tends to occur most often when a vehicle stops suddenly and animals are inadvertently 'pushed' into each other. This would be a major concern to producers in the event that the animals gore, scratch, or bruise each other and carcass quality is affected. Sufficient space allows enough room for the animals to adjust their posture naturally, brace themselves against the movement of the vehicle, and get up in the event that they fall down (17).

The effect of physical hazards and handling on meat quality

Some pre-slaughter handling losses may be attributed to damage caused by physical hazards. Sharp objects on cages

Rev. sci. tech. Off. int. Epiz., **25** (2)

679

and handling equipment and holes in the flooring and slippery conditions of vehicles and facilities at the slaughterhouse are sometimes overlooked hazards that can cause serious injury and loss (26). Transportation vehicles, containers, and holding facilities should be constructed to account for usage and a regular maintenance plan should be developed to ensure that these and other physical hazards are circumvented as much as possible.

It is the joint responsibility of all persons involved to make the appropriate handling of transported animals a number one priority. Meat quality is directly affected by the manner in which food animals are handled prior to slaughter. When dealing with unruly or stubborn animals, electric prods, and in some cases, sticks or other items may be used for control. At times, the use of these methods may be deemed necessary by trained handlers. However, problems arise when these methods are performed unnecessarily or incorrectly by improperly trained handlers. For example, significant bruising of sheep carcasses, particularly the neck and hind quarters, has been directly linked to wool-pulling and rough handling by human handlers (17). A physical blow or rough handling leading to bruising or other animal injury can result in parts of the carcass being condemned. Bruised meat is dark and bloody and must be removed for the carcass to pass federal inspection standards (4) (Fig. 3). This type of meat spoils rapidly and its appearance lacks consumer appeal.

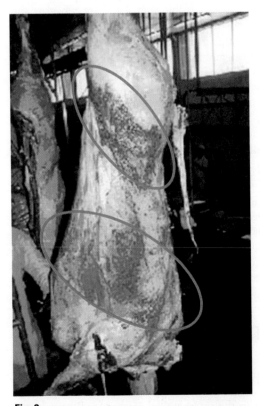

Fig. 3
Bruising on a cattle carcass
Source: Chambers and Grandin (2) courtesy of P.G. Chambers

Length of time in transit and rest stops

Another concern about transport conditions is the length of time in transit and the distance travelled. Time in transit does not necessarily coincide with the distance travelled and it may be impossible to avoid or reduce lengthy transportation times due to the location of farms in relation to slaughter establishments (27). A study by Cole *et al.* (5) concluded that the majority of losses due to transport stress take place during the early portions of the journey and that longer periods of travel may not significantly add to the amount of stress experienced (5, 7). The report suggested that adaptive mechanisms became effective as the time increased and that was reflected in the maintenance or decrease of stress levels (7). However, animals never fully calm down during transport and longer times may increase the amount of time required for rest and recovery at the slaughterhouse (8). Transport conditions may affect stress levels more than the length of transportation itself even though common sense would lead most people to view length in transit as a significant stressor. Some studies have shown that a reduction in transportation time by as little as an hour has a positive effect on meat quality (8). This may be because although fluid losses are highest early, losses continue throughout, albeit at a slower rate, and other physiological changes occur which can affect meat quality. Effects on meat quality and safety cannot be attributed solely to transport stress and/or time en route (5). Nonetheless, both should be minimised as much as possible to ensure public health safety, product quality standards and animal welfare.

The debate over the advantages and disadvantages of rest stops while in transit is on-going. The stresses associated with loading and unloading during rest stops are thought to be additive. Depending upon the length of the journey and the animals being transported, rest stops may involve stopping the vehicle with or without unloading. The stopping of the vehicle is beneficial in one way because it allows the animals to be temporarily relieved from constantly trying to keep their balance and, in some cases, it also provides them with access to water and feed (8). However, depending on the environmental conditions, the heat in a stopped vehicle can rise quickly, thereby increasing stress (10). The benefits of rest and feeding should be weighed against the stresses of loading and unloading to decide whether or not to stop (10). The method of transport, distance travelled, species, and age of the animals must also be taken into consideration when determining the frequency of rest stops and whether unloading, feeding and/or watering should take place.

Weather conditions

Weather influences the level of stress experienced during transport and variances in weather conditions affect the overall ability of the animals to recover at lairage (8).

680

Rev. sci. tech. Off. int. Epiz., **25** (2)

Severe increases or decreases in temperature can lead to livestock and poultry transportation losses. Insufficient vehicle ventilation and individual animal health status challenge the animal's ability to adequately adjust to varying temperatures. Some animals may experience heat exhaustion, sun burn (pigs) and dehydration when temperatures are elevated and hypothermia and frost bite when temperatures are low. These concerns are further heightened when travel involves long distances, such as in the event of international transportation. Adverse weather conditions cannot necessarily be predicted, but must be managed during the transportation process to limit the amount of added stress on the animal. In addition, caution must be taken to not introduce new hazards when attempts are made to protect the animals against the elements. An example of this would be how covering trailers in cold weather can trap truck fumes and cause carbon monoxide poisoning.

Lairage

Lairage, or holding prior to slaughter, allows animals to replenish muscle glycogen levels, rest, and recover from the effects of feed and water withdrawal and other transportation stressors (18, 20). Rest obtained in lairage also reduces the incidence of meat quality defects, though time in lairage has also been associated with an increase in the prevalence of pathogenic contamination (16, 20, 29).

The lairage environment and contamination

The lairage environment itself and the comingling of animals may inhibit the ability to recover from transportation and expose the animals to pathogens different from those from their farm of origin (18). Hurd *et al.* (16) reported increases in the number of pigs testing positive for *Salmonella* at slaughter versus those tested on the farm. This study also found a difference in the strains of *Salmonella* obtained at the slaughter establishment, suggesting that the pathogens originated from sources other than the farm (15, 16). These findings provide evidence that in addition to possible exposure during transportation, the holding pens for lairage are significant control points for reducing carcass contamination. External contamination may be compounded when the time in lairage is increased and the prevention of long lairage holding periods and overcrowding should help to reduce the amount of external contamination of animals at slaughter (21).

Time in lairage and meat quality

The time in lairage should be specific to the type of animals involved and the conditions of transport. Lairage times can be manipulated within certain limits and can vary from less than one hour to more than twenty (27). Most studies have shown that a lairage time of two to three hours is sufficient to ensure animal recovery and protection of the safety and quality of the resulting products (27). In pigs, the incidence of PSE is highest within the first two hours of lairage while the incidence of DFD meat increases with time in lairage (8). In cattle, especially males, increasing time in lairage has been linked to an increased incidence of dark-cutting beef and bruising on meat due to fighting (8). Table II provides a list of recommendations from various sources for optimising transportation and minimising stress in transit and at lairage.

Global considerations

Increased globalisation of trade markets has made it useful to establish domestic food standards for transportation that take into account the expectations of trading partners. The recommendations and material addressed in this paper are more easily applied to larger-scale food animal production systems, such as those in industrialised nations. The manner in which animals are transported and the distances travelled varies tremendously across the globe. Animals may be transported in large, tiered, vehicles across a country or continent or they may be gathered in groups and transported across a city on the back of a bicycle. Either case presents possible animal welfare concerns and provides opportunities for live animal and carcass contamination that need to be addressed from a global standpoint to ensure international public health safety.

Unfortunately, many small-scale producers often lack the resources to carry out the most humane transportation methods that limit stress and hazard exposure. In fact, these producers are unlikely to be exposed to information about the effects transportation can have on product safety and quality. Increased international production and trade of poultry and livestock has changed the scope of the associated public health safety risks (11). Therefore, it is critical that stakeholders continue to support the establishment of scientifically based methods and education concerning the movement of food animals that do not preclude small-scale disadvantaged producers from full access to local and international markets (11).

Economic considerations

Change in the global view of animal transport and welfare is directly affected by economics. There is growing competition in the international market for livestock and poultry and increased stocking densities may be in response to the economic factors required to maintain

Rev. sci. tech. Off. int. Epiz., **25** (2)

681

Table II
Recommendations for minimising stress while in transit and at lairage

Transport and lairage conditions	Recommendations
Facilities for in-transit monitoring	Drivers should check the effectiveness of transportation by being able to observe and tend to animals that may die in transport or be injured
Driving conditions	Drivers should try to account for varying weather and road conditions as much as possible to prevent unnecessary delays in arrival to the slaughterhouse
	The frequency, length and whether feeding, watering and unloading will take place during rest stops should be predetermined as much as possible
	Transportation should take place during the cooler/warmer parts of the day to minimise the effects of heat/cold stress in extreme conditions (8)
Vehicle conditions	The loading densities and the number of animals and their allocation to different compartments should be determined before loading takes place
	Space allowance should be calculated to avoid having groups which are too large and do not allow for comfortable transportation. There should be enough space for all animals to lie down at the same time and the stocking density should account for the season and climate (i.e. reduced density during warmer weather)
	Vehicles should be designed in a way that prevents faeces or urine from animals on the upper levels from contaminating the animals and their feed and water on lower levels
	Suitable bedding should be added to vehicle floors to assist absorption of urine, faeces and vomit and minimise slipping
	Vehicle design should adequately protect the animals from variations in climate so that the thermoregulatory needs of the animals in transit are met. Sufficient ventilation is enough to combat exhaust fumes and odours from the vehicle and the animals themselves
Lairage	Make sure the lairage environment has been adequately cleaned and disinfected prior to the arrival of the animals to lairage (14)
	Unload animals in a calm, unhurried manner
	Attempt to keep groups of animals from the same farm and/or transportation vehicle together to minimise the social stresses associated with the mixing of new animals and encourage rapid recovery
	Isolate sick or injured animals. Ensure that methods are in place for dealing with the humane handling of sick and injured animals
	Provide animals with clean drinking water upon arrival. Provide feed if slaughter will not take place within an acceptable amount of time (i.e. within 12 h)
	Make sure that the holding pens are secure to prevent animals from escaping and are free of physical hazards which may promote injury

commercial viability (6). 'Shrink', a term used to describe live weight loss occurring as a result of dehydration and feed deprivation, bruising, injury, and mortality during transportation are not only animal welfare and product quality concerns, but economic issues to all parties involved. It is a direct concern of producers when on-farm investments made to comply with regulations aimed at the protection of their product and public health, are essentially 'lost' in the process of transportation (23). In the US pork industry alone, transportation-associated losses have been estimated to be as much as US\$ 8 million annually (23).

Any government regulations disallowing the use of injured or downer animals for human consumption could have a direct effect on the economics of the livestock industry. A downer animal is any animal that is unable to maintain normal mobility due to disease or injury. Transportation is

an important control point to prevent a healthy animal from becoming injured due to poor conditions such that they would become labelled as a downer animal upon arrival to slaughter. In many developing countries, these types of losses are high because the marketing system does not always provide an economic incentive to reduce them (4). The practice of selling animals on a per head basis to the slaughter establishment is an example of a system in which the producer or transporter is not held liable for losses resulting from injuries or weight loss during transportation. As an alternative, some establishments pay for on-the-rail passed carcass weight, which means that the producer is paid for the weight of the animals after transportation rather than by head, or in other words, the number received at the establishment for slaughter. Under this alternative, the producer and transporters have an economic incentive to preserve the quality, and hence the value of the animal.

682

Rev. sci. tech. Off. int. Epiz., **25** (2)

Conclusion

Understanding the linkage between on-farm food safety operations and processing will contribute a great deal to enhancing food safety and increasing consumer confidence in meat, poultry, and egg products. Many of the hazards associated with transportation can be minimised; therefore, it is imperative that all persons involved at the different stages of transportation be educated and committed to understanding the effects that their actions can have on the safety and quality of meat, poultry, and egg products. Public perception of food safety and quality is changing and the proper support of industry and regulatory agencies is necessary to ensure that producers are able to maintain and exceed expectations both locally and globally.

Acknowledgements

The authors would like to thank Katrine Pritchard for her editorial assistance.

■

Les conditions de transport et la qualité des denrées alimentaires

K.J. Southern, J.G. Rasekh, F.E. Hemphill & A.M. Thaler

Résumé
De nombreux facteurs contribuent à l'innocuité des produits alimentaires d'origine animale. Les initiatives en faveur d'une approche intégrée de la sécurité sanitaire des aliments mettent l'accent sur la nécessité d'assurer des conditions de transport optimales afin de préserver la qualité sanitaire obtenue au niveau de la ferme. Les dangers physiques, microbiens et environnementaux inhérents au transport peuvent menacer la sécurité sanitaire et la qualité des produits de viandes, volailles et œufs. En outre, les conditions de transport sont potentiellement génératrices de stress, ce qui accroît la quantité de microorganismes pathogènes excrétés par les animaux porteurs, exposant les autres animaux au risque d'infection. Les effets physiologiques du stress ont un impact négatif sur la qualité des viandes, des volailles, des œufs et de leurs produits, ce qui diminue d'autant leur valeur économique. La mondialisation accrue des marchés constitue un incitatif pour l'application de normes pour le transport des animaux destinés à la consommation, et ce tant au niveau national qu'international.

Mots-clés
Bien-être animal – Manipulation des animaux avant l'abattage – Qualité de la viande – Sécurité sanitaire de la viande – Stabulation – Stress – Toxi-infection alimentaire – Transport.

■

Condiciones de traslado y calidad de los alimentos

K.J. Southern, J.G. Rasekh, F.E. Hemphill & A.M. Thaler

Resumen
Muchos son los factores que intervienen en la producción de alimentos de origen animal inocuos. Las iniciativas que promueven planteamientos integrados en la materia otorgan la debida importancia a la optimización de las condiciones de transporte con el fin de garantizar que las intervenciones practicadas en la

Rev. sci. tech. Off. int. Epiz., 25 (2)

683

explotación queden preservadas. Los peligros físicos, microbianos o ambientales que concurren durante el proceso de traslado pueden influir negativamente en la inocuidad y calidad de los productos elaborados con carne, aves de corral o huevos. Además, determinadas condiciones de transporte pueden elevar el nivel de estrés de los animales, cosa que a su vez puede incrementar la excreción de patógenos en ejemplares portadores y facilitar con ello la contaminación de animales sanos. Los efectos fisiológicos del estrés en los animales pueden mermar la calidad de los productos obtenidos a partir de la carne o los huevos de esos animales, reduciendo así su valor económico. La creciente mundialización de los mercados constituye un incentivo para aplicar, tanto dentro de un país como entre distintos países, reglas de transporte de animales destinados a la producción alimentaria.

Palabras clave

Bienestar de los animales – Calidad de la carne – Enfermedad transmitida por vía alimentaria – Estabulación – Estrés – Inocuidad de la carne – Manipulación previa al sacrificio – Transporte.

■

References

1. Blecha F., Boyles S.L. & Riley J.G. (1984). – Shipping suppresses lymphocyte blastogenic responses in angus and Brahman x angus feeder calves. *J. Anim. Sci.*, **59** (3), 576-583.

2. Brown S.N., Knowles T.G., Wilkins L.J., Chadd S.A. & Warriss P.D. (2005). – The response of pigs being loaded or unloaded onto commercial animal transporters using three systems. *Vet. J.*, **170** (1), 91-100.

3. Centers for Disease Control (CDC) (2004). – Preliminary FoodNet data on the incidence of infection with pathogens transmitted commonly through food: selected sites, United States, 2003. *MMWR*, **53** (16), 338-343. Available at: http://www.cdc.gov/mmwr/preview/mmwrhtml/mm5316a2. htm (accessed on 30 June 2005).

4. Chambers P.G. & Grandin T. (2001). – Guidelines for humane handling, transport and slaughter of livestock from the Food and Agriculture Organization of the United Nations Regional Office for Asia and the Pacific (G. Heinz & T. Srisuvan, eds). Available at: http://www.fao.org/docrep/ 003/x6909e/x6909e00.htm (accessed on 23 August 2005).

5. Cole N.A., Camp T.H., Rowe L.D., Stevens D.G. & Hutcheson D.P. (1988). – Effect of transport on feeder calves. *Am. J. vet. Res.*, **49** (2), 178-183.

6. Collins J.D. & Wall P.G. (2004). – Food safety and animal production systems: controlling zoonoses at farm level. *In* Emerging zoonoses and pathogens of public health concern (L.J. King, ed.). *Rev. sci. tech. Off. int. Epiz.*, **23** (2), 685-700.

7. Dousek J., Večerek V., Valcl O., Chloupek P. & Pištěková V. (2002). – Protection of animals against cruelty: transport of cattle, sheep, goats and pigs. *Acta. vet. (Brno)*, **71**, 555-562.

8. Fischer K. (1996). – Transport of slaughter animals: effects, weaknesses, measures. *Fleischwirtschaft*, **76** (5), 521-526.

9. Grandin T. (1998). – Handling methods and facilities to reduce stress on cattle. *Vet. Clin. N. Am. (Food Anim. Pract.)*, **14** (2), 325-341.

10. Grandin T. (2000). – Animal welfare during transport and slaughter. Sustainable Animal Production Consortium. Available at: http://www.agriculture.de/acms1/conf6/ ws5atransport.htm (accessed on 23 August 2005).

11. Hall D.C., Ehui S. & Delgado C. (2004). – The livestock revolution, food safety, and small-scale farmers: why they matter to us all. *J. agric. environ. Ethics*, **17** (4-5), 425-444.

12. Harvey R.B., Anderson R.C., Young C.R., Swindle M.M., Genovese K.J., Hume M.E., Droleskey R.E., Farrington L.A., Ziprin R.L. & Nisbet D.J. (2001). – Effects of feed withdrawal and transport on cecal environment and *Campylobacter* concentrations in a swine surgical model. *J. Food Protec.*, **64** (5), 730-733.

13. Hubbert W.T. & Hagstad H.V. (1991). – Food production technology: the food chain. *In* Food safety and quality assurance: foods of animal origin. Iowa State University Press, Ames, Iowa, 54-59.

14. Hurd H.S., Gailey J.K., McKean J.D. & Rostagno M.H. (2001). – Rapid infection in market-weight swine following exposure to a *Salmonella typhimurium*-contaminated environment. *Am. J. vet. Res.*, **62**, 1194-1197.

15. Hurd H.S., McKean J.D., Griffith R.W., Wesley I.V. & Rostagno M.H. (2002). – *Salmonella enterica* infections in market swine with and without transport and holding. *Appl. environ. Microbiol.*, **68** (5), 2376-2381.

16. Hurd H.S., McKean J.D., Wesley I.V. & Karriker L.A. (2001). – The effect of lairage on *Salmonella* isolation from market swine. *J. Food Protec.*, **64** (7), 939-944.

17. Jarvis A.M. & Cockram M.S. (1994). – Effects of handling and transport on bruising of sheep sent directly from farms to slaughter. *Vet. Rec.*, **135**, 523-527.

18. Jarvis A.M., Harrington D.W.J. & Cockram M.S. (1996). – Effect of source and lairage on some behavioural and biochemical measurements of feed restriction and dehydration in cattle at a slaughterhouse. *Appl. anim. Behav. Sci.*, **50**, 83-94.

19. Jarvis A.M., Messer C.D.A. & Cockram M.S. (1996). – Handling, bruising and dehydration of cattle at the time of slaughter. *Anim. Welf.*, **5**, 259-270.

20. Martoccia L., Brambilla G., Macri A., Moccia G. & Consentino E. (1995). – The effect of transport on some metabolic parameters and meat quality in pigs. *Meat Sci.*, **40**, 271-277.

21. Mulder R.W.A.W. (1995). – Impact of transport and related stresses on the incidence and extent of human pathogens in pigmeat and poultry. *J. Food Safety*, **15**, 239-246.

22. Rajkowski K.T., Eblen S. & Laubauch C. (1998). – Efficacy of washing and sanitizing trailers used for swine transport in reduction of *Salmonella* and *Escherichia coli*. *J. Food Protec.*, **61** (1), 31-35.

23. Speer N.C., Slack G. & Troyer E. (2001). – Economic factors associated with livestock transportation. *J. Anim. Sci.*, **79**, 166-170.

24. Stern N.J., Clavero M.R.S., Bailey J.S., Cox N.A. & Robach M.C. (1995). – *Campylobacter* spp. in broilers on the farm and after transport. *Poult. Sci.*, **74**, 937-941.

25. Voisinet B.D., Grandin T., O'Connor S.F., Tatum J.D. & Deesing M.J. (1997). – *Bos indicus*-cross feedlot cattle with excitable temperaments have tougher meat and a higher incidence of borderline dark cutters. *Meat Sci.*, **46** (4), 367-377.

26. Wadja S. & Denaburski J. (2003). – Pre-slaughter handling of pigs. *Anim. Sci. Papers Rep., Suppl. 1*, **21**, 173-181.

27. Warriss P.D., Brown S.N., Edwards J.E. & Knowles T.G. (1998). – Effect of lairage time on levels of stress and meat quality in pigs. *Anim. Sci.*, **66**, 255-261.

28. Warriss P.D., Knowles T.G., Brown S.N., Edwards J.E., Kettlewell P.J., Mitchell M.A. & Baxter C.A. (1999). – Effects of lairage time on body temperature and glycogen reserves of broiler chickens held in transport modules. *Vet. Rec.*, **145**, 218-222.

29. Wesley I.V., Muraoka W.T., Trampel D.W. & Hurd H.S. (2005). – Effect of preslaughter events on prevalence of *Campylobacter coli* in market-weight turkeys. *Appl. environ. Microbiol.*, **71** (6), 2824-2831.

Rev. sci. tech. Off. int. Epiz., 2006, **25** (2), 685-700

Meeting the requirements of importing countries: practice and policy for on-farm approaches to food safety

P.J. Dagg, R.J. Butler, J.G. Murray & R.R. Biddle

Australian Government Department of Agriculture, Fisheries and Forestry, G.P.O. Box 858, Canberra, ACT 2601, Australia

Summary

In light of the increasing consumer demand for safe, high-quality food and recent public health concerns about food-borne illness, governments and agricultural industries are under pressure to provide comprehensive food safety policies and programmes consistent with international best practice. Countries that export food commodities derived from livestock must meet both the requirements of the importing country and domestic standards.

It is internationally accepted that end-product quality control, and similar methods aimed at ensuring food safety, cannot adequately ensure the safety of the final product. To achieve an acceptable level of food safety, governments and the agricultural industry must work collaboratively to provide quality assurance systems, based on sound risk management principles, throughout the food supply chain. Quality assurance systems on livestock farms, as in other parts of the food supply chain, should address food safety using hazard analysis critical control point principles. These systems should target areas including biosecurity, disease monitoring and reporting, feedstuff safety, the safe use of agricultural and veterinary chemicals, the control of potential food-borne pathogens and traceability. They should also be supported by accredited training programmes, which award certification on completion, and auditing programmes to ensure that both local and internationally recognised guidelines and standards continue to be met. This paper discusses the development of policies for on-farm food safety measures and their practical implementation in the context of quality assurance programmes, using the Australian beef industry as a case study.

Keywords

Australia − Beef industry − Food safety − Livestock − Policy development − Quality assurance.

Introduction

As the global population continues to grow, so too does the value of the world food trade. From 1950 to the year 2000, the global population increased by more than 3.5 billion (to approximately six billion). According to recent predictions, the world population is estimated to rise by a further three billion to reach nine billion by the year 2050 (24) (Fig. 1).

Nearly all of this population growth is expected to occur in developing regions, including Africa, Asia and Latin America. The populations of industrialised countries are not expected to increase as dramatically and may, in fact, remain static. In some industrialised nations, the population is expected to decrease (8).

World population growth is also reflected in an increasing volume of food of animal origin in world trade. For example, world beef exports increased from

686

Rev. sci. tech. Off. int. Epiz., **25** (2)

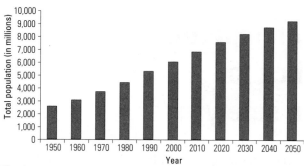

Fig. 1
The total midyear population for the world: 1950-2050 (in millions)
Source: United States Census Bureau website (24)

5,147,200 tonnes of carcass weight equivalent in 1998 to 6,060,800 tonnes of carcass weight equivalent in 2004 (11).

Owing to the increasing globalisation of trade and the industrialisation of food processing, consumers are potentially exposed to a greater number of food safety hazards than in previous generations. The reduction of trade barriers has improved the availability and security of international food markets. However, this may also contribute to the possibility of widespread and rapid dissemination of illness associated with the consumption of contaminated food (10).

Episodes of food-borne illness due to pathogenic organisms such as *Escherichia coli* O157, *Campylobacter jejuni* and *Listeria monocytogenes*, as well as international publicity about other disease issues, including bovine spongiform encephalopathy, antimicrobial resistance and dioxin contamination, have increased consumer food safety concerns over the past few decades. As a result, consumers are increasingly demanding safe, high-quality food from their governments and industries.

Since the international food trade is increasingly being regulated by disease control requirements, rather than tariffs and quotas, government authorities and agricultural and health organisations and industries are under increasing pressure to deliver comprehensive, integrated food safety policies, aimed at protecting public health and welfare (10). This applies to all aspects of the world food trade, including imported and exported foods, as well as food supply for the domestic market.

Food-borne illnesses cause major burdens on national economies and may interrupt international trade (19). As a result, many countries have undertaken fundamental reviews of national food safety regulations, generally with a view to optimising controls and restoring public confidence in food safety and security. A result of such reviews has been the establishment of new national food safety authorities and fundamental changes in the ways

that food safety policy is developed and implemented. For example, identifying the importance of pathogens such as *E. coli* O157:H7 and *Salmonella* Enteritidis in the United States of America (USA) between 1973 and 1988 was the catalyst for dramatic legislative changes in meat inspection, including mandatory hazard analysis critical control point (HACCP) programmes (25). An *E. coli* contamination of salami-style fermented meat produced in South Australia in 1995 was responsible for at least 150 cases of food-borne illness, including a number of cases of haemolytic uraemic syndrome and one death (13). This led to the Australian Government requesting the then Australia-New Zealand Food Authority (now known as Food Standards Australia New Zealand or FSANZ) to develop nationally uniform food safety standards.

Another result of these reviews was the realisation that relying on traditional end-product quality control methods was no longer adequate to ensure high standards of food quality and safety (9). Accompanying the organisational changes described above has been a move away from these traditional methods and end-product inspections towards preventative approaches using sound, science-based, risk management principles. Such risk management approaches aim to reduce the level of food-borne illness by:

– developing risk-based, sustainable, integrated food safety systems

– implementing science-based measures along the entire food production chain to prevent exposure to unacceptable levels of microbiological agents and chemicals in food

– assessment and management of food-borne risks, complemented by effective communication to address and allay consumer concerns (28).

However, in general, it has taken longer for these food-production-chain, risk management approaches to be adopted by livestock farmers. To produce and supply a safe final product, all interested parties throughout the food supply chain must be involved, including those who produce, process and trade in foods derived from livestock (i.e. farmers, slaughterhouse operators, food processors, transport operators and distributors).

It is important that, at each stage of the food supply chain, the safety of the product (whether animal or food) is 'certified' to the next party in the process. Additionally, systems should be in place to allow accurate and timely traceability of animals or food, in case either traceforward (to permit the withdrawal of the product) or traceback (to characterise its source) is required. Governments have an important role in providing policy guidance on the most appropriate quality assurance systems, and ensuring their implementation is verified/audited, to aid compliance with

Rev. sci. tech. Off. int. Epiz., **25** (2)

687

domestic requirements, as well as those of the importing country.

Policy development

The essential principles required to establish a policy framework to protect public health from food-borne risks include:

– developing a comprehensive, multidisciplinary approach to risk analysis, involving research organisations, agricultural and farming groups, governments, food industry bodies and community groups

– conducting independent, science-based risk assessments

– ensuring a consistent approach to the processes used throughout the entire production and supply chain

– complying with obligations under the Agreement on the Application of Sanitary and Phytosanitary Measures (the 'SPS Agreement') (31)

– consulting widely with all interested parties and ensuring transparency during decision-making and emergency planning and preparedness

– adequately identifying emerging risks and effectively co-ordinating the response

– ensuring effective risk communication

– overseeing emergency management and addressing emerging issues, such as the threat of bioterrorism.

On-farm quality systems for livestock should focus on food safety, using HACCP principles that target areas including:

– biosecurity

– disease monitoring and reporting

– safety of feed

– safe and responsible use of agricultural and veterinary chemicals

– minimising risk factors for potential food-borne pathogens

– traceability.

These systems should also be supported by national programmes such as:

– an accreditation/auditing programme

– registration of agricultural and veterinary chemicals

– quality assurance of prepared stockfeeds

– certification for intended purpose

– training.

In Australia, co-operative agreements exist between livestock industry representative organisations and the government at all levels. One example of this type of partnership is an organisation called 'SAFEMEAT' (please see more information at http://www.safemeat.com.au/). The primary role of SAFEMEAT is to promote and provide supervision for sound management systems with the aim of delivering safe and hygienic products to the marketplace. SAFEMEAT also seeks to ensure that effective emergency management strategies are in place and can be activated at appropriate times. The organisation has developed an incident response manual, which clearly defines roles and responsibilities in an emergency and promotes links between emergency management programmes, including the Australian Veterinary Emergency Plan (AUSVETPLAN) and state and territory government emergency response plans (22). SAFEMEAT members include the major red meat and livestock industry bodies and the Federal and state/territory government authorities. The terms of reference for the SAFEMEAT organisation are provided in Table I.

Table I

Terms of reference for the SAFEMEAT organisation, a partnership between the Australian Government and the Australian livestock industries

Terms of reference
To work with the objective of establishing world best practice in ensuring the safety of red meat products
To ensure that each red meat industry sector implements sound management systems to ensure safe and hygienic products are delivered to the marketplace
To ensure adequate and nationally consistent government standards and regulations on meat safety and hygiene
To ensure that effective crisis management strategies are put in place by the appropriate red meat industry sectors and, to this end, ensure that there is a fully integrated and effective communications network

Source: SAFEMEAT Partnership (22)

The Australian Stock Diseases Acts and related legislation regulate the control of livestock diseases, placing restrictions on the movement of diseased stock and specifying the exotic and serious endemic diseases which must be notified. This legislation gives certain powers to inspectors to enter premises where disease is suspected and allows certain actions to be taken with diseased stock, such as the power to quarantine.

The Trusted Information Sharing Network for Critical Infrastructure Protection (the 'Network') is a government/industry partnership that was established in 2003 under Australian national counter-terrorism arrangements. The role of the Network is to advise the

Rev. sci. tech. Off. int. Epiz., 25 (2)

industries comprising the national critical infrastructure, including the agricultural and food chain industries, about potential threats and appropriate risk management strategies (3).

The Network has developed a National Food Chain Safety and Security Strategy which is aimed at continually improving Australian preparedness to respond to potential incidents of deliberate terrorism in the agriculture and food supply chain. The strategy focuses on increasing industry capacity to protect the domestic food supply.

Australia is one of the largest exporters of livestock products in the world (Fig. 2) and regularly supplies over 70 different countries. The Australian beef industry can therefore be used as a case study to explore the practical implementation of on-farm safety approaches to meet the requirements of the importing country, as well as the domestic market. Although the authors have highlighted the beef industry, the principles of this discussion apply to all livestock industries.

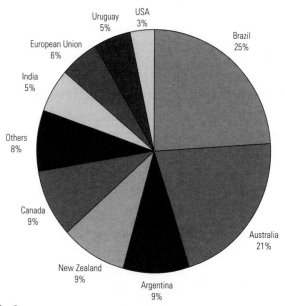

Fig. 2
World beef exports in 2004: percentages exported by exporting regions
Source: Food and Agriculture Organization (11)

Implementation

Australian on-farm beef quality assurance programmes

In Australia, a number of on-farm beef quality assurance programmes are operated and managed by livestock industry representative organisations, in partnership with the Federal Government and state and territory

governments. The major programmes which provide certification and verification to instil confidence in Australian beef are, as follows:

– the Livestock Production Assurance (LPA) programme

– the National Feedlot Accreditation Scheme (NFAS).

In addition to being supplemented by essential regulatory programmes on animal health, these quality assurance programmes are underpinned by the following supporting national programmes:

a) traceability programmes:

– national vendor declarations/Waybill (NVD/Waybill) and the electronic declaration programme

– property identification codes and a tailtag system

– the National Livestock Identification System (NLIS)

– the National Saleyard Quality Assurance (NSQA) programme

b) national programmes on chemicals and livestock feeds:

– the National Registration Scheme, administered by the Australian Pesticides and Veterinary Medicines Authority

– control of the use of agricultural and veterinary chemicals by state and territory governments

– *Chemcert* Australia (the national chemical certification programme for training chemical users)

– the National Residue Survey (NRS)

– targeted residue control programmes

– FeedSafe®

– the livestock fodder declarations programme.

The relationships between these national regulatory and quality assurance programmes in the Australian beef industry are illustrated in Figure 3, and described below.

Quality assurance programmes

The Livestock Production Assurance programme

For detailed information on the LPA programme, see the Meat and Livestock Australia website (http://www.mla.com.au/default.htm) (Fig. 4).

The LPA programme was introduced in early 2004 and is an on-farm food safety certification programme that provides guidelines to help farmers declare the food safety status of their cattle. The LPA programme supports the NVD/Waybill programme, and provides assurances to purchasers about on-farm quality systems through the application of on-farm food safety guidelines. Participation in the LPA programme is voluntary; however, cattle buyers often require an LPA NVD/Waybill for purchased livestock. Farms must be LPA-accredited to purchase and supply an LPA NVD/Waybill for cattle.

Rev. sci. tech. Off. int. Epiz., **25** (2)

689

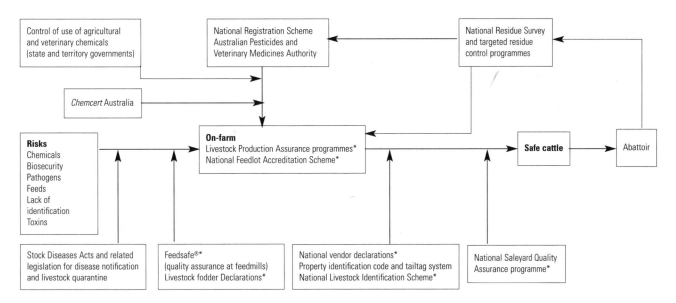

*Systems that are audited for compliance with requirements

Fig. 3

A simplified schematic diagram of the links between livestock regulatory systems and quality assurance systems in Australia

Level 1: food safety

Level 1 of the LPA programme, food safety, provides confirmation of the information provided by farmers in vendor declarations. By mid-2005, approximately 111,000 farms had provisional accreditation under the LPA programme and approximately 34,000 farms had full accreditation (22). The elements with which farmers must comply to maintain their accreditation are listed in Table II.

Once a farm is accredited with Level 1 – food safety, it is subject to random audits by qualified third-party personnel, who have the appropriate industry knowledge and auditing experience to ensure compliance with the requirements and guidelines of the programme.

Level 2: quality assurance

Level 2 of the LPA programme, quality assurance, is a group of programmes that are specific to each species of livestock and have additional elements beyond the

Fig. 4

Symbol of the Livestock Production Assurance programme in Australia

requirements of Level 1. The Level 2 LPA quality assurance programme for the Australian beef industry is called 'Cattlecare'. (Further information on the Cattlecare programme is available on the Ausmeat Limited website at: http://www.ausmeat.com.au/programmes/cattlecare/.)

Cattlecare was initiated by the Cattle Council of Australia and is based on the internationally recognised standards of ISO 9002 and HACCP. Cattlecare is a 'whole-of-farm' programme that ensures the products of accredited farms are based on the principles of quality assurance. Table III lists the requirements for Level 2 LPA – quality assurance.

The National Feedlot Accreditation Scheme

The NFAS, introduced in 1993, is a quality assurance programme for Australian feedlots and is mandatory for feedlots producing grain-fed beef for export markets. The NFAS is administered by Ausmeat Limited and overseen by the Feedlot Industry Accreditation Committee, comprising representatives from government and the industry. Approximately 97% of all Australian grain-fed beef for the domestic market (and 100% of exported grain-fed beef) is derived from NFAS-accredited feedlots (18).

To be accredited under the NFAS, a feedlot operator must:

– have documented procedures in place, specifically for the feedlot, that meet the requirements of the industry standards

– maintain records that these procedures have been adhered to for all cattle prepared at the feedlot

– undergo a third-party audit of these procedures, records and facilities at the feedlot.

690

Rev. sci. tech. Off. int. Epiz., **25** (2)

Table II
Requirements of the Livestock Production Assurance programme: food safety (Level 1)

Requirement	Details
Property risk assessment	To ensure that livestock are not exposed to areas on farms that are contaminated with organochlorines or other persistent chemicals
Safe and responsible animal treatments	To ensure that livestock intended for human consumption do not contain unacceptable chemical residues and/or are not exposed to physical hazards
Stock foods, fodder crops, grain and pasture treatments	To ensure that livestock are not exposed to feeds containing unacceptable contamination, specifically any food containing prohibited animal products (this includes materials that are prohibited to be fed to ruminants as part of bovine spongiform encephalopathy risk reduction measures in Australia) and/or unacceptable chemical residues
Preparation for dispatch of livestock	To ensure that livestock to be transported are fit for the journey, they are not unduly stressed and contamination is minimised during on-farm assembly and transport to the destination
Livestock transactions and movements	To ensure that purchasers of livestock can assess the chemical residue or food safety status of the animals and the movement of livestock can be traced if required

Source: Meat and Livestock Australia (16)

Table III
Requirements of the Livestock Production Assurance programme: quality assurance (Level 2)

Requirement	Details
Chemical residues in soil	A risk assessment must be carried out for each farm to ensure that cattle do not graze land that might contain unacceptable levels of persistent chemicals
Staff training	Training of staff should ensure that employees are able to meet the 'Cattlecare' requirements and records of training must be kept
Stock identification record	All cattle should be clearly identified from birth
Transaction and movement records	Accurate records should be kept of purchases, sales and movements. The National Livestock Identification System is an integral part of identifying cattle and tracing their movements
Prevention of bruising and hide damage	Attention to yard design, construction and maintenance is required to minimise obstructions and harsh contact points liable to cause bruising or hide damage
Transport	Cattle truck interiors should be free of obstruction and have non-slip floors
Labelling and storage of chemicals	Managers need to ensure that only legally available and properly labelled chemicals are obtained and used. Accurate records should be maintained of all chemicals used and where and how they were disposed of
The safe use of chemicals	Managers need to ensure that directions for use for chemicals are followed and that all treated cattle are identified and withheld from sale until the withholding period or export slaughter interval (an export slaughter interval is the time which should elapse between administration of a veterinary chemical to animals and their slaughter for export) has elapsed. Any adverse reactions should be recorded and reported
Treatment records	These should ensure that treatments of stock are adequately recorded to enable traceback. Application of chemicals to pastures and crops should be recorded to ensure that quarantine periods are observed prior to grazing or harvesting
Stock feeds	Care is needed to ensure that purchased stock feeds do not contain unacceptable chemical contamination or prohibited ingredients
Internal check procedures	All operators should carry out regular checks to verify continuing compliance and take any corrective or preventive action which may be required

Source: Meat and Livestock Australia (17)

Rev. sci. tech. Off. int. Epiz., 25 (2)

691

The NFAS is a self-regulatory system, based on compliance with the national standards outlined in the following codes of practice and reference documents:

– the national beef cattle feedlot environmental code of practice (15)

– the Australian model code of practice for the welfare of animals: cattle (5)

– the Australian Veterinary Association code of practice for the safe use of veterinary medicines on farms (7)

– the national guidelines for beef cattle feedlots in Australia (1)

– the AUSVETPLAN enterprise manual: feedlots (2).

The requirements of the NFAS are detailed in Table IV.

Traceability programmes

Farm-to-retail traceability permits both traceback (to identify the source of a product) and traceforward (to permit the withdrawal of a product). Traceability systems are becoming more important in ensuring the provision of safe food of acceptable quality for the marketplace (14). Traceability programmes may reduce the financial and social impact of a disease epidemic or contamination incident, due to the capability to accurately identify and

Table IV
Elements of the National Feedlot Accreditation Scheme

Element
Animal welfare
Environmental management
Stocking density
Stock identification systems
Livestock transactions and movements
Carcass quality, bruising and skin or hide damage
Cattle transportation
Safe and responsible chemical use
Cattle treatment records
Feedlot rations
Feed commodity control
Emergency response management
Persistent chemicals in soils
Obtaining and storing agricultural and veterinary chemicals
Paddock, crop and grain treatments
Training
Internal auditing and corrective action
Quality records
Document control

Source: SAFEMEAT Partnership (20)

rapidly trace any products from an infected animal. One study has estimated that the overall economic loss for Australia from a foot and mouth disease outbreak would be between Aus$ 2 billion and Aus$ 13 billion (6). Rapid tracing and effective disease response measures can limit the scale and distribution of a disease outbreak and offer the prospect of significant cost savings.

National vendor declarations/Waybill and the electronic declaration programme

Producers use the NVD/Waybill or electronic declarations programme to disclose relevant information about the cattle that they are selling. Information declared on the NVD/Waybill includes the following:

– identification of the owner and property (farm)

– the history of the treatment of the cattle with hormonal growth promotants and veterinary chemicals

– the history of the feeding of the cattle with feeds that have been treated with chemicals.

Table V contains further details of the NVD/Waybill requirements.

Although participation in the NVD/Waybill programme is voluntary, it has been adopted by almost 100% of cattle farms, due to commercial requirements. Cattle buyers rely on NVD/Waybill for accurate information on the livestock purchased and abattoir operators rely on the information to ensure that only safe food enters the food chain. The NVD/Waybill scheme is underpinned by the LPA programmes and managed by SAFEMEAT. (Further information is available at http://www.mla.com.au /default.htm.)

Property identification codes and the tailtag system

Australian beef farms must adhere to the requirements of the property identification code tailtag system. This mandatory system has been in place since the 1960s and was instrumental in the successful eradication of bovine tuberculosis and brucellosis in Australia. Each farm or parcel of land is assigned a unique identification number, which is printed on adhesive tags that are attached to the base of the tail of each animal before sale from the farm. This allows identification of the farm of last residence for each animal, for the purposes of traceability.

The tailtag system is in the process of being replaced with electronic identification systems that provide permanent whole-of-life animal identification, based on the property identification code. (Further information on the property identification code and tailtag system can be found on the Australian SAFEMEAT website at: http://www.safemeat. com.au/.)

Rev. sci. tech. Off. int. Epiz., 25 (2)

Table V
Questions and declarations contained in the National Vendor Declarations/Waybill programme

Question
Have any of the cattle in this consignment ever in their lives been treated with a hormonal growth promotant?
Have these cattle been raised consistent with the rules of an independently audited quality assurance programme on the farm, the PIC of which is shown above?
Has the owner stated above owned these cattle since their birth?
In the past 60 days, have any of these cattle been fed by-product stockfeeds?
In the past six months, have any of these cattle been on a farm listed on the ERP database or placed under grazing restrictions because of chemical residues?
Are any of the cattle in this consignment still within a withholding period or export slaughter interval following treatment with any veterinary drugs or chemical?
In the past 60 days, have any of these cattle consumed any stockfeed that was still within a withholding period when harvested or first grazed?
In the past 42 days, were any of these cattle:
– grazed in an endosulfan spray risk area?
– fed fodders cut from an endosulfan spray drift risk area?
I [FULL NAME] [FULL ADDRESS] declare that I am the owner or the person responsible for the husbandry of the cattle and that all the information in Part A of this document is true and correct. I also declare that I have read and understood all the questions that I have answered, that I have read and understood the explanatory notes, and that, while under my control, the cattle were not fed restricted animal material (including meat and bone meal) in breach of state or territory legislation

PIC: Property Identification Code
ERP: Extended Residues Program
Source: SAFEMEAT Partnership (21)

The National Livestock Identification System

The NLIS was a voluntary system for the identification and tracing of cattle, and became mandatory in 2005. It is a permanent identification system that enables individual cattle to be tracked from the farm of birth to the place of slaughter, to improve food safety, product integrity and access to markets.

All farms in Australia that run cattle must be registered with the relevant state or territory department of agriculture and each farm is assigned a property identification code.

The NLIS uses radio frequency identification devices in the form of ear tags or rumen bolus/ear tag combinations to identify cattle. Cattle are tagged with a unique NLIS device before they leave their farm of birth. Cattle implanted with NLIS devices can be electronically identified as they move through the livestock chain. All movements and deaths of cattle must be recorded in the national NLIS database.

Details of the National Livestock Identification System can be found on the Australian Meat and Livestock website at: http://www.mla.com.au/default.htm (Fig. 5).

The National Saleyard Quality Assurance programme

The NSQA programme is owned and operated by national saleyard owners. In Australia, the majority of cattle are sold

National Livestock Identification System

Fig. 5
Symbol of the National Livestock Identification System in Australia

to the market through saleyards. The NSQA programme was developed to support the National Standard for the Construction and Operation of Australian Saleyards. This standard was developed with participation from all sectors of the industry. The NSQA programme is a transparent, independently auditable means of managing and assessing compliance with the standard.

National programmes on chemicals and livestock feeds

In Australia, on-farm quality assurance systems are supported by national programmes aimed at ensuring compliance with national and international requirements for chemicals and livestock feeds. These national programmes are managed and administered by regulatory bodies such as the Australian Pesticides and Veterinary Medicines Authority (APVMA), state and territory

Rev. sci. tech. Off. int. Epiz., **25** (2)

693

governments, the Australian Government Department of Health and Ageing and FSANZ. These bodies and organisations are linked to ensure the overall co-ordination of activities and that livestock farmers do not operate in isolation.

The National Registration Scheme

The Australian Pesticides and Veterinary Medicines Authority is the Australian government statutory authority responsible for the assessment and registration of pesticides and veterinary medicines, and their regulation up to and including the point of retail sale. ('Pesticides and veterinary medicines' are also referred to as 'agricultural and veterinary chemicals'.) This body administers the National Registration Scheme for agricultural and veterinary chemicals in partnership with state and territory governments and with the active involvement of other Australian government agencies, such as the Australian Government Department of Health and Ageing and the Australian Government Department of Environment and Heritage.

In accord with domestic requirements and international guidelines (i.e. the Food and Agriculture Organization of the United Nations [FAO]/World Health Organization [WHO] Codex Alimentarius [Codex] Commission [CAC]), APVMA establishes maximum residue limits, as well as specifying export slaughter intervals.

A maximum residue limit is the highest concentration of the remainder of an agricultural and/or veterinary chemical permitted in food or animal feed. Maximum residue limits are monitored to ensure farmers comply with label 'withholding periods' when using chemicals (i.e. the amount of time that must be allowed to lapse between the use of the chemical and the sale or use of the animal or feed). Both APVMA and FSANZ work co-operatively to ensure that the use of chemical products and the level of any residues in food comply with the registered conditions of use.

An export slaughter interval is the time that should elapse between the administration of a veterinary chemical to an animal and its subsequent slaughter for export purposes. Export slaughter intervals may vary from withholding periods so as to manage the differences between maximum residue limits allowed in Australia and those allowed by trading partners. Export slaughter interval advice is particularly important for quality assurance schemes, and especially for producers completing NVDs as part of the whole-of-chain management of exported beef. Export slaughter intervals have been agreed to by the cattle industry and the registrant of the veterinary chemical.

In addition, APVMA operates a quality assurance programme which provides an effective reporting and feedback system to the National Registration Scheme for agricultural and veterinary chemicals. The Adverse Experience Reporting Program (AERP) reports on unintended or unexpected effects of agricultural and veterinary chemicals on animals, people and the environment. In turn, APVMA conducts science-based risk analyses of received adverse experience reports to improve the responsible management of agricultural and veterinary chemicals throughout their life cycle. The aim of the AERP is to ensure that products on the market remain safe and effective, are of acceptable quality, are used in the best possible way, and that the instructions and warnings on labels are appropriate.

State/territory control of chemical use

Australian provincial state and territory governments regulate the use of agricultural and veterinary chemicals after sale at the point of retail. These regulations cover:

– basic training requirements for users

– licensing of commercial pest control operators and ground and aerial spray operators

– residue monitoring

– arrangements to enforce the safe use of chemicals, including the use of codes of practice, spraydrift guidelines and other user-awareness-raising initiatives.

State and territory regulations use a national model to regulate dangerous substances in the workplace. State and territory government agencies for primary industry, agriculture, health and the environment also advise on agricultural and veterinary chemical use and promote other means of controlling pests and diseases. They undertake research, training and education to manage the possible risks from agricultural and veterinary chemical use and improve the ways they are used.

Chemical use quality assurance

Nationally accredited veterinary chemical training programmes are run in Australia by agricultural and veterinary chemical training providers. The aim of these training programmes for farmers is to ensure the safe and effective use of chemicals in animals for food production.

For example, the National Farmers' Federation and the Rural Training Council of Australia established *Chemcert* Australia as a national training and accreditation programme, based on recognised national industry competencies. *Chemcert* Australia trains farm chemical users to meet all regulations and laws requiring the safe use of agricultural and veterinary chemicals, as well as their obligations under industry quality assurance programmes. (Information on *Chemcert* Australia is available at: http://www.chemcert.org.au/index.shtm.)

Rev. sci. tech. Off. int. Epiz., **25** (2)

National Residue Survey

In partnership with various industries, the Australian Government Department of Agriculture, Fisheries and Forestry conducts the NRS, which randomly monitors chemical residues in raw food and fibre commodities. The participating industries, including the beef industry, pay for the operation of the survey. The NRS also surveys heavy metals and organochlorines, such as dichloro-diphenyl-trichloroethane (DDT), that could still be present in the environment as the result of past industry use. The general classes of chemicals, and some specific examples of chemicals included in the survey, are shown in Table VI.

The primary purpose of the NRS is to ensure that food commodities produced in Australia meet national and international residue requirements, to support access to key export and domestic markets for the participating industries. Traceback investigations are initiated when there are reasonable grounds to believe that any residue findings might have been the result of incorrect use of an agricultural or veterinary chemical.

The NRS conducts random residue and targeted monitoring and is involved in compliance and residue prevention projects. The NRS conducts random monitoring for the chemicals listed in Table VI, to collect data on the level of residues in agricultural and fisheries products. Its targeted monitoring, compliance testing, and residue prevention projects assist in obtaining information about known or potential residue problems, using a non-random sampling process. Table VII contains information on some targeted monitoring projects.

Table VI

The general classes of chemicals included in the National Residue Survey

Broad classes of chemicals	General categories of chemicals within each class
Anthelmintics	Macrocyclic lactones
	Benzimidazoles
	Salicylinamides
Antibiotics	Beta-lactams
	Aminoglycosides
	Tetracyclines
	Macrolides
	Cephalosporins
	Lincosamides
	Sulfonamides
	Others (e.g. chloramphenicol)
Hormones	Corticosteroids
	Resorcyclic acid lactones
	Steroids
	Stilbenes
Other veterinary drugs	Beta-agonists
	Non-steroidal anti-inflammatory drugs
Pesticides	Organochlorines
	Organophosphates
	Synthetic pyrethroids
	Benzoyl ureas
Environmental contaminants	Chlorinated biphenyls
	Metals (e.g. cadmium, lead, mercury)
	Mycotoxins

Source: National Residue Survey annual report, 2004-2005 (4)

FeedSafe

In 2003, the Stock Feed Manufacturers' Council of Australia (SFMCA) initiated a voluntary quality assurance programme for the Australian stock feed manufacturing industry, known as FeedSafe®. This programme demonstrates the commitment of the Australian stock feed industry to quality assurance and risk mitigation in the manufacture and use of animal feeds. Through FeedSafe®, the SFMCA has recognised the need for a broader industry approach to feed and food safety, and is providing greater security of supply to the Australian livestock industries. The central aspect of FeedSafe® is a code of good manufacturing practice, which has been developed in conjunction with the Veterinary Authorities. The main elements of FeedSafe® are summarised in Table VIII. Additional information on the programme is available at http://www.sfmca.com.au/feedsafe/about_feedsafe/.

Livestock fodder declarations

To provide assurances about the quality and safety of stockfeed, farmers should obtain a completed commodity vendor declaration or by-product vendor declaration from the suppliers of the livestock fodder. These vendor declarations indicate the chemicals that the product has been exposed to, if any. Commodity vendor declarations cover chemical treatments that might have been applied to stockfeed items. The by-product vendor declaration covers materials that have not been produced specifically for use as stockfeed, including fruit and vegetable wastes and crop-processing by-products, such as peel, pulp, stems, pressings and leaf material.

These vendor declarations include information on the following aspects of the commodity:
– the contact and address details of the supplier of the commodity

– whether the commodity comes from a farm accredited under a quality assurance scheme

– whether any residue testing has been performed on the commodity

– details of any chemicals applied to the farm (or neighbouring farms) where the crop was grown.

Rev. sci. tech. Off. int. Epiz., 25 (2)

695

Table VII
Targeted monitoring, compliance testing and residue prevention projects conducted by the National Residue Survey (NRS)

Project	Description
National Organochlorine Residue Management project	The National Organochlorine Residue Management project aims to minimise the potential for organochlorine residues in beef. The beef industry and the state governments jointly fund the project. The project collects information at abattoirs from testing cattle from at-risk farms for organochlorine residues (compliance testing), and also focuses on developing on-farm property management plans to minimise the risk of livestock grazing organochlorine-contaminated land
The National Antibacterial Residue Minimisation project	The National Antibacterial Residue Minimisation project aims to minimise antibacterial residues in cattle using advisory, analytical and regulatory techniques. The beef industry and the Australian state/territory governments are partners in the project. The NRS is responsible for national co-ordination of the project and management of financial disbursements to the state and territory governments
Targeted Antibacterial Residue Testing project	The Targeted Antibacterial Residue Testing project focuses on testing animals at abattoirs suspected by veterinary inspectors of having received recent antibacterial treatment. The project combines targeted testing, quality assurance, extension and regulation to minimise antibacterial residues in beef. The NRS co-ordinates the project and manages the financial disbursements to state and territory governments and laboratories
Endosulfan residues in beef	In conjunction with extension programmes to inform cotton and cattle producers how to minimise the risk of unacceptable endosulfan residues in cattle, endosulfan testing of slaughter cattle occurs each cotton spray season
Hormonal Growth Promotant Audit project	Australia has developed a hormonal growth promotant-free accreditation scheme that allows Australian cattle producers to supply the European Union market. On-farm third-party audits are routinely conducted to monitor compliance with accreditation requirements. The NRS manages the testing of samples taken during these audits

Source: National Residue Survey annual report, 2004-2005 (4)

Table VIII
The elements of FeedSafe®

Element
Premises and mill buildings
Personnel training and qualifications
Plant and equipment
Raw material sourcing and purchasing
Raw material quality and storage
Feed formulation and manufacturing
Product labelling
Loading, transport and delivery to clients
Product inspection, sampling and testing
Customer complaint investigation

Source: Stock Feed Manufacturers' Council of Australia (23)

Department of Agriculture, Fisheries and Forestry and the Australian Government Department of Health and Ageing. Thus, FSANZ is responsible for the following activities:

– developing standards for food manufacturing, labelling, processing and primary production

– providing information to consumers to enable better consumer choice

– co-ordinating national food surveillance, enforcement and food recall

– conducting consumer and industry research

– undertaking dietary exposure modelling and scientific risk assessments

– providing risk assessment advice on imported food.

Food safety standards

Domestic standards

Domestic food standards are developed by the independent statutory authority, FSANZ, in consultation with industry stakeholders, the public, the Australia and New Zealand Food Regulation Ministerial Council, and other government agencies, including the state and territory government, the Australian Government

International standards

As the global food trade continues to increase, the importance of uniform food standards for consumer protection is obvious. The SPS Agreement recognises the FAO/WHO CAC as the relevant body for setting international food standards, and Codex standards have therefore become the 'benchmark' (i.e. definitive standard) for evaluating national food controls (12). Codex, established in 1962, is the international, inter-

696

Rev. sci. tech. Off. int. Epiz., **25** (2)

governmental body that develops food safety and commodity standards to protect the health of consumers and ensure fair practices in the food trade.

A number of Codex Committees are responsible for addressing food safety issues, including:

- food hygiene
- food labelling
- pesticide residues
- milk and milk products
- fish and fish products
- fresh fruit and vegetables.

This work is facilitated by independent, expert, scientific advice from other committees that set maximum limits in food for additives, contaminants, and agricultural and veterinary chemicals.

In addition to Codex, WHO is involved in other activities that promote food safety, including:

- assisting the development of national food safety policies and infrastructures

- writing and enforcing food legislation

- promoting food safety technologies

- educating consumers

- generating data on epidemiological surveillance of food-borne diseases, food contaminants and the food safety infrastructure (27).

In 2000, WHO announced an expansion of its food safety programme in response to emerging food safety issues. These expanded activities include:

- obtaining better food-borne diseases data

- creating a WHO/FAO risk assessment body

- investigating the causes of increased food-borne disease

- defining food safety research needs (26).

The SPS Agreement recognises the World Organisation for Animal Health (OIE) as the international organisation responsible for establishing and maintaining animal health standards and guidelines for international trade in animals and animal products. In 2001, the OIE decided that the then *International Animal Health Code* (now the *Terrestrial Animal Health Code*) would include food safety in a context consistent with its mandate (i.e. pre-harvest controls over animal products) (30). Extra resources have been provided to allow this work to progress and to help the OIE strengthen its collaboration with the World Trade Organization, WHO, FAO and Codex (29).

The increased importance of international food standards has meant that obtaining international agreement to new or amended standards has become more difficult and controversial. International standards must continue to reflect legitimate global concerns, be based on sound science for the protection of consumer health, and not provide unjustified barriers to trade.

Conclusion

It is internationally recognised that traditional methods aimed at ensuring food safety, such as end-product quality control, do not adequately ensure the safety of the final food product. To achieve an acceptable standard of food safety, governments and the food industry must provide quality assurance systems based on sound risk management principles throughout the food supply chain. By controlling food safety hazards at the beginning of the process (i.e. on the farm), it is possible to reduce the challenge to food safety management systems at other steps along the supply chain.

In this paper, the authors have used the Australian beef industry as a case study to outline the development and implementation of on-farm quality assurance measures that encompass food safety using HACCP principles. These measures are further supported by auditing, the registration of chemicals, quality assurance systems for stockfeeds and various training and certification procedures.

Acknowledgements

The authors wish to thank Mr Ed Klim, Manager of the Product Integrity and Safety Branch, Australian Government Department of Agriculture, Fisheries and Forestry, for his assistance in sourcing information on Australian livestock quality systems and helping to prepare Figure 3, the schematic diagram of linkages between Australian livestock regulatory and quality systems. The authors would also like to thank Mr Alan Edwards, Manager of Biosecurity Coordination, the Australian Government Department of Agriculture, Fisheries and Forestry, for his assistance in preparing the information on the Network.

■

Rev. sci. tech. Off. int. Epiz., **25** (2)

697

Répondre aux exigences des pays importateurs : pratiques et politiques pour assurer la sécurité sanitaire des aliments au niveau de la ferme

P.J. Dagg, R.J. Butler, J.G. Murray & R.R. Biddle

Résumé

Compte tenu de la demande croissante des consommateurs en produits alimentaires de qualité et sans danger pour leur santé, et des récentes alarmes concernant les maladies transmises par les aliments, les gouvernements et le secteur agroalimentaire se doivent de mettre au point des politiques et des programmes de protection sanitaire des aliments correspondant aux meilleures pratiques au niveau international. Les pays exportateurs de denrées alimentaires issues de la production animale doivent se plier non seulement à leurs propres normes nationales, mais aussi aux exigences des pays importateurs.

Au niveau international, on considère désormais que les contrôles de qualité en fin de processus de production et les autres méthodes de ce type visant à contrôler la sécurité sanitaire des aliments sont insuffisants pour garantir la sécurité sanitaire du produit final. Pour atteindre un niveau acceptable de sécurité sanitaire, les gouvernements et le secteur agricole doivent travailler de concert pour mettre au point des systèmes d'assurance qualité fondés sur des principes solides de gestion du risque appliquée tout au long de la chaîne d'approvisionnement alimentaire. Les systèmes d'assurance qualité mis en œuvre dans les élevages ainsi qu'aux autres stades de la chaîne d'approvisionnement alimentaire devraient aborder la sécurité sanitaire des aliments en appliquant la méthode d'analyse des risques et de maîtrise des points critiques (HACCP). Ces systèmes doivent couvrir plusieurs aspects, dont la biosécurité, la surveillance des maladies et leur notification, la sécurité sanitaire des aliments destinés aux animaux, l'innocuité des produits chimiques utilisés dans l'agriculture et des médicaments vétérinaires, le contrôle des agents potentiellement responsables d'infections d'origine alimentaire et la traçabilité. Ils devraient également s'appuyer sur des plans de formation accrédités, avec délivrance d'un certificat en fin de formation, et sur des programmes d'audit permettant de s'assurer que les lignes directrices et les normes reconnues au niveau local et international continuent d'être respectées. En se basant sur l'exemple du secteur de production de viande bovine en Australie, les auteurs examinent les politiques à mener pour que les mesures de sécurité sanitaire des aliments soient prises au niveau de la ferme et appliquées concrètement dans le contexte des programmes d'assurance qualité.

Mots-clés

Animal d'élevage – Assurance qualité – Australie – Élaboration de politiques – Secteur de production de viande bovine – Sécurité sanitaire des aliments.

■

698

Rev. sci. tech. Off. int. Epiz., **25** (2)

Cumplimiento de los requisitos impuestos por los países importadores: principios y prácticas para garantizar la inocuidad de los alimentos desde la propia explotación

P.J. Dagg, R.J. Butler, J.G. Murray & R.R. Biddle

Resumen

Ante la creciente demanda de alimentos inocuos y de buena calidad por parte de los consumidores y los recientes problemas de salud pública relacionados con enfermedades transmitidas por vía alimentaria, los gobiernos y la industria agropecuaria se encuentran bajo presión para ofrecer políticas y programas integrales en materia de inocuidad que se ajusten además a las buenas prácticas reconocidas en el plano internacional. Los países que exportan artículos alimentarios obtenidos a partir del ganado deben cumplir tanto los requisitos del país importador como su propia normativa.

En los medios internacionales ya se admite que el control de calidad en el punto final y otros métodos similares para garantizar la inocuidad de los alimentos no sirven para que el producto acabado ofrezca las debidas garantías de inocuidad. Para lograr un nivel aceptable al respecto es menester que los gobiernos y la industria agropecuaria trabajen concertadamente para instituir, en toda la cadena de abastecimiento alimentario, sistemas de garantía de calidad basados en sólidos principios de gestión del riesgo. Los sistemas que se implanten en las explotaciones ganaderas y otros eslabones de la cadena deben tratar la cuestión de la inocuidad aplicando principios del análisis de riesgos y control de puntos críticos. Tales sistemas han de cubrir aspectos como la seguridad biológica, el control y la notificación de enfermedades, la inocuidad de los piensos, la utilización segura de productos químicos en agricultura y veterinaria, el control de eventuales patógenos transmitidos por vía alimentaria y la rastreabilidad. Es preciso además que vengan complementados con programas acreditados de entrenamiento que faciliten un certificado final de acreditación y programas de auditoría que aseguren el cumplimiento de las directrices y reglas reconocidas tanto local como internacionalmente. Los autores estudian la elaboración de políticas para instituir medidas de inocuidad en las explotaciones y su aplicación práctica como parte de programas de garantía de calidad, utilizando para ello el ejemplo de la industria australiana de carne vacuna.

Palabras clave

Australia – Bovinos – Elaboración de políticas – Garantía de calidad – Industria de carne vacuna – Inocuidad de los alimentos.

■

Rev. sci. tech. Off. int. Epiz., **25** (2)

699

References

1. Agriculture and Resource Management Council of Australia and New Zealand (ARMCANZ) (1997). – National guidelines for beef cattle feedlots in Australia, 2nd Ed. Primary Industries Report Series 47. Commonwealth Scientific and Industrial Research Organisation (CSIRO) Publishing/ Primary Industries Standing Committee (PISC)/ Standing Committee on Agriculture and Resource Management (SCARM), Collingwood, Victoria, Australia.

2. Animal Health Australia (1998). – Enterprise manual: feedlots (Version 2.1). Australian Veterinary Emergency Plan, Edition 2.0. Primary Industries Ministerial Council, Collingwood, Victoria, Australia.

3. Australian Government Attorney-General's Department (2006). – Australia's Critical Infrastructure Protection Arrangements. Available at: http://www.tisn.gov.au/agd/ WWW/rwpattach.nsf/VAP/(930C12A9101F61D43493D44C 70E84EAA)~Diagram+for+web+site.doc/$file/Diagram+for+ web+site.doc (accessed on 20 February 2006).

4. Australian Government Department of Agriculture, Fisheries and Forestry (DAFF) (2005). – National Residue Survey annual report 2004-2005. DAFF, Barton, Australian Capital Territory. Available at: http://www.affa.gov.au/content/ output.cfm?ObjectID=715E69E1-5C4B-4439- 84A2091FE098AD6D#0405 (accessed on 20 February 2006).

5. Australian Primary Industries Standing Committee (PISC) (2004). – Model code of practice for the welfare of animals: cattle, 2nd Ed. Primary Industries Report Series 85. Commonwealth Scientific and Industrial Research Organisation (CSIRO) Publishing/PISC/Standing Committee on Agriculture and Resource Management (SCARM), Collingwood, Victoria, Australia.

6. Australian Productivity Commission (2002). – Impact of a foot and mouth disease outbreak on Australia: research report. AusInfo, Melbourne.

7. Australian Veterinary Association (AVA) (1997). – Safe use of veterinary medicines on farms. AVA Code of Practice, prepared by the Therapeutics Subcommittee and adopted in February 1990. AVA, St Leonards, New South Wales, Australia.

8. Bongaarts J. & Bulatao R.A. (eds) (2000). – Beyond six billion: forecasting the world's population. Panel on Population Projections, Committee on Population, Commission on Behavioral and Social Sciences and Education, National Research Council. National Academy Press, Washington, DC.

9. Butler R.J., Murray J.G. & Tidswell S. (2003). – Quality assurance and meat inspection in Australia. *In* Veterinary Services: organisation, quality assurance, evaluation (E. Correa Melo & F. Gerster, eds). *Rev. sci. tech. Off. int. Epiz.*, **22** (2), 697-712.

10. Caporale V., Giovannini A., Di Francesco C. & Calistri P. (2001). – Importance of the traceability of animals and animal products in epidemiology. *In* Traceability of animals and animal products (H.A. MacDaniel & M.K. Sheridan, eds). *Rev. sci. tech. Off. int. Epiz.*, **20** (2), 372-378.

11. Food and Agriculture Organization of the United Nations (FAO) (2005). – Meat market assessment, commodities and trade. FAO, Rome. Available at: http://www.fao.org/es/ESC/en /20953/21014/highlight_27269en.html (accessed on 20 February 2006).

12. Food and Agriculture Organization of the United Nations (FAO) & World Health Organization (WHO) (1995). – Application of risk analysis to food standards issues. Report of the Joint FAO/WHO Expert Consultation, Geneva, 13- 17 March. WHO/FNU/FOS/95.3. FAO/WHO, Rome/Geneva.

13. Henning P.H., Tham E.B., Martin A.A., Beare T.H. & Jureidini K.F. (1998). – Haemolytic-uraemic syndrome outbreak caused by *Escherichia coli* O111:H-: clinical outcomes. *Med. J. Aust.*, **168** (11), 552-555.

14. McKean J.D. (2001). – The importance of traceability for public health and consumer protection. *In* Traceability of animals and animal products (H.A. MacDaniel & M.K. Sheridan, eds). *Rev. sci. tech. Off. int. Epiz.*, **20** (2), 363-371.

15. Meat and Livestock Australia (MLA) (2000). – National beef cattle feedlot environmental code of practice, 1st Ed. MLA, Sydney.

16. Meat and Livestock Australia (MLA) (2005). – Requirements of the Level 1 Livestock Production Assurance – food safety programme. Available at: http://www.mla.com.au/default.htm (accessed on 20 February 2006).

17. Meat and Livestock Australia (MLA) (2005). – Requirements of the Level 2 Livestock Production Assurance – quality assurance programme. Available at: http://www.mla.com.au/default.htm (accessed on 20 February 2006).

18. Meat and Livestock Australia in the Middle East (2006). – Quality assurance in Australia. Available at: http://www.meatlivestockaustralia.com/content.cfm?sid=760 (accessed on 20 February 2006).

19. Rocourt J., Moy G., Vierk K. & Schlundt J. (2003). – The present state of foodborne disease in OECD countries. Food Safety Department, World Health Organization (WHO), Geneva.

20. SAFEMEAT Partnership (2000). – National Feedlot Accreditation Scheme (NFAS). Available at: http://www. safemeat.com.au/English/Meat_Safety/On_farm_feedlot_sale yard/Livestock+Production+Assurance+(LPA)/LPA+Level+2/ National+Feedlot+Accreditation+Scheme.htm (accessed on 20 February 2006).

21. SAFEMEAT Partnership (2004). – National Vendor Declaration (Cattle) and Waybill (NVD). Available at http://www.mla.com.au/NR/rdonlyres/5927A1B7-B866-4D74-9583-BEC8FFADB64F/0/BlankCattleNVD2.pdf (accessed on 20 February 2006).

22. SAFEMEAT Partnership (2005). – 2004-2005 SAFEMEAT annual report. SAFEMEAT, Australia.

23. Stock Feed Manufacturers' Council of Australia (2003). – FeedSafe®. Available at: http://www.sfmca.com.au/feedsafe/about_feedsafe/ (accessed on 20 February 2006).

24. United States Census Bureau (2005). – US Census Bureau total midyear population for the world: 1950-2050. Available at: www.census.gov (accessed on 20 February 2006).

25. United States Food and Drug Administration (US FDA) (2001). – HACCP: a state-of-the-art approach to food safety. Backgrounder. US FDA, Washington, DC.

26. World Health Organization (WHO) (2000). – WHO responds to new challenges in food safety. Press release WHO/4, 25 January 2000. WHO, Geneva.

27. World Health Organization (WHO) (2002). – Food safety and foodborne illness. Fact sheet No. 237. WHO, Geneva.

28. World Health Organization (WHO) (2002). – WHO global strategy for food safety: safer food for better health. Food Safety Department, WHO, Geneva.

29. World Organisation for Animal Health (OIE) (2001). – Editorial from the Director General. Available at: http://www.oie.int/eng/Edito/en_edito_sept01.htm (accessed on 20 February 2006).

30. World Organisation for Animal Health (OIE) (2001). – International Animal Health Code: mammals, birds and bees, 10th Ed. OIE, Paris.

31. World Trade Organization (WTO) (1995). – Agreement on the application of sanitary and phytosanitary measures. *In* The results of the Uruguay Round of multilateral trade negotiations: the legal texts. WTO, Geneva.

Rev. sci. tech. Off. int. Epiz., 2006, **25** (2), 701-712

Sanitary and phytosanitary measures and food safety: challenges and opportunities for developing countries

M. Siméon

14 rue des Sauniers, 17000 La Rochelle, France

Summary

Because of fast-growing demand, export markets can absorb high value added products and offer high returns; for many developing countries export market development is thus a key requirement for rural income generation and rural growth.

Although developing countries face increasingly strict sanitary and phytosanitary standards in their export markets, they can maintain and improve market access – and improve domestic food safety and agricultural productivity – by adopting a strategic approach to food safety, agricultural health and trade. High-income countries should increase development flows to help developing countries build the capacity to plan and execute the necessary strategies.

The first proposal in this paper is to make two existing sets of guidelines widely available to interested parties, in particular through the World Bank and the World Organisation for Animal Health (OIE). The first covers the broad process of problem assessment, strategy development and action plan formulation; the second set deals with institutional analysis and training of staff of the official sanitary control services.

The second proposal is that interested countries and donors should speed up the ongoing development of guidelines, computer software tools and training material to help countries quantify the importance and impact of food safety issues. The focus here is on a 'multipurpose agricultural data analysis and modelization system'.

The third proposal is to carry out a case study to help demonstrate that a number of animal health issues related to food safety should be treated as relating to 'global public goods' and thus require intervention on a global scale. Possible candidates are foot and mouth disease and highly pathogenic avian influenza.

Keywords

Guideline – Market access – Modelization – Sector analysis – Sector strategy.

Issues and opportunities

What is food safety?

The basic definition of food safety is: 'what makes your food safe to consume'. But a few issues make such a definition over-simplistic:

– safety cannot be absolute, so 'safe' should be replaced by 'safe enough'. The concept of safety should then be replaced by the concept of 'acceptable level of risk';

– the level of risk depends on the way food is used: the same foodstuff can be perfectly safe if properly cooked but dangerous if consumed in raw form. The marketing of raw milk may be safe in a village in India where people traditionally boil their milk several times a day, and dangerous in a different context;

– safety and quality are distinct but closely related. For the economist, food safety is a public good, meaning that related costs and benefits cannot be captured by the mechanisms of the market, whereas food quality is a private good (though some amount of regulation is nevertheless needed, e.g. labelling). Quality management systems also help address safety issues;

– in a broader sense, safety also means safety with regard to animal (and plant) health. Food safety is thus closely linked to agricultural health. This is why the implications of food safety for international trade are governed in part by the Agreement on the Application of Sanitary and Phytosanitary Measures (the SPS Agreement) under the General Agreement on Tariffs and Trade rules supervised by the World Trade Organization.

Why is food safety becoming more important?

Food safety is important in two different domains: domestic consumption and access to export markets.

Demand for livestock products (as well as fruits and vegetables) is growing fast, particularly in developing countries. This growth helps to trigger change. Changes in consumption patterns create new hazards that can produce new food safety risks. In many large cities, for example, a growing number of people get their lunch from street vendors instead of at home. Changes in food processing and distribution systems, such as the development of supermarkets that are replacing traditional neighbourhood markets, also produce new types of risks. Food poisoning incidents spread to larger numbers of people, and trigger growing consumer concern about food safety. Improving food safety thus becomes an important element of better public health and food security.

Because of fast-growing demand, export markets can absorb high value added products and offer high returns, and for many developing countries export market development is a key requirement for rural income generation and rural growth. At the same time new risks and hazards are being identified, and the global burden of disease is growing, as exemplified by the recent major crises of foot and mouth disease (FMD) and bovine spongiform encephalopathy, and the current concerns with avian influenza. There is also growing consumer concern about food safety in importing countries, and as a result technical trade barriers are of increasing importance.

The Agreement on the Application of Sanitary and Phytosanitary Measures: what is it and what are the implications?

The SPS Agreement sets out a number of 'ground rules' about trade measures to protect the health of humans, animals or plant life, while aiming to ensure that such measures will not create unfair barriers to trade (10). There are seven of these ground rules, which relate to:

– transparency

– equivalence (recognition of different systems)

– the need for measures to be science-based and applied only to the extent necessary (using risk assessment to determine the 'appropriate level of protection')

– regionalisation

– the desirability of harmonisation

– the role of national sovereignty

– an established mechanism for dispute resolution.

In general terms the agreement can be said to have triggered regulatory reform and prompted action to open markets. However, there are concerns that it unduly favours advanced countries, which gain market access while less developed countries lack sufficient capacity to meet requirements for animal health and other safety and quality measures. Small, low-income countries might be particularly disadvantaged under the agreement, as they have limited public capacity, underdeveloped food systems, and higher costs per capita in regulating and monitoring food safety.

In addition, countries have differing ways of 'framing' problems, and large differences exist even among countries that are similar in other respects. As a result, there are still fundamental disagreements over the role of science versus the importance of consumer choice, as shown by ongoing controversies over genetically modified organisms, the beef hormone dispute, or issues related to the environment, labour regimes or animal welfare.

Recognising the problem

In spite of the growing importance of food safety, it is given low priority by a number of countries – and often also at the donor level. Too little attention is given to safety concerns, or to the impact of problems related to food safety and the linkages with development policies.

As a result, more often than not there is no comprehensive strategy at the national level, nobody is clearly in charge, and the issues receive attention only when there is a crisis. The situation is similar at donor level. Because food safety issues often cut across sector lines, nobody is in a position to take the lead.

From the perspective of development policy, trade raises more attention and can be used as the entry point. On the other hand, public opinion in developed countries will only focus on the issue of food safety when there is a crisis that threatens public health, as clearly illustrated by the current avian influenza crisis.

Rev. sci. tech. Off. int. Epiz., **25** (2)

703

First conclusion

The first conclusion one can draw from the above is that countries need to quantify the importance and impact of food safety issues with regard to:

– the cost of limitations to access to external markets

– the cost of the absence of quality

– the importance and priority of food safety with regard to public health

– the need to go beyond risk assessment, to assess relative importance as compared to other issues

– the economic implications for incomes of the SPS Agreement and in particular the impact on the rural poor.

Institutional capacity issues

Much of the policy discussion about trade and standards in developing countries centres on finding ways to help those countries to participate in international standard-setting bodies (the Codex Alimentarius Commission [Codex], the World Organisation for Animal Health [OIE] and the International Plant Protection Convention [IPPC]), or otherwise influence the level and nature of the standards themselves. There have also been some suggestions that the SPS Agreement itself should be re-examined, again with greater involvement from developing countries.

Risks and hazards differ from one country to the next. Typical issues that arise, and for which too many of the less-developed countries (LDCs) lack capacity to argue their views, include:

– debate over new risks (even though established risk sources may be more important to LDC trade)

– whether different standards and systems are equivalent

– whether regulations concerning hazard analysis critical control points are equivalent

– whether equivalent domestic regulation is necessary.

However, new findings from the World Bank's research programme on SPS standards (4) suggest that focusing on 'the rules of the game' represents only a partial solution, at best, and that the challenges and opportunities posed by standards can be better addressed by strengthening public and private capacities to manage food safety and agricultural health risks effectively.

In particular, the promotion of public/private partnerships is particularly important to help overcome the capacity gap.

The case for regionalisation

Small countries suffer special constraints, because their human resources are more limited, and also because they have to bear higher per capita costs of public investments than larger countries.

Such small countries thus need to explore whether some activities can be shared at regional level, and consider whether regional-level activities could bring added value. Examples of areas of potentially fruitful cooperation include:

– forming coalitions around issues of mutual regional interest

– pooling scientific and technical resources

– regional cooperation on laboratories and research

– forming regional networks that are better able to participate in the setting-up of international standards

– joint participation in standard-setting bodies

– information clearinghouses.

The limits of such cooperation, though, are set by the so-called subsidiarity principle: do not establish regional bodies for measures that can be undertaken better at the national level.

Second conclusion

Developing countries need to analyse their institutional set-up and capacity, and in particular:

a) clarify the roles of actors:

– public and private sector roles in the export trade

– the roles of government, consumers and civil society in domestic issues

b) identify the needs that could be better addressed through regional cooperation

c) identify needs for research, surveillance systems, monitoring of food systems, epidemiological monitoring and capacity building in risk assessment.

Policy implications

The general trend towards more intensive livestock production very often translates into increased concentration and vertical integration of input supply, production and processing. Altogether, this represents a very serious threat to small-scale producers.

Obviously, productivity gains from improved control of plant and animal disease may benefit the rural poor. At the same time, however, a strategy that sets higher standards

Rev. sci. tech. Off. int. Epiz., **25** (2)

might have damaging impacts on poorer producers. Controls set by the SPS, if not designed with small producers in mind, are likely to favour large-scale production units, further aggravating the threat.

The problems are particularly difficult in areas of market failure, and specific support needs to be provided in regulation, surveillance of diseases, training, extension and research.

Producer organisations can be crucial in moving the public agenda. Producers can make public services (research, extension, credit) more responsive to clients, but they need specific support to become effective.

Third conclusion

Developing countries need to identify and implement policies to enhance sustainable income opportunities for small farmers, in particular resource-poor livestock keepers, in order to mitigate potential negative impacts that measures for animal/plant health and food safety might have on the poor.

Overall conclusions

In order for developing countries to benefit more fully from the opportunities offered by international markets, they need to address food safety issues and comply with the provisions of the SPS Agreement.

There is a consensus that implementation of measures related to animal (and plant) health and food safety needs to be based on farm-to-table science-based (risk assessment) holistic approaches.

Developing countries faced with rising SPS standards in their export markets need to maintain and improve market access, position industries for long-term competitiveness, mitigate potential effects on vulnerable groups, and improve domestic food safety and agricultural productivity. Recent research work carried out by the World Bank (4) indicates that LDCs can achieve these goals by: 'adopting a strategic approach to food safety, agricultural health, and trade. For those countries and suppliers who are well prepared, rising standards represent an opportunity; for those who are poorly prepared, they pose safety and market access risks. High-income countries should increase development flows to help developing countries build the capacity to plan and execute the necessary strategies.'

This translates in particular into the need for such countries to:

– formulate specific strategies, programmes and policies designed in particular to mitigate the problems of the poor

– assess the countries' institutional capacity to cope with SPS requirements

– quantify the importance and impact of food safety issues

– increase the legitimacy of international standards by more participation in the standard-setting process, in particular through resource sharing and regional cooperation.

Proposals

General

Of the four points listed in the overall conclusion of the previous section, the last one (on international standard setting) is dealt with in other parts of this *Review* (1, 3, 5, 6, 8, 11), so this article will limit its proposals to the other three topics.

Regarding the first two points – strategy and policy formulation and institutional capacity – one of the limitations often faced by LDCs is that they do not know how to develop these aspects. The World Bank has sponsored the production of tool kits or sets of guidelines to help countries build capacity in those two areas (2, 9).

The first set, entitled 'Guidelines for food safety, SPS and trade', covers the broad process of problem assessment, strategy development and action plan formulation. The second set, entitled 'Formation des personnels des services officiels de contrôle sanitaire des pays en développement' (available only in French) deals with training for staff of the official sanitary control services, and for that purpose includes guidelines for their institutional analysis.

The two sets of guidelines are described in the two following sections. The first proposal of this article (as mentioned in the introduction) is to make such guidelines widely available to interested parties, in particular through the World Bank and the OIE; this will entail getting them translated into more languages (the two sets of guidelines should be made available at least in English, French and Spanish). Members of the international development community are also invited, in line with their commitments under the SPS Agreement, to offer technical assistance to the countries willing to undertake such comprehensive reviews.

In the same way that many LDCs face problems in strategy and policy formulation and institutional capacity, a similar capacity gap exists regarding the need to quantify the importance and impact of food safety issues. This is particularly the case in sub-Saharan Africa, and has been recognised as a priority issue by the African Livestock Programme (ALive), the recently established partnership

Rev. sci. tech. Off. int. Epiz., **25** (2)

705

for livestock development, poverty reduction and sustainable growth in sub-Saharan Africa. One of the constraints identified by ALive is that most countries lack the capacity to analyse the livestock sector, and in particular its poverty dimensions, formulate strategies, and propose programmes for international and national funding. To address this constraint, ALive has included in its work programme a project to provide the countries with a number of interrelated tools (a tool kit), including guidelines, computer software, and the corresponding training modules. This has resulted, alongside other proposed activities, in the specification of a software tool called the 'multipurpose agricultural data analysis and modelization system' (DAMS), which could be used to develop quantitative analyses of food safety issues.

The second proposal of this paper is that interested countries and donors should speed up the development process. Donors and technical agencies such as the OIE should also help an initial group of countries develop their own sector analysis capacity, in order to test and improve upon the various tools that are currently available. The focus here will be on the main software proposal, and the key features of DAMS are presented in a later section (the ALive toolkit).

The third proposal – outlined in the fourth and last section – is to carry out a case study (using a tool such as DAMS) to help demonstrate that, where food safety is concerned, a number of animal health issues should be treated as issues relating to 'global public goods'. This implies that the costs and benefits of such issues are global in scope, and are not captured by the operation of market forces, but on the contrary require global intervention on a global scale. Well-known examples are FMD or highly pathogenic avian influenza (HPAI).

Guidelines for food safety and trade in the context of the Agreement on the Application of Sanitary and Phytosanitary Measures

The case has been made in the first part of this paper that countries need to formulate specific strategies and programmes in order to deal properly with food safety issues in relation with the SPS Agreement and trade, and in particular to develop policies to mitigate the problems of poverty.

The international agriculture and health institutes (the World Health Organization, Food and Agriculture Organization, Codex, IPPC, OIE), the World Bank, and some key traders in the global market such as the European Union and United States of America (USA) have published various guidelines to help policy-makers cope with food safety issues. Most publications tend to focus on the collection of data and analytical work for the analysis

of problems, and some also discuss the possible elements of interventions; few, however, give help with the difficult step of linking data to the development of policy. In 2002, in order to bridge this gap, the World Bank commissioned a team from the University of Wageningen, the Netherlands, to prepare guidelines to help countries formulate and implement such strategies. The outcome (9) is presented here.

The solution to the lack of methodological support in this matter (i.e. how to link analytical data to policy development) lies in taking a participatory approach to policy-making. While in this approach the analytical work remains of enormous importance, it is merely the input into the interaction of policy-makers with the stakeholders affected by the policy. The guidelines aim to support this pivotal interaction by providing guidance about both analysis and consultation for policy evaluation *ex ante* (i.e. at the earliest stage of policy-making) at a national level. The challenge was to bring to the surface mechanisms of evaluation that help in such situations. In this way, these guidelines contribute to a more rational and less emotional policy process. Further added value comes from the fact that these guidelines were designed to address specifically the problems that may occur in developing countries.

The Wageningen document thus offers a set of guidelines and decision-support tools for developing policies on food safety in low-income and middle-income countries. Targeted users are officials in key positions in national governments, and outside consultants. Aims are to give food authorities insights into the basic policy dilemmas, to identify shortcomings and priorities, and to provide guidance about the design of interventions. These guidelines go beyond the mere description of policy issues in the field of food safety, and suggest practical options. The user is to be supported in the activities of setting the objectives for food safety policy, assessing the food safety situation and identifying priority problems to be addressed, and developing a policy strategy and an action plan for implementation. The guidelines cover the policy-making process from the earliest stages to the final go/no-go decision on the proposed action plan.

The first part of the document, setting out the guidelines, presents a process in seven steps, going from the initial activities to the preparation of an action plan, as shown in Figure 1.

Developing food safety policy is not the work of a single official, nor is it a desk exercise only. As food safety touches on the policy fields of public health, agriculture/fisheries, and trade/commerce, a cooperative effort between government officials is needed to develop sound policies. Moreover, policies need support from stakeholders in food control: consumers, producers, retailers, traders and the like. The management of the various stakes in food safety

706

Rev. sci. tech. Off. int. Epiz., **25** (2)

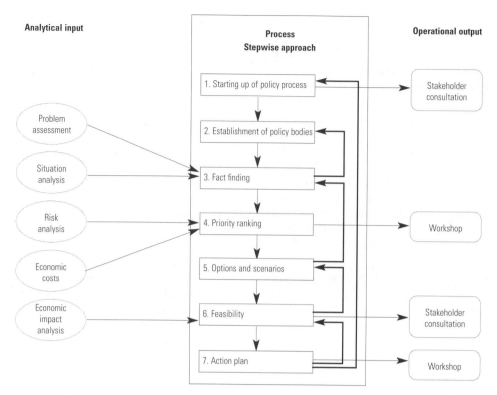

Fig. 1
Food safety strategy formulation process
Source: Wageningen report (9)

issues poses substantial coordination challenges to the process of policy development.

The Wageningen document focuses on the need for the process to be participatory, emphasising stakeholder consultation supported by analytical work. See the left-hand side of the figure for the analytical input into the process; the right-hand side shows the operational side in terms of interactive activities and consultations (Fig. 1).

The second part of the document is a resource book for food safety policy. Its first section includes a discussion of the objectives that policy-makers in the domain of food safety may define. Subsequently some options are presented to support the development of a policy strategy. The third section suggests a range of measures and actions to achieve progress towards the objectives of food safety policy. This part concludes with a summary section aimed at decision support.

The document is partly based on field research in South Africa in 2002 and 2003. The last part of the document presents the case of contaminated groundnut as an example of how to match food policy to markets. Although this is not an animal product, the discussion should be of interest to the readers of the OIE *Review* as an illustrative account of real-life experience.

Guidelines on training for official sanitary control services

Recognising the key importance of the official control and certification services in the implementation of any food safety improvement programme, and the need to provide assistance to developing countries that lack institutional capacity, the World Bank commissioned a second piece of work in 2002 to complement the one described above, focusing on training for such services.

The work was undertaken by a consortium of French organisations, including the livestock department of the Centre de coopération internationale en recherche agronomique pour le développement, the National School of Veterinary Services, the Training Institute (INFOMA) and the Quality and Plant Protection Sub-Directorate of the Ministry of Agriculture, and the Engineers-for-Development Network. So far the guidelines are available in French only.

The guidelines are based in part on fieldwork carried out by the team in Senegal, South Africa and Vietnam. They cover three areas.

The first part presents a broad array of reference material, mostly in the form of pointers to websites where detailed information can be found. It is organised in three sections:

– the world market for food products

– sanitary and phytosanitary requirements, by geographical area

– international, regional or national support organisations.

The second part presents guidelines for the institutional analysis of official services dealing with food safety and official control and certification. The guidelines also cover food safety management by private companies and companies providing control or certification on behalf of governments, as well as the use of support structures providing services such as laboratories, risk assessment or research.

The guidelines are organised around a series of templates designed to help the user put together the relevant information concerning:

– an overview of the agriculture and food situation in the country, including a brief description of the main issues and objectives relating to the improvement of food safety

– a detailed picture of the government services in charge of control and certification, in terms of statutes, missions, administrative and judicial power, and human resources and their management

– an inventory and analysis of the organisations dealing with laboratory services, risk assessment, research and university training, and of private organisations dealing with control on behalf of governments

– a review of the food companies, by sector, in terms of implementation of risk control plans or good practice processes

– an assessment of the missions and effectiveness of public/private sector coordination mechanisms.

Finally, the guidelines will help analyse the situation regarding the production of the information and arguments that will be required to convince stakeholders that the policy is worthwhile, namely the system of surveys and other surveillance systems (occurrence and epidemiology of disease incidents), including the way incidents are analysed and how the results of such analysis are used.

The third part presents guidelines on designing and developing training systems. One outcome of the institutional analysis is to identify the training needs of the various stakeholders in order to improve the sanitary condition of a given sector or product line. Then the guidelines help in drafting training specifications that can

be used when requesting training suppliers to submit proposals, help appraise such proposals, and finally propose monitoring and evaluation tools.

Although the guidelines are geared towards the identification of training needs, they provide valuable guidance for the detailed analysis of a country's institutional set-up, and as such complement very well the broader guidelines presented in the previous section.

The ALive toolkit: a set of tools for quantitative analysis

ALive is planning to provide countries with a number of interrelated tools (a tool kit), including guidelines, computer software, and the corresponding training modules. The need for modelization of the livestock sector is acknowledged by the methodological guidelines being developed under ALive for the analysis of a country's livestock sector.

A DAMS is thus proposed (7). The objective is to develop a system that can not only undertake sector analysis of poverty reduction strategies but can also be used as a decision tool for testing policy scenarios, for sector monitoring, and for regional and project level analysis. In particular it could be used for modelling in economic terms the impact of animal diseases and of programmes designed to control them better.

The core model would represent a livestock system, defined as a herd (or flock or any other grouping) of a size corresponding to a typical production unit, and specified by suitable animal production parameters. Production systems are represented by production-unit/farm models defined as a linear combination of livestock systems and other activities (e.g. crop cultivation, non-farm activities). A region, a development programme or the entire livestock sector of a country is then represented as a linear combination of production units.

It is proposed that the system, at least in its initial version, would be based on simple deterministic cost–benefit analysis models; in other words, the user is responsible for determining the value of the parameters (e.g. milk production per lactation of a cow, yield of a crop), and the software merely compiles the data to produce results.

The DAMS approach aims to be a synthesis between the manipulation of non-typed variables and the detailed structuring of data found in other software. The idea is to structure the data in order to allow for maximum pre-definition of calculations and output tables, as well as to provide for mechanisms that would let the user specify additional calculations and define the format of customised reports (tables). The number of data types is kept relatively limited by combining generic and specific data structures in order to provide maximum power and flexibility. The DAMS would offer two specialised data structures to handle livestock models (herd and feed) plus two primary generic data structures (data object types), called commodity and plan, which are meant to be general enough to accommodate most basic analysis situations. At the lowest level, plans can be thought of as representing activities as a combination of herds, feed and commodities produced or consumed. These activities can in turn be combined linearly into higher-level plans. For example, one can define a farm model as a plan comprising herd and crop plans, and a given sector, region or project as a plan composed of farm plans. The plan is thus the structure that represents a particular model. Calculations will be performed and reports produced for a given plan. In addition, DAMS would offer additional generic data structures to handle investments and credit, to schedule the different components of a plan, to calculate sub-totals and explore alternative scenarios, and would also offer mechanisms to specify user-defined calculations and to produce summary tables and user-defined reports.

Figure 2 presents a very simple example of the way data can be structured to define crop budgets, farm models and the entire study area.

If for example one wants to use the system to model the impact of FMD in a country where the disease is endemic, the steps would be as follows:

a) first identify all stakeholders, and in particular identify representative production or farm models, ideally by drawing on recent surveys and national statistics that indicate the typology of production systems;

b) each model would eventually be represented in DAMS, and for each model a weighting parameter would be estimated, so that the weighted sum of the models would give total values (e.g. herd size, milk production) for the study area;

c) each model corresponds to a projection into the future of what is likely to happen in a 'normal' situation in the absence of specific events or programmes;

d) an FMD outbreak would be simulated by modifying the parameters of a herd model to represent the impact of the disease on mortality or fertility; the weighting parameters of such modified models would be derived from available epidemiological data on the frequency of outbreaks. The dynamic nature of the herd models would be a major improvement over traditional 'static' models, as it would show that perturbations in the herd caused by the outbreak extend well beyond the year of the event;

e) a second set of models would represent what would happen if a better control programme were put in place. A higher vaccination coverage could be expected to result

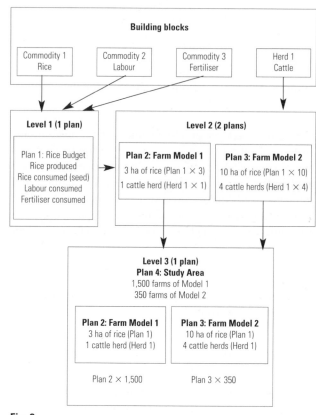

Fig. 2

Multipurpose agricultural data analysis and modelization system (DAMS) data structure: simple example of the way data can be structured to define crop budgets, farm models and an entire study area

in a lower frequency of outbreaks, as well as in less severe impacts at the level of individual outbreaks (lower mortality and less loss of fertility);

f) the difference between the cost and benefit flows corresponding to the two sets of projections would give an estimate of the returns from the control programme.

Overall, the proposed system should be able to deal with the following:

– herd model (static or demographic) and feed balance

– other activities model (e.g. crops, support services)

– production system/farm/enterprise model/product line analysis/regional or national level analysis

– financing, debt service, cash flow and other financial analysis

– poverty indicators

– financial versus economic pricing

Rev. sci. tech. Off. int. Epiz., **25** (2)

709

– variability, vulnerability/resilience of production systems

– 'what-if' scenarios

– investment return analysis (present value, internal rate of return).

Obviously the availability of the right tool is of no use if sufficient data is not available, so countries might also need to improve their statistical systems and strengthen their capacity to carry out surveys and analyse survey data. Guidelines and computer software would also be required for that purpose, but the inventory of what is already available is beyond the scope of this paper.

More information on the ALive initiative, including the draft specifications of DAMS, can be found at their website (www.alive-online.org).

Case study on food-safety-related disease control as a global public good

In order to go beyond what can be achieved by the kind of analysis presented in the above section, one should look at the rationale for viewing the control of food-safety-related disease as a global public good. This could be considered through one or more case studies that would look at the rationale, technical feasibility and economic justification of global or regional programmes to control specific diseases that draw their main justification from a decrease in the risks of new crises in Europe, the USA or worldwide. Possible candidates could be a global programme for the elimination of FMD, or the control of HPAI in countries where it is endemic or pandemic.

Let us take the case of FMD as an example. The initial process is not that different from the one at national level. It would involve assessing:

– what is currently known of the epidemiology of the disease

– whether it is possible to achieve consensus on the technical approach (i.e. vaccination versus culling)

– whether it is realistic to expect that the probability of success of a control programme can be reasonably estimated

– whether the impact on livestock productivity at national level would be a sufficient incentive for affected countries to undertake the programme, even assuming they get financing and technical assistance from outside, or whether something more would be needed (as a comparison, the interest of the rich world in protecting biodiversity in developing countries has translated into the establishment of the Global Environment Facility)

– what approach would be used to quantify benefits at the global level.

The donor community, possibly with the OIE taking the lead, should establish a working group of carefully selected experts and ask them, as a first step, to carry out a theoretical analysis of the kind outlined above, using readily available information. If the outcome is convincing enough, it would provide the rationale and justification for mobilising more resources and launching whatever activities would be required to move from theory to reality and prepare fully fledged feasibility studies.

710

Rev. sci. tech. Off. int. Epiz., **25** (2)

Mesures sanitaires et phytosanitaires et sécurité sanitaire des aliments : enjeux et opportunités pour les pays en développement

M. Siméon

Résumé

En raison de l'augmentation rapide de la demande, les marchés d'exportation peuvent absorber des produits à fortes valeur ajoutée et rentabilité ; pour de nombreux pays en développement, augmenter les exportations est donc un moyen essentiel de générer des revenus pour le secteur rural et d'y favoriser la croissance.

Bien que les marchés d'exportation imposent aux pays en développement des normes sanitaires et phytosanitaires de plus en plus rigoureuses, ceux-ci peuvent conserver et améliorer leur accès à ces marchés (et améliorer en même temps l'inocuité des aliments vendus localement et la productivité du secteur agroalimentaire) en adoptant une approche stratégique intégrant à la fois la sécurité sanitaire des aliments, la qualité sanitaire des productions agricoles et le commerce. Les pays à revenu élevé devraient intensifier l'aide au développement afin d'aider les pays en développement à renforcer leurs capacités de planification et de mise en œuvre des stratégies nécessaires.

La première proposition avancée par l'auteur consiste à diffuser parmi les parties prenantes deux séries de lignes directrices déjà existantes, en particulier par l'intermédiaire de la Banque mondiale et de l'Organisation mondiale de la santé animale (OIE). La première série de lignes directrices concerne les processus d'évaluation des problèmes, d'élaboration de stratégies et de formulation de plans d'action. La deuxième série concerne l'analyse institutionnelle et la formation du personnel des services officiels de police sanitaire.

En second lieu, l'auteur propose que les pays intéressés et les organisations donatrices progressent dans l'élaboration de lignes directrices, d'outils progiciels et de matériel didactique afin d'aider les pays à quantifier l'ampleur et l'impact des questions liées à la sécurité sanitaire des aliments. L'emphase est mise sur un « système pluri-fonctionnel d'analyse des données agricoles et de modélisation ».

La troisième proposition consiste à réaliser une étude de cas visant à démontrer qu'il conviendrait d'aborder certaines questions zoosanitaires liées à la sécurité sanitaire des aliments en les rattachant à la notion de « bien public international », ce qui suppose d'admettre qu'elles requièrent une intervention à l'échelle mondiale. Deux problèmes pourraient d'ores et déjà relever de cette approche, à savoir la fièvre aphteuse et l'influenza aviaire hautement pathogène.

Mots-clés

Accès au marché – Analyse sectorielle – Ligne directrice – Modélisation – Stratégie sectorielle.

■

Rev. sci. tech. Off. int. Epiz., **25** (2)

711

Medidas sanitarias y fitosanitarias e inocuidad de los alimentos: desafíos y oportunidades para los países en desarrollo

M. Siméon

Resumen

Habida cuenta del rápido crecimiento de la demanda, los mercados de exportación pueden absorber productos de gran valor añadido y ofrecer un elevado rendimiento. Para muchos países en desarrollo, ampliar los mercados de exportación es pues un requisito clave para lograr que el medio rural genere ingresos y entre en la senda del crecimiento.

Aunque los mercados de exportación imponen reglas sanitarias y fitosanitarias cada vez más estrictas a los países en desarrollo, éstos pueden mantener y mejorar su acceso a esos mercados (y a la vez mejorar la inocuidad de los alimentos y la productividad agrícola en su propio territorio) trabajando estratégicamente sobre las cuestiones de la inocuidad, la sanidad agropecuaria y el comercio. Los países de elevado nivel de renta deben incrementar sus actividades de asistencia para ayudar a que los países en desarrollo adquieran la capacidad de planificar y aplicar las estrategias necesarias.

La primera propuesta que el autor formula consiste en dar amplia difusión a los dos conjuntos de directrices existentes, en particular a través del Banco Mundial y la Organización Mundial de Sanidad Animal (OIE), para hacerlos llegar a todas las partes interesadas. El primer conjunto se refiere al proceso general de evaluar problemas, concebir estrategias y formular planes de acción; el segundo trata del análisis de instituciones y la formación del personal de los servicios oficiales de control sanitario.

La segunda propuesta es que los países y donantes interesados incrementen el ritmo actual de producción de directrices, aplicaciones y programas informáticos y material didáctico para ayudar a los países a valorar cuantitativamente la importancia y las repercusiones de los problemas de inocuidad. A este respecto, el autor pone el acento en un 'sistema polivalente de análisis de datos y elaboración de modelos agrícolas'.

La tercera propuesta consiste en realizar un estudio de caso que ayude a demostrar que hay una serie de problemas zoosanitarios ligados a la inocuidad de los alimentos que conviene considerar temas de 'interés público mundial', merecedores por lo tanto de una intervención a escala planetaria (dos enfermedades en las que podría centrarse el estudio son la fiebre aftosa y la influenza aviar altamente patógena).

Palabras clave

Acceso al mercado – Análisis por sectores – Directriz – Elaboración de modelos – Estrategia sectorial.

References

1. Acar J.F. & Moulin G. (2006). – Antimicrobial resistance at farm level. *In* Animal production food safety challenges in global markets. *Rev. sci. tech. Off. int. Epiz.*, **25** (2), 775-792.

2. Barbet A., Cardinale E., Thonnat J., Mallet E., Vareille S. & Ehret P. (2003). – Formation des personnels des services officiels de contrôle sanitaire des pays en développement. Centre de coopération internationale en recherche agronomique pour le développement, Montpellier.

3. Droppers W.F.G.L. (2006). – OIE philosophy, policy and procedures for the development of food safety standards. *In* Animal production food safety challenges in global markets. *Rev. sci. tech. Off. int. Epiz.*, **25** (2), 805-812.

4. Jaffee S. (ed.) (2005). – Food safety and agricultural health standards: challenges and opportunities for developing country exports. World Bank Report No. 31207, 10 January. World Bank, Washington, DC.

5. McKenzie A.I. & Hathaway S.C. (2006). – The role and functionality of Veterinary Services in food safety throughout the food chain. *In* Animal production food safety challenges in global markets. *Rev. sci. tech. Off. int. Epiz.*, **25** (2), 837-848.

6. Schnöller A. (2006). – Pautas para los procedimientos de inspección en animales y carnes en un matadero [Guidelines for animal and meat inspection procedures in the slaughterhouse]. *In* Animal production food safety challenges in global markets. *Rev. sci. tech. Off. int. Epiz.*, **25** (2), 849-860.

7. Siméon M. (2005). – Multipurpose agricultural data analysis and modelization system (DAMS): draft functional specifications. ALive report, June. Available at www.Alive-online.org.

8. Slorach S.A. (2006). – Assuring food safety: the complementary tasks and standards of the World Organisation for Animal Health and the Codex Alimentarius Commission. *In* Animal production food safety challenges in global markets. *Rev. sci. tech. Off. int. Epiz.*, **25** (2), 813-821.

9. Smelt A., Achterbosch T., Aalberts C., Löffler H., Merx R. & van Vugt F. (2003). – Guidelines for food safety, SPS and trade. Report to the World Bank. Wageningen University and Research Centre (Wageningen UR), the Netherlands.

10. Unnevehr L. & Hirschhorn N. (2000). – Food safety issues in the developing world. World Bank Technical Paper No. 469, May. World Bank, Washington, DC.

11. World Organisation for Animal Health (OIE) Animal Production Food Safety Working Group (2006). – Guide to good farming practices for animal production food safety. *In* Animal production food safety challenges in global markets. *Rev. sci. tech. Off. int. Epiz.*, **25** (2), 823-826.

Rev. sci. tech. Off. int. Epiz., 2006, **25** (2), 713-737

Organisation et fonctionnement des Services vétérinaires : bilan d'une enquête réalisée auprès des Pays Membres de l'Organisation mondiale de la santé animale en 2005

J.J. Bénet [1], B. Dufour [1] & V. Bellemain [2]

(1) École nationale vétérinaire d'Alfort, 7 avenue du Général de Gaulle, 94704 Maisons-Alfort Cedex, France
(2) École nationale des services vétérinaires, Centre collaborateur de l'OIE pour la formation des vétérinaires officiels, 1 avenue Bourgelat, 69280 Marcy-l'Étoile, France

Résumé
Un questionnaire a été diffusé aux 167 Pays Membres de l'Organisation mondiale de la santé animale (OIE) en 2004 et 2005. L'organisation et le fonctionnement des Services vétérinaires ont pu être analysés à partir des réponses de 85 de ces pays. Au-delà de la variabilité nationale, les Services vétérinaires sont très généralement impliqués dans le contrôle de la sécurité sanitaire au niveau de l'élevage (y compris l'alimentation animale), de la première et de la deuxième transformation, seuls ou en partage avec d'autres services ; les compétences sont davantage partagées en aval, notamment pour la distribution et la restauration. Les Services vétérinaires assument une responsabilité centrale lors des échanges internationaux d'animaux comme de produits. Les principaux points faibles de la chaîne de contrôle sanitaire se situent au niveau des moyens logistiques et financiers des services, ainsi que de l'implication des éleveurs, voire des vétérinaires de terrain. Les réformes récentes, nombreuses, tendent à améliorer la cohérence d'une approche intégrée des contrôles sanitaires, de l'étable à la table.

Mots-clés
Chaîne alimentaire – Enquête – Organisation mondiale de la santé animale – Pays Membre – Sécurité sanitaire des aliments – Service vétérinaire.

Introduction

L'Organisation mondiale de la santé animale (OIE) accorde une importance croissante aux capacités des Services vétérinaires de ses Pays Membres. C'est en effet sur eux que reposent la qualité des informations sanitaires collectées par l'OIE, la mise en œuvre des normes sanitaires internationales, la sécurité sanitaire du commerce des animaux et de leurs produits et, d'une façon plus générale, la déclinaison nationale des travaux de l'Organisation.

La sécurité sanitaire a évolué, ou évolue, vers une approche intégrée sur l'ensemble de la chaîne de production des aliments, de l'étable à la table – ou de la fourche à la fourchette. L'action des Services vétérinaires s'appréhende dans ce nouveau contexte.

Lors de la 21e Conférence de la Commission régionale de l'OIE pour l'Europe, en septembre 2004, une communication sur la « structure et l'organisation des Services vétérinaires pour mettre en œuvre le concept de l'étable à la table » (1) avait été présentée. Le rapport de ce thème technique s'était appuyé sur un questionnaire diffusé aux Délégués des 50 Pays Membres d'Europe, auquel 31 d'entre eux avaient répondu.

L'intérêt des informations recueillies a amené à étendre l'étude au niveau mondial et à en approfondir l'analyse.

714

Rev. sci. tech. Off. int. Epiz., **25** (2)

Le questionnaire a été adressé par l'OIE aux Délégués des 136 Pays Membres qui n'y avaient pas encore répondu (167 Pays Membres moins 31 réponses déjà collectées en Europe), en juillet 2005.

Les réponses de 85 pays (31 pour le premier envoi, 54 pour le second, liste en Annexe 1) ont été recueillies et analysées, notamment en comparant les réponses des pays en développement (PED) et celles des pays développés (PD).

Matériels et méthodes

Un questionnaire (Annexe 2), élaboré par les auteurs en 2004, a été adressé par le Directeur général de l'OIE aux Délégués des 167 Pays Membres de l'Organisation, par courrier papier et électronique, en deux phases. Les 50 pays de la Commission régionale de l'OIE pour l'Europe ont reçu le questionnaire en 2004 ; tous les autres Pays Membres, ainsi que les pays européens n'ayant pas répondu en 2004, ont été sollicités en juillet 2005, avec un rappel en octobre.

Le questionnaire, élaboré en français, avait été traduit en anglais et en espagnol, et chaque pays a pu le recevoir dans celle de ces trois langues officielles de l'OIE lui correspondant le mieux.

Le questionnaire comprenait 22 questions fermées et une question ouverte finale. Certaines questions fermées comportaient plusieurs sous-parties et plusieurs items possibles pour chaque réponse.

Les sujets abordés visaient à décrire et à évaluer l'organisation des contrôles sanitaires sur l'ensemble de la chaîne de production des aliments, de l'étable à la table, en abordant plus précisément :

– l'importance économique des productions animales,

– l'organisation des Services sanitaires centraux, territoriaux et de terrain,

– l'organisation de l'analyse des risques sanitaires,

– la répartition des compétences et des responsabilités entre les différents services potentiellement impliqués,

– la coordination entre les différentes administrations impliquées,

– les participations aux travaux des instances internationales,

– les réorganisations récentes ou envisagées,

– les effectifs et l'implication des différents acteurs,

– une auto-évaluation générale de satisfaction,

– le rôle de l'OIE.

Toutes les réponses reçues avant le 6 décembre 2005 ont été analysées. La saisie et les traitements des données ont été effectués à l'aide du logiciel Sphinx Lexica (version 4.5).

La classification retenue par la Conférence des Nations Unies sur le commerce et le développement (CNUCED) pour le Programme spécial en faveur des pays les moins avancés (3) a permis de ventiler les pays en PD et PED.

Les résultats sont présentés avec les effectifs observés, accompagnés des pourcentages correspondants lorsque les effectifs le permettaient.

Les comparaisons entre groupes ont été réalisées grâce au test de chi carré de Pearson, ou, si besoin, le test exact de Fisher, en retenant un seuil de signification de 5 %.

Résultats commentés

Les réponses au questionnaire reçues de 85 pays ont été analysées, ce qui correspond à un Pays Membre de l'OIE sur deux. Néanmoins, la plupart des questionnaires présentaient des non-réponses à certaines questions, ce qui explique qu'il est rare que l'analyse porte sur 85 pays répondeurs. Quand les chiffres sont présentés, le nombre de pays répondeurs est donc systématiquement indiqué.

Répartition des pays répondeurs

Le Tableau I et la Figure 1 présentent la répartition des pays répondeurs en fonction de leur niveau de développement (d'après la classification de l'Organisation des Nations Unies) et de leur situation géographique (d'après la classification de l'OIE).

Les pays d'Europe ont été beaucoup plus nombreux à répondre, du fait vraisemblablement d'une sollicitation plus intense (premier questionnaire en 2004, puis deux envois en 2005). Les PED ont été proportionnellement un peu moins nombreux que les PD à renseigner le questionnaire, sans que l'écart soit toutefois significatif, et sans doute en lien avec le fait que les PED sont beaucoup moins nombreux en Europe.

Certains pays faisant l'objet d'un classement par l'OIE dans deux régions, en raison soit de leur étendue, soit de la dispersion de certaines parties de leur territoire, soit de leur position intermédiaire au plan géographique, pour le Moyen-Orient et l'Asie en particulier, il a été choisi de les classer selon une cohérence géographique, et non politique.

Rev. sci. tech. Off. int. Epiz., **25** (2)

715

Tableau I
Nombre de pays sollicités et ayant répondu, dans les délais permettant l'analyse, au questionnaire sur l'organisation des Services vétérinaires

Région	Pays en développement		Pays développés		Total	
	Sollicités	Répondeurs	Sollicités	Répondeurs	Sollicités	Répondeurs
Afrique	34	11	15	8	49	19
Amériques	8	4	20	11	28	15
Asie	10	6	18	7	28	13
Europe	3	3	46	33	49	36
Moyen-Orient	1	0	12	2	13	2
Total	**56**	**24**	**111**	**61**	**167**	**85**

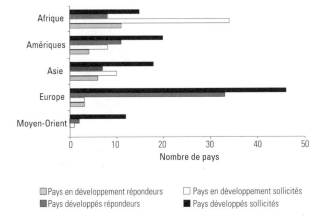

Fig. 1
Pays sollicités et ayant répondu au questionnaire sur l'organisation des Services vétérinaires, par région et niveau de développement

Importance économique des productions animales

Le poids économique de l'élevage était assez important ou important pour la plupart des pays répondeurs (70/84, soit 83 %). Par ailleurs, une différence est apparue entre les PED et les PD sur l'importance économique des industries agroalimentaires, qui était significativement plus marquée pour les PD (55 pays sur 64, soit 86 %) que pour les PED (12 pays sur 21, soit environ 57 %).

D'une façon générale, le poids économique de l'élevage était corrélé positivement de façon significative à celui des industries agroalimentaires : sur 83 répondants, il était important dans ces deux domaines pour 62 pays et faible pour 9 d'entre eux.

Organisation des services centraux, territoriaux et de terrain

Dans la majorité des cas (70/84, soit 83 %) et de manière identique pour les PED et les PD, les Services vétérinaires

dépendaient du ministère de l'agriculture. Le ministère de la santé apparaissait comme le deuxième ministère de rattachement des Services vétérinaires. Il est à noter que, dans deux pays, les Services vétérinaires étaient directement rattachés au Premier Ministre.

Le nom de l'Administration vétérinaire différait selon qu'il s'agissait de PED ou de PD. Pour tous les pays, le mot « vétérinaire » était le plus fréquemment cité ; c'était le cas pour 48 pays sur 85 (56 %), respectivement 14 PED (sur 21) et 34 PD (sur 64). Les PED mettaient ensuite l'accent, principalement, sur l'élevage (11/21) ; de façon beaucoup moins fréquente, apparaissaient les termes de santé (2), inspection (1), animal (1), agriculture (1), publique (1). Pour les PD, les termes les plus cités après vétérinaire étaient aliment ou alimentation (17/64) et santé (17) ; venaient ensuite animal (10), agriculture (8), inspection (7), sécurité (5), végétaux (5), élevage (4), qualité (3), consommateur (2), industrie (1), protection (1), publique (1).

Plusieurs questions visaient à évaluer le niveau de décentralisation des décisions et actions sanitaires. Pour la majorité des répondants (83), l'État gardait, en santé animale, la responsabilité de l'évaluation des risques (75, soit 90 %), l'élaboration de la réglementation (81, soit 98 %), la surveillance et le contrôle (71, soit 86 %) ; en sécurité sanitaire des aliments, l'évaluation des risques (71, soit 86 %), l'élaboration de la réglementation (78, soit 94 %) et la surveillance et le contrôle (64, soit 77 %). Seuls certains pays semblaient avoir mis en place une véritable décentralisation allant jusqu'à l'élaboration de la réglementation sanitaire (21, soit 33 %, en santé animale ; 18, soit 29 %, en sécurité sanitaire des aliments). Aucune différence significative n'a été notée sur ces différents points entre les PED et les PD.

Les Services vétérinaires de terrain étaient sous la responsabilité de l'État dans la majorité des pays répondeurs (80/85 soit 94 % des cas), sans distinction entre les PED et les PD. Par contre, 11 PD (sur 62, soit 13 %) (aucun PED) déclaraient que tout ou partie des

716

Rev. sci. tech. Off. int. Epiz., **25** (2)

Services vétérinaires de terrain étaient placés sous la responsabilité d'une agence.

Organisation de l'analyse des risques sanitaires

Cinquante-huit des 81 pays répondeurs (72 %) (sans différence entre les PD et les PED) ont indiqué que l'analyse des risques sanitaires était réalisée par différentes organisations, seulement 23 pays (28 %) déclarant avoir une organisation unique. Les organisations citées relevaient du ministère de l'agriculture (55 pays, soit 68 %) puis du ministère de la santé (12 pays, soit 15 %, dont les quatre pays pour lesquels le ministère de la santé était responsable de l'Administration centrale vétérinaire) et, beaucoup plus rarement, du ministère de l'économie (deux pays, pour lesquels ce ministère était également responsable de l'Administration centrale vétérinaire). Cinq pays

disposaient d'une agence indépendante par rapport aux Services vétérinaires.

Quarante-deux pays sur 79 répondeurs (53 %) ont indiqué qu'un document préconise ou favorise une approche intégrée « de l'étable à la table » pour l'application des mesures de sécurité sanitaire des aliments. Bien que la différence ne soit pas significative, les PED étaient proportionnellement moins nombreux que les PD à disposer d'un tel document.

Répartition des compétences et des responsabilités entre les différents services

Le Tableau II et la Figure 2 présentent l'implication des Services vétérinaires dans les différentes activités liées à la santé animale (identification des animaux, prophylaxies,

Tableau II
Responsabilités des activités concernant la santé animale : assumées par les Services vétérinaires (SV) seuls, en partage avec d'autres services ou exclusivement par d'autres services

Activité	Responsabilité			
	SV seuls	SV et autres services	Autres services seuls	Total
Identification	40 (51 %)	35 (45 %)	3 (4 %)	78 (100 %)
Prophylaxies	57 (70 %)	23 (28 %)	2 (2 %)	82 (100 %)
Police sanitaire	65 (78 %)	18 (22 %)	0	83 (100 %)
Laboratoire en santé animale	53 (64 %)	26 (31 %)	4 (5 %)	83 (100 %)
Certification à l'exportation d'animaux vivants	77 (93 %)	6 (7 %)	0	83 (100 %)
Contrôle à l'importation d'animaux vivants	70 (85 %)	11 (13 %)	1 (2 %)	82 (100 %)
Traçabilité des animaux	52 (65 %)	26 (32 %)	2 (3 %)	80 (100 %)

Les nombres correspondent au nombre de pays ayant répondu à la question, et les pourcentages sont établis par rapport à ce nombre

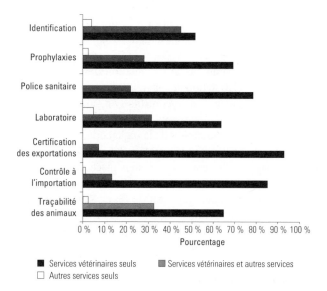

Fig. 2
Responsabilités des activités concernant la santé animale, par services

police sanitaire, traçabilité des animaux, laboratoire, certificats à l'exportation, contrôle à l'importation).

Sans surprise, les Services vétérinaires étaient très impliqués dans ces activités, dont ils étaient, dans la majorité des pays, seuls responsables (écart significatif par rapport à un taux d'indifférence supposée de 50 %). Seule l'identification des animaux était aussi souvent sous la responsabilité exclusive des Services vétérinaires que partagée avec d'autres services.

Le Tableau III et la Figure 3 présentent l'implication des Services vétérinaires dans des activités en relation avec la sécurité et l'hygiène des aliments.

Les Services vétérinaires étaient moins impliqués, seuls, dans les activités de sécurité sanitaire des aliments que dans les activités de santé animale (Tableau II) ; pour beaucoup de segments, ils partageaient en effet cette responsabilité avec d'autres acteurs. Ils étaient toutefois largement dominants pour la certification à l'exportation

Rev. sci. tech. Off. int. Epiz., **25** (2)

717

Tableau III
Responsabilités des activités concernant la sécurité des denrées animales et d'origine animale (DAOA) : assumées par les Services vétérinaires (SV) seuls, en partage avec d'autres services ou exclusivement par d'autres services

Activité	Responsabilité			
	SV seuls	SV et autres services	Autres services seuls	Total
Abattoir	48 (59 %)	29 (36 %)	4 (5 %)	81 (100 %)
Traçabilité des aliments	16 (21 %)	51 (67 %)	9 (12 %)	76 (100 %)
Sécurité de la production de DAOA	37 (46 %)	36 (44 %)	8 (10 %)	81 (100 %)
Sécurité de la transformation	30 (37 %)	40 (49 %)	11 (14 %)	81 (100 %)
Sécurité du transport	35 (42 %)	34 (41 %)	14 (17 %)	83 (100 %)
Sécurité de l'entreposage	28 (35 %)	35 (43 %)	18 (22 %)	81 (100 %)
Sécurité de la distribution	27 (35 %)	25 (32 %)	26 (33 %)	78 (100 %)
Sécurité de la restauration	12 (15 %)	27 (35 %)	39 (50 %)	78 (100 %)
Certification à l'exportation de DAOA	65 (78 %)	17 (20 %)	1 (1 %)	83 (100 %)
Contrôle à l'importation de DAOA	54 (64 %)	28 (33 %)	2 (2 %)	84 (100 %)
Laboratoire d'hygiène des aliments	16 (19 %)	58 (69 %)	10 (12 %)	84 (100 %)

Les nombres correspondent au nombre de pays ayant répondu à la question, et les pourcentages sont établis par rapport à ce nombre

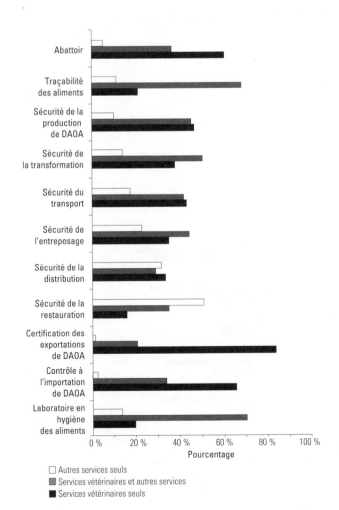

□ Autres services seuls
▓ Services vétérinaires et autres services
■ Services vétérinaires seuls

Fig. 3
Responsabilités des activités concernant la sécurité des denrées animales et d'origine animale (DAOA), par services

des denrées d'origine animale (65/83, soit 78 %) et pour leur contrôle à l'importation (54/82, soit 64 %).

Inversement, les Services vétérinaires n'avaient aucune responsabilité dans la sécurité et le contrôle de la distribution dans 26 pays (33 %) et de la restauration dans 39 (50 %) des 78 pays pour lesquels une réponse a été obtenue à ces questions.

Les différences observées entre les PED et les PD ne sont pas significatives, excepté au stade de la distribution, où les Services vétérinaires des PED étaient significativement moins impliqués que ceux des PD.

Le Tableau IV et la Figure 4 présentent l'implication des Services vétérinaires dans des activités liées à l'alimentation animale et aux médicaments vétérinaires.

Les activités liées à l'alimentation animale et au médicament étaient aussi fréquemment sous la responsabilité des Services vétérinaires seuls qu'en partage avec d'autres services. Les Services vétérinaires n'avaient aucune responsabilité en alimentation animale dans 22 % (production) à 33 % (distribution) des pays. Pour les médicaments, si d'autres services étaient seuls responsables de la production dans 21 % des pays, les Services vétérinaires étaient presque toujours en charge du contrôle de leur utilisation – ce qui est cohérent avec la présence de ces services au niveau des élevages.

Le Tableau V et la Figure 5 présentent l'implication des Services vétérinaires dans diverses autres activités.

Les Services vétérinaires étaient très impliqués dans le bien-être animal (dans 96 % des pays, dont 45 % où ils

718

Rev. sci. tech. Off. int. Epiz., **25** (2)

Tableau IV

Responsabilités des activités liées à l'alimentation animale et aux médicaments vétérinaires : assumées par les Services vétérinaires (SV) seuls, en partage avec d'autres services ou exclusivement par d'autres services

Activité	Responsabilité			
	SV seuls	SV et autres services	Autres services seuls	Total
Production de l'alimentation animale	31 (38 %)	32 (40 %)	18 (22 %)	81 (100 %)
Distribution des aliments pour animaux	27 (35 %)	25 (32 %)	26 (33 %)	78 (100 %)
Fabrication d'aliments à la ferme	28 (35 %)	31 (39 %)	20 (25 %)	79 (100 %)
Production de médicaments	34 (44 %)	27 (35 %)	16 (21 %)	77 (100 %)
Distribution des médicaments	39 (48 %)	31 (38 %)	12 (15 %)	82 (100 %)
Utilisation des médicaments	46 (56 %)	32 (39 %)	4 (5 %)	82 (100 %)

Les nombres correspondent au nombre de pays ayant répondu à la question, et les pourcentages sont établis par rapport à ce nombre

Tableau V

Responsabilités dans diverses activités : assumées par les Services vétérinaires (SV) seuls, en partage avec d'autres services ou exclusivement par d'autres services

Activité	Responsabilité			
	SV seuls	SV et autres services	Autres services seuls	Total
Bien-être animal	35 (45 %)	39 (51 %)	3 (4 %)	77 (100 %)
Animaux aquatiques	28 (36 %)	36 (47 %)	13 (17 %)	77 (100 %)
Protection des végétaux	10 (14 %)	12 (16 %)	52 (70 %)	74 (100 %)
Organismes génétiquement modifiés	11 (18 %)	24 (39 %)	27 (43 %)	62 (100 %)
Environnement	3 (4 %)	35 (42 %)	45 (54 %)	83 (100 %)

Les nombres correspondent au nombre de pays ayant répondu à la question, et les pourcentages sont établis par rapport à ce nombre

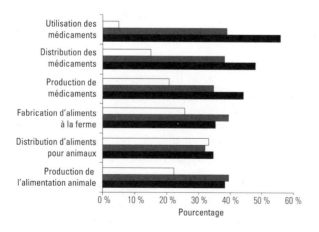

■ Services vétérinaires seuls
□ Autres services seuls
■ Services vétérinaires et autres services

Fig. 4

Responsabilités des activités liées à l'alimentation animale et aux médicaments vétérinaires, par services

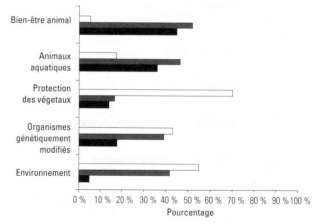

■ Services vétérinaires seuls
□ Autres services seuls
■ Services vétérinaires et autres services

Fig. 5

Responsabilités d'activités diverses (bien-être animal, animaux aquatiques, protection des végétaux, organismes génétiquement modifiés et environnement), par services

Rev. sci. tech. Off. int. Epiz., **25** (2)

719

étaient seuls responsables) et dans le contrôle sanitaire des animaux aquatiques (83 % des pays, dont 36 % où ils étaient seuls responsables). Logiquement, ils étaient plus rarement concernés par la protection des végétaux (30 %), les organismes génétiquement modifiés (OGM) (57 %) et l'environnement (46 %).

Les responsabilités des Services vétérinaires des PED étaient globalement moins diversifiées que dans les PD. La différence est significative entre ces deux catégories de pays pour les OGM et les animaux aquatiques. Ceci traduit vraisemblablement – et logiquement, une moindre préoccupation ou une moins grande activité des PED dans ces secteurs.

La Figure 6 reprend l'intégralité de ces données, organisée selon le concept de l'étable à la table, en distinguant les

secteurs suivants : l'amont (alimentation animale et médicament) ; l'élevage comprenant les différentes activités de santé animale, y compris celles relatives aux importations et exportations correspondantes, ainsi que les activités de contrôle indispensables (identification, traçabilité, laboratoire) ; la transformation, qui inclut l'abattoir et les différentes étapes de transformation ultérieures, qui sont en interface avec le secteur suivant, lequel réunit la distribution et la restauration. Les autres secteurs, qui sont collatéraux à cette perspective linéaire, sont placés à droite du schéma. La représentation fait appel au diagramme en ligne brisée, afin de faciliter la perception du rôle relatif de chaque acteur par rapport à la continuité conceptuelle examinée. Les symboles propres à chaque acteur sont en clair lorsque l'écart par rapport aux autres acteurs concernés par la comparaison n'est pas significatif et en noir lorsque cet écart est significatif.

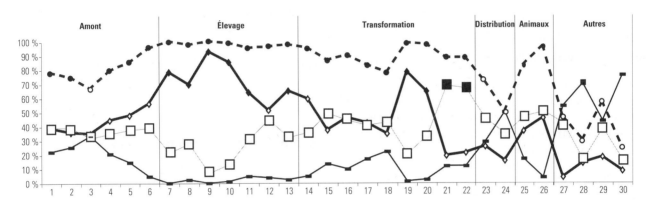

Amont
1. Aliments pour animaux : production
2. Aliments pour animaux : fabrication à la ferme
3. Aliments pour animaux : distribution
4. Médicaments : production
5. Médicaments : distribution
6. Médicaments : utilisation

Élevage
7. Police sanitaire
8. Prophylaxies
9. Certification des exportations : animaux vivants
10. Contrôle à l'importation : animaux vivants
11. Laboratoire en santé animale
12. Identification des animaux
13. Traçabilité des animaux

Transformation
14. Abattage
15. Denrées d'origine animale : transformation

16. Denrées d'origine animale : production
17. Denrées d'origine animale : transport
18. Denrées d'origine animale : entreposage
19. Certification des exportations de produits d'origine animale
20. Contrôle des importations de produits d'origine animale
21. Laboratoire en sécurité sanitaire des aliments
22. Traçabilité des aliments

Distribution
23. Denrées d'origine animale : distribution
24. Denrées d'origine animale : restauration

Animaux
25. Animaux aquatiques
26. Bien-être animal

Autres
27. Environnement
28. Protection des végétaux
29. Organismes génétiquement modifiés
30. Autres

◆ ◇ Services vétérinaires seuls responsables
(◆ écart significatif ; ◇ écart non significatif)

■ □ Services vétérinaires partageant la responsabilité avec d'autres services
(■ écart significatif ; □ écart non significatif)

■ – Autres services seuls responsables
(■ écart significatif ; – écart non significatif)

● ○ Cumul Services vétérinaires seuls ou partageant la responsabilité
(● écart significatif ; ○ écart non significatif)

Fig. 6
Distribution de fréquence des pays selon la répartition des compétences et des responsabilités au long de la chaîne de sécurité sanitaire des aliments

720

Rev. sci. tech. Off. int. Epiz., **25** (2)

Cette figure permet de souligner différents points. Tout d'abord, elle montre l'implication nettement majoritaire des Services vétérinaires, seuls, pour ce qui concerne directement l'animal (élevage, bien-être animal, animaux aquatiques), et la présence continue des Services vétérinaires, qu'ils fussent seuls responsables ou en association avec d'autres services, tout au long de la chaîne. Aux extrémités de la chaîne, l'implication des Services vétérinaires seuls était plus faible : alimentation animale, distribution et surtout restauration. La certification et le contrôle à l'importation sont des activités où les Services vétérinaires étaient fortement représentés, non seulement en ce qui concerne les animaux vivants, mais aussi pour les produits d'origine animale. Inversement, les activités de gestion de la qualité nécessaires à la sécurité (traçabilité, identification, laboratoire) étaient plus souvent partagées avec d'autres services, voire majoritairement confiées à d'autres services.

Coordination entre les différentes administrations

Les réponses portant sur les modalités de coordination entre les différentes administrations impliquées s'avérant délicates à interpréter sur le plan synthétique, seule la question concernant l'évaluation de la qualité de cette coordination a été analysée.

La qualité de la coordination a été jugée correcte par 55 des 62 PD répondeurs (89 %), seuls sept PD (11 %) l'estimant insuffisante ou à l'origine de graves dysfonctionnements.

Les PED apparaissaient moins satisfaits de la qualité de la coordination, puisque parmi eux plus de la moitié des répondeurs (11/20) l'estimaient insuffisante ou à l'origine de graves dysfonctionnements.

Sur 53 pays ayant répondu et pour lesquels l'Administration vétérinaire était sous tutelle du ministère de l'agriculture, 41 étaient satisfaits ou très satisfaits. Sur les 25 pour lesquels elle était sous une autre tutelle, 21 étaient également satisfaits. La différence n'est pas significative.

Participations aux travaux des instances internationales

Lorsqu'ils se sont prononcés sur la qualité de la coordination nationale pour préparer les travaux des instances internationales, les pays ont répondu très majoritairement (60/67, soit 90 %) qu'elle était bonne ou très bonne s'agissant des travaux de l'OIE. Les Services vétérinaires nationaux en étaient responsables, seuls ou en association avec d'autres instances, dans la grande majorité des cas (64/69, soit 93 %).

Pour ce qui concerne l'Organisation des Nations Unies pour l'agriculture et l'alimentation (FAO), la coordination nationale a été jugée d'assez bonne qualité (55/68, soit 81 %). Elle était assurée, majoritairement, soit par des services du ministère de l'agriculture (32/67, soit 48 %), soit par les Services vétérinaires (28/67, soit 42 %).

S'agissant de l'Organisation mondiale de la santé (OMS), la coordination a été jugée d'assez bonne qualité par 75 % des pays répondeurs (50/67). Ce sont les services en charge de la santé qui assuraient le plus souvent cette coordination (56/65, soit 86 %).

La proportion d'avis positifs est la même en ce qui concerne la coordination liée au Codex alimentarius (48/64, soit 75 %), dont la responsabilité était partagée au niveau national entre les services de santé (19/60, soit 32 %), les Services vétérinaires (17/60, soit 28 %), le ministère de l'agriculture (11/60, soit 18 %) et d'autres instances (13/60, soit 22 %).

Il conviendrait peut-être de vérifier si les appréciations émises signifient que la coordination était bien réalisée conformément à ce qui était prévu – ou si ce qui était prévu était satisfaisant.

Réorganisations récentes ou envisagées

Soixante-neuf des 82 pays répondeurs (soit 84 %, sans différence entre les PED et les PD) ont indiqué que l'organisation des services impliqués dans la sécurité sanitaire de la chaîne alimentaire « de l'étable à la table » a fait l'objet de réformes récentes (au cours des dix dernières années) ou que des réformes étaient en projet.

Dans la majorité des cas (42/59, soit 71 %), ces réformes visaient explicitement l'instauration d'une cohérence de l'approche sanitaire de l'étable à la table.

Implication des différents types d'acteurs

L'action sanitaire des services publics ne peut être efficace que si elle est adaptable, pour faire face aux crises éventuelles, et si elle est relayée par les différents acteurs du monde socioprofessionnel, éleveurs et vétérinaires de terrain en amont, professionnels de l'agroalimentaire en aval.

Possibilité de mobiliser des personnels complémentaires pour faire face à des crises de santé animale et à des crises de sécurité sanitaire des aliments

Le renforcement des équipes était envisagé dans au moins 80 % des pays aussi bien pour des crises de santé animale que pour des crises liées aux aliments, ce qui est cohérent

Rev. sci. tech. Off. int. Epiz., **25** (2)

721

avec la nécessité d'une réaction rapide, par exemple, lors de l'apparition d'une épizootie. La mobilisation d'étudiants vétérinaires apparaissait moins fréquente (environ 60 %) (Tableau VI).

Modalités de la participation des vétérinaires privés

Les vétérinaires privés participaient de manière variable aux activités placées sous la responsabilité des Services vétérinaires. Leur participation était assez générale pour la prophylaxie (67/85, soit 79 %), majoritairement grâce à un mandat sanitaire (44/67, soit 66 %) et, dans les autres cas, dans le cadre d'un contrat. Leur participation était plus restreinte dans les secteurs tels que la police sanitaire, l'abattoir, les zoonoses, le laboratoire et le bien-être animal, secteurs dans lesquels seulement 32 à 40 pays (38 % à 47 %, sur 85) déclaraient leur confier des tâches ; elle était encore moins fréquente pour la sécurité sanitaire des aliments (24 pays, soit 28 %) et les animaux aquatiques (22 pays, soit 26 %). Pour toutes ces activités, c'est le mandat sanitaire qui constituait la modalité dominante de sujétion des vétérinaires.

Aucune différence significative n'est à signaler entre les PD et les PED pour cette question (Tableau VII et Figure 7).

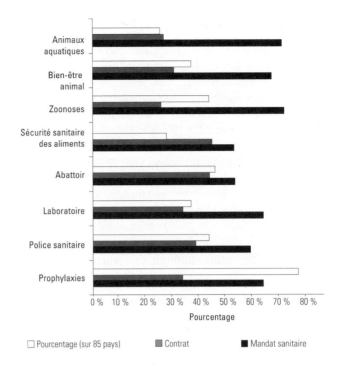

□ Pourcentage (sur 85 pays) ■ Contrat ■ Mandat sanitaire

Fig. 7
Participation des vétérinaires privés dans les différentes activités sanitaires

Tableau VI
Personnels additionnels pouvant être mobilisés en cas de crise sanitaire

Personnels mobilisés	Oui	Non	Total
Crises en santé animale			
Agents de sécurité sanitaire des aliments	67 (84 %)	13 (16 %)	80 (100 %)
Étudiants vétérinaires	43 (60 %)	29 (40 %)	72 (100 %)
Autres services	64 (84 %)	12 (16 %)	76 (100 %)
Autres	42 (86 %)	7 (14 %)	49 (100 %)
Crises en sécurité sanitaire des aliments			
Agents de santé animale	71 (90 %)	8 (10 %)	79 (100 %)
Étudiants vétérinaires	38 (53 %)	34 (47 %)	72 (100 %)
Autres services	60 (80 %)	15 (20 %)	75 (100 %)
Autres	51 (71 %)	21 (29 %)	72 (100 %)

Les nombres correspondent au nombre de pays ayant répondu à la question, et les pourcentages sont établis par rapport à ce nombre

Tableau VII
Mode de participation des vétérinaires privés dans les différentes activités sanitaires

Activité	Mandat sanitaire [a]		Contrat [b]		Total	Pourcentage (sur 85)
Prophylaxies	44	(66 %)	23	(34 %)	67	79 %
Police sanitaire	23	(61 %)	15	(39 %)	38	45 %
Laboratoire	21	(66 %)	11	(34 %)	32	38 %
Abattoir	22	(55 %)	18	(45 %)	40	47 %
Sécurité sanitaire des aliments	13	(54 %)	11	(46 %)	24	28 %
Zoonoses	28	(74 %)	10	(26 %)	38	45 %
Bien-être	22	(69 %)	10	(31 %)	32	38 %
Animaux aquatiques	16	(73 %)	6	(27 %)	22	26 %

a) mandat sanitaire : ce terme désigne le contrat entre l'administration et le vétérinaire privé, qui confie à ce dernier des missions permanentes (surveillance sanitaire, intervention en cas d'épizootie, etc.)
b) contrat : ce terme désigne les vétérinaires privés, salariés de l'administration à temps partiel

722

Rev. sci. tech. Off. int. Epiz., **25** (2)

Implication des éleveurs

Les liens avec les éleveurs apparaissaient, globalement, insuffisamment formalisés, eu égard à l'importance de leur rôle en santé animale. Les éleveurs avaient des responsabilités sanitaires réglementaires dans 65 pays sur 83 (78 %), avec une différence significative entre PD (86 %) et PED (55 %). Mais le taux de pays disposant d'organisations d'éleveurs interlocutrices de l'administration était faible (60 % environ), sans différence significative entre PD et PED. La formalisation de partenariats avec ces organisations n'était pas systématique, même dans les PD (59 %), et peu fréquente dans les PED (3/20, soit 15 %) (Tableau VIII).

Implication des professionnels de l'agroalimentaire

La plupart des pays, qu'ils soient développés ou en développement, confiaient par voie réglementaire des responsabilités aux professionnels de l'agroalimentaire dans le domaine de la maîtrise de la qualité de produits fournis (67/78, soit 86 %). Dans les PD, les industries agro-alimentaires étaient significativement plus organisées que dans les PED (Tableau IX).

Auto-évaluation générale de satisfaction

Chaque répondant a évalué les points forts et les points faibles de l'organisation visant à assurer la sécurité sanitaire de la filière de production, à partir d'une liste de 19 items, qui ont permis d'établir un score par pays (Fig. 8).

Le code utilisé dans le questionnaire allait de – – (aspect insuffisant) à ++ (point fort), ce qui a été transformé pour le traitement en notes allant de –2 (– –) à +2 (++). Le score était constitué de la somme algébrique des 19 notes obtenues aux 19 questions. Les PED avaient un score moyen de 0, les PD de 16, les valeurs étant dans tous les cas relativement dispersées.

Tableau VIII

Modalités d'implication des éleveurs dans les décisions et actions sanitaires

Modalité	Pays en développement			Pays développés			Total
	Oui	Non	Total	Oui	Non	Total	
Responsabilité réglementaire *	11 (55 %)	9 (45 %)	20	54 (86 %)	9 (14 %)	63	83
Existence d'une organisation d'éleveurs	12 (60 %)	8 (40 %)	20	39 (62 %)	24 (38 %)	63	83
Partenariats formalisés avec les Services vétérinaires *	3 (15 %)	17 (85 %)	20	36 (59 %)	25 (41 %)	61	81

* écart significatif entre les pays développés et les pays en développement

Tableau IX

Implication des professionnels de l'agroalimentaire dans la sécurité sanitaire

Modalité	Pays en développement			Pays développés			Total
	Oui	Non	Total	Oui	Non	Total	
Responsabilité réglementaire	14 (74 %)	5 (26 %)	19	53 (90 %)	6 (10 %)	59	78
Existence d'une organisation *	5 (28 %)	13 (72 %)	18	41 (71 %)	17 (29 %)	58	76

* écart significatif entre les pays développés et les pays en développement

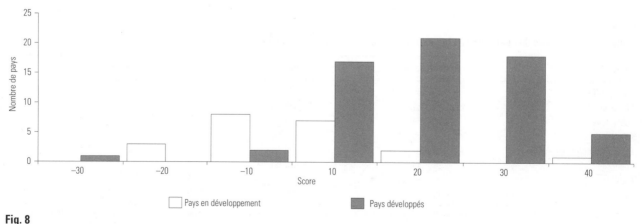

Fig. 8

Distribution des pays en développement et des pays développés selon leur score à l'auto-évaluation générale

Rev. sci. tech. Off. int. Epiz., **25** (2)

723

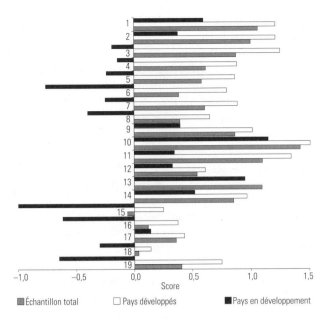

1. Organisation générale
2. Lisibilité des missions des Services vétérinaires
3. Indépendance des Services vétérinaires
4. Cohérence de la chaîne de décision
5. Circulation de l'information
6. Articulation évaluation / gestion des risques
7. Coordination entre acteurs
8. Traçabilité
9. Efficacité en action de routine
10. Réactivité en cas de crise en santé animale
11. Réactivité en cas de crise alimentaire
12. Moyens humains
13. Qualification des vétérinaires officiels
14. Qualification des autres agents des Services vétérinaires
15. Moyens logistiques et financiers
16. Implication des vétérinaires privés
17. Organisation des éleveurs
18. Qualification des éleveurs
19. Responsabilisation des industriels

Fig. 9
Score moyen aux questions relatives à l'appréciation générale, pour l'échantillon total, les pays en développement et les pays développés

La Figure 9 illustre les scores moyens par questions, en distinguant la totalité de l'échantillon, PED et PD. Le score maximal est de 2.

Seule la réactivité en cas de crise en santé animale (score 1,4) approchait la valeur seuil de 1,6, correspondant à 80 % de la note maximale pour l'ensemble de l'échantillon, ce qui peut être considéré comme satisfaisant.

Le seuil, beaucoup moins ambitieux, d'un score atteignant 50 % de la valeur maximale (c'est-à-dire la valeur 1) était atteint pour d'autres items, dont l'organisation générale (1,1), la lisibilité des missions des Services vétérinaires (1,0), la réactivité en cas de crise alimentaire (1,1) et la qualification des vétérinaires officiels (1,1).

Si nous considérons comme faible un score inférieur ou égal à 40 % de la valeur maximale (0,8), les items suivants constituaient des points faibles pour l'ensemble de l'échantillon : la cohérence de la chaîne de décision (0,6), la circulation de l'information (0,6), l'articulation entre l'évaluation et la gestion des risques (0,4), la coordination entre les acteurs (0,6), la traçabilité (0,4), les moyens humains (0,5), mais surtout l'implication des vétérinaires privés (0,1), l'organisation des éleveurs (0,4) et leur qualification (0,04), la responsabilisation des industriels (0,4) ainsi que, de façon criante, les moyens logistiques et financiers (– 0,1).

De façon significativement différente, les PD reconnaissaient comme points forts l'indépendance des services sanitaires (1,2), la cohérence de la chaîne de décision (0,9), la circulation de l'information (0,9), l'articulation entre l'évaluation et la gestion des risques (0,8), la coordination entre les acteurs (0,9), la traçabilité tout au long de la filière (0,65), la réactivité dans le cas de crise de sécurité sanitaire des aliments (1,5), la responsabilisation des industriels (0,75).

Ces mêmes points étaient reconnus par les PED comme autant de points de faiblesse, à l'exception de la réactivité en cas de crise alimentaire. La faiblesse des moyens logistiques et financiers, ainsi que le manque d'implication des vétérinaires privés, étaient significativement plus aigus pour les PED.

Rôle de l'Organisation mondiale de la santé animale

La presque totalité des répondants considérait que l'OIE pourrait apporter un appui à ses Pays Membres pour assurer une meilleure maîtrise de la sécurité des aliments d'origine animale, dans le domaine de l'organisation des services publics, en :

– organisant des séminaires de réflexion et d'échange au niveau régional ou mondial (78/80) ;

– sensibilisant les décideurs politiques (75/79) ;

– développant des approches communes avec l'OMS, la FAO et le Codex alimentarius sur ces aspects (79/80) ;

– précisant les dispositions du *Code sanitaire pour les animaux terrestres* en ce sens (75/78).

Ces souhaits, exprimés par les Délégués des Pays Membres auprès de l'OIE, sont en cohérence avec l'implication croissante de l'Organisation en faveur des Services vétérinaires de ses Pays Membres.

Discussion générale

a) Le taux de réponse (environ 50 % des pays sollicités) a été, toute proportion gardée, relativement élevé. Ce taux

724

Rev. sci. tech. Off. int. Epiz., **25** (2)

était fort pour l'Europe (trois répondeurs sur quatre sollicités), moyen pour l'Afrique, les Amériques et l'Asie (un sur deux), et faible pour le Moyen-Orient (un sur six). Différentes hypothèses peuvent être envisagées pour expliquer cette variabilité, sans qu'il soit possible d'en vérifier la validité : sensibilité au thème de la sécurité sanitaire des aliments ; relation locale entre les pays et la Représentation régionale de l'OIE ; autres priorités, qu'elles soient sanitaires, économiques ou politiques…

Malgré ce fort taux de participation, les questionnaires reçus ne peuvent pas être considérés comme représentatifs des Pays Membres de l'OIE, le biais introduit par le caractère volontaire des réponses ne permettant pas d'extrapoler à l'ensemble des pays les réponses obtenues. De ce fait, l'effet éventuel de certains facteurs ou les interactions entre différentes variables n'ont pu être analysés, puisque les interprétations auraient pu être contredites par une analyse conduite sur un fichier plus complet. Les résultats présentés tiennent compte de cette difficulté et sont volontairement prudents quant à l'interprétation épidémiologique qui pourrait être tirée.

Les résultats ont été analysés en tenant compte du classement entre PD et PED utilisé par la CNUCED, dans la mesure où il semblait *a priori* que les moyens disponibles dans un pays constituaient un des éléments clés de l'organisation des Services vétérinaires. Le faible nombre de pays classés « en développement » ayant finalement répondu au questionnaire n'a pas permis une analyse plus fine en fonction du niveau de développement.

La rédaction du questionnaire a posé des difficultés de réponse à certains correspondants, ce qui a conduit à ne pas pouvoir analyser en détail toutes les questions.

La réponse à de nombreuses questions laissait place à la subjectivité, mais si les réponses devaient avoir reposé sur des faits à documenter, le taux de réponse aurait très certainement été nettement moins bon.

Malgré toutes ces contraintes et biais, de grands axes semblent pouvoir être dégagés de cette étude.

b) L'organisation des Services vétérinaires et, de façon plus large, celle des services intervenant dans la chaîne de contrôle des aliments, est fortement déterminée par l'organisation administrative du pays (État centralisé, décentralisé, régionalisé) et par l'importance des productions agroalimentaires dans l'économie du pays. L'organisation des Services vétérinaires semble plus centralisée dans les PED que dans les PD, pour lesquels on peut observer une tendance à la décentralisation des prises de responsabilité.

c) Les missions confiées aux Services vétérinaires varient selon les pays, d'autres services de contrôle pouvant partager leurs attributions ou prendre le relais, à un niveau ou à un autre de la chaîne.

Au-delà de cette inévitable variabilité et de la complexité des organisations nationales, dans la très grande majorité des pays, les Services vétérinaires semblent être présents, seuls ou non, à presque tous les stades de l'élevage et de la transformation.

Historiquement, les Services vétérinaires ont été mis en place pour lutter contre les maladies animales au niveau des élevages. Ils peuvent y assurer aussi, outre les missions de santé et de protection animale, le contrôle des mesures nécessaires pour assurer la sécurité ultérieure des produits alimentaires issus des animaux.

L'enquête a confirmé que la place des Services vétérinaires était prédominante, voire exclusive, en élevage. Ils avaient toujours la charge de la police sanitaire, presque toujours des prophylaxies, et interviennent dans l'identification animale et la traçabilité des animaux. Leur implication, souvent partagée, était très fréquente au niveau de l'alimentation animale (plus de 73 % des pays) et du médicament vétérinaire (95 % des pays pour ce qui est du contrôle de son utilisation).

En aval de l'élevage, l'intervention des Services vétérinaires s'est prolongée au niveau de l'abattoir, avec une double mission : d'une part, compléter leurs informations relatives à la santé animale (lésions), d'autre part, évaluer la salubrité et l'acceptabilité des viandes pour le consommateur.

L'enquête a confirmé que les Services vétérinaires étaient très généralement présents, seuls ou non, au niveau de l'abattoir, de la deuxième transformation, du contrôle de la traçabilité des denrées alimentaires ainsi que, dans 80 % des pays, du transport et de l'entreposage. Dans environ la moitié des pays, les compétences sur ces segments étaient partagées avec d'autres services.

Il est difficile cependant de déduire que les Services vétérinaires sont en capacité d'assurer, dans chaque pays, un continuum sanitaire de l'amont à l'aval de la chaîne de production. Seule une analyse au cas par cas permettrait d'identifier les éventuelles ruptures. La cohérence de la chaîne de décision n'était pas jugée très satisfaisante dans de nombreux pays, notamment en développement, bien que certains pays l'estimassent *a contrario* de qualité. Les éventuelles ruptures d'organisation, les questions sensibles de coordination interservice, ne pourraient être identifiées que par une analyse fine, par pays.

À l'extrémité de la chaîne de production, pour la distribution et, plus encore, la restauration, l'implication des Services vétérinaires était moins systématique et, le

Rev. sci. tech. Off. int. Epiz., **25** (2)

725

plus souvent, partagée. Compte tenu de la nature des contrôles à ces stades, ceci ne remet pas *a priori* en cause une approche sanitaire intégrée.

Justifiant l'importance que leur accorde l'OIE, les Services vétérinaires jouaient un rôle clef dans la sécurisation des échanges internationaux. Ils assuraient, souvent seuls, la responsabilité des contrôles sanitaires à l'importation et, plus encore, à l'exportation (signature des certificats sanitaires), que ce soit pour les animaux vivants ou pour les denrées alimentaires, et ce quelle que soit par ailleurs la répartition des attributions entre services de contrôle.

Notons enfin que les Services vétérinaires étaient des acteurs incontournables dans le domaine du bien-être animal (96 % des pays), souvent de façon partagée – ceci sans préjuger de l'importance accordée ou non par chaque pays au bien-être. Ils étaient très présents pour le contrôle sanitaire des animaux aquatiques, compétence là encore souvent partagée.

Enfin, les Services vétérinaires d'un nombre non négligeable de pays exerçaient des attributions pour les questions environnementales relatives aux élevages et aux entreprises agroalimentaires (46 %) et le contrôle des OGM (57 %).

Les PED étaient plus souvent tournés vers la santé animale, tandis que les PD avaient très nettement amorcé leur orientation vers la sécurité sanitaire des aliments et d'autres préoccupations, comme le bien-être animal et, même si c'était minoritaire, vers la maîtrise des risques sanitaires pour l'environnement.

d) L'action sanitaire des services de contrôle n'est efficace que si elle est relayée par les différents acteurs du monde socioprofessionnel, éleveurs et vétérinaires de terrain en amont, professionnels de l'agroalimentaire en aval.

Les éleveurs sont les premières sentinelles pour la détection précoce des maladies animales, condition première d'une réaction rapide appropriée. Leurs pratiques ont par ailleurs un impact sur la qualité des produits alimentaires en aval : utilisation des médicaments vétérinaires ou d'autres intrants (facteurs de croissance) susceptibles de laisser des résidus dans les produits, salmonelles en production aviaire, etc. Pour agir de façon responsable, il importe qu'ils soient suffisamment formés. Cette formation peut être délivrée par des organisations d'éleveurs, avec l'appui technique des services publics ou de vétérinaires privés mandatés par l'administration. Les vétérinaires de terrain, ou les paraprofessionnels vétérinaires travaillant sous leur responsabilité, jouent également un rôle déterminant dans les élevages. Le *Code sanitaire pour les animaux terrestres* de l'OIE (2) intègre d'ailleurs ces acteurs, sous certaines conditions, dans l'évaluation des Services Vétérinaires.

L'enquête a mis en évidence des faiblesses importantes au niveau des organisations d'éleveurs à vocation sanitaire et, plus encore, de la formation des éleveurs. Exception faite des moyens alloués aux Services vétérinaires, ces points étaient jugés comme les moins efficients du système, que ce soit pour les PD ou pour les PED (même si la situation était encore moins bonne dans ces derniers).

L'intervention des vétérinaires ne semblait pas pallier ces insuffisances, puisque leur implication était jugée très insatisfaisante, notamment dans les PED. Les missions qui leur étaient confiées contractuellement, portant principalement sur des opérations de prophylaxie, ne leur permettraient pas d'être des appuis efficaces.

Il semblerait donc que le premier maillon des systèmes de surveillance des maladies animales (zoonotiques ou non) et de la chaîne de production des denrées alimentaires d'origine animale, soit aussi, au niveau mondial, le plus faible.

Pour ce qui est des industriels, leur responsabilisation apparaissait comme moyennement satisfaisante dans les PD, alors qu'elle était nettement déficiente dans les PED. Ceci est vraisemblablement à corréler, dans les PD, avec le transfert sur les opérateurs de la responsabilité première de la qualité des produits qu'ils mettent sur le marché, les services officiels assurant alors un contrôle de second niveau, alors que cette conception moderne restait embryonnaire ou absente dans les PED.

e) En ce qui concerne l'organisation, les moyens et l'efficience du contrôle sanitaire, des différences significatives apparaissaient entre PD et PED. Certes, les réponses à ces questions étaient, par construction, éminemment subjectives, mais une évaluation moyens/missions/résultats ne pouvait être conduite dans le cadre de l'étude.

Les responsables des Services vétérinaires étaient relativement satisfaits de l'organisation générale du contrôle sanitaire, de la lisibilité des missions des services sanitaires, de la qualification des vétérinaires officiels.

L'indépendance des services sanitaires, la cohérence de la chaîne de décision, la circulation de l'information, la coordination entre les acteurs, l'articulation entre évaluation et gestion des risques, la traçabilité tout au long de la filière, points forts pour les PD, étaient considérées comme des faiblesses dans les PED, notamment la circulation de l'information.

La réactivité en cas de crise était considérée comme le point fort des Services vétérinaires, notamment en santé animale. En cas de crise liée à la sécurité des aliments, les PED semblaient moins efficaces ; un lien peut sans doute être établi avec l'absence de responsabilisation des industriels, et donc de partenariat avec eux pour gérer les crises, ainsi qu'avec une moindre intégration de la gestion des risques sur l'ensemble de la chaîne de production.

Les Services vétérinaires de tous les pays déploraient une insuffisance de leurs moyens logistiques et financiers, notamment, de façon criante, dans les PED. Cet item obtenait le plus mauvais score lorsque les responsables évaluaient leurs services. L'enquête a donc confirmé, si besoin était, la nécessité des politiques d'amélioration des capacités des Services vétérinaires, qui devraient se développer, avec l'appui des bailleurs de fonds internationaux (notamment de la Banque mondiale) suite à l'épizootie d'influenza aviaire. Le manque de moyens humains était également souvent déploré.

f) Une très forte proportion (84 %) des pays ayant répondu au questionnaire a connu une réforme des services de contrôle entre 1997 et 2005, ou en prévoyait une, ce qui témoigne de la nécessité ressentie par les décideurs d'adapter les organisations aux évolutions du contexte d'action. Dans 71 % des cas, cette réorganisation visait explicitement à assurer une meilleure cohérence de l'étable à la table.

Bien que les données ne soient constituées que d'une image à un moment donné pour chaque pays, la juxtaposition des résultats suggérait très nettement une dynamique de progression du concept de l'étable à la table, même s'il reste, de façon inégale selon les pays, du chemin à parcourir.

Conclusion

L'organisation et les domaines de compétence des Services vétérinaires varient fortement d'un pays à l'autre, mais de grands axes peuvent être dégagés au niveau mondial.

Le concept de la maîtrise intégrée des risques sanitaires de l'étable à la table tend à s'imposer, suivant une dynamique variable selon les pays. Ce concept implique la responsabilisation des différents acteurs professionnels. Si, dans une proportion élevée de pays, la réglementation responsabilise les industriels et les éleveurs, la pratique se heurte à l'absence d'organisations spécifiques de ces catégories d'acteurs dans une proportion notable de ces pays.

Dans la majorité des pays, les Services vétérinaires sont impliqués dans les actions de maîtrise sanitaire tout au long de la chaîne alimentaire, que ce soit seuls, ou en association avec d'autres instances. Le degré de développement économique constitue indiscutablement un facteur important dans l'appropriation de cette approche dans un pays.

Les Délégués ayant répondu au questionnaire souhaitaient de façon quasi unanime que l'OIE apporte un appui à la promotion et au développement des capacités des Services vétérinaires nationaux, eu égard aux lacunes qu'ils relèvent, la première d'entre elles étant liée aux moyens. La présente étude pourra être utilisée dans ce cadre, notamment lors de l'évaluation des Services vétérinaires d'un pays, en permettant de les situer par rapport aux Services vétérinaires nationaux d'autres pays.

Remerciements

Les auteurs remercient Mme Sophie Desage, de l'École nationale vétérinaire d'Alfort (France), pour la saisie des réponses au questionnaire, ainsi que le Dr Dugas, Mme Souyri et Mlle Banaszak, du Service des publications de l'OIE, pour la diffusion et la collecte des questionnaires.

Rev. sci. tech. Off. int. Epiz., **25** (2)

727

Resultados de una encuesta sobre la organización y el funcionamiento de los Servicios Veterinarios en los Países Miembros de la Organización Mundial de Sanidad Animal en 2005

J.J. Bénet, B. Dufour & V. Bellemain

Resumen
En 2004 y 2005 se distribuyó un cuestionario a los 167 Países Miembros de la Organización Mundial de Sanidad Animal (OIE). Las respuestas remitidas por 85 países permitieron sintetizar la organización y el funcionamiento de sus Servicios Veterinarios. Más allá de las diferencias nacionales, en la mayoría de los países los Servicios Veterinarios participan en el control de la seguridad sanitaria (comprendida la alimentación animal) en las explotaciones y, también, en el curso de la primera y segunda transformación de los productos alimenticios, ya sea solos, o en colaboración con otros servicios. Asimismo, las responsabilidades están mucho más fraccionadas en las últimas etapas de la cadena alimentaria, en particular en los sectores de la distribución y la restauración. Pero en los intercambios internacionales de animales y sus subproductos, la responsabilidad central recae en los Servicios Veterinarios. Los medios logísticos y financieros de esos Servicios, así como la limitada participación de los criadores e, incluso, de los veterinarios de terreno, son las principales deficiencias de la cadena de control sanitario. Recientemente se han efectuado numerosas reformas con objeto de armonizar los métodos integrados de los controles sanitarios que se efectúan desde el establo hasta la mesa.

Palabras clave
Cadena alimentaria – Encuesta – Organización Mundial de Sanidad Animal – País Miembro – Seguridad sanitaria de los alimentos – Servicio Veterinario.
∎

Bibliographie

1. Bellemain V. (2004). – Structure et organisation des Services vétérinaires pour mettre en œuvre le concept « de l'étable à la table ». 21e Conférence de la Commission régionale de l'OIE pour l'Europe, Avila (Espagne), 28 septembre-1er octobre. *In* Recueil des thèmes techniques présentés au Comité international de l'OIE ou aux Commissions régionales en 2004. Organisation mondiale de la santé animale (OIE), Paris.

2. Organisation mondiale de la santé animale (OIE) (2005). – Code sanitaire pour les animaux terrestres, 14e édit. OIE, Paris.

3. United Nations Office of the High Representative for the Least Developed Countries, Landlocked Developing and Small Island Developing States (UN-OHRLLS) (2005). – List of Least Developed Countries (http://www.un.org/special-rep/ohrlls/ldc/list.htm) ; List of Landlocked Developing Countries (http://www.un.org/special-rep/ohrlls/lldc/ list.htm) ; List of Small Island Developing States (http://www.un.org/special-rep/ohrlls/sid/list.htm) (pages consultées le 18 décembre 2005).

∎

728

Rev. sci. tech. Off. int. Epiz., **25** (2)

Annexe 1

Liste des 85 Pays Membres de l'OIE ayant répondu au questionnaire

Afrique du Sud, Albanie, Algérie, Allemagne, Argentine, Arménie, Australie, Autriche, Azerbaïdjan, Bangladesh, Barbade, Belgique, Belize, Bénin, Belarus, Bolivie, Brésil, Burkina-Faso, Chili, Chypre, Colombie, Côte d'Ivoire, Croatie, Cuba, Danemark, Égypte, El Salvador, Espagne, Estonie, États-Unis d'Amérique, Finlande, France, Géorgie, Grèce, Guatemala, Guinée, Guinée-Bissau, Irlande, Islande, Israël, Italie, Jamaïque, Japon, Kenya, Koweït, Lettonie, Lituanie, Luxembourg, Maroc, Mexique, Moldavie, Mongolie, Mozambique, Myanmar, Namibie, Népal, Nicaragua, Norvège, Nouvelle-Calédonie, Pays-Bas, Pérou, Philippines, Pologne, Portugal, République tchèque, Roumanie, Royaume-Uni, Russie, Sénégal, Serbie-et-Monténégro, Slovaquie, Slovénie, Suède, Suisse, Swaziland, Taipei China, Tanzanie, Tchad, Thaïlande, Tunisie, Turquie, Ukraine, Vanuatu, Zambie, Zimbabwe.

■

Annexe 2
Questionnaire diffusé aux Pays Membres de l'OIE

Questionnaire utilisé pour le IIème thème technique de la Commission régionale Europe de sept. 2004
Diffusé à l'ensemble des Pays membres de l'OIE en juin 2005, dans le cadre de la *revue scientifique et technique* de l'OIE
VB//13/06/2005

Revue scientifique et technique de l'OIE - 2005

Questionnaire de préparation

**Structure et organisation des Services vétérinaires
pour mettre en œuvre le concept "de l'étable à la table"**

Rapporteur : Véronique BELLEMAIN

Pays : ....
Nom du Délégué : ....
Date : ....

Présentation

Le concept "de l'étable à la table" (ou "de la fourche à la fourchette") implique une approche intégrée des questions sanitaires sur l'ensemble de la chaîne de production, un continuum dans l'évaluation et la gestion des risques depuis l'amont (y compris les conditions de production d'aliments pour animaux), jusqu'à l'aval, la délivrance des produits au consommateur. La sécurité sanitaire est assurée par des contrôles et garanties adaptés à chaque étape de la production et par des liens et interactions permanents entre les étapes.

Définitions :

Code zoosanitaire international, Titre 1.1, chapitre 1.1.1 (définitions générales) (Edition 2003) :

- *Administration vétérinaire* désigne le *Service vétérinaire* gouvernemental ayant compétence sur tout le pays pour mettre en œuvre les mesures zoosanitaires et les procédures de certification vétérinaire internationale que l'OIE recommande, et en surveiller ou auditer l'application.

- *Autorité vétérinaire* désigne le *Service vétérinaire*, sous l'autorité de l'*Administration vétérinaire*, qui est directement responsable de l'application des mesures zoosanitaires dans un territoire déterminé du pays. Il peut aussi être responsable de la délivrance ou de la supervision de la délivrance des *certificats vétérinaires internationaux* dans ce territoire.

- Les *Services vétérinaires* sont composés de l'*Administration vétérinaire* et de l'ensemble des *Autorités vétérinaires*.

Remarque :

Ce questionnaire porte sur les animaux producteurs de denrées destinées à la consommation humaine, ainsi que sur les denrées issues de ces animaux. Les animaux de compagnie, les déchets, etc., ne sont pas concernés.

Notation :

Pour plusieurs questions, il est proposé une grille de notation qualitative : *"- -" (faible), "-" (plutôt faible), "0" (neutre, moyen), "+" (plutôt important) ou "++" (important, positif)*.

1

Rev. sci. tech. Off. int. Epiz., **25** (2)

Questionnaire utilisé pour le IIème thème technique de la Commission régionale Europe de sept. 2004
Diffusé à l'ensemble des Pays membres de l'OIE en juin 2005, dans le cadre de la *revue scientifique et technique* de l'OIE
VB//13/06/2005

Eléments de contexte : Importance des productions animales

1 - Quel est le poids économique des productions animales dans l'économie de votre pays ?
(de - - à ++)

Elevage ……………………………	
Industries agro-alimentaires ………	
Exportations ……………………	

2 - Quelle est l'importance économique des différentes filières animales pour la production de denrées destinées à la consommation humaine ? *(de - - à ++)*

Bovins (viande) ……………………	
Bovins (lait)………………………	
Petits ruminants……………………	
Porcs………………………………	
Volailles (chair et œufs)……………	
Chevaux de boucherie………………	
Lamas ……………………………	
Animaux aquatiques………………	
Abeilles……………………………	
Autres (préciser) …………………	

Services intervenant dans la sécurité sanitaire de l'étable à la table : organisation administrative et domaines d'intervention

3 - Services centraux

Administration vétérinaire :

Ministère de tutelle des Services vétérinaires : ....
....

Dénomination complète de l'Administration vétérinaire : ....
....

Sigle *(à utiliser dans le reste du document si besoin)* : ....

Autres structures concernées : *(répéter cette rubrique autant de fois que nécessaire)*

Ministère de tutelle : ....
....

Dénomination complète : ....
....

Sigle : ....

Ministère de tutelle : ....
....

Dénomination complète : ....
....

Sigle : ....

4 - Organisation de l'analyse des risques sanitaires

Rev. sci. tech. Off. int. Epiz., **25** (2)

Questionnaire utilisé pour le IIème thème technique de la Commission régionale Europe de sept. 2004
Diffusé à l'ensemble des Pays membres de l'OIE en juin 2005, dans le cadre de la *revue scientifique et technique* de l'OIE
VB//13/06/2005

Evaluation et gestion dépendent   - d'une seule structure   [ ]
                                            - de structures indépendantes   [ ]

Structure(s) en charge de l'évaluation des risques sanitaires : *(répéter cette rubrique autant de fois que nécessaire)*

Dénomination : ....
Lien avec un ou des ministère(s) : ....
....
Domaine de compétences : ....
....
....
Sigle : ....

Dénomination : ....
Lien avec un ou des ministère(s) : ....
....
Domaine de compétences : ....
....
....
Sigle : ....

5 - <u>Organisation territoriale</u>

Quels sont les niveaux administratifs en charge des missions suivantes ?

Niveau d'organisation	(1) Dénomination de la division administrative concernée	(2) Nombre total dans le pays	(3) Présence de structures en charge de :					
			L'évaluation des risques		L'élaboration de la réglementation		La surveillance et le contrôle	
			en SA*	en SSA*	en SA*	en SSA*	en SA*	en SSA*
Etat central	*Etat*	*1*						
Régions								
Niveau local								
Municipalité								
Autres ...								
....								

* : SA = santé animale, SSA = sécurité sanitaire des aliments
(1) : donner la dénomination exacte (land, département, judet...)
(2) : nombre de ces divisions administratives pour l'ensemble du pays
(3) : mettre une croix dans les cases correspondant à la situation dans votre pays

Donner toutes les précisions utiles : ....
....
....
....

6 - <u>Services de terrain</u>

Autorités vétérinaires :

Les Autorités vétérinaires sont :
-    des services de l'Etat
-    des services dépendant d'une autorité régionale ou locale   [ ]
-    intégrés dans une structure indépendante (Agence)   [ ]
Dénomination complète : ....
....

Questionnaire utilisé pour le IIème thème technique de la Commission régionale Europe de sept. 2004
Diffusé à l'ensemble des Pays membres de l'OIE en juin 2005, dans le cadre de la *revue scientifique et technique* de l'OIE
VB//13/06/2005
Sigle *(à utiliser dans le reste du document si besoin)* : ....

Autres structures : *(répéter cette rubrique autant de fois que nécessaire)*

Dénomination complète : ....
....
Sigle *(à utiliser dans le reste du document si besoin)* : ....

Dénomination complète : ....
....
Sigle *(à utiliser dans le reste du document si besoin)* : ....

7 - <u>Répartition des compétences et responsabilités pour les questions vétérinaires aux niveaux central et déconcentré (hors évaluation des risques)</u>

		1 Attribution exclusive des SV	2 Attribution partagée des SV	3 Attribution exclusive d'autres services	4 Autres structure(s) concernée(s) (si colonne 2 ou 3 cochée)
Identification des animaux					
Traçabilité des mouvements d'animaux					
Traçabilité des produits alimentaires					
Santé animale	Prophylaxies				
	Police sanitaire				
Sécurité sanitaire des denrées animales et d'origine animale	Abattage				
	Production				
	Transformation				
	Transport				
	Entreposage				
	Distribution				
	Restauration				
Alimentation animale	Production d'aliments				
	Distribution				
	Fabrication à la ferme				
Médicaments vétérinaires	Production				
	Distribution				
	Utilisation				
Bien-être animal					
Animaux aquatiques					
Environnement					
Laboratoire	Santé animale				
	Sécurité des aliments				
Certification à l'exportation	Animaux vivants				
	Produits d'origine animale				
Contrôles à l'importation	Animaux vivants				
	Produits d'origine animale				
OGM					
Protection des végétaux					
Autre :					

SV = Services vétérinaires
(1), (2) et (3) = répondre par "oui" ou par "non"
(4) : utiliser les sigles définis dans les questions précédentes

Rev. sci. tech. Off. int. Epiz., **25** (2)

Questionnaire utilisé pour le IIème thème technique de la Commission régionale Europe de sept. 2004
Diffusé à l'ensemble des Pays membres de l'OIE en juin 2005, dans le cadre de la *revue scientifique et technique* de l'OIE
VB//13/06/2005

8 - Coordination entre les différentes administrations impliquées dans le contrôle de la sécurité sanitaire de la chaîne alimentaire

Rappeler les structures concernées : ....
....

pour : ...	la préparation des négociations internationales	la définition de la réglementation	l'évaluation des risques	la gestion des risques	les services centraux	les services de terrain
La coordination est organisée systématiquement :						
- dans un cadre réglementaire						
- par l'existence d'une structure spécifique						
- par les habitudes de travail						
La coordination se fait de façon informelle						
La coordination est occasionnelle						
La coordination est faite par les Services vétérinaires						
Il n'y a pas de coordination réelle						

Répondre par OUI ou par NON

Considérez-vous que la coordination est globalement :

- très satisfaisante..[ ]
- correcte ....[ ]
- insuffisante ....[ ]
- à l'origine de dysfonctionnements importants ....[ ]

Commentaires : ....
....
....
....

9 - Des documents officiels ont-ils été publiés qui préconisent (et/ou favorisent) une approche intégrée "de l'étable à la table" pour l'application des mesures de sécurité sanitaire des aliments ?

OUI   [ ]   NON   [ ]

Si oui, lesquels ? Quel est leur statut juridique ? ....
....
....
....

5

Rev. sci. tech. Off. int. Epiz., **25** (2)

Questionnaire utilisé pour le IIème thème technique de la Commission régionale Europe de sept. 2004
Diffusé à l'ensemble des Pays membres de l'OIE en juin 2005, dans le cadre de la *revue scientifique et technique* de l'OIE
VB//13/06/2005

10 - Participation aux instances internationales

Quelle est la structure chef de file dans les travaux préparatoires et autres activités des instances internationales suivantes ? Quelles sont les autres structures impliquées ?

	(1) chef de file (ou compétence exclusive)	(2) autres structures impliquées	(3) qualité de la coordination
OIE			
OMS			
FAO			
Codex alimentarius			

(1) et (2) = utiliser les sigles définis dans les questions précédentes
(3) : de -- à ++

11 - Réorganisations récentes ou envisagées

L'organisation des services impliqués dans la sécurité sanitaire de la chaîne alimentaire "de l'étable à la table" a-t-elle fait l'objet de réformes récentes (au cours des 10 dernières années), ou des réformes sont-elles en cours ou en projet ?   OUI   [ ]   NON   [ ]

Si oui : quand et lesquelles : ....
....
....
....
....
....

12 - Synthèse

Pour synthétiser les réponses aux questions précédentes, décrivez schématiquement l'organisation administrative des services impliqués dans la maîtrise de la sécurité sanitaire tout au long de la chaîne alimentaire (joindre éventuellement un schéma en annexe) :
....
....
....
....
....
....
....
....

Rev. sci. tech. Off. int. Epiz., **25** (2)

Questionnaire utilisé pour le IIème thème technique de la Commission régionale Europe de sept. 2004
Diffusé à l'ensemble des Pays membres de l'OIE en juin 2005, dans le cadre de la *revue scientifique et technique* de l'OIE
VB//13/06/2005

Effectifs

13 - Effectifs des agents publics dans les Services vétérinaires

Définition : Sont concernés les personnels qui travaillent à temps plein pour les Services vétérinaires officiels et ne sont pas autorisés à exercer parallèlement une activité privée dans les mêmes domaines de compétence.

Nombre (approximatif) d'agents publics dans les Services vétérinaires :

- Administration centrale (y compris les niveaux régionaux):   ....
  dont vétérinaires :   ....

- Administration décentralisée :   ....
  dont vétérinaires :   ....

- Services déconcentrés ou de terrain :   ....
  dont vétérinaires :   ....

14 – Possibilité de mobiliser des effectifs complémentaires

En cas de crise sanitaire grave, comme, par exemple, la survenue d'une épizootie qui se propage rapidement sur l'ensemble du territoire, y a-t-il la possibilité de mobiliser **facilement** des effectifs complémentaires, autres que ceux chargés du domaine concerné en temps normal ?

Pour faire face à une crise en santé animale :

-	Mobilisation d'agents chargés de la sécurité sanitaire des produits alimentaires ?	OUI [ ]	NON [ ]
-	Mobilisation d'étudiants vétérinaires ?	OUI [ ]	NON [ ]
-	Mobilisation d'agents d'autres services officiels ?	OUI [ ]	NON [ ]
-	Autres ?	OUI [ ]	NON [ ]

Pour faire face à une crise en sécurité sanitaire des aliments :

-	Mobilisation d'agents chargés de la santé animale ?	OUI [ ]	NON [ ]
-	Mobilisation d'étudiants vétérinaires ?	OUI [ ]	NON [ ]
-	Mobilisation d'agents d'autres services officiels ?	OUI [ ]	NON [ ]
-	Autres ?	OUI [ ]	NON [ ]

Si oui, dans quel cadre réglementaire ? Sous quelle autorité ?...
....
....
....
....

Citez un exemple de crise ayant donné lieu à une telle mobilisation : ....
....
....

15 - Participation des vétérinaires privés à la maîtrise de la sécurité sanitaire et du bien-être animal

Est-ce que des vétérinaires privés réalisent des missions sous l'autorité des SV ?
          OUI   [ ]   NON   [ ]

Si oui, dans quel(s) domaine(s) et dans quel(s) cadre(s) juridique(s) ? Combien de vétérinaires privés sont-ils concernés ? Quelle proportion ceux-ci représentent-ils parmi le nombre total de vétérinaires privés (différencier éventuellement ruraux, mixtes et canins) ?

Rev. sci. tech. Off. int. Epiz., **25** (2)

735

Questionnaire utilisé pour le IIème thème technique de la Commission régionale Europe de sept. 2004
Diffusé à l'ensemble des Pays membres de l'OIE en juin 2005, dans le cadre de la *revue scientifique et technique* de l'OIE
VB//13/06/2005

	(1) cadre juridique			(2) vétérinaires concernés	
	Mandat sanitaire (3)	Employé à temps partiel (contrats)	autre (préciser)	nombre	proportion
Campagnes de prophylaxie					
Police sanitaire					
Laboratoires					
Abattoirs					
Sécurité sanitaire des aliments (hors abattoir)					
Zoonoses					
Bien-être animal					
Animaux aquatiques					
Santé des abeilles					
Autres : préciser					

(1) : répondre par OUI ou NON
(2) : indiquer le nombre (ordre de grandeur) et le pourcentage par rapport au nombre total de vétérinaires privés, ou un commentaire (exemple : "presque tous les vétérinaires ruraux")
(3) : le mandat sanitaire est un contrat entre l'administration et le vétérinaire privé, qui confie à ce dernier des missions permanentes (surveillance sanitaire, intervention en cas d'épizootie, etc.)

Commentaires : ....
....
....
....

Implication des producteurs

Les éleveurs

16 - Les éleveurs ont-ils des responsabilités réglementaires dans la maîtrise de la santé animale et de la qualité des produits fournis ?

OUI   [ ]   NON   [ ]

Si oui, lesquelles ? ....
....
....

17 - Les éleveurs sont-ils organisés pour la lutte contre les maladies animales ?

OUI   [ ]   NON   [ ]

Si oui, comment ? ....
....
....

18 - Des partenariats sont-ils formalisés avec l'administration ?

OUI   [ ]   NON   [ ]

Si oui, lesquels ? ....
....
....

Rev. sci. tech. Off. int. Epiz., **25** (2)

Questionnaire utilisé pour le IIème thème technique de la Commission régionale Europe de sept. 2004
Diffusé à l'ensemble des Pays membres de l'OIE en juin 2005, dans le cadre de la *revue scientifique et technique* de l'OIE
VB//13/06/2005

Les professionnels de l'agro-alimentaire

19 - Les producteurs de denrées alimentaires ont-ils des responsabilités réglementaires dans la maîtrise de la qualité des produits fournis ?

OUI   [ ]   NON   [ ]

Si oui, lesquelles ? ....
....
....

20 - Sont-ils organisés pour promouvoir la qualité sanitaire de leurs produits ?

OUI   [ ]   NON   [ ]

Si oui, comment ? ....
....
....
....

Appréciation générale

21 - Quels sont, selon vous, les points forts et les points faibles de l'organisation de votre pays pour assurer la maîtrise continue de la sécurité sanitaire de la chaîne alimentaire <u>de l'étable à la table</u> ? *(de "- -" pour les aspects insuffisants à "++" pour les points forts)*

Organisation générale des services concernés	....
Lisibilité des missions des services sanitaires	....
Indépendance des services sanitaires	....
Cohérence de la chaîne de décision	....
Circulation de l'information	....
Articulation évaluation – gestion des risques	....
Coordination entre les acteurs	....
Traçabilité tout au long de la filière	....
Efficacité en action de routine	....
Réactivité en cas de crise en santé animale	....
Réactivité en cas de crise alimentaire	....
Moyens humains	....
Qualification des vétérinaires officiels	....
Qualification des autres agents des Services vétérinaires	....
Moyens logistiques et financiers	....
Implication des vétérinaires privés	....
Organisation des éleveurs	....
Qualification des éleveurs	....
Responsabilisation des industriels	....
Autre :	....
Autre :	....

Commentaires : ....
....
....
....

Rev. sci. tech. Off. int. Epiz., **25** (2)

Questionnaire utilisé pour le IIème thème technique de la Commission régionale Europe de sept. 2004
Diffusé à l'ensemble des Pays membres de l'OIE en juin 2005, dans le cadre de la *revue scientifique et technique* de l'OIE
VB//13/06/2005

Rôle de l'OIE

22 - Pensez-vous que l'OIE pourrait apporter un appui à ses Pays membres, pour assurer une meilleure maîtrise de la sécurité des aliments d'origine animale, dans le domaine de l'organisation des services publics ?

OUI   [ ]   NON   [ ]

Si oui, sous quelle forme ?

- Séminaires de réflexion et d'échanges de pratiques
  - . au niveau régional   OUI [ ]   NON [ ]
  - . au niveau mondial   OUI [ ]   NON [ ]
- Sensibilisation des décideurs politiques aux nécessités d'une approche intégrée des questions sanitaires ?   OUI [ ]   NON [ ]
- En développant les approches communes avec l'OMS et la FAO, le Codex alimentarius, sur ces aspects   OUI [ ]   NON [ ]
- En précisant les dispositions du Code zoosanitaire international en ce sens   OUI [ ]   NON [ ]
- Autre (préciser) ....   OUI [ ]   NON [ ]

Autres informations - Commentaires

23 - ....
....
....
....
....
....
....
....

10

Rev. sci. tech. Off. int. Epiz., 2006, **25** (2), 739-761

The organisation and functioning of Veterinary Services: results of a 2005 survey of Member Countries of the World Organisation for Animal Health

J.J. Bénet [1], B. Dufour [1] & V. Bellemain [2]

(1) École nationale vétérinaire d'Alfort, 7 avenue du Général de Gaulle, 94704 Maisons-Alfort Cedex, France
(2) École nationale des services vétérinaires, Centre collaborateur de l'OIE pour la formation des vétérinaires officiels, 1 avenue Bourgelat, 69280 Marcy-l'Etoile, France

Summary
A questionnaire was sent to the 167 Member Countries of the World Organisation for Animal Health (OIE) in 2004 and 2005. The organisation and functioning of national Veterinary Services were analysed based on the responses from 85 of these countries. Leaving aside variations between countries, Veterinary Services are very involved in animal health and food safety controls at farm level (including animal feed), and during primary and secondary processing, whether alone or in conjunction with other services. At the lower end of the chain, namely distribution and the food service industry, responsibilities tend to be more widely shared. Veterinary Services have a central responsibility in international trade in animals and animal products. The main weaknesses in the chain of controls concern the logistical and financial resources of Veterinary Services, and insufficient involvement of livestock producers and even of field veterinarians. The many recent reforms are tending to provide a more consistent, integrated approach to animal health and food safety controls 'from the stable to the table'.

Keywords
OIE Member Countries – Veterinary Services – World Organisation for Animal Health (OIE).

Introduction

The World Organisation for Animal Health (OIE) attaches increasing importance to the capacities of its Member Countries' Veterinary Services. Indeed, the quality of the animal health information collected by the OIE depends on the Veterinary Services, as does the implementation of international animal health standards, the safety of trade in animals and animal products and, more generally, the way the Organisation's work is applied at national level.

Animal production food safety has evolved, indeed is still evolving, towards an integrated approach throughout the food production chain, 'from the stable to the table' – or 'from farm to fork'. The action of Veterinary Services must be viewed in this new context.

The 21st Conference of the OIE Regional Commission for Europe, held in September 2004, included a technical item entitled 'Structure and organisation of Veterinary Services to implement the concept "from the stable to the table"' (1). The report for the technical item was based on the 31 responses to a questionnaire sent to the Delegates of the 50 OIE Member Countries of Europe.

Given the value of the information collected, it was decided to extend the study worldwide and conduct a more detailed analysis.

In July 2005, the OIE sent the questionnaire to the Delegates of the remaining 136 Member Countries (i.e. 167 Member Countries, minus the 31 in Europe that had already replied).

740

Rev. sci. tech. Off. int. Epiz., **25** (2)

Responses were received from 85 countries (31 for the first group of questionnaires and 54 for the second group; see list in Appendix 1) and subsequently analysed. Particular attention was given to comparing the responses from developing countries with those from developed countries.

Materials and methods

A questionnaire (Appendix 2), prepared by the authors in 2004, was sent by the Director General of the OIE to the Delegates of the 167 Member Countries, in hard copy and electronic format, in two phases. The 50 countries of the OIE Regional Commission for Europe received the questionnaire in 2004. All the other Member Countries, and those European countries that had not replied in 2004, were contacted in July 2005, with a reminder in October.

The questionnaire was written in French and translated into English and Spanish so that each country could receive it in whichever of the three official OIE languages was most appropriate.

The questionnaire comprised 22 closed-ended questions and a final open-ended question. Some of the closed-ended questions included sub-sections and several possible responses to choose from.

The topics covered were chosen with the aim of obtaining a description and evaluation of the organisation of animal health and food safety controls throughout the food production chain 'from the stable to the table' and dealt specifically with the following:

– economic importance of animal production

– organisation of central and field Veterinary Services

– organisation of animal health and food safety risk analysis

– distribution of tasks and responsibilities among the various services

– coordination between the different administrations involved

– participation in the work of international organisations

– recent or planned reorganisations

– staff numbers and involvement of the various stakeholders

– a general self-assessment

– the role of the OIE.

All the responses received before 6 December 2005 were analysed. Data entry and processing were carried out using the computer application Sphinx Lexica (v 4.5).

Countries were divided into developed countries and developing countries in accordance with the classification adopted by the United Nations Conference on Trade and Development (UNCTAD) for the Special Programme for Least Developed, Landlocked and Island Developing Countries (2).

Throughout this paper the results are presented with the number and, where meaningful, the percentage of countries that replied.

Group comparisons were performed using the Pearson chi-square test and, where appropriate, the Fisher exact test, with a 5% significance level.

Annotated results

The analysis covers the information provided by the 85 different countries who returned the questionnaire, representing approximately half the Member Countries of the OIE. However, most of the questionnaires contained one or more non-responses, which explains why the analysis rarely relates to all 85 respondents. Whenever figures are presented, the number of respondents is therefore systematically indicated.

Distribution of responding countries

Table I and Figure 1 show the distribution of responding countries according to their level of development (United Nations) and their geographical location (source: OIE).

European countries provided the highest proportion of responders, most likely due to their having been canvassed on more occasions (first questionnaire in 2004, then twice in 2005). Though the difference did not reach significance, a smaller proportion of developing countries than developed countries completed the questionnaire, probably due to there being far fewer developing countries in Europe.

The OIE classifies some countries in two different regions due to their size, the dispersal of parts of their territory or their geographically intermediate position. However, for the purposes of this study, it was decided to classify them on a geographical rather than a political basis.

Economic importance of animal products

The economic importance of livestock was deemed major or fairly major by most of the responding countries (70/84; 83%). A difference was found between developing countries and developed countries for the economic importance of agrifood industries, which was significantly

Rev. sci. tech. Off. int. Epiz., **25** (2)

741

Table I
Questionnaire on the organisation of Veterinary Services: number of countries approached and number of countries that responded in time for inclusion in the study

Region	Developing countries		Developed countries		Total	
	Approached	Responded	Approached	Responded	Approached	Responded
Africa	34	11	15	8	49	19
Americas	8	4	20	11	28	15
Asia	10	6	18	7	28	13
Europe	3	3	46	33	49	36
Middle East	1	0	12	2	13	2
Total	**56**	**24**	**111**	**61**	**167**	**85**

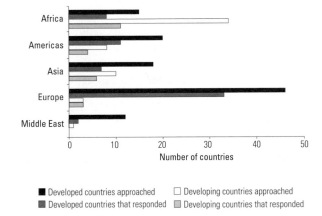

- ■ Developed countries approached
- □ Developing countries approached
- ■ Developed countries that responded
- ▨ Developing countries that responded

Fig. 1
Countries approached and countries that replied to the questionnaire on the organisation of Veterinary Services in time for inclusion in the study

higher for developed countries (55/64; 86%) than for developing countries (12/21; approximately 57%).

Generally speaking, the importance of livestock production was positively correlated with that of agrifood industries: out of 83 respondents, the importance of both these sectors was considered to be high in 62 countries and low in 9 countries.

Organisation of central and field services

In the majority of cases (70/84; 83%), with no difference between developing and developed countries, Veterinary Services are supervised by the Ministry of Agriculture. The Ministry of Health is in second place as the ministry responsible for Veterinary Services. It should be noted that, in two countries, Veterinary Services are directly responsible to the Prime Minister.

The name of the Veterinary Administration differs depending on whether a country is a developing country or a developed country. Among all the countries, the term

'veterinary' was the most frequently cited, by 48 countries out of 85 (56%), comprising 14/21 developing countries and 34/64 developed countries. For developing countries, the next most frequent term was 'livestock' (11/21), with the following terms cited far less frequently: 'health' (2), 'inspection' (1), 'animal' (1), 'agriculture' (1) and 'public' (1). For the developed countries, the terms most commonly cited after 'veterinary' were 'food' (17/64) and 'health' (17); these were followed by 'animal' (10), 'agriculture' (8), 'inspection' (7), 'safety' (5), 'plant' (5), 'livestock/animal production' (4), 'quality' (3), 'consumer' (2), 'industry' (1), 'protection' (1) and 'public' (1).

Several questions sought to evaluate the level of decentralisation in decisions and actions relating to animal health and food safety. In the field of animal health, for most of the respondents (83), the State retains responsibility for risk evaluation (75; 90%), drafting regulations (81; 98%), surveillance and control (71; 86%); in the field of food safety the State is responsible for risk evaluation (71; 86%), drafting regulations (78; 94%) and surveillance and control (64; 77%). Only a few countries have instituted a true system of decentralisation extending as far as the drafting of animal health and food safety regulations (21 [33%] in animal health and 18 [29%] in food safety). No significant differences were found between developing and developed countries on any of these points.

The field Veterinary Services are under the responsibility of the State in the majority of the responding countries (80/85; 94%), with no difference between developing countries and developed countries. However, 11/62 developed countries (13%) (but no developing countries) declared that all or part of the field Veterinary Services are placed under the responsibility of an agency.

Organisation of animal health and veterinary public health risk analysis

Fifty-eight of the 81 responding countries (72%) (no difference between developed and developing countries) indicated that animal health and veterinary public health risk analysis is performed by more than one organisation, only 23 countries (28%) stating that it is performed by a single organisation. The organisations mentioned come under the Ministry of Agriculture (55 countries [68%]), followed by the Ministry of Health (12 countries [15%], including the four countries where the Ministry of Health is responsible for the central Veterinary Administration) and, far more rarely, the Ministry for Economic Affairs (two countries, where this ministry is also responsible for the central Veterinary Administration). Five countries have an agency that is independent of the Veterinary Services.

Forty-two of the 79 responding countries (53%) indicated the existence of a document recommending or promoting a 'stable to table' approach for the application of food safety measures. Although the difference did not reach

significance, a smaller proportion of developing countries than developed countries had a document of this type.

Distribution of tasks and responsibilities between the different services

Table II and Figure 2 present the involvement of Veterinary Services in the various activities related to animal health (animal identification, prophylactic treatment, health policing, animal traceability, laboratory activities, export certification).

Not surprisingly, Veterinary Services are heavily involved in these activities, for which they are, in the majority of countries, solely responsible (significant difference from a 50% indifference level). Only animal identification is as

Table II

Responsibilities in animal health activities: assumed by the Veterinary Services (VS) alone, by the VS and other services or by other services only

Activity	Responsibility			
	VS alone	VS and other services	Other services	Total
Identification	40 (51%)	35 (45%)	3 (4%)	78 (100%)
Disease prevention campaigns	57 (70%)	23 (28%)	2 (2%)	82 (100%)
Health policing	65 (78%)	18 (22%)	0	83 (100%)
Animal health laboratory	53 (64%)	26 (31%)	4 (5%)	83 (100%)
Live animal export certification	77 (93%)	6 (7%)	0	83 (100%)
Live animal import controls	70 (85%)	11 (13%)	1 (2%)	82 (100%)
Animal traceability	52 (65%)	26 (32%)	2 (3%)	80 (100%)

The figures correspond to the number of countries that responded to the relevant question and the percentages have been established accordingly

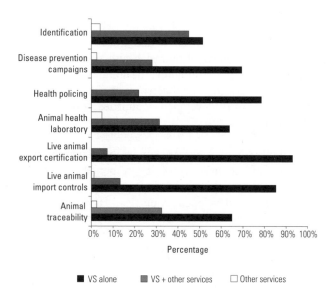

Fig. 2

Responsibilities in animal health activities: assumed by the Veterinary Services (VS) alone, by the VS and other services or by other services only

frequently the exclusive responsibility of the Veterinary Services as it is shared with other services.

Table III and Figure 3 present the involvement of Veterinary Services in activities related to food safety and hygiene.

Veterinary Services are less frequently solely responsible for food safety activities than they are for animal health activities (Table II and Table III). For many food safety functions, responsibility is shared with other bodies. Veterinary Services are, however, largely predominantly responsible for matters relating to the export certification of animal products (65/83; 78%) and for import controls on animal products (54/82; 64%).

Conversely, in the 78 countries that replied to questions about safety and control during food transportation and in the food service industry, Veterinary Services have no responsibility for food distribution in 26 countries (33%) and no responsibility for the food service industry in 39 countries (50%). The differences observed between

Rev. sci. tech. Off. int. Epiz., **25** (2)

743

Table III
Responsibilities in activities related to food safety of animal products: assumed by the Veterinary Services (VS) alone, by the VS and other services or by other services only

Activity	Responsibility			
	VS alone	VS and other services	Other services	Total
Slaughter	48 (59%)	29 (36%)	4 (5%)	81 (100%)
Traceability of food products	16 (21%)	51 (67%)	9 (12%)	76 (100%)
Food safety in production	37 (46%)	36 (44%)	8 (10%)	81 (100%)
Food safety in processing	30 (37%)	40 (49%)	11 (14%)	81 (100%)
Food safety in transport	35 (42%)	34 (41%)	14 (17%)	83 (100%)
Food safety in storage	28 (35%)	35 (43%)	18 (22%)	81 (100%)
Food safety in distribution	27 (35%)	25 (32%)	26 (33%)	78 (100%)
Food safety in the food service industry	12 (15%)	27 (35%)	39 (50%)	78 (100%)
Export certification of animal products	65 (78%)	17 (20%)	1 (1%)	83 (100%)
Import controls on animal products	54 (64%)	28 (33%)	2 (2%)	84 (100%)
Food safety laboratory	16 (19%)	58 (69%)	10 (12%)	84 (100%)

The figures correspond to the number of countries that responded to the relevant question and the percentages have been established accordingly

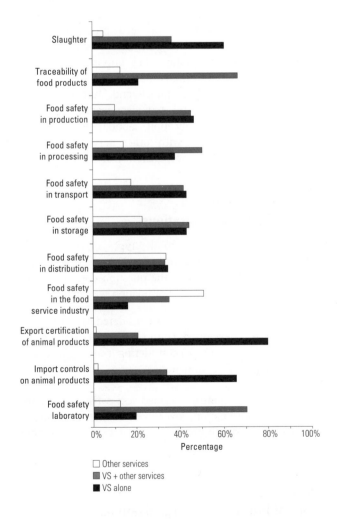

Fig. 3
Responsibilities in activities related to food safety of animal products: assumed by the Veterinary Services (VS) alone, by the VS and other services or by other services only

developing countries and developed countries are not significant except at the distribution stage, where the Veterinary Services of developing countries are significantly less involved than those of the developed countries.

Table IV and Figure 4 present the involvement of Veterinary Services in activities relating to animal feed and veterinary medicinal products. These types of activities are just as frequently under the responsibility of Veterinary Services alone as they are shared with other services. Veterinary Services have no responsibility in the area of animal feed production or distribution in 22% and 33% of countries, respectively. While other services have sole responsibility for the production of veterinary medicinal products in 21% of countries, Veterinary Services are almost always responsible for controlling their use – which is consistent with the presence of these services at farm level.

Table V and Figure 5 present the involvement of Veterinary Services in various other activities. Veterinary Services are heavily involved in animal welfare (96% of countries, with sole responsibility in 45%) and aquatic animal issues (83% of countries, with sole responsibility in 36%). Logically, they are more rarely concerned with plant protection (30%), genetically modified organisms (GMOs) (57%) or the environment (46%).

The responsibilities of the Veterinary Services of developing countries are globally less diversified than those of developed countries. The difference between these two categories of countries is significant in terms of their involvement in GMO and aquatic animal issues. This most likely – and logically – reflects a lower level of concern or less activity in such areas in developing countries.

744

Rev. sci. tech. Off. int. Epiz., **25** (2)

Table IV
Responsibilities in activities related to animal feed and veterinary medicinal products: assumed by the Veterinary Services (VS) alone, by the VS and other services or by other services only

Activity	Responsibility			
	VS alone	VS and other services	Other services	Total
Animal feed production	31 (38%)	32 (40%)	18 (22%)	81 (100%)
Animal feed distribution	27 (35%)	25 (32%)	26 (33%)	78 (100%)
Animal feed produced on the farm	28 (35%)	31 (39%)	20 (25%)	79 (100%)
Production of veterinary medicinal products	34 (44%)	27 (35%)	16 (21%)	77 (100%)
Distribution of veterinary medicinal products	39 (48%)	31 (38%)	12 (15%)	82 (100%)
Use of veterinary medicinal products	46 (56%)	32 (39%)	4 (5%)	82 (100%)

The figures correspond to the number of countries that responded to the relevant question and the percentages have been established accordingly

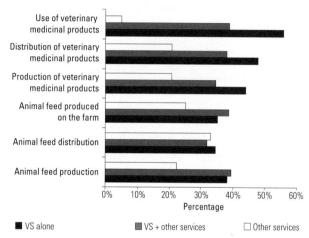

Fig. 4
Responsibilities in activities related to animal feed and veterinary medicinal products: assumed by the Veterinary Services (VS) alone, by the VS and other services or by other services only

Figure 6 collates all these data, arranged according to the concept 'from the stable to the table', and differentiates between the following sectors: upstream (farm inputs: animal feed and veterinary medicines); livestock production (comprising the various animal health activities, including those related to imports and exports and to essential control activities such as identification, traceability and laboratory procedures); processing (including abattoir procedures and the subsequent stages of processing which interface with the final distribution stage), and, lastly, distribution and the food service industry. The other sectors, which are collateral to this linear view, are shown on the right of the figure. The broken-line diagram makes it easier to grasp the relative role of each player in the continuum. The symbols for each of the players are open when the difference compared to the other players is not significant and closed when the difference is significant.

This figure emphasises a number of points. First of all, it shows that in a large majority of cases Veterinary Services are involved, with sole responsibility, in everything directly concerned with animals (livestock production, animal welfare, aquatic animal issues), and that Veterinary Services are continuously present, whether with sole responsibility or in association with other services, throughout the chain. At both ends of the chain, there are far more areas in which Veterinary Services do not have sole responsibility, e.g. animal feed production, food transportation and, especially, the activities of the food service industry. Certification and import controls are activities where Veterinary Services are strongly represented, both for live animals and animal products. Conversely, quality control activities needed to ensure safety (traceability, identification, laboratory procedures) are more often shared with other services, or even predominantly under the responsibility of other services.

Coordination between the different administrations

As the responses relating to the types of coordination between the different administrations involved could not readily be synthesised, only the question concerning the evaluation of the quality of coordination was analysed.

The quality of coordination was considered satisfactory by 55 of the 62 developed countries (89%), only seven developed countries (11%) considering it unsatisfactory or a source of serious malfunctions.

The developing countries seemed less satisfied with the quality of coordination, over half of the respondents (11/20) considering it unsatisfactory or a source of serious malfunctions.

Participation in the work of international organisations

When asked for their assessment of the quality of national coordination in preparing the country's participation in the work of international organisations, a large majority of countries (60/67; 90%) answered that it was 'good' or 'very

Rev. sci. tech. Off. int. Epiz., **25** (2)

745

Table V

Responsibilities in various other activities: assumed by the Veterinary Services (VS) alone, by the VS and other services or by other services only

Activity	Responsibility			
	VS alone	VS and other services	Other services	Total
Animal welfare	35 (45%)	39 (51%)	3 (4%)	77 (100%)
Aquatic animals	28 (36%)	36 (47%)	13 (17%)	77 (100%)
Plant protection	10 (14%)	12 (16%)	52 (70%)	74 (100%)
GMOs	11 (18%)	24 (39%)	27 (43%)	62 (100%)
Environment	3 (4%)	35 (42%)	45 (54%)	83 (100%)

GMOs: genetically modified organisms
The figures correspond to the number of countries that responded to the relevant question and the percentages have been established accordingly

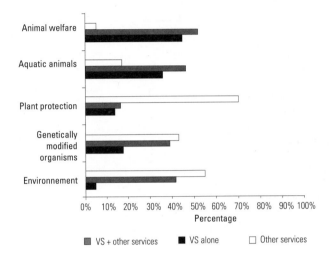

Fig. 5
Responsibilities in various other activities: assumed by the Veterinary Services (VS) alone, by the VS and other services or by other services only

good' for the work of the OIE. In the majority of cases, national Veterinary Services are the lead organisation in this respect, either alone or in conjunction with other authorities (64/69; 93%).

For the Food and Agriculture Organization of the United Nations (FAO), the quality of national coordination was considered 'quite good' (55/68; 81%). In the majority of cases, this is organised either by services within the Ministry of Agriculture (32/67; 48%) or by the Veterinary Services (28/67; 42%).

For the World Health Organization (WHO), the quality of national coordination was considered 'quite good' by only 75% of the responding countries (50/67). Responsibility for coordinating this lies with the health services in most cases (56/65; 86%).

A similar proportion of countries considered the quality of coordination in the work of the Codex Alimentarius Commission to be 'quite good' (48/64; 75%). National responsibility for coordinating this lies with the health

services (19/60; 28%), the Veterinary Services (17/60; 32%), the Ministry of Agriculture (11/60; 18%) or other authorities (13/60; 22%).

There is perhaps a need to verify whether the assessments given mean that the existing procedures result in effective participation or merely that the arrangements themselves are deemed satisfactory.

Recent or planned reorganisation

Sixty-nine of the 82 responding countries (84%; no difference between developing and developed countries) indicated that the services involved in the safety of the food chain 'from the stable to the table' had recently been reorganised (i.e. during the previous ten years) or that reorganisations were planned.

In the majority of cases (42/59; 71%), these reorganisations were explicitly aimed at establishing a coherent approach to food safety, 'from the stable to the table'.

Involvement of different categories of players

The animal health and food safety actions of the public services can only be effective if they are adaptable, so as to be able to deal with any crises, and if all the various socio-professional groups play their part in turn, namely livestock farmers and field veterinarians at one end of the chain and agrifood professionals at the other.

The possibilities that exist for mobilising supplementary personnel to deal with animal health and food safety crises

The possibility of strengthening teams exists in at least 80% of the responding countries, both for animal health crises and for food safety crises, which is consistent with the need for a rapid response, as for example in the event of an epizootic. The mobilisation of veterinary students appears to be less common (approximately 60%) (Table VI).

746

Rev. sci. tech. Off. int. Epiz., **25** (2)

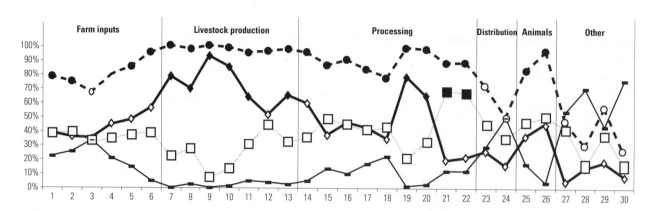

Farm inputs
1. Animal feed : production
2. Animal feed : on-farm production
3. Animal feed: distribution
4. Veterinary medicinal products: production
5. Veterinary medicinal products: distribution
6. Veterinary medicinal products: use

Livestock production
7. Health policing
8. Prophylactic treatment
9. Export certification: live animals
10. Import controls: live animals
11. Animal health laboratory
12. Animal identification
13. Animal traceability

Processing
14. Slaughter
15. Animal products: processing

16. Animal products: production
17. Animal products: transport
18. Animal products: storage
19. Animal products: export certification
20. Animal products: import controls
21. Food safety laboratory
22. Traceability of food products

Distribution
23. Distribution of animal products
24. Food safety industry

Animals
25. Aquatic animals
26. Animal welfare

Other
27. Environment
28. Plant protection
29. Genetically modified organisms
30. Other

◆ ◇ Sole responsibility of the Veterinary Services
(◆ significant difference; ◇ non significant difference)

■ □ Shared responsibility of the Veterinary Services and other services
(■ significant difference; □ non significant difference)

■ – Sole responsibility of other services
(■ significant difference; – non significant difference)

● ○ Responsibility of the Veterinary Services
(either sole or shared – cumulative frequency)
(● significant difference; ○ non significant difference)

Fig. 6
Frequency distribution of the ways in which countries allocate tasks and responsibilities throughout the food safety chain

Table VI
Additional personnel that can be mobilised in the event of a health crisis

Personnel	Yes	No	Total
Animal health crises			
Food safety officials	67 (84%)	13 (16%)	80 (100%)
Veterinary students	43 (60%)	29 (40%)	72 (100%)
Other service personnel	64 (84%)	12 (16%)	76 (100%)
Other	42 (86%)	7 (14%)	49 (100%)
Food safety crises			
Animal health officials	71 (90%)	8 (10%)	79 (100%)
Veterinary students	38 (53%)	34 (47%)	72 (100%)
Other services	60 (80%)	15 (20%)	75 (100%)
Other	51 (71%)	21 (29%)	72 (100%)

The figures correspond to the number of countries that responded to the relevant question and the percentages have been established accordingly

Rev. sci. tech. Off. int. Epiz., **25** (2)

747

The different ways in which private veterinarians participate

Private veterinarians participate to varying degrees in activities that are under the responsibility of the Veterinary Services. They are quite widely involved in disease prevention campaigns (67/85; 79%), mostly under the terms of an animal health accreditation mandate (44/67; 66%) or else under contract. Their participation is more restricted in sectors such as animal health policing, abattoirs, zoonoses, laboratories and animal welfare, sectors in which only 32 to 40 countries (38% to 47%, out of 85) stated that they were assigned these tasks. They are even less frequently involved in food safety (24 countries, 28%) and matters concerning aquatic animals (22 countries, 26%). For all these activities, the animal health accreditation mandate is the most commonly used method of assigning official duties to veterinarians. There was no significant difference between developed countries and developing countries on this point (Table VII and Figure 7).

The involvement of livestock producers

On the whole, the links with livestock producers appear to be insufficiently formal given the importance of their role in animal health. Livestock producers have statutory animal health responsibilities in 65 countries out of 83 (78%), with a significant difference between developed countries (86%) and developing countries (55%). However, the proportion of countries with livestock producers' organisations that can liaise with the administration is low (approximately 60%), without any significant difference between developed countries and developing countries. The existence of formal partnerships with these organisations is not systematic, even in developed countries (59%), and is very infrequent in developing countries (3/20; 15%) (Table VIII).

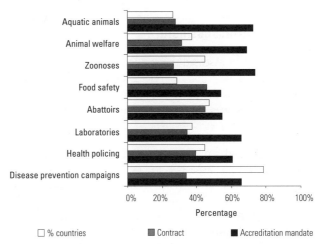

% countries = % out of 85 countries that responded
Contract: private veterinarians employed part-time by the State
Accreditation mandate (*'mandat sanitaire'*): contract between the Administration and the private veterinarian, entrusting permanent tasks to the veterinarian (disease surveillance, intervention in the case of an epizootic, etc.)

Fig. 7
Participation of private veterinarians in official animal health and food safety activities

Table VII
Framework for participation of private veterinarians in official animal health and food safety activities

Activity	Accreditation mandate [a]		Contract [b]		Total	Total (% out of 85)
Disease prevention campaigns	44	(66%)	23	(34%)	67	79%
Health policing	23	(61%)	15	(39%)	38	45%
Laboratories	21	(66%)	11	(34%)	32	38%
Abattoirs	22	(55%)	18	(45%)	40	47%
Food safety	13	(54%)	11	(46%)	24	28%
Zoonoses	28	(74%)	10	(26%)	38	45%
Animal welfare	22	(69%)	10	(31%)	32	38%
Aquatic animals	16	(73%)	6	(27%)	22	26%

a) Accreditation mandate (*'mandat sanitaire'*): contract between the Administration and the private veterinarian, entrusting permanent tasks to the veterinarian (disease surveillance, intervention in the case of an epizootic, etc.)
b) Contract: private veterinarians employed part-time by the State

Table VIII
Involvement of livestock producers in animal health decisions and actions

Type of involvement	Developing countries			Developed countries			Total
	Yes	No	Total	Yes	No	Total	
Statutory responsibilities *	11 (55%)	9 (45%)	20	54 (86%)	9 (14%)	63	**83**
Existence of a producers' organisation	12 (60%)	8 (40%)	20	39 (62%)	24 (38%)	63	**83**
Formal partnerships with the Veterinary Services *	3 (15%)	17 (85%)	20	36 (59%)	25 (41%)	61	**81**

* significant difference between developed countries and developing countries

748

Rev. sci. tech. Off. int. Epiz., **25** (2)

The involvement of agrifood professionals

The majority of countries, regardless of whether they are developed or developing countries, place statutory responsibilities on agrifood professionals to control the quality of the products they provide (67/78; 86%). In the developed countries, agrifood industries are significantly more highly organised than in the developing countries (Table IX).

General self-assessment

Each respondent assessed the strengths and weaknesses of their country's Veterinary Services for guaranteeing food safety throughout the production chain, based on a list of 19 items. This was used to determine a score for each country (Fig. 8).

The scale used in the questionnaire ranged from -- ('unsatisfactory aspects') to ++ ('strong points'). To establish a global score, each response was assigned a score, ranging from -2 (--) to +2 (++). The global score was the sum of the scores for each of the 19 questions. Developing countries had a mean score of 0, and developed countries a mean score of 16, with a relatively high degree of dispersion of values in each case.

Figure 9 shows the mean score for each question, for the whole sample, for developing countries and for developed countries. The maximum score for any given question is 2. Only responsiveness to an animal health crisis (score: 1.4)

was close to the threshold value of 1.6, corresponding to 80% of the maximum score for the whole sample, a proportion that can be considered satisfactory.

A far less ambitious threshold, namely a score corresponding to 50% of the maximum value (i.e. a value of 1) was reached for some other items, including general organisation (1.1), transparency of the tasks of Veterinary Services (1.0), responsiveness to a food safety crisis (1.1) and qualifications of official veterinarians (1.1).

If one considers that a score equal to or less than 40% of the maximum value (0.8) is low, the following items are weaknesses for the whole of the sample: coherence of the decision-making chain (0.6), circulation of information (0.6), coordination between risk assessment and risk management (0.4), coordination between the people in charge (0.6), traceability (0.4), human resources (0.5) and especially the involvement of private veterinarians (0.1), organisation of livestock producers (0.4) and qualifications of livestock producers (0.04), accountability of manufacturers (0.4), and, most glaringly, logistical and financial resources (-0.1).

Developed countries differed significantly from developing countries in that they considered their main strengths to be independence of the veterinary public health services (1.2), coherence of the decision-making chain (0.9), circulation of information (0.9), integration between risk

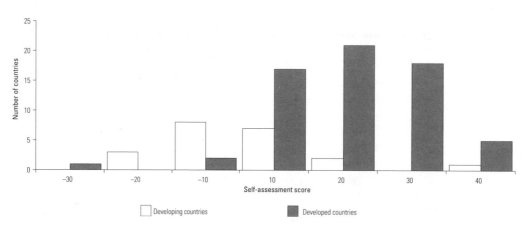

Fig. 8
Distribution of developing countries and developed countries according to their general self-assessment score

Table IX
Involvement of agrifood professionals in food safety

Type of involvement	Developing countries			Developed countries			Total
	Yes	No	Total	Yes	No	Total	
Statutory responsibilities	14 (74%)	5 (26%)	19	53 (90%)	6 (10%)	59	**78**
Existence of an organisation *	5 (28%)	13 (72%)	18	41 (71%)	17 (29%)	58	**76**

* significant difference between developed countries and developing countries

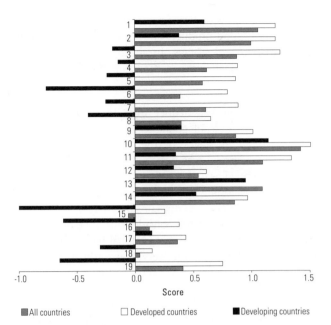

■ All countries   □ Developed countries   ■ Developing countries

1. General organisation
2. Transparency of the tasks of Veterinary Services
3. Independence of the Health Services
4. Coherence of the decision-making chain
5. Circulation of information
6. Integration between risk assessment and management
7. Coordination between the people in charge
8. Traceability
9. Effectiveness in routine activities
10. Responsiveness to an animal health crisis
11. Responsiveness to a food safety crisis
12. Human resources
13. Qualifications of official veterinarians
14. Qualifications of other Veterinary Services officials
15. Logistical and financial resources
16. Involvement of private veterinarians
17. Organisation of livestock producers
18. Qualifications of livestock producers
19. Accountability of manufacturers

Fig. 9
Mean score on individual self-assessment questions: all countries, developing countries and developed countries

assessment and risk management (0.8), coordination between the people in charge (0.9), traceability throughout the chain (0.65), responsiveness to a food safety crisis (1.5) and accountability of manufacturers (0.75).

Developing countries considered these same points to be among their weaknesses, with the exception of responsiveness to a food safety crisis. The weakness of logistical and financial resources and the lack of involvement of private veterinarians were significantly more acute for developing countries.

The role of the OIE

Nearly all the respondents considered that the OIE could support its Member Countries in the area of public service

organisation, to guarantee better control of the safety of animal foodstuffs, by:

– organising study seminars and exchanges of practice at regional or international level (78/80)

– raising the awareness of political decision-makers (75/79)

– developing common approaches with WHO, FAO and the Codex Alimentarius Commission regarding these aspects (79/80)

– indicating the relevant provisions of the *Terrestrial Animal Health Code* (75/78).

These wishes, expressed by the Delegates of OIE Member Countries, are consistent with the growing involvement of the Organisation in support of the Veterinary Services of its Member Countries.

General discussion

a) The response rate (approximately 50% of the countries approached) was relatively high for a survey of this type. The response rate was high for Europe (three-quarters of the countries approached), average for Africa, the Americas and Asia (half of the countries approached), and low for the Middle East (one sixth). Various hypotheses can be put forward to try to account for this variability but they cannot be verified: sensitivity to the food safety issue; relations between countries and the local OIE Regional Representation; other priorities, be they health, economic or political.

Despite the high rate of participation, the returned questionnaires cannot be considered representative of the Member Countries of the OIE, since the respondents' willingness to reply introduces a bias that prevents the results obtained being extrapolated to all countries. As a result, the possible effect of certain factors or interactions between different variables could not be analysed, since these interpretations might have been contradicted by an analysis performed on a more complete sample. The results presented take this difficulty into account and are intentionally cautious as to any epidemiological interpretation that might be drawn from them.

The results have been analysed taking into account the definitions of developed and developing countries used by UNCTAD insofar as it seemed *a priori* that the available resources in a country constituted one of the key factors in the organisation of its Veterinary Services. The small number of developing countries that actually replied to the questionnaire did not allow a finer analysis according to the level of development.

The wording of the questionnaire was a source of difficulty for some of the respondents and as a result not all the questions could be analysed in detail.

Many of the questions made provision for subjective answers, because if the questions had principally asked for documented facts the response rate would undoubtedly have been lower.

Yet, despite the various constraints and potential bias, several main themes seem to emerge from this study.

b) The organisation of Veterinary Services and, in a wider sense, that of the services involved in controlling the safety of the food chain, is largely determined by the administrative organisation of the country (centralised, decentralised or regionalised) and the importance of agrifood production for the economy of the country. The organisation of Veterinary Services seems to be more centralised in developing countries than in developed countries, where there is a trend towards the decentralisation of responsibilities.

c) The missions assigned to Veterinary Services vary from country to country, and other control services may share their responsibilities or take over responsibility at one or other point in the chain.

Beyond the inevitable variability and complexity of national organisations, in the vast majority of countries Veterinary Services seem to be present, either alone or with other services, at almost all stages of animal production and processing.

Historically, Veterinary Services were set up to control animal diseases at farm level. Now, in addition to animal health and protection missions, they may also carry out the control measures needed to guarantee the subsequent safety of animal-derived food products.

The survey confirms that Veterinary Services have a predominant, or even exclusive, role in livestock farming. They are always responsible for animal health policing and nearly always for prophylactic treatment, and are involved in animal identification and the traceability of animals. They are very frequently involved, often with shared responsibility, in animal feed issues (over 73% of countries) and the use of veterinary medicinal products (95% of countries for controls on their use).

Downstream from livestock production, the involvement of Veterinary Services has extended to include the abattoir, with a dual mission: firstly, to obtain additional animal health information (lesions), and secondly to assess whether meat is fit for consumption.

The survey confirms that Veterinary Services are very generally present, alone or with shared responsibility, at the abattoir, in secondary processing, in controlling the traceability of food products and, in 80% of countries, in their transport and storage. In approximately half of the countries, responsibilities in these areas are shared with other services.

One cannot, however, deduce from this that Veterinary Services are capable of guaranteeing a health and safety continuum at all stages of the production chain. An analysis on a case by case basis would be the only way of identifying breaks in the chain. In many countries, especially developing countries, the coherence of the decision-making chain is not considered very satisfactory. In contrast, some countries consider this to be one of their strengths. To identify any organisational failures and study the sensitive issue of inter-service coordination would require a detailed analysis on an individual country basis.

At the end of the production chain, namely distribution and, especially, the food service industry, Veterinary Services are less systematically involved, and in most cases responsibilities are shared. Given the nature of the controls at these stages, this does not at first sight call into question an integrated approach to sanitary control.

Fully justifying the importance attached to them by the OIE, Veterinary Services play a key role in the safety of international trade. They assume responsibility, and often sole responsibility, for sanitary controls on imports and more particularly exports (signing of sanitary certificates), whether for live animals or for food products, regardless of the distribution of responsibilities between control services.

It should also be noted that Veterinary Services are key players in the field of animal welfare (96% of countries), often with shared responsibilities, though this is not necessarily an indication of whether or not a country attaches importance to the welfare issue. They have a strong presence in the sanitary control of aquatic animals, a responsibility that is also often shared.

Lastly, in an appreciable number of countries Veterinary Services have responsibility for environmental matters relating to farms and agrifood firms (46%) and the control of GMOs (57%).

Developing countries generally direct their efforts towards animal health, whereas developed countries have clearly begun to turn their attention to food safety and other concerns, such as animal welfare and, albeit in a minority of cases, health risks for the environment.

d) The animal health and food safety actions of the control services can only be effective if they are coordinated with the various socio-professional groups involved, namely farmers and field veterinarians at one end of the chain, and agrifood sector professionals at the other.

Rev. sci. tech. Off. int. Epiz., **25** (2)

751

Livestock producers are the first sentinels for the early detection of animal diseases, a vital condition for implementing the appropriate rapid response. Their practices also have an impact on the subsequent quality of food products: use of veterinary medicinal products and other inputs (growth factors) likely to leave residues in products, salmonellas in poultry production, etc. If livestock producers are to act responsibly they must be adequately trained. Training of this kind can be provided by livestock producers' organisations, with the technical support of the public services or private veterinarians operating under the terms of an animal health accreditation mandate. Field veterinarians, or veterinary paraprofessionals under their responsibility, also play a key role at farm level. The OIE *Terrestrial Animal Health Code* (3) does in fact provide for these players to be included, under certain conditions, in an evaluation of Veterinary Services.

The survey reveals major weaknesses at the level of livestock producers' organisations and their veterinary public health responsibilities, and especially for training of livestock producers. Apart from the resources allocated to Veterinary Services, these points were considered the least effective in the system, whether for developed countries or for developing countries (though in the latter the situation was even worse).

The intervention of veterinarians does not appear to compensate for these inadequacies, since their involvement was considered very unsatisfactory, especially in developing countries. The tasks they are contracted to perform, mainly involving disease prevention campaigns, do not enable them to provide effective support.

It would therefore appear that the first link in the chain of surveillance systems for animal diseases (zoonotic or otherwise) and the production chain for food products of animal origin is the weakest at a worldwide level.

The accountability of manufacturers appears to be only moderately satisfactory in developed countries, whereas it is markedly deficient in developing countries. In developed countries, this is probably correlated with primary responsibility for the quality of the products they place on the market having been transferred to the operators, the official services now providing a second level of control, whereas this modern concept is still at the embryonic stage or totally absent in developing countries.

e) Regarding the organisation, resources and effectiveness of animal health and food safety controls, significant differences were found between developed and developing countries. The responses to these questions were, by design, highly subjective, and an evaluation of resources/missions/results was beyond the scope of this study.

The respondents were relatively satisfied with the overall organisation of food safety control, the transparency of the tasks of the health services and the qualifications of official veterinarians.

Independence of the health services, coherence of the decision-making chain, circulation of information, coordination between the people in charge, integration between risk assessment and management, and traceability throughout the chain were seen by developed countries as among their strengths, whereas they were seen as weaknesses in developing countries, especially with regard to circulation of information.

Responsiveness to crises was seen as the major strength of Veterinary Services, especially in the area of animal health. Developing countries, however, seem less effective in dealing with food safety crises. This could well be related to the lack of accountability of manufacturers and therefore of any partnership with them in the management of crises, as well as to a poorer integration of risk management throughout the production chain.

Veterinary Services of all the responding countries complained of insufficient logistical and financial resources, the most glaring inadequacies being in the developing countries. This item received the lowest score when the respondents assessed their services. The survey therefore provides confirmation, if any were required, of the need for capacity-building policies for Veterinary Services, which can now be expected to develop, with the help of international funding agencies (in particular the World Bank), as a consequence of the avian influenza epizootic. Many respondents also complained of a lack of human resources.

f) A very high proportion (84%) of countries that completed the questionnaire underwent a reorganisation of their control services between 1997 and 2005, or reported that one was planned, which clearly shows that policy-makers have felt the need to adapt the administrative organisation to suit changes in the situation in which they work. In 71% of cases, the reorganisation was specifically aimed at ensuring greater consistency 'from the stable to the table'.

Although the data relate to a single moment in time for each country, the juxtaposition of the results very clearly suggests a general movement towards implementing the concept 'from the stable to the table', even if countries still have, albeit to varying degrees, some way to go.

Conclusion

While the organisation of Veterinary Services and their areas of competence vary considerably from one country to another, several major themes can be identified worldwide.

Rev. sci. tech. Off. int. Epiz., **25** (2)

The concept of integrated control of sanitary risks 'from the stable to the table' is becoming widely accepted, though the pace of introduction varies from country to country. This concept implies that all the different professionals involved are accountable. While a high proportion of countries have regulations making manufacturers and livestock producers accountable, many of these countries lack specific organisations for these categories of professionals.

In the majority of countries Veterinary Services are involved in sanitary control activities throughout the food chain, whether alone or in conjunction with other authorities. The degree of economic development is unquestionably an important factor in determining whether a country adopts this approach.

The Delegates who completed the questionnaire were almost unanimous in wishing to see the OIE help to promote and develop the capacities of national Veterinary Services, in view of the weaknesses they reported, the main one being the lack of resources. The present study should prove helpful in this context, particularly during the evaluation of a country's Veterinary Services, by showing how they compare to the national Veterinary Services of other countries.

Acknowledgements

The authors wish to thank Mrs Sophie Desage, École Nationale Vétérinaire d'Alfort, France, who processed the questionnaire returns, and Dr Dugas, Mrs Souyri and Mrs Banaszak of the OIE Publications Department, who distributed and collected the questionnaires.

References

1. Bellemain V. (2004). – Structure and organisation of Veterinary Services to implement the concept 'from the stable to the table'. 21st Conference of the OIE Regional Commission for Europe, Avila (Spain), 28 September-1 October. *In* Compendium of Technical items presented to the OIE International Committee or to Regional Commissions in 2004, trilingual. World Organisation for Animal Health (OIE), Paris.

2. United Nations Office of the High Representative for the Least Developed Countries, Landlocked Developing and Small Island Developing States (UN-OHRLLS) (2005). – List of Least Developed Countries (http://www.un.org/special-rep/ohrlls/ldc/list.htm); List of Landlocked Developing Countries (http://www.un.org/special-rep/ohrlls/lldc/list. htm); List of Small Island Developing States (http://www.un.org/special-rep/ohrlls/sid/list.htm) (accessed on 18 December 2005).

3. World Organisation for Animal Health (OIE) (2005). – Terrestrial Animal Health Code, 14th Ed. OIE, Paris.

Appendix 1

List of the 85 countries that completed the questionnaire

Albania, Algeria, Argentina, Armenia, Australia, Austria, Azerbaijan, Bangladesh, Barbados, Belarus, Belgium, Belize, Benin, Bolivia, Brazil, Burkina Faso, Chad, Chile, Colombia, Côte d'Ivoire, Croatia, Cuba, Cyprus, Czech Republic, Denmark, Egypt, El Salvador, Estonia, Finland, France, Georgia, Germany, Greece, Guatemala, Guinea, Guinea-Bissau, Iceland, Ireland, Israel, Italy, Jamaica, Japan, Kenya, Kuwait, Latvia, Lithuania, Luxembourg, Mexico, Moldavia, Mongolia, Morocco, Mozambique, Myanmar, Namibia, Nepal, Netherlands, Nicaragua, Norway, New Caledonia, Peru, Philippines, Poland, Portugal, Romania, Russia, Senegal, Serbia and Montenegro, Slovakia, Slovenia, South Africa, Spain, Swaziland, Sweden, Switzerland, Taipei China, Tanzania, Thailand, Tunisia, Turkey, Ukraine, United Kingdom, United States of America, Vanuatu, Zambia, Zimbabwe.

Rev. sci. tech. Off. int. Epiz., **25** (2)

753

Appendix 2

Questionnaire sent to OIE Member Countries

Questionnaire used to prepare the IInd technical theme of the OIE Regional Commission for Europe – september 2004
Sent to all the OIE Member Countries on JUNE 2005, in the framework of the OIE *Scientific and Technical Review*
VB//13/06/2005

OIE Scientific and Technical Review - 2005

Questionnaire

Structure and organisation of Veterinary Services
to implement the concept 'from the stable to the table'

Rapporteur: Véronique BELLEMAIN

Country: . ...

Delegate's name:...

Date: ....

Introduction

The 'stable to table' (or 'farm to fork') concept calls for an integrated approach to health issues throughout the production chain, a risk assessment and management continuum that starts upstream (including the conditions for producing animal feed) and extends downstream with the delivery of products to the consumer. Food safety is assured by controls and guarantees geared to each production phase and by constant links and interactions between the phases.

Definitions:

International Animal Health Code, Part 1.1, Chapter 1.1.1 (general definitions) (Edition 2003):

- *Veterinary Administration* means the governmental *Veterinary Service* having authority in the whole country for implementing the animal health measures and international veterinary certification process which the OIE recommends, and supervising or auditing their application.

- *Veterinary Authority* means a *Veterinary Service*, under the authority of the *Veterinary Administration*, which is directly responsible for the application of animal health measures in a specified area of the country. It may also have responsibility for the issuing or supervision of the issuing of *international veterinary certificates* in that area.

- The *Veterinary Services* comprise the *Veterinary Administration* and all the *Veterinary Authorities*.

Note:

This questionnaire relates to animals used to produce food for human consumption, as well as to products derived from these animals. It does not concern companion animals, waste, etc.

Grading:

For several of the questions, a qualitative grading scale is proposed: **"- -" (minor), "-" (fairly minor), "0" (neutral, average), "+" (fairly major) or "++" (major, positive)**.

1

Questionnaire used to prepare the IInd technical theme of the OIE Regional Commission for Europe – september 2004
Sent to all the OIE Member Countries on JUNE 2005, in the framework of the OIE *Scientific and Technical Review*
VB//13/06/2005

Contextual elements: Importance of animal products

1 – What is the economic importance of animal products in your country's economy? *(from - - to ++)*

Livestock
production....................................
Agrifood industries ....
Exports ....

2 – What is the economic importance of the different animal sectors in the production of foodstuffs for human consumption? *(from - - to ++)*

Cattle (meat) ....
Cattle (dairy)..............................
Small ruminants...........................
Pigs..
Poultry (meat and eggs)................
Horses for meat...........................
Lamas ....
Aquatic animals...........................
Bees..
Other (specify) ....

Services involved in food safety from the stable to the table: administrative organisation and fields of intervention

3 – Central Services

Veterinary Administration:

Ministry supervising the Veterinary Services: ....
....
Full name of the Veterinary Administration: ....
....
Acronym *(to be used throughout the rest of the document where required)*: ....

Other structures concerned: *(repeat this section as many times as necessary)*

Supervisory ministry: ....
....
Full name: ....
....
Acronym: ....

Supervisory ministry: ....
....
Full name: ....
....
Acronym: ....

Questionnaire used to prepare the IInd technical theme of the OIE Regional Commission for Europe – september 2004
Sent to all the OIE Member Countries on JUNE 2005, in the framework of the OIE *Scientific and Technical Review*
VB//13/06/2005

4 - Organisation of health risk analysis

Evaluation and management depend- on a single organisation   [ ]
                            - on separate organisations   [ ]

Organisation(s) in charge of evaluating health risks: *(repeat this section as many times as necessary)*

Name: ....
....
Link with one or more ministries: ....
....
Field of competence: ....
....
Acronym: ....

Name: ....
....
Link with one or more ministries: ....
....
Field of competence: ....
....
Acronym: ....

Name: ....
....
Link with one or more ministries: ....
....
Field of competence: ....
....
Acronym:...

5 – Territorial organisation

What are the administrative levels responsible for the following tasks?

Organisational level	(1) Name of the administrative division concerned	(2) Total number in the country	(3) Existence of organisations responsible for:					
			Risk assessment		Drafting regulations		Surveillance and control	
			for AH*	for FS*	for AH*	for FS*	for AH*	For FS*
Central government								
Regions								
Local level								
Municipality								
Other ...								
....								

*AH = animal health, FS = food safety
(1): Give the exact name (land, département, judet, etc.)
(2): Number of these administrative divisions throughout the country
(3): Put a cross in the boxes corresponding to the situation in your country

Provide any further details: See org. chart...
....
....

6 – Field services

Questionnaire used to prepare the IInd technical theme of the OIE Regional Commission for Europe – september 2004
Sent to all the OIE Member Countries on JUNE 2005, in the framework of the OIE Scientific and Technical Review
VB//13/06/2005

Veterinary Authorities:

The Veterinary Authorities are:
- State services   [ ]
- Services reporting to a regional or local authority   [ ]
- Integrated into an independent organisation (Agency)   [ ]

Full name: ....

Acronym *(to be used throughout the rest of the document where required)*: ....

Other structures: *(repeat this section as many times as necessary)*

Full name: ....
....

Acronym *(to be used throughout the rest of the document where required)*: ....

7 – Distribution of tasks and responsibilities for veterinary issues at the central and devolved levels (other than for risk assessment)

		1	2	3	4
		Sole responsibility of the VS	Shared responsibility of the VS	Sole responsibility of other services	Other structure(s) involved (if column 2 or 3 ticked)
Animal identification					
Traceability of animal movements					
Traceability of food products					
Animal health	Prophylactic treatment				
	Health policing				
Food safety of animals and animal products	Slaughter				
	Production				
	Processing				
	Transport				
	Storage				
	Distribution				
	Catering				
Animal feed	Food production				
	Distribution				
	Farm production				
Veterinary medicinal products	Production				
	Distribution				
	Use				
Animal welfare					
Aquatic animals					
Environment					
Laboratory	Animal health				
	Food safety				
Export certificates	Live animals				
	Animal products				
Import controls	Live animals				
	Animal products				
GMOs					
Plant protection					
Other:					
Cosmetics					
Drinking water					

VS = Veterinary Services
(1), (2) and (3) = answer "yes" or "no"
(4): Use the acronyms defined in the previous questions

4

Rev. sci. tech. Off. int. Epiz., **25** (2)

Questionnaire used to prepare the IInd technical theme of the OIE Regional Commission for Europe – september 2004
Sent to all the OIE Member Countries on JUNE 2005, in the framework of the OIE *Scientific and Technical Review*
VB//13/06/2005

8 - <u>Coordination between the different administrations involved in controlling the safety of the food chain</u>

List the organisations concerned:

....

....

	for:	Preparing inter-na-tional nego-tia-tions	Defining regulations	Risk as-sess-ment	Risk man-age-ment	Central ser-vices	Field ser-vices
Coordination is systematically organised:							
- Within a regulatory framework							
- By a specific organisation							
- By customary work practices							
Coordination is informal							
Coordination is occasional							
The Vet. Services are responsible for coordination							
There is no proper coordination							

Answer YES or NO

Overall you consider coordination to be:

- Highly satisfactory .... [ ]
- Satisfactory .... [ ]
- Unsatisfactory .... [ ]
- A source of serious malfunctions .... [ ]

Comments: ....

....

....

....

9 – Have official documents been published that recommend (and/or promote) an integrated "stable to table" approach for the application of food safety measures?

          YES   []   NO   [ ]

If you answered yes, which ones? What is their legal status?

....

....

....

10 - <u>Participation in international organisations</u>

What is the lead organisation in the preparatory work and other activities of the following international organisations? Which other organisations are involved?

	(1) Lead organisation (or sole competence)	(2) Other organisations involved	(3) Quality of coordination
OIE			
WHO			
FAO			
Codex Alimentarius			

(1) and (2) = use the acronyms defined in the previous questions
(3): From -- to ++

Rev. sci. tech. Off. int. Epiz., **25** (2)

Questionnaire used to prepare the IInd technical theme of the OIE Regional Commission for Europe – september 2004
Sent to all the OIE Member Countries on JUNE 2005, in the framework of the OIE *Scientific and Technical Review*
VB//13/06/2005

11 – Recent or planned reorganisations

Has the organisation of the services involved in the safety of the food chain "from stable to table" been reformed in the past ten years, or are reforms planned or in progress?

YES   [ ]   NO   [ ]

If you answered yes, state when and which ones:

....
....
....
....
....

12 - Summary

To summarise the answers to the previous questions, briefly describe the administrative organisation of the services involved in controlling safety throughout the food chain (append a diagram if possible):

....
....
....
....
....
....
....
....

Staff numbers

13 – Number of public officials employed by the Veterinary Services

Definition: This concerns staff working full time for the official Veterinary Services who are prohibited from engaging in private practice in the same fields of competence.

Number (approximate) of public officials in the Veterinary Services:

- Central Administration (including regional levels):   ....
- Number of these who are veterinarians: ....
- Decentralised administration: ....
  Number of these who are veterinarians: ....
- Devolved or field services: ....
  Number of these who are veterinarians: ....

14 – Possibility of mobilising supplementary personnel

In the event of a serious health crisis, such as the occurrence of an epizootic that spreads rapidly throughout the territory, is it possible **easily** to mobilise extra personnel, other than those normally responsible for the field concerned?

To cope with an animal health crisis:

- Mobilisation of food safety officials?	YES	[ ]	NO	[..]
- Mobilisation of veterinary students?	YES	[..]	NO	[ ]
- Mobilisation of officials from other official services?	YES	[ ]	NO	[..]
- Other?	YES	[ ]	NO	[..]

Rev. sci. tech. Off. int. Epiz., **25** (2)

759

Questionnaire used to prepare the IInd technical theme of the OIE Regional Commission for Europe – september 2004
Sent to all the OIE Member Countries on JUNE 2005, in the framework of the OIE *Scientific and Technical Review*
VB//13/06/2005

To cope with a food safety crisis:

- Mobilisation of animal health officials?	YES	[ ]	NO	[..]
- Mobilisation of veterinary students?	YES	[..]	NO	[ ]
- Mobilisation of officials from other official services?	YES	[ ]	NO	[..]
- Other?	YES	[..]	NO	[ ]

If you answered yes, within which regulatory framework? Under which authority?.............................
....
....
....
....
....

Cite an example of a crisis that led to such extra personnel being mobilised: ....
....
....
....
....

15 - Participation of private veterinarians in controlling food safety and animal welfare

Do private veterinarians carry out tasks under the authority of the VS?

YES   [ ]   NO   [ ]

If you answered yes, in which field(s) and within which legal framework(s)? How many private veterinarians are involved? What proportion do they represent of the total number of private veterinarians? (differentiate between rural, mixed and canine veterinarians where appropriate)

	(1) Legal framework			(2) Veterinarians involved	
	Animal health accreditation mandate (3)	Employed part time (contracts)	Other (specify)	Number	Proportion
Disease prevention campaigns					
Health policing					
Laboratories					
Abattoirs					
Food safety (outside the abattoir)					
Zoonoses					
Animal welfare					
Aquatic animals					
Bee health					
Other: specify					

(1): Answer YES or NO
(2): State the number (order by size) and the percentage of the total number of private veterinarians, or a comment
(e.g.: "nearly all rural veterinarians")
(3): The animal health accreditation mandate *("mandat sanitaire")* is a contract between the Administration and the private veterinarian, entrusting permanent tasks to the veterinarian (disease surveillance, intervention in the case of an epizootic, etc.)

Comments: ....
....
....
....

Rev. sci. tech. Off. int. Epiz., **25** (2)

Questionnaire used to prepare the IInd technical theme of the OIE Regional Commission for Europe – september 2004
Sent to all the OIE Member Countries on JUNE 2005, in the framework of the OIE *Scientific and Technical Review*
VB//13/06/2005

Involvement of producers

Livestock producers

16 – Do livestock producers have statutory responsibilities in controlling animal health and the quality of the products supplied?

YES   [..]   NO   [ ]

If you answered yes, which ones? ....
....
....

17 – Are livestock producers organised to control animal diseases?

YES   [..]   NO   [ ]

If you answered yes, how? ....
....
....
....

18 – Are there formal partnerships with the Administration?

YES   [..]   NO   [ ]

If you answered yes, which ones? ....
....
....

Agrifood professionals

19 – Do food producers have statutory responsibilities in controlling the quality of the products supplied?

YES   [..]   NO   [ ]

If you answered yes, which ones? ....
....
....

20 – Are they organised to promote the health quality of their products?

YES   [ ]   NO   [..]

If you answered yes, how? ....
....

General assessment

21 – What, in your view, are the strengths and weaknesses of your country's organisation for guaranteeing the continuous control of safety of the food chain <u>from the stable to the table</u>? *(from "- -" for unsatisfactory aspects to "++" for strong points)*

General organisation of the services concerned   ....
Transparency of the tasks of the health services   ....
Independence of the health services   ....
Coherence of the decision-making chain   ....
Circulation of information   ....
Integration between risk assessment and management   ....

Rev. sci. tech. Off. int. Epiz., **25** (2)

761

Questionnaire used to prepare the IInd technical theme of the OIE Regional Commission for Europe – september 2004
Sent to all the OIE Member Countries on JUNE 2005, in the framework of the OIE *Scientific and Technical Review*
VB//13/06/2005

Coordination between the people in charge . . . .
Traceability throughout the chain . . . .
Effectiveness in routine activities . . . .
Responsiveness to an animal health crisis . . . .
Responsiveness to a food safety crisis . . . .
Human resources . . . .
Qualifications of official veterinarians . . . .
Qualifications of other Veterinary Service officials . . . .
Logistical and financial resources . . . .
Involvement of private veterinarians . . . .
Organisation of livestock producers . . . .
Qualifications of livestock producers . . . .
Accountability of manufacturers . . . .
Other: . . . .
Other: . . . .

Comments: ....
....

Role of the OIE

22 – Do you think the OIE could support its Member Countries in the area of public service organisation, to guarantee better control of the safety of animal foodstuffs?

        YES   [..]   NO   [ ]

If you answered yes, how?

- Study seminars and exchanges of practice
  - At regional level   YES [ ]   NO [..]
  - At international level   YES [..]   NO [ ]
- Raising the awareness of political decision-makers of
  the need for an integrated approach to health issues   YES [..]   NO [ ]
- Developing common approaches with the WHO, FAO and
  Codex Alimentarius regarding these aspects   YES [..]   NO [ ]
- Specifying the relevant provisions of the International Animal
  Health Code   YES [ ]   NO [..]
- Other (specify) ....   YES [ ]   NO [ ]

Further information - Comments

23 - ....

Rev. sci. tech. Off. int. Epiz., 2006, **25** (2), 763-773

The implementation of traceability systems

S. Ammendrup[1] & L.O. Barcos[2]

(1) Danish Veterinary and Food Administration, Region East, Soendervang 4, DK-4100 Ringsted, Denmark
(2) Regional Representation of the World Organisation for Animal Health (OIE) for the Americas,
Cerviño 3101 2°, 1425 Buenos Aires, Argentina

Summary
Traceability is a tool to help countries meet their objectives of controlling, preventing and eradicating animal diseases. This article sets out the required steps in a traceability system.
Before designing a system of traceability, one must identify the different characteristics that need to be traced throughout the various steps in the food production chain. The interaction between different sectors in defining the objectives and the resulting needs of a traceability system is fundamental. A clear legal framework is also indispensable.
European Union (EU) legislation requires identification and registration for cattle, pigs, sheep and goats. For intra-EU trade these animals must be accompanied by a health certificate providing information on their identity and health status. The required identification is harmonised on an EU-wide basis with the aim of ensuring traceability for veterinary purposes. Furthermore EU legislation requires that the traceability of food, feed and food-producing animals be established at all stages of production.

Keywords
Animal identification – Cattle – European Union – Goat – Passport – Pigs – Sheep – Traceability.

Introduction

Before we can consider the implementation of animal identification and traceability in the field certain concepts need to be clarified.

Traceability is not an end in itself, but rather a tool or concept which, in certain circumstances, may be used to gather information, or verify the accuracy of existing information where appropriate, and to carry out surveillance, isolation or even destruction of products or animals in the framework of public health (food safety) or animal health measures (1).

The objectives of a traceability system must be clearly defined, and their scope must be broad, since Veterinary Services work with many animal species and the foodstuffs derived therefrom. Thus, if we are required to trace a piece of meat from the plate to the farm or animal of origin, how extensive does traceability need to be to cover the case of a hamburger, or pieces of chicken (2)?

What the authors are trying to say is that the approach to traceability must be an integrated approach: the point is not merely to trace a product from the plate back to the animal of origin, but to cover all the related processes, to record, recover and analyse all the information required to meet specific objectives, e.g. the prevention of disease, the acquisition of health certificates, etc. (1, 2, 3, 4, 20).

Whatever the specific objectives, animal species, system or country may be, there is a series of factors that are common to all situations, and that must be considered when developing a traceability system, such as legislation, standards, procedures and the competent authority (27).

764

Rev. sci. tech. Off. int. Epiz., 25 (2)

Moreover, the identification of animals, primary and industrial production sites, diagnostic laboratories and the various components of the traceability system chosen is indispensable. Each of these elements must be identified using the most appropriate system available (1, 2, 24).

As we look at the basic elements of a system of animal identification and traceability, we become aware that many of the requisite components are often already in place, since all countries that take animal health measures, and that therefore have operational surveillance systems, are implementing some form of identification and traceability (1, 2, 24, 27).

For traceability systems to be properly implemented or improved in the various countries, a clear distinction must be drawn between identification and traceability, and between objectives or missions and the instruments needed to carry them out (1, 2, 4, 27).

Since 1964 European Community (EC) legislation has included provisions for the identification and registration of live animals. Council Directive 64/432/EEC on animal health problems affecting intra-Community trade in bovine animals and swine (8) requires animals to be identified for certification purposes. This Directive also refers to the creation of computer databases for bovine and porcine animals to store information on animals and their movements. Community rules for the control of classical swine fever and foot and mouth disease were laid down in 1980 (Council Directive 80/217/EEC [9]) and in 1985 (Council Directive 85/511/EEC [10]), respectively. These rules included provisions for monitoring movements of animals which were essential to prevent any spread of disease in the event of an outbreak. However, the detailed arrangements for identifying the animals or for tracing the holding of origin were to be determined by the competent authority of the Member State involved. These directives had been substantially amended over the years to take account of developments and were replaced by the 2001 Council Directive 2001/89/EC (15) on classical swine fever and the 2003 Council Directive 2003/85/EC (17) on foot and mouth disease.

In 1990, with a view to the completion of the internal market, the Council adopted Directive 90/425/EEC (11), which laid down rules concerning veterinary and zootechnical checks applicable in intra-Community trade in certain live animals. According to these rules animals must be identified in accordance with Community rules and be registered in such a way that the original or transit holding, centre or organisation can be traced.

Community rules on identification and registration of bovine, porcine, ovine and caprine animals were laid down in 1992 (Council Directive 92/102/EEC [12]). The two basic objectives of these rules were:

a) the localisation and tracing of animals for veterinary purposes, which are of crucial importance for the control of contagious diseases

b) the management and supervision of livestock premiums as part of the reform of the agricultural policy.

In 2002 the general principles and requirements of food law were laid down in Regulation (EC) No. 178/2002 of the European Parliament and of the Council (16). This Regulation includes the general requirement that 'the traceability of food, feed, food-producing animals, and any other substance, intended to be, or expected to be, incorporated into a food or feed shall be established at all stages of production, processing and distribution'.

Developing a traceability system

The implementation of a national traceability system is a process comprising certain basic steps, in which the public sector must be involved since the process encompasses regulations, standards, international certification, and epidemiological considerations. Private enterprises also may participate, with their own standards and procedures. There will undoubtedly be many similarities and synergies between the two, to their mutual benefit. Some of the points that must be considered when designing a traceability system are outlined below (1, 2, 4, 21, 27).

Objectives

The starting point for any analysis prior to the implementation of a traceability system is a precise description of its objectives, the level of depth sought, and the characteristics to consider. A programme for developing a traceability system should include the various basic elements presented below. However, such a programme would have to be adapted to specific needs and objectives, keeping in mind a series of factors that require discussion by the country's public and private sectors, and by its trading partners (1, 4, 19, 27).

For the system to function, the Veterinary Service must identify its needs with regard to animal health, zoonoses and international certification, and the private sector and trading partners must provide their input as well (1, 2, 23, 24).

The precise objectives of implementing a traceability system will vary from country to country, but for many systems the purposes, requirements and scope could be summarised as follows:

Rev. sci. tech. Off. int. Epiz., **25** (2)

765

– a system to protect and improve a country's animal health status through surveillance measures that meet World Organisation for Animal Health (OIE) standards

– a system which enables preventive measures to be taken, e.g. when a suspected animal or public health problem is detected the source can be swiftly located and appropriate measures taken to avoid its spread

– a system that is applied to animals and animal products, be they for domestic consumption or for export

– a system that is comparable to systems in other countries and provides transparency and confidence to trading partners (25, 26).

Description of the local situation

Once the objectives have been defined, the following step is a clear and detailed description of the country's current situation. This will help determine the necessary changes, although often some of the elements of a traceability system will already exist in different public or private bodies.

Some of the factors that should enter into a diagnosis of the local situation, and that are common to all countries and traceability systems, are as follows (further details on each of these points are given below):

– farms (location, type, practices)

– animal owners

– animal stocks

– movements

– means of transport

– documentation

– legal framework

– establishments where animals are sold.

Farms: location, type, practices

In order to meet the objectives of a traceability system, including disease surveillance, the location of each farm containing animals must be known, by means of maps and polar or satellite coordinates. In many countries, such information is available, but the public and private sectors must join forces to collate it and adapt it to the system's needs.

Such information must be kept up-to-date by means of a specific procedure; for example, the data provided by the different users may be subject to annual authorisation or updating where necessary. The information thereby obtained should be used to establish a farm registry in the form of a database. The information contained in such registries must be analysed to determine whether it is sufficient to meet traceability needs, if it is not, the necessary correction should be made (1, 24).

The information should make it possible to evaluate the various criteria needed to meet the defined animal health and epidemiological objectives. Data regarding the location of the farm, its neighbours, its proximity to cities, the type of farm it is (e.g. livestock only, livestock and crops, tourism, etc.), the animal acquisition practices implemented, the people present, the foodstuffs used, and other inputs, can prove valuable when undertaking epidemiological analyses. The dynamic nature of such information must also be taken into account, along with the need for constant updating.

It is important that information be gathered, and a registry compiled, on all farms, and the system of codification must be standardised. This is because it may be necessary, for a certification procedure or the analysis of a health problem, to obtain information on the use of chemicals, pesticides, veterinary drugs, etc., and, moreover, there may be fields devoted to several activities, such as cropping, livestock, horticulture, tourism, etc. (1, 23, 24).

Animal owners

Animal owners must be identified, along with the farms on which their animals are kept, since they shoulder primary responsibility for animal management and for notification of disease events. In the final analysis, the owner is legally responsible for compliance with standards, and up-to-date data is needed for each one.

The owner of an animal, and the owner of the farm on which it lives, are not necessarily one and the same person. For all the reasons set forth above, it is important to know the geographical location of a farm; the identity of the owner is, however, no less important, albeit for legal rather than epidemiological reasons (1, 2, 24).

Animal stocks

Accurate figures are needed with regard to animal stocks per species and the type of production (breeding, fattening, etc.), and procedures for updating these figures must be specified. Such figures are of epidemiological significance, and necessary to plan surveillance and prevention actions. For example, how can a country take preventive measures, or respond rapidly to an emergency situation, if it does not know how many animals it must deal with, nor their characteristics? Species is also an important criterion, and we should not lose sight of the important role in many diseases of wild animal species, although farm owners do not own them, nor are they responsible for them. Information on the species present can be of great epidemiological significance, when related to data on the farm, zone or region, and the destination or use of the animals concerned (1, 2, 4, 23, 24).

Movements

This section concerns the movement of animals beyond farm boundaries, irrespective of destination or, in the case of transhumance, the movement of animals when they change their grazing region.

In many countries, in which the purpose of traceability is to protect animal health, monitoring animal movements is of fundamental importance. It is, however, necessary to clarify certain concepts regarding the management and processing of this information; epidemiologists in countries where existing systems of traceability are being implemented, modified or improved must specify what needs to be known with regard to the movement of animals. Therefore, epidemiologists should determine their needs on the basis of their surveillance programmes and many other factors, such as flow data, which will provide valuable information for the analysis of preventive measures and surveillance systems, and draw attention to changes in flow that result from trade (25, 26).

Furthermore, the time frame for monitoring animal movements, in order to meet the assigned traceability objectives, should be defined, as it has a decisive bearing on many other factors. The decision to perform analyses on a weekly, monthly, quarterly or annual basis will depend on a set of factors that should be analysed when deciding on objectives. When a specific epidemiological situation arises information on animal movements must be provided within a specific time period, which will vary depending on the disease. The closer one gets to the minimum time period for retrieving such information (for example, 24 h in the case of foot and mouth disease), the better one will be able to halt disease spread through the movement of animals and animal products. It is vital, therefore, that the relevant databases can be consulted within an appropriate time frame.

It is important to establish if the available resources are capable of supplying the necessary information quickly enough. To this end, the relevant documents, registries and databases should be analysed, as should the way in which they interact with each other within the existing legal framework. Changes can then be made if it becomes apparent that information requirements are not being met as quickly as they could be.

Moreover, the systems should be capable of using information held by different agencies, both public and private (1, 4, 24).

Means of transport

Means of transport, on the one hand, and the tool of traceability, on the other, have different roles to play in an animal health system. The OIE animal transport standards must be met for sanitary reasons, and transport owners must be responsible for transporting animals in a way that complies with existing sanitary legislation. To give an example, all animal transport enterprises, even the smallest, know which trips their vehicles have made. Therefore, when an epidemiological analysis of flows is needed, or if an outbreak occurs requiring rapid data on the origin and destination of a consignment of animals, the databases kept by animal transport enterprises can provide, within hours, information on all trips made, for example, in the previous 30, 15 or 5 days within a radius of 10 km from a given farm. Immediate measures can then be taken to prohibit animal movement in these zones, epidemiological analyses can be made, and the farms of destination inspected in order to prevent disease spread.

To that end, on-line information on animal movements is not necessary, but the animal transport enterprises must be registered so that they can be contacted if the need arises. Moreover, the informational needs of Veterinary Services when it comes to flow analysis should be determined, as should the ways in which this information will be processed in the event of an emergency. National Veterinary Services will need to adapt their needs for information according to their objectives, and extract useful information from the databases of transporters.

Documentation

This is another basic issue in the implementation of traceability systems, disease prevention plans and other animal health measures. The first step is to review all existing documentation, such as notifications or reports of suspected cases, farm inspection reports, documents on the movement of animals and animal products, etc. The location of such documentation and its degree of accessibility must be noted, and, if necessary, modifications should be made to bring it in line with the requirements and objectives of the traceability system adopted (1, 2, 4, 23, 24, 27).

Legal framework

A basic aspect in implementing a traceability system, or in taking any national action, is a review of the existing relevant legislation and, on that basis, the unambiguous choice of the competent authority. Subsequently, the details of the programme can be worked out with regard to the responsibilities of each party, compulsory documentation, movement of animals and animal products and the system of registry. In other words, all programme actions must be clearly developed in relation to their legal framework if they are to be properly implemented in the field.

Other aspects to consider when establishing the legal framework are:

– the definition, roles and scope of the competent authority

Rev. sci. tech. Off. int. Epiz., **25** (2)

767

– the definition of system components and the role and obligations of each one

– the documentation/notification of animal health-related events, the transport of animals and animal products and the registration system

– the animal identification system, livestock farms, processing plants, and animal and animal product transport vehicles (1, 2, 4, 23, 24, 25, 26).

Establishments where animals are sold

Available information must be collected in order to determine the location of all establishments where animals are sold, as is the case with transport enterprises. This central register of all establishments may also contain information on animal movements into and out of the establishments, but in any event, this information must be held by the establishments themselves to be used for epidemiological analyses in order to plan preventive action; when a disease event occurs, additional information may be requested in order to trace the origin of the problem and avoid its spread. Each time new information is collected, the corresponding registries and databases should be updated accordingly.

Identification

Ever since traceability has been a topical issue, the concept has been confused with that of identification in many countries and sectors. Indeed, identification is indispensable for traceability to work, but in addition to the identification of animals the establishments where they are kept or processed should be identified as well, and all these data should be cross-checked. Therefore, in each country it is necessary first of all to set the objectives of a traceability system, which is a tool to pursue various actions, such as prevention, control and eradication of diseases or health certification. It must be kept clearly in mind that identification and traceability are not ends in themselves, but rather means or tools to achieve a given objective.

Once objectives have been assigned to the various components involved in a system of traceability and identification in a given country a decision can be taken as to which identification system to use, and how to move from the current to the desired system.

It must be decided which identification system to implement for:

– animals

– farms where animals are kept

– processing plants

– animal transport vehicles

– products.

Furthermore, the registry format must allow for the necessary correlations, for example, products with processing plant, or animals with farms of origin or with any other farm through which they pass during transit.

There is much written documentation on available elements of identification. Whichever choices are made, they must correspond to the set objectives and needs (1, 2, 4, 22, 24).

Analysis of information

The key point and greatest challenge is to understand that traceability is about keeping up-to-date records of disease and other health-related events, and maintaining accessible data on laboratory results, movement of animals and their products. These data will enable Veterinary Services to pursue their specific objectives of prevention, control and eradication of animal diseases and international certification (25, 26).

What is essential is to have access to information and to registries, but the system chosen to enable these analyses will differ from country to country. Some may establish centralised databases containing all necessary information, whereas others may establish regional or local databases. No single recipe can be provided, but it is indispensable for health and certification programme officials to have access to necessary information (1, 2, 19, 21).

Implementation in the field

Once needs have been defined and the situation has been diagnosed, we can go on to the next step: implementation in the field, for which the following items, *inter alia*, must be considered (1, 24):

– planning

– training

– legislation

– financing

– administration

– timetable for implementation.

European Union legislation

The European Union (EU) has laid down requirements for the identification and registration of bovine animals, pigs,

Rev. sci. tech. Off. int. Epiz., **25** (2)

sheep and goats taking into account the specific needs of the various species and the different production systems involved.

Bovine animals

Council Directive 92/102/EEC stated that bovine animals should be identified with an eartag bearing a code which made it possible to identify each animal individually, as well as the holding on which it was born. However, experience, and notably the bovine spongiform encephalopathy crisis, showed that the implementation of Directive 92/102/EEC was not entirely satisfactory and needed further improvement. Therefore, it became clear that it would be necessary to adopt a specific regulation for bovine animals in order to reinforce the provisions of the Directive. Hence, in 1997, Council Regulation (EC) No. 820/97 establishing a system for the identification and registration of bovine animals and regarding the labelling of beef and beef products (13) was adopted. According to this Regulation bovine animals must be identified by an eartag applied to each ear and accompanied by a passport whenever they are moved. These requirements are upheld in the current Regulation (EC) No. 1760/2000 of the European Parliament and of the Council of 17 July 2000 establishing a system for the identification and registration of bovine animals and regarding the labelling of beef and beef products and repealing Council Regulation (EC) No. 820/97 (14).

The EU system for the identification and registration of bovine animals comprises several different elements, all of which are outlined below.

Eartags

According to the detailed rules laid down in Commission Regulation (EC) No. 911/2004 (6), an eartag must be worn in each ear and both tags must contain at least the name and the code or logo of the competent authority or the central competent authority of the Member State which allocated them, the two-letter country code and a numeric code not exceeding 12 digits. An additional bar code may be authorised by the central competent authorities of the Member States. Furthermore the replacement eartags used in the event of eartag losses may contain a mark which indicates that the eartag is a replacement and which includes a Roman numeral indicating how many times the tag has been replaced.

Cattle passports

Commission Regulation (EC) No. 911/2004 also states that a passport, which will accompany the individual animal whenever it is moved, must be issued for each bovine animal within 14 days of the notification of its birth, or, in the case of animals imported from third countries, within

14 days of the notification of its re-identification by the Member State concerned. Passports may be issued for animals from another Member State under the same conditions. In such cases, the passport accompanying the animal on its arrival must be surrendered to the competent authority, which then returns it to the issuing Member State. Whenever a bovine animal is moved, it must be accompanied by its passport. The exception to this requirement is that animals can move within a Member State without being accompanied by a passport provided the Member State has a computerised database which the Commission deems fully operational. In the case of the death of an animal, the passport must be returned by the keeper to the competent authority. When animals are sent to the slaughterhouse, the operator of the slaughterhouse must return the passport to the competent authority. When animals are exported to third countries, the passport must be surrendered by the last keeper to the competent authority at the place where the animal is exported. Commission Regulation (EC) No. 911/2004 specifies that the passport must contain information on the animal (identification code, date of birth, sex, breed or colour of coat), the identification code of the mother or, in the case of an animal imported from a third country, the identification number given by the country of origin and the new identification number issued when the animal entered the EU, an identification number of the holding where the animal was born, and identification numbers of all holdings where the animal has been kept and the dates of each change of holding. In addition the passport must contain the signature of the keeper(s), with the exception of the transporter, and the name of the issuing authority.

Individual registers on each holding

According to Commission Regulation (EC) No. 911/2004 registers kept on each holding must contain up-to-date information on each animal (identification code, date of birth, sex, breed or colour of coat), the date of death of the animal on the holding, or, in the case of departure, the identification code of the holding of destination and the date for departure, and, in the case of arrival, the identification code of the holding of dispatch and the date of arrival. In addition, checks carried out by the competent authority must be recorded in the register.

Computerised national databases

In accordance with the requirements laid down in Council Directive 64/432/EEC computerised national databases for bovine animals have been fully operational since 31 December 1999. These national databases must contain information for each bovine animal (identification code, date of birth, sex, breed or colour of coat), identification code of the mother or, in the case of an animal imported from a third country, the identification number given in the country of origin and the new identification number given when the animal entered the EU, the identification number of the holding where the animal was born, and identification numbers of all holdings where the animal has been kept, the dates of each change of holding and date of death or slaughter. In addition, the database must contain information for each holding (identification number and name and address of the holder). The database must be able to supply at any time a list of identification numbers for all bovine animals present on a holding, and a list of all changes of holding for each bovine animal, starting from the holding of birth or holding of importation.

During 2002 the Commission's Food and Veterinary Office carried out a series of inspection missions in all Member States in order to evaluate the operation of traceability systems and labelling of beef and minced beef. In general the inspection teams found that the requirements for the registration of holdings and the identification of bovine animals were understood in all Member States, and official control systems were in place to monitor their performance. Whilst operational shortfalls were frequently seen, they did not cast doubt on the validity of the basic structure in place.

Electronic identification

The current system already allows countries to use an optional electronic identifier in addition to the two compulsory eartags; however, in accordance with Regulation (EC) No. 1760/2000 of the European Parliament and of the Council, the Commission has submitted a report on the possibility of introducing more extensive use of electronic identification for bovine animals (7). This report is based on the outcome of a large-scale research project on livestock electronic identification (IDEA) launched by the Commission in 1998 and finalised in 2002. This project, which was lead by the Joint Research Centre of the Commission, has demonstrated that in principle, the use of electronic identifiers can deliver a substantial improvement in animal identification systems provided a number of conditions concerning the accompanying measures are fulfilled. The conclusions of this project allow recommendations to be made on technical issues and conclusions to be drawn concerning the conditions of introducing electronic identification arrangements for bovine animals in the EU.

Based on this study electronic identification could be introduced for bovine animals either as a compulsory system in all Member States or as an optional system, where Member States could authorise the replacement of the second eartag with an electronic identifier. The third option would be to maintain the status quo, i.e. the use of an optional electronic identifier in addition to the two eartags.

In view of the direction already taken with regard to the reinforced system for the identification and registration of sheep and goats as laid down in Regulation (EC) No. 21/2004 (18) (see the section on sheep and goats below) the preferred option is the introduction of an optional system that would, over time, become a compulsory system. A decision on the compulsory system should take into account the practical experience gained by those Member States which choose to introduce the system on an optional basis.

Pigs

According to Council Directive 92/102/EEC pigs must be marked as soon as possible, and certainly before they leave the holding, with an eartag or tattoo. The identification mark must make it possible to determine the holding from which they came and enable reference to be made to any accompanying document which must mention the eartag or tattoo. Furthermore, the mark must enable reference to be made to the list of all holdings with animals of the relevant species which must be kept in each Member State.

The identification mark can only be removed or replaced with the permission of the competent authority, and the keeper must record any new mark in the register establishing a link with the previous mark applied to the animal.

The national systems for movements of pigs in their territories must enable the holding from which the animals came and the holding on which the animals were born to be identified.

Pig keepers must keep a register stating the number of animals present on the holding. The register must include an up-to-date record of movements (number of animals involved in each entering and leaving operation) stating as appropriate their origin or destination and the date of such movements and the identification mark.

For animals to be moved to or from a market or collection centre the keeper must provide a document, setting out details of the animals, to the operator at the market or collection centre who is a keeper of the animals on a temporary basis.

Animals imported from a third country must be identified by a mark within 30 days, or before they leave the holding of destination, whichever is sooner. This requirement does not apply if the holding of destination is a slaughterhouse situated on the territory of the Member State in which the veterinary border checks are carried out and the animals are actually slaughtered within the 30-day period. For the purposes of traceability both the identification provided by the third country and the identification allocated by the Member State of destination must be recorded in the holding register.

Rev. sci. tech. Off. int. Epiz., **25** (2)

For movements to other Member States pigs must be accompanied by a health certificate in accordance with Community rules on health problems affecting intra-Community trade in bovine animals and swine (Council Directive 64/432/EEC). The health certificate includes information on the official individual identification of the animals concerned.

In accordance with Council Directive 64/432/EEC computerised national databases which contain information on pig holdings and of the movements of pigs from all holdings have been compulsory since 31 December 2002. Information on each movement of groups of pigs must include the number of pigs being moved, the identification number of the holding or herd of departure as well as the date of departure, and the identification number of the holding or herd of arrival, as well as the date of arrival. To ensure the appropriate implementation of functional databases for recording the movements of porcine animals Community rules for computerised national databases and rules for the registration of holdings were laid down in 2000 by amendment of Council Directive 64/432/EEC and Commission Decision 2000/678/EC (5), respectively.

Sheep and goats

Experience, and particularly the foot and mouth disease crisis in 2001, had shown that the implementation of the provisions for the identification and registration of sheep and goats laid down in Council Directive 92/102/EEC, which were much the same as they were for pigs, had not been satisfactory. However, Council Regulation (EC) No. 21/2004 addressed this acknowledged need for more stringent provisions by establishing a system for the identification and registration of ovine and caprine animals (18) that reinforced the provisions of Council Directive 92/102/EEC. This new system comprises various different elements, most of which are outlined below.

Means of identification

There must be a means of identification, approved by the competent authority, which will enable individual animals to be identified. As a general rule this means two eartags to ensure that identification remains possible even if one eartag is lost. Member States may authorise the use of an electronic identifier instead of the second eartag. Technical characteristics are laid down to ensure the compatibility of readers and identifiers so that the electronic identifiers can be read throughout the EU. For animals not involved in intra-Community trade the competent authority may authorise the use of a tattoo or a national system approved by the Commission instead of the second eartag.

Individual registers on each holding

Keepers must keep a register on the holding with up-to-date information on movements of animals to and from the holding, including information on the holding of departure and the holding of destination. From the date when electronic identification becomes compulsory information on the individual identification codes will be included in these registers.

Movement documents

Movement documents must accompany each group of animals throughout the movement. This document must contain the following: information on the holding of departure, the number of animals moved, the holding of destination or the next keeper, and data concerning the transport as well as the date of departure and the signature of the keeper. From the date when electronic identification becomes compulsory information on the individual identification codes will be included in the documentation.

Computerised national databases

Member States must establish a computerised database with information on all holdings. From the date when electronic identification becomes compulsory all movements of groups of animals will be recorded in the database.

Other provisions

The reinforced system as outlined in Council Regulation (EC) No. 21/2004 entered into force on 9 July 2005 and since then all animals born on a holding have been identified according to the new provisions. Options are given to Member States to apply the measures slightly differently in certain circumstances, e.g. the current system requires that animals be identified by the time they are six months of age, but this period may be extended to nine months if animals are kept in free-range or extensive farming conditions. All animals must, however, be identified before they leave the holding. In addition, for animals intended for slaughter before 12 months of age, the competent authority of the Member States may authorise a system by which animals are identified by means of one eartag bearing the code of the holding of birth instead of the individual identification code. Whenever a batch of these animals is moved the only information recorded in the holding register and the movement document is the code of the holding of birth and the total number of animals being transported. When electronic identification becomes compulsory some animals will be provided with individual identification codes which will be recorded in the holding register and movement document, other animals will continue to be identified by the holding of origin as mentioned above.

With regard to electronic identification, the IDEA Project included sheep and goats as well as bovine animals. The main conclusion of the IDEA Project was that the technology involved in the electronic identification of

Rev. sci. tech. Off. int. Epiz., **25** (2)

771

sheep and goats has been developed to such an extent that it can be applied. However, the implementing measures required for the proper introduction of the system of electronic identification on a Community-scale have not yet been developed, although the final report of the IDEA project provides some recommendations. Council Regulation (EC) No. 21/2004 foresees that further guidelines and procedures for the implementation shall be adopted through the Standing Committee on the Food Chain and Animal Health so that the general electronic identification of sheep and goats can be implemented by 1 January 2008. This date shall be confirmed or amended in view of the practical experience gained by those countries implementing an optional system.

be clearly defined in order to make an assessment of the situation and, on that basis, design an appropriate traceability system. When defining the objectives, needs and means of implementation, the different sectors involved, both public and private, and the trading partners must cooperate very closely.

To implement traceability, it is important to bear in mind that it is a tool to assist in the prevention, control and eradication of animal diseases, including zoonoses, and in certification. To the extent that it is understood that traceability is a tool, that identification is one of the aspects of traceability, and that it goes hand-in-hand with the analysis of recorded information, the various components involved can be successfully implemented.

Conclusions

When defining the purpose of a traceability system national objectives regarding the prevention, control and eradication of animal diseases, including zoonoses, must

La mise en place des systèmes de traçabilité

S. Ammendrup & L.O. Barcos

Résumé
La traçabilité est un instrument dont les pays peuvent se servir pour remplir leurs objectifs de prophylaxie, de prévention et d'éradication des maladies animales. Les auteurs décrivent les étapes successives de la mise en place réussie d'un système de traçabilité.
Avant de concevoir un système de traçabilité, il convient de définir les caractéristiques que l'on cherche à surveiller tout au long de la chaîne de production d'aliments. Il est fondamental que les différents secteurs concernés participent à la définition des objectifs du système de traçabilité et des besoins qui en résultent. De même, il est indispensable de disposer d'un cadre juridique clair.
L'identification et l'enregistrement des animaux sont obligatoires dans l'Union européenne pour les espèces bovine, porcine, ovine et caprine. Lors des échanges intracommunautaires, ces animaux doivent être accompagnés d'un certificat indiquant leur identité et leur statut sanitaire. Les critères d'identification ont été harmonisés au sein de l'Union européenne afin de garantir la traçabilité pour motifs sanitaires. En outre, la législation européenne impose la traçabilité des denrées alimentaires, des aliments pour animaux et des animaux destinés à l'alimentation, et ce à tous les stades de la production.

Mots-clés
Bovin – Caprin – Identification animale – Ovin – Passeport – Porcin – Traçabilité – Union européenne.

Rev. sci. tech. Off. int. Epiz., **25** (2)

Aplicación de los sistemas de trazabilidad

S. Ammendrup & L.O. Barcos

Resumen
Los países recurren a los sistemas de trazabilidad para alcanzar sus objetivos de control, prevención y erradicación de enfermedades animales. En este artículo se exponen los componentes obligatorios de los sistemas de trazabilidad.
Antes de desarrollar un sistema de trazabilidad deben determinarse las distintas características que se rastrearán en las diferentes etapas de la cadena de producción de alimentos. Es de fundamental importancia que los distintos sectores trabajen en colaboración a la hora de definir los objetivos y las necesidades consiguientes de un sistema de trazabilidad. También es indispensable que se disponga de un marco legal claro.
La normativa de la Unión Europea (UE) exige la identificación y el registro del ganado bovino, porcino, ovino y caprino. Para que puedan comercializarse dentro de la UE, los animales deben ir acompañados por un certificado sanitario con información sobre su identidad y estado sanitario. La identificación obligatoria se armonizó en todos los países de la UE para garantizar la trazabilidad con fines veterinarios. Además, la reglamentación de la UE impone que se establezca la trazabilidad de los alimentos, piensos y animales para producción de alimentos en todas las etapas de la cadena alimentaria.

Palabras clave
Bovino – Caprino – Identificación de los animales – Ovino – Pasaporte – Porcino – Trazabilidad – Unión Europea.
■

References

1. Barcos L.O. (2001). – Recent developments in animal identification and the traceability of animal products in international trade. *In* Traceability of animals and animal products (H.A. MacDaniel & M.K. Sheridan, eds). *Rev. sci. tech. Off. int. Epiz.*, **20** (2), 640-651.

2. Barcos L.O. (2004). – Identificación animal y trazabilidad [Animal identification and traceability]. Technical Item II. *In* Proc. 72nd OIE General Session, 23-28 May, Paris. Document 72 SG/10. World Organisation for Animal Health, Paris.

3. Canadian Food Inspection Agency (CFIA) (1999). – Enforcement of the National Cattle Identification Program (R. Robinson & J.A. Kellar, eds.). CFIA, Ottawa, 1-24.

4. Canadian Food Inspection Agency (CFIA) (1999). – Regulation amending the health of animals regulations. Section 172. Animal Identification. CFIA, Ottawa.

5. Commission of the European Communities (2000). – Commission Decision 2000/678/EC of 7 November 2000 laying down detailed rules for registration of holdings in national databases for porcine animals as foreseen by Council Directive 64/432/EEC. *Off. J. Eur. Union*, **L 281**, 16-17.

6. Commission of the European Communities (2004). – Commission Regulation (EC) No. 911/2004 of 29 April 2004 implementing Regulation (EC) No. 1760/2000 of the European Parliament and of the Council as regards eartags, passports and holding registers. *Off. J. Eur. Union*, **L 163**, 65-70.

7. Commission of the European Communities (2005). – Report from the Commission to the Council and the European Parliament on the possibility of introduction of electronic identification for bovine animals. COM(2005) 9 final. European Commission, Brussels.

8. Council of the European Communities (1964). – Council Directive 64/432/EEC of 26 June 1964 on animal health problems affecting intra-Community trade in bovine animals and swine. *Off. J. Eur. Union*, **121**, 1977-2012.

9. Council of the European Communities (1980). – Council Directive 80/217/EEC of 22 January 1980 introducing Community measures for the control of classical swine fever. *Off. J. Eur. Union*, **L 47**, 11-23.

10. Council of the European Communities (1985). – Council Directive 85/511/EEC of 18 November 1985 introducing Community measures for the control of foot-and-mouth disease. *Off. J. Eur. Union*, **L 315**, 11-18.

11. Council of the European Communities (1990). – Council Directive 90/425/EEC of 26 June 1990 concerning veterinary and zootechnical checks applicable in intra-Community trade in certain live animals and products with a view to the completion of the internal market. *Off. J. Eur. Union*, **L 224**, 29-41.

12. Council of the European Communities (1992). – Council Directive 92/102/EEC of 27 November 1992 on the identification and registration of animals. *Off. J. Eur. Union*, **L 355**, 32-36.

13. Council of the European Communities (1997). – Council Regulation (EC) No. 820/97 of 21 April 1997 establishing a system for the identification and registration of bovine animals and regarding the labelling of beef and beef products. *Off. J. Eur. Union*, **L 117**, 1-8.

14. Council of the European Communities (2000). – Regulation (EC) No. 1760/2000 of the European Parliament and of the Council of 17 July 2000 establishing a system for the identification and registration of bovine animals and regarding the labelling of beef and beef products and repealing Council Regulation (EC) No. 820/97. *Off. J. Eur. Union*, **L 204**, 1-10.

15. Council of the European Communities (2001). – Council Directive 2001/89/EC of 23 October 2001 on Community measures for the control of classical swine fever. *Off. J. Eur. Union*, **L 316**, 5-35.

16. Council of the European Communities (2002). – Regulation (EC) No. 178/2002 of the European Parliament and of the Council of 28 January 2002 laying down the general principles and requirements of food law, establishing the European Food Safety Authority and laying down procedures in matters of food safety. *Off. J. Eur. Union*, **L 31**, 1-24.

17. Council of the European Communities (2003). – Council Directive 2003/85/EC of 29 September 2003 on Community measures for the control of foot-and-mouth disease repealing Directive 85/511/EEC and Decisions 89/531/EEC and 91/665/EEC and amending Directive 92/46/EEC. *Off. J. Eur. Union*, **L 306**, 1-87.

18. Council of the European Communities (2004). – Council Regulation (EC) No. 21/2004 of 17 December 2003 establishing a system for the identification and registration of ovine and caprine animals and amending Regulation (EC) No. 1782/2003 and Directives 92/102/EEC and 64/432/EEC regarding the labelling of beef and beef products. *Off. J. Eur. Union*, **L 5**, 8-17.

19. Disney W.T., Green J.W., Forsythe K.W., Wiemers J.F. & Weber S. (2001). – Benefit-cost analysis of animal identification for disease prevention and control. *In* Traceability of animals and animal products (H.A. MacDaniel & M.K. Sheridan, eds). *Rev. sci. tech. Off. int. Epiz.*, **20** (2), 385-405.

20. Hunter S. (1996). – Tracing single animals for quality control purposes. Allflex Europe SA, France.

21. Instituto Argentino de Normalización (IRAM) (1994). – Normas IRAM-IACC-ISO sobre gestión y aseguramiento de la calidad. Cuarta edición ampliada en 1998. IRAM, Buenos Aires.

22. Landais E. (2001). – Le marquage du bétail dans les systèmes pastoraux traditionnels. *In* Traceability of animals and animal products (H.A. MacDaniel & M.K. Sheridan, eds). *Rev. sci. tech. Off. int. Epiz.*, **20** (2), 445-462.

23. Neophytou G. (1999). – Systems of animal identification and their importance for disease surveillance. *In* Comprehensive reports on Technical Items presented to the International Committee or to Regional Commissions. OIE, Paris.

24. Van Vugt F., Ferri G., Scudamore J., Vallat B., Chaisemartin D., Bonbon E., Zwingmann E., Caja G., Almanza de Lara V., Kellar J., Marshall B., Clifford J., Hammerschmidt N., McCutcheon S. & Barcos L. (1998). – Seminario Internacional de la OIE sobre identificación permanente de animales y trazabilidad. Del Campo al Plato, 25-26 November, Buenos Aires. Secretaría de Agricultura, Ganadería, Pesca y Alimentos (SAGPyA)/ Servicio Nacional de Sanidad y Calidad Agroalimentaria (SENASA), Buenos Aires.

25. Wilson D.W. & Beers P.T. (2001). – Global trade requirements and compliance with World Trade Organization agreements: the role of tracing animals and animal products. *In* Traceability of animals and animal products (H.A. MacDaniel & M.K. Sheridan, eds). *Rev. sci. tech. Off. int. Epiz.*, **20** (2), 379-384.

26. World Organisation for Animal Health (OIE) (2003). – Terrestrial Animal Health Code, 12th Ed. OIE, Paris.

27. World Organisation for Animal Health (OIE) (2003). – Veterinary Services: organisation, quality assurance, evaluation. *Rev. sci. tech. Off. int. Epiz.*, **22** (2).

Rev. sci. tech. Off. int. Epiz., 2006, **25** (2), 775-792

Antimicrobial resistance at farm level

J.F. Acar [1] & G. Moulin [2]

(1) Université Pierre et Marie Curie, Paris, and World Organisation for Animal Health, 14 rue de Prony, 75017, Paris, France.
(2) AFSSA Fougères, Agence Nationale du Médicament Vétérinaire, B.P. 90203, La Haute Marche, Javené, 35302 Fougères Cedex, France

Summary

Bacteria that are resistant to antimicrobials are widespread. This article reviews the distribution of resistant bacteria in farm environments. Humans, animals, and environmental sites are all reservoirs of bacterial communities that contain some bacteria that are susceptible to antimicrobials and others that are resistant.

Farm ecosystems provide an environment in which resistant bacteria and genes can emerge, amplify and spread. Dissemination occurs via the food chain and via several other pathways.

Ecological, epidemiological, molecular and mathematical approaches are being used to study the origin and expansion of the resistance problem and its relationship to antibiotic usage.

The prudent and responsible use of antibiotics is an essential part of an ethical approach to improving animal health and food safety. The responsible use of antibiotics during research is vital, but to fully contribute to the containment of antimicrobial resistance 'prudent use' must also be part of good management practices at all levels of farm life.

Keywords

Antibiotic residue – Antimicrobial resistance – Bacterial clone – Farm – Food safety – Resistance gene.

Introduction

Resistance to an antimicrobial agent was first recognised by scientists soon after penicillin was used for the first time. It became clear that there were two types of bacterial strain: those naturally resistant to penicillin, already known as out of the spectrum of the compound; and those which had acquired an ability to survive and multiply in the presence of the compound. The first type of strain has not been widely studied and deserves epidemiological consideration when exploring the effect of an antibiotic on a microbial community. The second type of strain has been extensively studied because its acquired mechanism of resistance has had major consequences for human health.

The loss of a previously effective antibiotic stimulates research into a means of overcoming the resistance mechanism and developing another therapeutic agent. The story of the discovery of antibiotics, the emergence of resistant bacteria shortly afterwards (usually within two years), and the race to develop new antibacterial agents, is well known and has been reported many times.

Antimicrobial resistance is a natural phenomenon which is an inherent risk associated with any use of antimicrobial medication (3).

As a background to this article, it is important to keep the following points in mind:

a) since the late 1980s, the number of new antibiotics coming on to the market has declined. In fact, no new chemical class of antibacterial has been discovered. This situation has prompted a reevaluation of antimicrobial usage and generated multidirectional efforts to optimise the use of antibiotics in hospitals and in the community. In addition, more widespread surveillance of resistant bacteria has opened the door to extensive research into the biochemical mechanisms, molecular identity and genetics of resistance traits (68);

b) since the discovery of plasmids in the early 1960s, bacterial systems that allow the acquisition and transmission of genetic material between members of their community have been explored. Strains of *Salmonella* were among the first species of zoonotic bacteria to be studied (6, 14).

Rev. sci. tech. Off. int. Epiz., **25** (2)

Studies on bacterial resistance have shown that there is a huge diversity of resistance mechanisms, the distribution and interaction of which is complex and mostly unknown. Moreover, resistance mechanisms can change and evolve as quickly as bacterial cells multiply, which sometimes means within very short periods of time (4).

Bacterial clones that are resistant to one or more antibiotics are now everywhere. Containment of bacterial resistance is a key issue in human medicine (nosocomial infections and resistant pathogens acquired in the community). The World Health Organization (WHO) (107) has extensively developed strategies to contain bacterial resistance, e.g.:

– updating knowledge of pathogen resistance

– using appropriate antibiotics in defined circumstances and with a defined treatment duration

– ending the use of antibiotics in cases where bacteria are not likely to be the cause of disease.

It is assumed that reducing the amount of antibiotics used will reduce their selective pressure and will help to control the incidence of resistant strains. Studies are needed to scientifically document this hypothesis.

Antibiotic usage in animals has definitely contributed to the current situation as regards resistant bacteria. Antibacterials contribute to the development of resistance in animal pathogens and commensals, and thus increase the risk that humans will be colonised and/or infected with resistant zoonotic bacteria (1, 37). This important consequence has been reviewed in many previous publications, and will not be detailed in this article (59, 95).

The aim of this paper is to present the actual situation of antimicrobial resistance at farm level and demonstrate how the prudent and responsible use of antibiotics may contribute to its containment and improved food safety, as well as reduce the hazards of the transmission of zoonotic food-borne pathogens that are resistant to antibiotics.

Resistant bacterial clones on the farm

The farm is as a large ecosystem composed of several compartments with different niches. Overlapping between niches and compartments allows microbes to disseminate.

Resistant bacterial strains are found everywhere. A review of the literature reveals that they are reported in all studies exploring animate or inanimate niches. Enterocci, Enterobacteriacae, and non fermentative Gram-negative

rods are the most frequently studied species. The prevalence of resistant microorganisms is variable and the species affected depends on the niches explored. Resistant microorganisms have been found in conventional farms and also in organic farms, showing how widespread is the bacterial resistance phenomenon (74, 80, 81, 96, 98).

The principal compartments on the farm are:

– the humans who live and work there

– food animals (cattle, sheep, pigs, poultry), horses, pets, wild animals (rodents, insects, birds)

– the environment, e.g. water, soil, feeds, wastewaters, sewage, manure, lagoons, etc.

Humans on the farm

All human beings, including farm workers and their families, have huge numbers of commensal bacteria on their skin and in their digestive tract.

Only a small number of studies on antimicrobial resistance have been performed in healthy individuals in the community, but they have all shown that humans were colonised with resistant clones of bacteria, even months after having received antibiotics (15, 49, 66).

Studies in adults and children documented that among Gram-positive, Gram-negative and anaerobic bacteria found in intestinal flora a number of strains are resistant to one or more antibiotics; resistance to tetracyclins, β-lactam compounds, sulfonamide and trimethoprim is often found. The extent of the colonisation with resistant strains appears to be related to geographical location and environmental conditions (46).

It is recognised that crowding, poor hygiene, and extensive antibiotic use in the community increase the risk that healthy humans will carry resistant strains. Antibiotic absorption – even in appropriate amounts following a justified treatment – favours the carriage of strains that are resistant to antibiotics.

A large number of studies have been conducted on farms. They were mostly focused on exploring the similarity between resistant strains carried by humans and resistant strains carried by food animals after receiving an antibiotic treatment, e.g. enterococci resistant to glycopeptides (avoparcin, vancomycin) or enteroccoci resistant to virginiamycin (44, 52, 105). The farm workers and farm inhabitants often have strains similar to those isolated in the animals. Comparison with healthy persons living elsewhere or workers less exposed to animals sometimes shows that farm workers carry more resistant bacteria in their faecal flora than the control population. In other studies, such difference is not found. The type of work and the period of exposure may explain the different results (62, 63, 85, 93, 101).

Animals on the farm

Food animals

For four decades food animals have been known to harbour bacteria that are resistant and multiresistant to the antibiotics used in the farm. The resistant strains are found mostly among the commensal flora. Animal pathogens can be also resistant. Antibiotics given orally and for a long period of time have a stronger selective pressure and facilitate the prevalence of resistant strains (26, 42, 48, 53, 70).

The digestive tract of animals is a major bacterial reservoir where resistance genes can be acquired and from where resistant strains can be disseminated (36, 105, 109).

Antimicrobial substances given in low doses for growth promotion were recognised as selectors for resistant strains in the 1960s. The possible consequences for human health were discussed by the Swan committee (1969), which advised that antibiotics used to treat human infections should not be used for growth promotion. More recently, following the Danish experiment (108), the European Community decided to ban the use of antibiotics as growth promoters in Europe.

The food animals on a farm are at present a very large reservoir of resistant bacteria. We will not try to review the large number of publications which have established that all antibiotics used in animals have their corresponding resistant strains. Moreover, as happens in humans, multiple resistant strains are often found since they have a survival advantage in environments where multiple antibiotics are used.

Food animals may be colonised with bacteria present in their feed. *Salmonella* is a dangerous contaminant, often reported in feed, and must be controlled (20, 21, 22, 43, 79).

Other animals

Food animals are not the only reservoir of antibiotic-resistant bacteria: pets, wild rodents, birds, and insects may also harbour resistant bacteria and spread them among all compartments of the farm (18, 33, 103). The ways in which these bacteria spread from animal to animal are very intricate and this complex transmission network has yet to be fully explored.

Environmental sites

Much of the work undertaken on farms contributes to the contamination of the environment with resistant bacteria.

The faecal and urine waste of the animals contains both resistant bacteria and antibiotic residues. Sewage, slurries, manure, surface water, sediments, even groundwater may contain, in addition to their specific bacterial flora, resistant bacteria from animals, and some antibiotic residues. This type of environment favours the emergence of resistance, the transfer of genes, and the amplification of resistant strains. New studies are carefully exploring environmental reservoirs and have documented the survival of bacteria in the environment and some of their patterns of antibiotic resistance (11, 12, 13, 41, 45, 84, 88).

Horizontal transfer and the spread of resistant clones

The spread of resistant clones is never monodirectional; it occurs between the different compartments as they overlap. The amplification of resistant bacteria, which facilitates their spread, is generally caused by antibiotics or their residues in the reservoir. When resistant bacteria are pathogens, the amplification occurs in the diseased animals (or humans). Adequate treatment with the appropriate antibiotic and the isolation of the patient are essential for controlling bacterial spread.

The strategy for controlling infections in food animals varies according to the disease and to the species. Bacterial cells, genes, and antibiotic residues interact in various ways. Antibiotics tend to diminish compartmentalisation: i.e. the presence of the same antibiotics in different niches means that resistant bacteria in one compartment can spread and survive in another (64).

It is important to note that clonal transmission and horizontal transfer of genes may occur together in a bacterial population. The relative frequency of each of these mechanisms of spread is unknown. It may depend upon the compartment, the bacteria and the antibiotic being used. However, we do know that horizontal transfer is a slow and complex process that takes place slowly in the environment and in the gut; while clonal transmission can occur very quickly between one host or niche and another.

It has been known for several decades that antimicrobial-resistant bacteria can spread from animals to humans (48). It was shown that small amounts of oxytetracyclin given to animals could select in their intestinal flora *Escherichia coli* resistant to tetracycline. Surprisingly, a few weeks later, resistant *E. coli* were also found in the intestinal flora of people living on the same farm.

A very large number of publications demonstrate that resistant strains in animals can be shared with farm

778

Rev. sci. tech. Off. int. Epiz., **25** (2)

workers and families living on the farm. An early experiment was done with the antibiotic nurseothricin, which is not used in humans; strains resistant to it were recovered in both animals and farm workers (106). More recent studies (principally concerned with enterococci and Enterobacteriaceae [2, 27, 36, 100]) confirm that resistant bacteria can be transmitted from animals to humans.

The transmission from animals to other animals and to humans can happen from direct or indirect contact (7, 93, 97, 103). Resistant bacterial strains originating from a calf were demonstrated to have colonised mice, pigs, chickens, flies, turkeys, and humans (56).

Moreover, airborne transmission has been documented in concentrated swine-feeding operations. The bacterial concentration can be as high as 104 colony-forming units (CFU)/m³ to 107 CFU/m³. Enterococci, staphylococci, *Pseudomonas, Listeria, Bacillus, E. coli* were recovered. Resistant enterococci were also recognised as airborne transmissible (16).

The spread of resistant bacteria from humans to animals has not been well documented. A study mentioned by S. Levy, in Ambroseli park in Kenya, showed that baboons that ate human refuse and garbage had a flora with resistant strains similar to those isolated from humans, while baboons from the wild did not (48).

Recently, methicillin-resistant *Staphylococcus aureus* colonising dogs, cats and horses were suspected to have originated from attendant personnel (65, 86). It is likely that the probability of transmission from humans to animals depends upon the geographical location, the level of hygiene, the size of the farm, and the type of integrated farming which takes place.

The magnitude and the dynamic of the spread of resistant strains between the different niches of the farm ecosystems are unknown. Spatial and temporal epidemiology studies might in the future bring new insight into the problem (29, 58).

Farms, like hospitals, are places where a large number of various bacteria coexist and different antibiotics are used. New resistance traits may emerge and horizontal transfer of genes between bacterial cells may result in new resistant microorganisms and new combinations of resistance genes, leading to different patterns of resistance.

In humans and animals the gut is the site for the horizontal transfer of genes. The emergence of clones that have acquired resistance genes in the gut has been documented in several papers (30, 94). A recent study has shown the transfer of plasmid encoding CMY-2 beta-lactamase from *E. coli* to *Salmonella* Newport in turkey intestinal tracts, even without the selective pressure of an antibiotic (73).

Beta-lactamase CMY-2 was discovered in a *Klebsiella* infection affecting a patient in a hospital in Greece in 1990. Four years later CMY-2 was found in a *Salmonella* from Algeria. Since then, CMY-2 has spread and can now be found in a large number of *Salmonella* serotypes. The journey of this beta-lactamase from human *Klebsiella* to *Salmonella* remains a mystery. It is worth noticing that both species are epidemic nosocomial pathogens; in the case of *Salmonella* this is mostly in developing countries (5, 69).

Horizontal transfers have been documented in environmental sites such as wastewater, surface water, sediments and manure. The microbial communities at these sites may contain different amounts of antibiotic residues and genetic material encoding resistance.

There is a lot that is not known about environmental bacteria and which deserves to be investigated, e.g. the role of uncultured bacteria and of *Pseudomonas, Acinetobacter,* anaerobes and enterococci, in the emergence and dissemination of resistance (67, 75).

Recently, two mechanisms of resistance originating in *Shewanella* (class D beta-lactamase and the new plasmid-mediated trait qnR governing quinolone resistance) were reported to have been transmitted horizontally to other bacteria (35, 71, 72).

Bacteria in the genera *Shewanella* and *Xanthomonas* also have chromosomal super-integrons similar to those found in the family Enterobacteriaceae. Are they the origin of such structures (76)?

Exchanges in and out of the farm ecosystem

The farm ecosystem is open: an exchange of bacteria resistant and susceptible to antibiotics occurs at the local level and also at regional, national and international levels as a result of modern systems of farming and export. Resistant strains entering the farm are transported by people, new food animals, birds, rodents, insects, water and feed. Contaminated feed as a vehicle for salmonella is an important problem which needs a surveillance and control strategy (82).

The dissemination of resistant bacteria out of the farm follows multiple pathways, but wastewater, effluent, and manure are important in this regard; in such vehicles, both resistant and susceptible bacteria come into contact with antibiotic residues, and although the amount can be low it is sometimes high enough to maintain the selective pressure. Antibiotics may accumulate in sediments and they take varying amounts of time to degrade.

Rev. sci. tech. Off. int. Epiz., **25** (2)

779

To antibiotic residues, we must add other pharmaceuticals: disinfectants, heavy metals, coccidiostats and many other compounds that have some antibacterial effect (11, 45).

Animals waste is also an important vehicle of dissemination for resistant bacteria and genes. When used as fertilizer vegetables can be contaminated (40, 87). Contamination of drinking and domestic water has also been documented (8).

If there are any resistant bacteria (pathogenic, commensal or zoonotic) present in food animals at the time of slaughter this can start a chain of contamination which may reach the retail food sector and the consumer (19, 54, 102).

Dissemination from the farm by sewage and neighbouring spread may account for resistant bacteria found in rivers and sediments (9, 17). Human waste may also contribute to that contamination (55, 83).

The big picture of the farm with its different compartments and the constant exchange between a widespread community of bacteria, some of which are resistant and some of which are susceptible to antibiotics, raises a major question about how resistant microorganisms survive.

In sites where some antibiotics are present, the selective pressure maintains the resistant strains and amplifies them. This selective pressure can have a direct effect on strains harbouring the corresponding resistance mechanism. It can also have an indirect effect if cross resistance between bacterial species allows for antibiotics with similar modes of action to select for bacterial species with similar mechanisms of resistance, or if selection by one antibiotic for a sequence in which all traits of resistance are linked together genetically results in co-resistance of a bacterial species to more than one type of antibiotic.

In sites where antibiotics are absent, resistant bacterial strains tend to reach an equilibrium with susceptible strains. Resistant strains may persist at different levels of prevalence; they usually do not disappear completely (78). Several mechanisms have been described which aim to maintain resistant plasmids and to ensure the survival of the resistant strain:

– compensatory mutations, which improve the fitness of the strain, occur in order to adapt to the cost of fitness that occurs in response to the acquisition of resistance (47).

– plasmids themselves may enhance the host fitness (25).

– plasmids may regulate killer genes in the host and maintain themselves by protecting the bacterial cell (31).

Other mechanisms are likely to exist to stabilise resistance genes in the bacterial cell.

It is remarkable to note that resistant traits once acquired are difficult to eliminate (24, 78, 94).

Human and animal bacteria may survive outside of the host for some time in the environment. *Salmonella*, in particular, can survive for long periods in the environment, promoting transmission to a new host. Because *Salmonella* are able to infect a large number of animal species, including flies, there is a complex cycle of host to non-host survival which results in recurring outbreaks that are difficult to manage (104).

The prudent use of antibiotics

We have not detailed the different types of antibiotic use in animals (therapy, metaphylaxis and feed efficiency) as they do not fall within the scope of this paper. However, whatever the reason for using antibiotics, a few important points should be noted:

– selection of resistant strains is more likely to occur when antibiotics are given for a long time. The role of antibiotics used as growth promoters has been established as mentioned earlier. Differences between antibiotics as selectors for resistance should be clarified in the future (39, 43);

– antibiotics facilitate the emergence of resistant strains. High concentrations of antibiotics in contact with the bacterial reservoir (gut, or environment) kill susceptible bacteria and increase the prevalence of pre-existing resistant strains. Subinhibitory concentrations may favour horizontal transfer of genes because at such concentrations, potential receiver strains are not killed. However the effect of various antibiotic concentrations on bacterial cell functions has not been fully explored. The words 'subinhibitory concentrations' are vague because inhibitory concentrations are different for each bacterial species and there is never any definition of what constitutes a subinhibitory concentration;

– no general law or general statement can be applied to the interaction of bacteria and antimicrobials. It depends upon the microbial community, the local and environmental factors, the microbial species and the antibiotic being used;

– a huge number of resistance genes and mechanisms have been recognised to date. Usually resistant strains have multiple mechanisms of resistance for the same antibiotic as well as different mechanisms of resistance for different antibiotics;

– some types of resistance are easy to select among the susceptible bacterial populations: e.g. mutations to quinolones or rifamycin;

– other types of resistance emerge more slowly from a covert evolution of genes whose origin are often unknown: e.g. vancomycin and avoparcin and the VanA gene;

– an advantage for multiple-resistant strains is that they can survive in the presence of various antibiotics; the use of just one antibiotic may maintain the whole set of resistance traits;

– co-selective as well as cross-selective pressure are part of the reason why resistant strains are so difficult to eliminate;

– factors underlying the difficulty in eliminating resistant strains include the dynamics of the ecosystem considered, the fitness and ability to survive of the resistant strains in their community, and the influx of susceptible strains to replace the resistant ones (50).

Future health problems related to infectious diseases depend upon the interplay of the epidemicity, antibiotic resistance, and pathogenicity acquired by bacteria (57).

Antibiotic resistant bacteria are now everywhere in the farm. Antibiotics and their residues contribute to their prevalence. Although the dissemination and transmission pathways of antibiotic resistant bacteria are very complex and not fully understood, the links between the farm on one side and colonised or diseased humans on the other have been documented for *Campylobacter, Salmonella, E. coli,* enterococci, *Listeria, Yersinia.*

It is important to note that the impact of agricultural antibiotic use on the emergence and dissemination of resistance traits and its contribution to antibiotic resistant pathogens in humans (hospital and community) remains poorly quantified (51, 89, 90, 91).

In human medicine, efforts to decrease the unnecessary use of antibiotics, which includes unnecessary prolonged treatment and use in the treatment of non-bacterial infections, have been going on for 15 years. The prudent use of antibiotics is a large part of the strategy for containment of antimicrobial resistance recommended by the WHO (107). It is legitimate to think that a similar effort among those working in animal medicine may have a positive impact on the problem.

Some experiences are paving the way for a better use of antibiotics in animals. Scandinavian countries, Denmark in particular, have addressed the issue of antibiotics administered as growth promoters and of animals carrying resistant strains. Results of the ban on growth promoters in this country were evaluated and a decline of resistance was observed. Integrated systems which monitor bacteria and the level of antimicrobial use have been established (108).

The treatement of *Campylobacter* infections with fluoroquinolones has been the subject of several studies in the United Kingdom (UK). Many results confirmed that removing bacterial populations from exposure to antimicrobial drugs eliminates the survival advantage of resistant bacteria, thus the carriage of resistant bacteria declines and they are replaced by susceptible strains. It must be mentioned that in most cases, a small number of resistant clones survive the discontinuation of antibiotics. No actions have been proven to completely restore susceptibility (23, 32, 38, 74).

The proper use of antibiotics for treating human diseases in hospitals, in the community, in the farm and in veterinarian hospitals, is likely to help prolong the useful life of antimicrobials. Using antibiotics prudently (appropriately, judiciously) as a strategy to contain antimicrobial resistance is an ethical obligation toward patients (humans or animals).

Treating an infection by eradicating the pathogenic microorganism creates a unique situation where the host, the pathogen, the commensals and the therapeutic agents must be considered. Since the discovery of penicillin we have learnt that antibiotics are a powerful trigger of bacterial evolution. The patient (human or animal) must be effectively treated, taking into account his status, his/its social position (protection of the group) and the ecological aspects of the treatment.

The prudent use of antimicrobial agents in veterinary medicine is a key issue for animal health and one which is inextricably linked to the production of safe food. The principles developed in the last decade to implement the prudent use of antibiotics in veterinary medicine have taken into account the animal species, its bacterial diseases, the most effective approach to delivering the compound, the duration of the treatment, the strategy toward the herd, and the consequences in term of benefits and risks (60). The guidelines developed by the World Organisation for Animal Health (OIE) in agreement with Codex Alimentarius are given in Annex 1 (110). The prudent use of antimicrobial agents in veterinary medicine is just one of the steps that can be taken to control the contamination of food with bacteria of animal origin and the spread of bacterial resistance. Other actions include:

– monitoring zoonotic pathogens and their antibiotic resistance pattern, in animals and in humans (28, 34, 109)

– monitoring animal pathogens and a few indicator bacteria among their commensals to detect new resistance traits (28)

– monitoring antibiotic consumption (61).

The information collected on bacterial surveillance and antibiotic consumption is very important for risk assessment and for interpreting the follow-up studies of management decisions (77, 99).

Rev. sci. tech. Off. int. Epiz., **25** (2)

781

The prudent use of antimicrobial products must be integrated into the whole concept of good management, which includes good husbandry practices, veterinary attention, vaccine programmes, site hygiene, and programmes to control zoonotic pathogen hazards. Safe water, appropriate wildlife control, safe feed, effective effluent management, and stress reduction are key issues. The education of farmers and stockmen is essential to successful on-farm improvement of animal health. Every effort should be made to protect the consumer from resistant as well as susceptible food-borne pathogens.

The key issues for the prudent use of antibiotics are:

- using them when they can be useful

- knowing when to stop using them (as soon as possible)

- knowing about pK, pD characteristics

- knowing about their residues

- respecting the withdrawal period

- knowing that antibiotics are only part of the treatment of sick animals.

As a conclusion let us consider the current situation. Resistance now exists everywhere and to all antibiotics used in humans (even to those which were never used in animals), and to all antibiotics used in animals.

There are four large areas where resistant bacteria emerge, amplify, evolve and disseminate:

- wild environment

- farms

- human communities

- hospitals.

Many countries have already established large systems of surveillance (e.g. the United States of America, Canada, Japan, Australia, the UK, Denmark, Sweden, Norway, the European Union) and others are following their example. Integrated and comparative surveillance technologies should be used to analyse national data and provide international comparisons (64).

It is reasonable to expect an improvement in the way in which we handle antimicrobials. The prudent use of them in humans and in animals is an important task and we must develop studies to assess the impact on patients and keep developing research to better understand the interaction between the bacterial world (human, animal, environmental) and antibiotics (92).

It can be expected that the incidence of resistant bacteria will decline, or at least stabilise, in some locations (hospitals, animal husbandry establishments).

Food safety is already improving because of programmes designed to improve the health of food animals, such as those aimed at decreasing the dissemination and the load of *Salmonella* and *Campylobacter* (10).

With our current knowledge it is impossible to quantify the contribution of antibiotics in agriculture to the emergence and incidence of resistant bacteria in human beings. However, we can develop studies to explore the 'portfolio' of antibiotics that are shared between human and animals, and their corresponding resistance mechanisms. It is important to try to establish a science-based rationale to accurately approach the use of old, new and future antibiotics.

Annex 1
The guidelines for antimicrobial use contained in the OIE *Terrestrial Animal Health Code*

Appendix 3.9.3
Guidelines for the responsible and prudent use of antimicrobial agents in veterinary medicine

Article 3.9.3.1
Purpose

These guidelines provide guidance for the responsible and prudent use of antimicrobial agents in veterinary medicine, with the aim of protecting both animal and human health. The Competent Authorities responsible for the registration and control of all groups involved in the production, distribution and use of veterinary antimicrobials have specific obligations.

Prudent use is principally determined by the outcome of the marketing authorisation procedure and by the implementation of specifications when antimicrobials are administered to animals.

Article 3.9.3.2
Objectives of prudent use

Prudent use includes a set of practical measures and recommendations intended to prevent and/or reduce the selection of antimicrobial-resistant bacteria in animals to:

a) maintain the efficacy of antimicrobial agents and to ensure the rational use of antimicrobials in animals with the purpose of optimising both their efficacy and safety in animals

782

Rev. sci. tech. Off. int. Epiz., **25** (2)

b) comply with the ethical obligation and economic need to keep animals in good health

c) prevent, or reduce, as far as possible, the transfer of micro-organisms (with their resistance determinants) within animal populations

d) maintain the efficacy of antimicrobial agents used in food-producing animals

e) prevent or reduce the transfer of resistant micro-organisms or resistance determinants from animals to humans

f) maintain the efficacy of antimicrobial agents used in human medicine and prolong the usefulness of the antimicrobials

g) prevent the contamination of animal-derived food with antimicrobial residues that exceed the established maximum residue limit (MRL)

h) protect consumer health by ensuring the safety of food of animal origin with respect to residues of antimicrobial drugs, and the ability to transfer antimicrobial drug resistant micro-organisms to humans.

Article 3.9.3.3
Responsibilities of the regulatory authorities

Marketing authorisation

The national regulatory authorities are responsible for granting marketing authorisation. This should be done in accordance with the provisions of the *Terrestrial Code.* They have a significant role in specifying the terms of this authorisation and in providing the appropriate information to the veterinarian.

Submission of data
for the granting of the marketing authorisation

The pharmaceutical industry has to submit the data requested for the granting of the marketing authorisation. The marketing authorisation is granted only if the criteria of safety, quality and efficacy are met. An assessment of the potential risks and benefits to both animals and humans resulting from the use of antimicrobial agents in food-producing animals should be carried out. The evaluation should focus on each individual antimicrobial product and the findings not be generalised to the class of antimicrobials to which the particular active principle belongs. Guidance on usage should be provided for all dose ranges or different durations of treatment that are proposed.

Market approval

Regulatory authorities should attempt to expedite the market approval process of a new antimicrobial in order to address a specific need for the treatment of disease.

Registration procedures

Countries lacking the necessary resources to implement an efficient registration procedure for veterinary medicinal products (VMPs), and whose supply principally depends on imports from foreign countries, should undertake the following measures:

a) check the efficacy of administrative controls on the import of these VMPs

b) check the validity of the registration procedures of the exporting and manufacturing country as appropriate

c) develop the necessary technical co-operation with experienced authorities to check the quality of imported VMPs as well as the validity of the recommended conditions of use.

Regulatory authorities of importing countries should request the pharmaceutical industry to provide quality certificates prepared by the Competent Authority of the exporting and manufacturing country as appropriate. All countries should make every effort to actively combat the manufacture, advertisement, trade, distribution and use of unlicensed and counterfeit bulk active pharmaceutical ingredients and products.

Quality control of antimicrobial agents

Quality controls should be performed:

a) in compliance with the provisions of good manufacturing practices

b) to ensure that analysis specifications of antimicrobial agents used as active ingredients comply with the provisions of approved monographs

c) to ensure that the quality and concentration (stability) of antimicrobial agents in the marketed dosage form(s) are maintained until the expiry date, established under the recommended storage conditions

d) to ensure the stability of antimicrobials when mixed with feed or drinking water

e) to ensure that all antimicrobials are manufactured to the appropriate quality and purity in order to guarantee their safety and efficacy.

Assessment of therapeutic efficacy

Preclinical trials

a) Preclinical trials should:

– establish the range of activity of antimicrobial agents on both pathogens and non-pathogens (commensals)

– assess the ability of the antimicrobial agent to select for resistance *in vitro* and *in vivo,* taking into consideration pre-existing resistant strains

Rev. sci. tech. Off. int. Epiz., **25** (2)

783

– establish an appropriate dosage regimen necessary to ensure the therapeutic efficacy of the antimicrobial agent and limit the selection of antimicrobial resistance. (Pharmacokinetic and pharmacodynamic data and models can assist in this appraisal);

b) the activity of antimicrobial agents towards the targeted micro-organism should be established by pharmacodynamics.

The following criteria should be taken into account:

– spectrum of activity and mode of action

– minimum inhibitory and bactericidal concentrations

– time- or concentration-dependent activity or co-dependency

– activity at the site of infection;

c) the dosage regimens allowing maintenance of effective antimicrobial levels should be established by pharmacokinetics. The following criteria should be taken into account:

– bio-availability according to the route of administration

– concentration of the antimicrobial at the site of infection and its distribution in the treated animal

– metabolism that may lead to the inactivation of antimicrobials

– excretion routes

– use of combinations of antimicrobial agents should be scientifically supported.

Clinical trials

Clinical trials should be performed to confirm the validity of the claimed therapeutic indications and dosage regimens established during the preclinical phase. The following criteria should be taken into account:

a) diversity of the clinical cases encountered when performing multi-centre trials

b) compliance of protocols with good clinical practice, such as Veterinary International Cooperation on Harmonisation guidelines

c) eligibility of studied clinical cases, based on appropriate criteria of clinical and bacteriological diagnoses

d) parameters for qualitatively and quantitatively assessing the efficacy of the treatment.

Assessment of the potential of antimicrobials to select for resistance

Other studies may be requested in support of the assessment of the potential of antimicrobials to select for resistance. The party applying for market authorisation should, where possible, supply data derived in target animal species under the intended conditions of use. For this the following may be considered:

a) the concentration of active compound in the gut of the animal (where the majority of potential food-borne pathogens reside) at the defined dosage level

b) the route and level of human exposure to food-borne or other resistant organisms

c) the degree of cross-resistance within the class of antimicrobials and between classes of antimicrobials

d) the pre-existing level of resistance in the pathogens of human health concern (baseline determination) in both animals and humans.

Establishment of acceptable daily intake, maximum residue level and withdrawal periods for antimicrobial compounds

a) When setting the acceptable daily intake (ADI) and MRL for an antimicrobial substance, the safety evaluation should also include the potential biological effects on the intestinal flora of humans

b) the establishment of an ADI for each antimicrobial agent, and an MRL for each animal-derived food, should be undertaken

c) for each VMP containing antimicrobial agents, withdrawal periods should be established in order to produce food in compliance with the MRL, taking into account:

– the MRL established for the antimicrobial agent under consideration

– the composition of the product and the pharmaceutical form

– the target animal species

– the dosage regimen and the duration of treatment

– the route of administration

d) the applicant should provide methods for regulatory testing of residues in food.

Protection of the environment

An assessment of the impact of the proposed antimicrobial use on the environment should be conducted. Efforts should be made to ensure that the environmental impact of antimicrobial use is restricted to a minimum.

Establishment of a summary of product characteristics for each veterinary antimicrobial product

The summary of product characteristics contains the information necessary for the appropriate use of veterinary antimicrobial products (VAPs) and constitutes the official reference for their labelling and package insert. This summary should contain the following items:

a) active ingredient and class

b) pharmacological properties

c) any potential adverse effects

d) target animal species and age or production category

e) therapeutic indications

f) target micro-organisms

g) dosage and administration route

h) withdrawal periods

i) incompatibilities

j) shelf-life

k) operator safety

l) particular precautions before use

m) particular precautions for the proper disposal of unused or expired products

n) information on conditions of use relevant to the potential for selection of resistance.

Post-marketing antimicrobial surveillance

The information collected through existing pharmacovigilance programmes, including lack of efficacy, should form part of the comprehensive strategy to minimise antimicrobial resistance. In addition to this, the following should be considered:

General epidemiological surveillance

The surveillance of animal micro-organisms resistant to antimicrobial agents is essential. The relevant authorities should implement a programme according to the *Terrestrial Code*.

Specific surveillance

Specific surveillance to assess the impact of the use of a specific antimicrobial may be implemented after the granting of the marketing authorisation. The surveillance programme should evaluate not only resistance development in target animal pathogens, but also in food-borne pathogens and/or commensals. Such surveillance will also contribute to general epidemiological surveillance of antimicrobial resistance.

Supply and administration
of the antimicrobial agents used in veterinary medicine

The relevant authorities should ensure that all the antimicrobial agents used in animals are:

a) prescribed by a veterinarian or other authorised person

b) supplied only through licensed/authorised distribution systems

c) administered to animals by a veterinarian or under the supervision of a veterinarian or by other authorised persons

d) the relevant authorities should develop effective procedures for the safe collection and destruction of unused or expired VAPs.

Control of advertising

All advertising of antimicrobials should be controlled by a code of advertising standards, and the relevant authorities must ensure that the advertising of antimicrobial products:

a) complies with the marketing authorisation granted, in particular regarding the content of the summary of product characteristics

b) is restricted to authorised professionals, according to national legislation in each country.

Training of antimicrobial users

The training of users of antimicrobials should involve all the relevant organisations, such as regulatory authorities, pharmaceutical industry, veterinary schools, research institutes, veterinary professional organisations and other approved users such as food-animal owners. This training should focus on:

a) information on disease prevention and management strategies

b) the ability of antimicrobials to select for resistance in food-producing animals

c) the need to observe responsible use recommendations for the use of antimicrobial agents in animal husbandry in agreement with the provisions of the marketing authorisations.

Research

The relevant authorities should encourage public- and industry-funded research.

Article 3.9.3.4
Responsibilities of the veterinary pharmaceutical industry

Marketing authorisation
of veterinary antimicrobial products

The veterinary pharmaceutical industry has responsibilities to:

a) supply all the information requested by the national regulatory authorities

Rev. sci. tech. Off. int. Epiz., **25** (2)

785

b) guarantee the quality of this information in compliance with the provisions of good manufacturing, laboratory and clinical practices

c) implement a pharmacovigilance programme and on request, specific surveillance for bacterial susceptibility and resistance.

Marketing and export of veterinary antimicrobial products

For the marketing and export of VAPs:

a) only licensed and officially approved VAPs should be sold and supplied, and then only through licensed/authorised distribution systems

b) the pharmaceutical industry should provide quality certificates prepared by the Competent Authority of the exporting and/or manufacturing countries to the importing country

c) the national regulatory authority should be provided with the information necessary to evaluate the amount of antimicrobial agents marketed.

Advertising

The veterinary pharmaceutical industry should:

a) disseminate information in compliance with the provisions of the granted authorisation

b) ensure that the advertising of antimicrobials directly to the food animal producer is discouraged.

Training

The veterinary pharmaceutical industry should participate in training programmes as defined in point 14 of Article 3.9.3.3.

Research

The veterinary pharmaceutical industry should contribute to research as defined in point 15 of Article 3.9.3.3.

Article 3.9.3.5
Responsibilities of wholesale and retail distributors

Retailers distributing VAPs should only do so on the prescription of a veterinarian or other suitably trained person authorised in accordance with national legislation, and all products should be appropriately labelled.

The guidelines on the responsible use of antimicrobials should be reinforced by retail distributors who should keep detailed records of:

a) date of supply

b) name of prescriber

c) name of user

d) name of product

e) batch number

f) quantity supplied.

Distributors should also be involved in training programmes on the responsible use of antimicrobials, as defined in point 14 of Article 3.9.3.3.

Article 3.9.3.6
Responsibilities of veterinarians

The concern of the veterinarian is to promote public health and animal health and welfare. The veterinarian's responsibilities include preventing, identifying and treating animal diseases. The promotion of sound animal husbandry methods, hygiene procedures and vaccination strategies (good farming practice) can help to minimise the need for antimicrobial use in food-producing animals.

Veterinarians should only prescribe antimicrobials for animals under their care.

Use of antimicrobial agents

The responsibilities of veterinarians are to carry out a proper clinical examination of the animal(s) and then:

a) only prescribe antimicrobials when necessary

b) make an appropriate choice of the antimicrobial based on experience of the efficacy of treatment.

Choosing an antimicrobial agent

a) The expected efficacy of the treatment is based on:

– the clinical experience of the veterinarian

– the activity towards the pathogens involved

– the appropriate route of administration

– known pharmacokinetics/tissue distribution to ensure that the selected therapeutic agent is active at the site of infection

– the epidemiological history of the rearing unit, particularly in relation to the antimicrobial resistance profiles of the pathogens involved.

Should a first-line antimicrobial treatment fail or should the disease recur, a second line treatment should ideally be based on the results of diagnostic tests.

To minimise the likelihood of antimicrobial resistance developing, it is recommended that antimicrobials be targeted to pathogens likely to be the cause of infection.

On certain occasions, a group of animals that may have been exposed to pathogens may need to be treated without recourse to an accurate diagnosis and antimicrobial susceptibility testing to prevent the development of clinical disease and for reasons of animal welfare.

b) Use of combinations of antimicrobials should be scientifically supported. Combinations of antimicrobials may be used for their synergistic effect to increase therapeutic efficacy or to broaden the spectrum of activity.

Appropriate use of the antimicrobial chosen

A prescription for antimicrobial agents should indicate precisely the treatment regime, the dose, the treatment intervals, the duration of the treatment, the withdrawal period and the amount of drug to be delivered, depending on the dosage and the number of animals to be treated.

The off-label use of a veterinary antimicrobial drug may be permitted in appropriate circumstances and should be in agreement with the national legislation in force including the withdrawal periods to be used. It is the veterinarian's responsibility to define the conditions of responsible use in such a case, including the therapeutic regimen, the route of administration, and the duration of the treatment.

Recording

Records on veterinary antimicrobial drugs should be kept in conformity with national legislation. Information records should include the following:

a) quantities of medication used

b) a list of all medicines supplied to each food-producing animal holding

c) a list of medicine withdrawal period

d) a record of antimicrobial susceptibilities

e) comments concerning the response of animals to medication

f) the investigation of adverse reactions to antimicrobial treatment, including lack of response due to antimicrobial resistance. Suspected adverse reactions should be reported to the appropriate regulatory authorities.

Veterinarians should also periodically review farm records on the use of VAPs to ensure compliance with their directions and use these records to evaluate the efficacy of treatment regimens.

Labelling

All medicines supplied by a veterinarian should be labelled according to national legislation.

Training

Veterinary professional organisations should participate in the training programmes as defined in point 14 of Article 3.9.3.3. It is recommended that veterinary professional organisations develop for their members species-specific clinical practice guidelines on the responsible use of VAPs.

Article 3.9.3.7
Responsibilities of food-animal producers

Food-animal producers with the assistance of a veterinarian are responsible for implementing health and welfare programmes on their farms (good farming practice) in order to promote animal health and food safety. Food-animal producers should:

a) draw up a health plan with the attending veterinarian that outlines preventative measures (feedlot health plans, mastitis control plans, endo- and ectoparasite control and vaccination programmes, etc.)

b) use antimicrobial agents only on prescription, and according to the provisions of the prescription

c) use antimicrobial agents in the species, for the uses and at the dosages on the approved/registered labels and in accordance with product label instructions or the advice of a veterinarian familiar with the animals and the production site

d) isolate sick animals, when appropriate, to avoid the transfer of pathogens; dispose of dead or dying animals promptly under conditions approved by the relevant authorities

e) comply with the storage conditions of antimicrobials in the rearing unit, according to the provisions of the leaflet and package insert

f) address hygienic conditions regarding contacts between people (veterinarians, breeders, owners, children) and the animals treated

g) comply with the recommended withdrawal periods to ensure that residue levels in animal-derived food do not present a risk for the consumer

h) dispose of surplus antimicrobials under safe conditions for the environment; medicines should only be used within the expiry date, for the condition for which they were prescribed and, if possible, in consultation with the prescribing veterinarian

i) maintain all the laboratory records of bacteriological and susceptibility tests; these data should be made available to the veterinarian responsible for treating the animals

j) keep adequate records of all medicines used, including the following:

– name of the product/active substance and batch number

– name of prescriber and/or the supplier

– date of administration

– identification of the animal or group of animals to which the antimicrobial agent was administered

Rev. sci. tech. Off. int. Epiz., **25** (2)

787

- clinical conditions treated
- dosage
- withdrawal periods
- result of laboratory tests

– effectiveness of therapy

k) inform the responsible veterinarian of recurrent disease problems.

■

La résistance antimicrobienne au niveau de l'exploitation agricole

J.F. Acar & G. Moulin

Résumé

Les bactéries résistantes aux agents antimicrobiens sont extrêmement répandues. Les auteurs font le point sur la distribution des bactéries résistantes dans les exploitations agricoles. Les populations humaines et animales et les sites dans lesquels ces populations évoluent constituent autant de réservoirs pour les colonies de bactéries susceptibles de devenir résistantes aux antimicrobiens.

L'écosystème des exploitations agricoles offre un cadre dans lequel les bactéries et les gènes résistants ont tout loisir d'émerger, de proliférer et de se propager. La dissémination se produit tout au long de la chaîne alimentaire ou par plusieurs autres voies.

La recherche écologique, épidémiologique, moléculaire et mathématique est mobilisée pour élucider l'origine et le développement du problème de la résistance aux agents antimicrobiens ainsi que ses liens avec l'utilisation d'antibiotiques.

L'utilisation prudente et responsable des antibiotiques est un aspect essentiel de la démarche éthique visant à protéger la santé animale et à assurer la sécurité sanitaire des aliments. Si l'utilisation responsable des antibiotiques est indispensable pour les besoins de la recherche, un réel progrès dans la maîtrise de la résistance aux agents antimicrobiens exige qu'une « utilisation prudente » soit instaurée à tous les niveaux de l'activité des élevages, en tant que partie intégrante des bonnes pratiques de gestion.

Mots-clés

Clone bactérien – Exploitation agricole – Gène de la résistance – Résidu d'antibiotique – Résistance aux agents antimicrobiens – Sécurité sanitaire des aliments.

■

Resistencia a los antimicrobianos en las explotaciones

J.F. Acar & G. Moulin

Resumen

Las bacterias resistentes a los antimicrobianos se han generalizado. En este artículo se examina la distribución de las bacterias resistentes en los seres humanos, los animales y el entorno de las explotaciones, es decir, en los reservorios de las colonias que pueden desarrollar esa resistencia.

Rev. sci. tech. Off. int. Epiz., **25** (2)

Los ecosistemas de las explotaciones constituyen un medio en el que pueden aparecer, desarrollarse y propagarse las bacterias y genes resistentes los cuales, posteriormente, se diseminan por conducto de la cadena alimentaria y otras vías.

Para estudiar el origen y la extensión del fenómeno de la resistencia, así como su relación con la administración de antibióticos, se utilizan métodos ecológicos, epidemiológicos, moleculares y matemáticos.

Para conferir una dimensión ética a los métodos destinados a mejorar la sanidad animal y la seguridad sanitaria de los alimentos deberá incluirse, necesariamente, la administración prudente y responsable de antibióticos. Si bien la "administración responsable" de antibióticos en la investigación es crucial, su "administración prudente" debe formar parte de las buenas prácticas de gestión de las explotaciones para contribuir plenamente a la contención de la resistencia a los antimicrobianos.

Palabras clave

Clon bacteriano – Explotación – Gen de resistencia – Inocuidad de los alimentos – Residuo de antibiótico – Resistencia antimicrobiana.

■

References

1. Aarestrup F.M. (2005). – Veterinary drug usage and antimicrobial resistance in bacteria of animal origin. *Basic clin. Pharmacol. Toxicol.*, **96** (4), 271-281.

2. Aarestrup F.M. & McNicholas P.M. (2002). – Incidence of high-level evernimicin in enterococcus faecium among food animals and humans. *Antimicrob. Agents Chemother.*, **46**, 3088-3090.

3. Acar J.F. & Goldstein F.W. (1998). – Consequences of increasing resistance to antimicrobial agents. *Clin. infect. Dis.*, **27**, (Suppl. 1), S125-S130.

4. Acar J.F. & Rostel B. (2001). – Antimicrobial resistance: an overview. *Rev. sci. tech. Off. int. Epiz.*, **20** (3), 797-810.

5. Allen K.J. & Poppe C. (2002). – Occurrence and characterization of resistance to extended spectrum cephalosporins mediated by beta-lactamase CMY-2 in *Salmonella* isolated from food-producing animals in Canada. *Can. J. vet. Res.*, **66**, 137-144.

6. Anderson E.S. & Lewis M.J. (1965). – Drug resistance and its transfer in *Salmonella typhimurium*. *Nature*, **206**, 579-583.

7. Armand-Lefevre L., Ruimy R. & Andremont A. (2005). – Clonal comparison of *Staphylococcus aureus* isolates from healthy farmers, human controls, and pigs. *Emerg. infect. Dis.*, **11** (5), 711-714.

8. Armstrong J.L., Shigeno D.S., Calomiris J.J. & Seidler R.J. (1981). – Antibiotic-resistant bacteria in drinking water. *Appl. environ. Microbiol.*, **42**, 277-283.

9. Aubron C., Poirel L., Ash R.J. & Nordmann P. (2005). – Carbapenemase-producing enterobacteriaceae, US rivers. *Emerg. infect. Dis.*, **11**, 260-264.

10. Berends B.R., Van Knapen F., Mossel D.A., Burt S.A. & Snijders J.M. (1998). – Impact on human health of *Salmonella* spp. on pork in the Netherlands and the anticipated effects of some currently proposed control strategies. *Int. J. Food Microbiol.*, **44** (3), 219-229.

11. Boxall A.B., Fogg L.A., Blackwell P.A., Kay P., Pemberton E.J. & Croxford A. (2004). – Veterinary medicines in the environment. *Rev. environ. Contam. Toxicol.*, **180**, 1-91.

12. Callaway T.R., Morrow J.L., Johnson A.K., Dailey J.W., Wallace F.M., Wagstrom E.A., McGlone J.J., Lewis A.R., Dowd S.E., Poole T.L., Edrington T.S., Anderson R.C., Genovese K.J., Byrd J.A., Harvey R.B. & Nisbet D.J. (2005). – Environmental prevalence and persistence of *Salmonella* spp. in outdoor swine wallows. *Foodborne Pathog Dis.*, **2** (3), 263-273.

13. Campagnolo E.R., Johnson K.R., Karpati A., Rubin C.S., Kolpin D.W., Meyer M.T., Esteban J.E., Currier R.W., Smith K., Thu K.M. & McGeehin M. (2002). – Antimicrobial residues in animal waste and water resources proximal to large-scale swine and poultry feeding operations. *Sci. total Environ.*, **299**, 89-95.

14. Chabbert Y.A. & Baudens J.G. (1966). – Transmissible resistance to six groups of antibiotic in *Salmonella* infections. *Antimicrob. Agents Chemother.*, **1965**, 380-383.

Rev. sci. tech. Off. int. Epiz., **25** (2)

789

15. Chachaty E., Youssef M.T., Bourneix C. & Andremont A. (1995). – Shedding of antibiotic-resistant members of the family Enterobacteriaceae in healthy residents of France and Jordan. *Res. Microbiol.,* **146**, 175-182.

16. Chapin A., Rule A., Gibson K., Buckley T. & Schwab K. (2005). – Airborne multidrug-resistant bacteria isolated from a concentrated swine feeding operation. *Environ. Hlth Perspect.,* **113**, 137-142.

17. Chee-Sanford J.C., Aminov R.I., Krapac I.J., Garrigues-Jeanjean N. & Mackie R.I. (2001). – Occurrence and diversity of tetracycline resistance genes in lagoons and groundwater underlying two swine production facilities. *Appl. environ. Microbiol.,* **67**, 1494-1502.

18. Cole D., Drum D.J., Stalknecht D.E., White D.G., Lee M.D., Ayers S., Sosbey M. & Maurer J.J. (2005). – Free-living Canada geese and antimicrobial resistance. *Emerg. infect. Dis.,* **11**, 935-938.

19. Collins J.D. & Wall P.G. (2004). – Food safety and animal production systems: controlling zoonoses at farm level. *In* Emerging zoonoses and pathogens of public health concern. *Rev. sci. tech. Off. int. Epiz.,* **23** (2), 685-700.

20. Crump J.A., Griffin P.M. & Angulo F.J. (2002). – Bacterial contamination of animal feed and its relationship to human foodborne illness. *Clin. infect. Dis.,* **35**, 859-865.

21. Davies P.R., Scott Hurd H., Funk J.A., Fedorka-Cray P.J. & Jones F.T. (2004). – The role of contaminated feed in the epidemiology and control of *Salmonella enterica* in pork production. *Foodborne Pathog. Dis.,* **1** (4), 202-215.

22. Davis M.A., Hancock D.D., Rice D.H., Call D.R., DiGiacomo R., Samadpour M. & Besser T.E. (2003). – Feedstuffs as a vehicle of cattle exposure to *Escherichia coli* O157:H7 and *Salmonella enterica*. *Vet. Microbiol.,* **95**, 199-210.

23. Desmonts M.H., Dufour-Gesbert F., Avrain L. & Kempf I. (2004). – Antimicrobial resistance in *Campylobacter* strains isolated from French broilers before and after antimicrobial growth promoter bans. *J. antimicrob. Chemother.,* **54**, 1025-1030.

24. Dugatkin L.A., Perlin M., Lucas J.S. & Atlas R. (2005). – Group-beneficial traits, frequency-dependent selection and genotypic diversity: an antibiotic resistance paradigm. *Proc. Biol. Sci.,* **272** (1558), 79-83.

25. Enne V.I., Bennett P.M., Livermore D.M. & Hall L.M. (2004). – Enhancement of host fitness by the sul2-coding plasmid p9123 in the absence of selective pressure. *J. antimicrob. Chemother.,* **53**, 958-963.

26. Fairchild A.S., Smith J.L., Idris U., Lu J., Sanchez S., Purvis L.B., Hofacre C. & Lee M.D. (2005). – Effects of orally administered tetracycline on the intestinal community structure of chickens and on tet determinant carriage by commensal bacteria and *Campylobacter jejuni*. *Appl. environ. Microbiol.,* **71**, 5865-5872.

27. Fey P.D., Safranek T.J., Rupp M.E., Dunne E.F., Ribot E., Iwen P.C., Bradford P.A., Angulo F.J. & Hinrichs S.H. (2000). – Ceftriaxone-resistant salmonella infection acquired by a child from cattle. *N. Engl. J. Med.,* **342**, 1242-1249.

28. Franklin A., Acar J., Anthony F., Gupta R., Nicholls T., Tamura Y., Thompson S., Threlfall E.J., Vose D., van Vuuren M., White D.G., Wegener H.C. & Costarrica M.L. (2001). – Antimicrobial resistance: harmonisation of national antimicrobial resistance monitoring and surveillance programmes in animals and animal-derived food. *Rev. sci. tech. Off. int. Epiz.,* **20** (3), 859-870.

29. French N., Barrigas M., Brown P., Ribeiro P., Williams N., Leatherbarrow H., Birtles R., Bolton E., Fearnhead P. & Fox A. (2005). – Spatial epidemiology and natural population structure of *Campylobacter jejuni* colonizing a farmland ecosystem. *Environ. Microbiol.,* **7**, 1116-1126.

30. Gebreyes W.A. & Thakur S. (2005). – Multidrug-resistance *Salmonella enterica* serovar Muenchen from pigs and humans and potential interserovar transfer of antimicrobial resistance. *Antimicrob. Agents Chemother.,* **49**, 503-511.

31. Gerdes K., Poulsen L.K., Thisted T., Nielsen A.K., Martinussen J. & Andreasen P.H. (1990). – The hok killer gene family in gram-negative bacteria. *New Biol.,* **2** (11), 946-956.

32. Griggs D.J., Johnson M.M., Frost J.A., Humphrey T., Jorgensen F. & Piddock L.J. (2005). – Incidence and mechanism of ciprofloxacin resistance in *Campylobacter* spp. isolated from commercial poultry flocks in the United Kingdom before, during, and after fluoroquinolone treatment. *Antimicrob. Agents Chemother.,* **49**, 699-707.

33. Guardabassi L., Schwarz S. & Lloyd D.H. (2004). – Pet animals as reservoir of antimicrobial-resistant bacteria. *J. antimicrob. Chemother.,* **54** (2), 321-332.

34. Hald T., Vose D., Wegener H.C. & Koupeev T. (2004). – A Bayesian approach to quantify the contribution of animal-food sources to human salmonellosis. *Risk Analysis,* **24**, 255-269.

35. Heritier C., Poirel L. & Nordmann P. (2004). – Genetic and biochemical characterization of a chromosome-encoded carbapenem-hydrolyzing ambler class D beta-lactamase from *Shewanella algae*. *Antimicrob. Agents Chemother.,* **48**, 1670-1675.

36. Hershberger E., Oprea S.F., Donabedian S.M., Perri M., Bozigar P., Bartlett P. & Zervos M.J. (2005). – Epidemiology of antimicrobial resistance in enterococci of animal origin. *J. antimicrob. Chemother.,* **55**, 127-130.

37. Holmberg S.D., Wells J.G. & Cohen M.L. (1984). – Animal-to-man transmission of antimicrobial-resistant salmonella: investigations of US outbreaks, 1971-1983. *Science,* **225**, 883-885.

38. Humphrey T.J., Jorgensen F., Frost J.A., Wadda H., Domingue G., Elviss N.C., Griggs D.J. & Piddock L.J. (2005). – Prevalence and subtypes of ciprofloxacin-resistant *Campylobacter* spp. in commercial poultry flocks before, during, and after treatment with fluoroquinolones. *Antimicrob. Agents Chemother.*, **49**, 690-698.

39. Inglis G.D., McAllister T.A., Busz H.W., Yanke L.J., Morck D.W., Olson M.E. & Read R.R. (2005). – Effects of subtherapeutic administration of antimicrobial agents to beef cattle on the prevalence of antimicrobial resistance in *Campylobacter jejuni* and *Campylobacter hyointestinalis*. *Appl. environ. Microbiol.*, **71**, 3872-3881.

40. Islam M., Morgan J., Doyle M.P., Phatak S.C., Millner P. & Jiang X. (2004). – Persistence of *Salmonella enterica* serovar *typhimurium* on lettuce and parsley and in soils on which they were grown in fields treated with contaminated manure composts or irrigation water. *Foodborne Pathog. Dis.*, **1** (1), 27-35.

41. Jensen L.B., Agerso Y. & Sengelov G. (2002). – Presence of erm genes among macrolide-resistant Gram-positive bacteria isolated from Danish farm soil. *Environ. int.*, **28** (6), 487-491.

42. Kim L.M., Gray J.T., Harmon B.G., Jones R.D. & Fedorka-Cray P.J. (2005). – Susceptibility of *Escherichia coli* from growing piglets receiving antimicrobial feed additives. *Foodborne Pathog. Dis.*, **2** (4), 304-316.

43. Korsak N., Jacob B., Groven B., Etienne G., China B., Ghafir Y. & Daube G. (2003). – *Salmonella* contamination of pigs and pork in an integrated pig production system. *J. Food Protec.*, **66**, 1126-1133.

44. Kuhn I., Iversen A., Finn M., Greko C., Burman L.G., Blanch A.R., Vilanova X., Manero A., Taylor H., Caplin J., Dominguez L., Herrero I.A., Moreno M.A. & Mollby R. (2005). – Occurrence and relatedness of vancomycin-resistant enterococci in animals, humans, and the environment in different European regions. *Appl. environ. Microbiol.*, **71**, 5383-5390.

45. Kummerer K. (2004). – Resistance in the environment. *J. antimicrob. Chemother.*, **54**, 311-320.

46. Lester S.C., del Pilar Pla M., Wang F., Perez Schael I., Jiang H. & O'Brien T.F. (1990). – The carriage of *Escherichia coli* resistant to antimicrobial agents by healthy children in Boston, in Caracas, Venezuela, and in Qin Pu, China. *N. Engl. J. Med.*, **323** (5), 285-289.

47. Levin B.R., Perrot V. & Walker N. (2000). – Compensatory mutations, antibiotic resistance and the population genetics of adaptive evolution in bacteria. *Genetics*, **154** (3), 985-997.

48. Levy S.B. (1992). – The antibiotic paradox. Plenum Press, New York, 157-182.

49. Levy S.B., Marshall B., Schluederberg S., Rowse D. & Davis J. (1988). – High frequency of antimicrobial resistance in human fecal flora. *Antimicrob. Agents Chemother.*, **32** (12), 1801-1806.

50. Lipsitch M. (2001). – The rise and fall of antimicrobial resistance. *Trends Microbiol.*, **9**, 438-444.

51. Lipsitch M., Singer R.S. & Levin B.R. (2002). – Antibiotics in agriculture: when is it time to close the barn door? *Proc. natl Acad. Sci. USA*, **99**, 5752-5754.

52. McDermott P.F., Cullen P., Hubert S.K., McDermott S.D., Bartholomew M., Simjee S. & Wagner D.D. (2005). – Changes in antimicrobial susceptibility of native *Enterococcus faecium* in chickens fed virginiamycin. *Appl. environ. Microbiol.*, **71**, 4986-4991.

53. McEwen S.A. & Fedorka-Cray P.J. (2002). – Antimicrobial use and resistance in animals. *Clin. infect. Dis.*, **34** (suppl. 3), S93-S106.

54. MacKenzie A.A., Allard D.G., Perez E. & Hathaway S. (2004). – Food systems and the changing patterns of food-borne zoonoses. *In* Emerging zoonoses and pathogens of public health concern. *Rev. sci. tech. Off. int. Epiz.*, **23** (2), 677-684.

55. Marcinek H., Wirth R., Muscholl-Silberhorn A. & Gauer M. (1998). – *Enterococcus faecalis* gene transfer under natural conditions in municipal sewage water treatment plants. *Appl. environ. Microbiol.*, **64**, 626-632.

56. Marshall B., Petrowski D. & Levy S.B. (1990). – Inter- and intraspecies spread of *Escherichia coli* in a farm environment in the absence of antibiotic usage. *Proc. natl Acad. Sci. USA*, **87**, 6609-6613.

57. Martinez J.L. & Baquero F. (2002). – Interactions among strategies associated with bacterial infection: pathogenicity, epidemicity, and antibiotic resistance. *Clin. Microbiol. Rev.*, **15**, 647-679.

58. Michel P., Wilson J.B., Martin S.W., Clarke R.C., McEwen S.A. & Gyles C.L. (1999). – Temporal and geographical distributions of reported cases of *Escherichia coli* O157:H7 infection in Ontario. *Epidemiol. Infect.*, **122**, 193-200.

59. Molbak K. (2005). – Human health consequences of antimicrobial drug-resistant *Salmonella* and other foodborne pathogens. *Clin. infect. Dis.*, **41** (11), 1613-1620.

60. Morley P.S., Apley M.D., Besser T.E., Burney D.P., Fedorka-Cray P.J., Papich M.G., Traub-Dargatz J.L. & Weese J.S. (2005). – Antimicrobial drug use in veterinary medicine. *J. vet. internal Med.*, **19**, 617-629.

61. Nicholls T., Acar J., Anthony F., Franklin A., Gupta R., Tamura Y., Thompson S., Threlfall E.J., Vose D., van Vuuren M., White D.G., Wegener H.C. & Costarrica M.L. (2001). – Antimicrobial resistance: monitoring the quantities of antimicrobials used in animal husbandry. *Rev. sci. tech. Off. int. Epiz.*, **20** (3), 841-847.

62. Nijsten R., London N., van den Bogaard A. & Stobberingh E. (1994). – Resistance in faecal *Escherichia coli* isolated from pigfarmers and abattoir workers. *Epidemiol. Infect.*, **113**, 45-52.

63. Nijsten R., London N., van den Bogaard A. & Stobberingh E. (1996). – Antibiotic resistance among *Escherichia coli* isolated from faecal samples of pig farmers and pigs. *J. antimicrob. Chemother.*, **37**, 1131-1140.

64. O'Brien T.F. (2002). – Emergence, spread, and environmental effect of antimicrobial resistance: how use of an antimicrobial anywhere can increase resistance to any antimicrobial anywhere else. *Clin. infect. Dis.* **34** (Suppl. 3), S78-S84.

65. O'Mahony R., Abbott Y., Leonard F.C., Markey B.K., Quinn P.J., Pollock P.J., Fanning S. & Rossney A.S. (2005). – Methicillin-resistant *Staphylococcus aureus* (MRSA) isolated from animals and veterinary personnel in Ireland. *Vet. Microbiol.*, **109**, 285-296.

66. Osterblad M., Hakanen A., Manninen R., Leistevuo T., Peltonen R., Meurman O., Huovinen P. & Kotilainen P. (2000). – A between-species comparison of antimicrobial resistance in enterobacteria in fecal flora. *Antimicrob. Agents Chemother.*, **44** (6), 1479-1484.

67. Petersen A., Andersen J.S., Kaewmak T., Somsiri T. & Dalsgaard A. (2002). – Impact of integrated fish farming on antimicrobial resistance in a pond environment. *Appl. environ. Microbiol.*, **68**, 6036-6042.

68. Pfaller M.A., Acar J., Jones R.N., Verhoef J., Turnidge J. & Sader H.S. (2001). – Integration of molecular characterization of microorganisms in a global antimicrobial resistance surveillance program. *Clin. infect. Dis.*, **32** (suppl. 2), S156-S167.

69. Philippon A., Arlet G. & Jacoby G.A. (2002). – Plasmid-determined AmpC-type β-lactamases. *Antimicrob. Agents Chemother.*, **46**, 1-11.

70. Phillips I., Casewell M., Cox T., De Groot B., Friis C., Jones R., Nightingale C., Preston R. & Waddell J. (2004). – Does the use of antibiotics in food animals pose a risk to human health? A critical review of published data. *J. antimicrob. Chemother.*, **53**, 28-52.

71. Poirel L., Heritier C. & Nordmann P. (2004). – Chromosome-encoded ambler class D beta-lactamase of *Shewanella oneidensis* as a progenitor of carbapenem-hydrolyzing oxacillinase. *Antimicrob. Agents Chemother.*, **48**, 348-351.

72. Poirel L., Rodriguez-Martinez J.M., Mammeri H., Liard A. & Nordmann P. (2005). – Origin of plasmid-mediated quinolone resistance determinant QnrA. *Antimicrob. Agents Chemother.*, **49**, 3523-3525.

73. Poppe C., Martin L.C., Gyles C.L., Reid-Smith R., Boerlin P., McEwen S.A., Prescott J.F. & Forward K.R. (2005). – Acquisition of resistance to extended-spectrum cephalosporins by *Salmonella enterica* subsp. *enterica* serovar newport and *Escherichia coli* in the Turkey poult intestinal tract. *Appl. environ. Microbiol.*, **71**, 1184-1192.

74. Price L.B., Johnson E., Vailes R. & Silbergeld E. (2005). – Fluoroquinolone-resistant *Campylobacter* isolates from conventional and antibiotic-free chicken products. *Environ. Hlth Perspect.*, **113**, 557-560.

75. Riensenfeld C.S., Goodman R.M. & Handelsman J. (2004). – Uncultured soil bacteria are a reservoir of new antibiotic resistance genes. *Environ. Microbiol.*, **6**, 981-989.

76. Rowe-Magnus D.A., Guerout A.M., Ploncard P., Dychinco B., Davies J. & Mazel D. (2001). – The evolutionary history of chromosomal super-integrons provides an ancestry for multiresistant integrons. *Proc. natl Acad. Sci. USA*, **98**, 652-657.

77. Salisbury J.G., Nicholls T.J., Lammerding A.M., Turnidge J. & Nunn M.J. (2002). – A risk analysis framework for the long-term management of antibiotic resistance in food-producing animals. *Int. J. antimicrob. Agents*, **20**, 153-164.

78. Salyers A.A. & Amabile-Cuevas C.F. (1997). – Why are antibiotic resistance genes so resistant to elimination? *Antimicrob. Agents Chemother.*, **41**, 2321-2325.

79. Sanderson M.W., Sargeant J.M., Renter D.G., Griffin D.D. & Smith R.A. (2005). – Factors associated with the presence of coliforms in the feed and water of feedlot cattle. *Appl. environ. Microbiol.*, **71**, 6026-6032.

80. Sato K., Bennedsgaard T.W., Barlett P.C., Erskine R.J. & Kaneene J.B. (2004). – Comparison of antimicrobial susceptibility of *Staphylococcus aureus* isolated from bulk tank milk in organic and conventional dairy herds in the midwestern United States and Denmark. *J. Food Protec.*, **67**, 1104-1110.

81. Sato K., Bartlett P.C. & Saeed M.A. (2005). – Antimicrobial susceptibility of *Escherichia coli* isolates from dairy farms using organic versus conventional production methods. *J. Am. vet. med. Assoc.*, **226**, 589-594.

82. Sauli I., Danuser J., Geeraerd A.H., Van Impe J.F., Rufenacht J., Bissig-Choisat B., Wenk C. & Stark K.D. (2005). – Estimating the probability and level of contamination with *Salmonella* of feed for finishing pigs produced in Switzerland: the impact of the production pathway. *Int. J. Food Microbiol.*, **100**, 289-310.

83. Sayah R.S., Kaneene J.B., Johnson Y. & Miller R. (2005). – Patterns of antimicrobial resistance observed in *Escherichia coli* isolates obtained from domestic and wild-animal fecal samples, human septage, and surface water. *Appl. environ. Microbiol.*, **71**, 1394-404.

84. Schwartz T., Kohnen W., Jansen B. & Obst U. (2003). – Detection of antibiotic-resistant bacteria and their resistance genes in wastewater, surface water, and drinking water biofilms. *FEMS Microbiol. Ecol.*, **43**, 325-335.

85. Scott H.M., Campbell L.D., Harvey R.B., Bischoff K.M., Alali W.Q., Barling K.S. & Anderson R.C. (2005). – Patterns of antimicrobial resistance among commensal *Escherichia coli* isolated from integrated multi-site housing and worker cohorts of humans and swine. *Foodborne Pathog. Dis.*, **2** (1), 24-37.

86. Seguin J.C., Walker R.D., Caron J.P., Kloos W.E., George C.G., Hollis R.J., Jones R.N. & Pfaller M.A. (1999). – Methicillin-resistant *Staphylococcus aureus* outbreak in a veterinary teaching hospital: potential human-to-animal transmission. *J. clin. Microbiol.*, **37**, 1459-1463.

87. Sengelov G., Agerso Y., Halling-Sorensen B., Baloda S.B., Andersen J.S. & Jensen L.B. (2003). – Bacterial antibiotic resistance levels in Danish farmland as a result of treatment with pig manure slurry. *Environ. int.*, **28**, 587-595.

88. Seveno N.A., Kallifidas D., Smalla K., van Elsas J.D., Collard J.M., Karagouni A.D. & Wellington E.M.H. (2002). – Occurrence and reservoirs of antibiotic resistance genes in the environment. *Rev. med. Microbiol.*, **13**, 15-27.

89. Shryock T.R. (1999). – Relationship between usage of antibiotics in food-producing animals and the appearance of antibiotic resistant bacteria. *Int. J. antimicrob. Agents*, **12**, 275-278.

90. Smith D.L., Harris A.D., Jonhson J.A., Silbergeld E.K. & Morris J.G. Jr (2002). – Animal antibiotic use has an early but important impact on the emergence of antibiotic resistance in human commensal bacteria. *Proc. natl Acad. Sci. USA*, **99**, 6434-6439.

91. Smith D.L., Dushoff J. & Morris J.G. (2005). – Agricultural antibiotics and human health. *Plos Med.*, **2** (8), e232.

92. Soulsby E.J. (2005). – Resistance to antimicrobials in humans and animals. *Br. med. J.*, **331**, 1219-1220.

93. Stobberingh E., van den Bogaard A., London N., Driessen C., Top J. & Willems R. (1999). – Enterococci with glycopeptide resistance in turkeys, turkey farmers, turkey slaughterers, and (sub)urban residents in the south of the Netherlands: evidence for transmission of vancomycin resistance from animals to humans? *Antimicrob. Agents Chemother.*, **43**, 2215-2221.

94. Summers A.O. (2002). – Generally overlooked fundamentals of bacterial genetics and ecology. *Clin. infect. Dis.*, **34** (suppl. 3), S85-S92.

95. Swartz M.N. (2002). – Human diseases caused by foodborne pathogens of animal origin. *Clin. infect. Dis.*, **34** (suppl. 3), S111-S122.

96. Thakur S. & Gebreyes W.A. (2005). – Prevalence and antimicrobial resistance of *Campylobacter* in antimicrobial-free and conventional pig production systems. *J. Food Protec.*, **68** (11), 2402-2410.

97. Threlfall E.J., Teale C.J., Davies R.H, Ward L.R., Skinner J.A., Graham A., Cassar C. & Speed K. (2003). – A comparison of antimicrobial susceptibilities in nontyphoidal Salmonellas from humans and food animals in England and Wales in 2000. *Microbiol. Drug Resistance*, **9** (2), 183-188.

98. Tikofsky L.L., Barlow J.W., Santisteban C. & Schukken Y.H. (2003). – A comparison of antimicrobial susceptibility patterns for *Staphylococcus aureus* in organic and conventional dairy herds. *Microbiol. Drug Resist.*, **9** (suppl. 1), S39-S45.

99. Tollefson L. (2004). – Developing new regulatory approaches to antimicrobial safety. *J. vet. Med., B, Infect. Dis. vet. public Hlth*, **51**, 415-418.

100. Van den Bogaard A.E. (1997). – Antimicrobial resistance-relation to human and animal exposure to antibiotics. *J. antimicrob. Chemother.*, **40**, 453-454.

101. Van den Bogaard A.E., Willems R., London N., Top J. & Stobberingh E.E. (2002). – Antibiotic resistance of faecal enterococci in poultry, poultry farmers and poultry slaughterers. *J. antimicrob. Chemother.*, **49**, 497-505.

102. White D.G., Zhao S., Singh R. & McDermott P.F. (2004). – Antimicrobial resistance among gram-negative foodborne bacterial pathogens associated with foods of animal origin. *Foodborne Pathog. Dis.*, **1** (3), 137-152.

103. Wilson J.S., Hazel S.M., Williams N.J., Phiri A., French N.P. & Hart C.A. (2003). – Nontyphoidal salmonellae in United Kingdom badgers: prevalence and spatial distribution. *Appl. environ. Microbiol.*, **69**, 4312-4315.

104. Winfield M.D. & Groisman E.A. (2003). – Role of nonhost environments in the lifestyles of *Salmonella* and *Escherichia coli*. *Appl. environ. Microbiol.*, **69**, 3687-3694.

105. Witte W. (2000). – Selective pressure by antibiotic use in livestock. *Int. J. antimicrob. Agents*, **16** (suppl. 1), S19.

106. Witte W., Heier H., Klare I., Ludwig H., Hummel R., Ziesche K., Ludke H., Schmidt S. & Rische H. (1984). – The development of antibiotic resistance of coliform bacteria in connection with the nutritional use of nourseothricin in swine. *Arch. experim. VetMed.*, **38** (6), 807-815.

107. World Health Organization (WHO) (2001). – Global strategy for containment of antimicrobial resistance WHO/CDS/CSR/DRS. WHO, Geneva.

108. World Health Organization (WHO) (2003). – Impacts of antimicrobial growth promoter termination in Denmark. WHO/CDS/CPE/ZFK, 6-9 November 2002, Foulum. WHO, Geneva.

109. World Health Organization (WHO)/Food and Agriculture Organization (FAO)/World Organisation for Animal Health (OIE) (2003). – Joint FAO/OIE/WHO Expert Workshop on non-human antimicrobial usage and antimicrobial resistance, 1-5 December, Geneva. WHO, Geneva.

110. World Organisation for Animal Health (OIE) (2005). – Appendix 3.9.3.: Guidelines for the responsible and prudent use of antimicrobial agents in veterinary medicine. *In* Terrestrial Animal Health Code, 14th Ed. OIE, Paris, 555-563.

Rev. sci. tech. Off. int. Epiz., 2006, **25** (2), 793-803

Public investment in strengthening Veterinary Services and other food safety authorities: issues affecting developed and developing countries

M. Roberts

Agriculture and Commodities Division, World Trade Organization, Centre William Rappard, Rue de Lausanne 154, Case Postale, CH 1211 Genève 21, Switzerland

This paper has been prepared by the author in a personal capacity, and the opinions expressed should be attributed solely to the author. They are not meant to represent the positions or opinions of the World Trade Organization (WTO) Secretariat or of its Members and are without prejudice to Members' rights and obligations under the WTO. Any errors or omissions are the responsibility of the author. Any citation of this paper should ascribe authorship to staff of the WTO Secretariat and not to the WTO.

Summary

During the negotiation of the Agreement on the Application of Sanitary and Phytosanitary Measures (the SPS Agreement), there was clear recognition of the problems that developing countries would face in complying with the SPS Agreement. The agreement included provisions related to technical assistance and special differential treatment for developing countries. Both topics are discussed in the SPS Committee as a regular agenda item and have been subject to substantive consideration during both reviews of the SPS Agreement, in 1999 and latterly in 2005. The SPS Committee is currently considering proposals to make these provisions more precise, effective and operational.

The Standards and Trade Development Facility (STDF) was formally established in mid-2002 by the Food and Agriculture Organization, World Organisation for Animal Health (OIE), World Bank, World Health Organization and World Trade Organization as a financing and coordinating mechanism. The STDF maintains a database which provides information on SPS-related technical assistance and capacity-building projects. From the limited data gathered, it would appear that the focus of the technical assistance provided so far has been knowledge transfer. Only a small minority of the projects reported deal with the strengthening of hard infrastructure such as laboratory facilities. It is also clear that in terms of the overall number and value of projects, animal health lags well behind the food safety sector. The World Bank estimates that annual expenditure by donor agencies on trade-related SPS programmes has been running at some US\$ 65 million to US\$ 70 million annually. However, there is under-reporting of technical cooperation activities in the STDF database.

Keywords

Agreement on the Application of Sanitary and Phytosanitary Measures – Animal health – Consumer protection – Food inspection systems – Food safety – Standards and Trade Development Facility – Technical assistance.

Introduction

Demand in developing countries for assistance related to sanitary and phytosanitary (SPS) measures is on the rise. Requirements for ever-higher levels of consumer protection, coupled with technological progress (for example in new testing equipment that can detect ever-lower concentrations of contaminants and pathogens), is leading to stricter agricultural and food inspection systems in markets in developed countries. This reinforcement of inspection and testing systems is raising the costs of entry for countries seeking to diversify away from their

Rev. sci. tech. Off. int. Epiz., **25** (2)

traditional raw-commodity export base into higher-value products such as processed fish, meat and horticultural products; stricter controls are raising the risk of rejection for all market players. Furthermore, much of the dynamic of this process is being generated by large commercial buyers in developed markets where food safety and plant and animal protection have become significant factors in supermarket or brand differentiation. The range and breadth of commercial SPS requirements, and the concomitant demand for public regulation, are having ever-greater impacts on market relations and on the competitiveness of suppliers in both developed and developing countries. Finally, South–South trade in SPS-sensitive products is growing rapidly, offering new commercial opportunities, but also posing greater challenges in managing SPS requirements.

The Agreement on the Application of Sanitary and Phytosanitary Measures and technical assistance

The World Trade Organization (WTO) celebrated its tenth anniversary on 1 January 2005. Among the body of texts that form the legal basis for the multilateral trading system enshrined in the WTO is the Agreement on the Application of Sanitary and Phytosanitary Measures (the SPS Agreement) (2). Although a decade has passed since the Marrakech Agreement was signed and brought the WTO into legal force, the SPS Agreement is a relative newcomer, and Members are still in the process of adjusting to the expanded disciplines it has established.

During the negotiation of the SPS Agreement there was clear recognition of the problems that developing countries would face in complying with it. This recognition figured in the preamble to the agreement in which the signatories, who now number 149, recognised that: 'developing country Members may encounter special difficulties in complying with the sanitary or phytosanitary measures of importing Members, and as a consequence in access to markets, and also in the formulation and application of sanitary or phytosanitary measures in their own territories.'

The SPS Agreement also stated the desire of the Members to assist developing countries in their endeavours in this regard.

One response to the implementation problems of developing countries was to delay the SPS Agreement's entry into force for these Members. Thus for developing country Members, most of the provisions of the agreement became applicable only as of January 1997; for the least-

developed countries (LDCs), the date of application was January 2000.

The agreement also included provisions related to technical assistance and special and differential treatment for developing countries. Articles 9 and 10 of the SPS Agreement are given below.

Article 9: technical assistance

1. Members agree to facilitate the provision of technical assistance to other Members, especially developing country Members, either bilaterally or through the appropriate international organisations. Such assistance may be, *inter alia*, in the areas of processing technologies, research and infrastructure, including in the establishment of national regulatory bodies, and may take the form of advice, credits, donations and grants, including for the purpose of seeking technical expertise, training and equipment to allow such countries to adjust to, and comply with, sanitary or phytosanitary measures necessary to achieve the appropriate level of sanitary or phytosanitary protection in their export markets.

2. Where substantial investments are required in order for an exporting developing country Member to fulfil the sanitary or phytosanitary requirements of an importing Member, the latter shall consider providing such technical assistance as will permit the developing country Member to maintain and expand its market access opportunities for the product involved.

Article 10: special and differential treatment

1. In the preparation and application of sanitary or phytosanitary measures, Members shall take account of the special needs of developing country Members, and in particular of the least-developed country Members.

2. Where the appropriate level of sanitary or phytosanitary protection allows scope for the phased introduction of new sanitary or phytosanitary measures, longer time-frames for compliance should be accorded on products of interest to developing country Members so as to maintain opportunities for their exports.

3. With a view to ensuring that developing country Members are able to comply with the provisions of this Agreement, the Committee is enabled to grant to such countries, upon request, specified, time-limited exceptions in whole or in part from obligations under this Agreement, taking into account their financial, trade and development needs.

4. Members should encourage and facilitate the active participation of developing country Members in the relevant international organisations.

Rev. sci. tech. Off. int. Epiz., **25** (2)

795

Technical assistance and the Sanitary and Phytosanitary Committee

In the SPS Committee, technical assistance is discussed as a regular agenda item. Under this agenda item, Members are invited to identify any specific technical assistance needs which they may have, and/or to report on any SPS-related capacity building activities in which they are involved. The WTO Secretariat and observer organisations report on their assistance activities.

Two questionnaires have been circulated to Members, seeking information on technical assistance provided and on technical assistance needs. Most replies to the first questionnaire circulated in July 1999 reported on assistance provided. A summary of the replies to this questionnaire (3) are contained in WTO document G/SPS/GEN/143/Rev.1 (5) and its addenda. Replies to the same questionnaire have also been provided separately by Australia (16); the United States of America (USA) (6, 9, 13, 15, 17); and New Zealand (12, 19). Information has also been provided by the European Commission (8). The second questionnaire, focusing on technical assistance needs, was circulated to WTO Members in July 2001 and has been used as a basis for technical assistance discussions (7). By June 2005, 33 Members had submitted responses to the questionnaire about their technical assistance needs (these responses are circulated as addenda to document G/SPS/GEN/295 (14).

The WTO's technical assistance activities in the SPS area help strengthen the capacities of developing countries to meet standards for market access of food and other agricultural commodities. The activities increase the awareness of participants about rights and obligations under the SPS Agreement, and about its implications at the national level. The programmes of national/regional activities include presentations on the work undertaken by the three standard-setting organisations referenced in the SPS Agreement (the Codex Alimentarius Commission [Codex], World Organisation for Animal Health [OIE] and International Plant Protection Convention [IPPC]).

Since 1999, SPS technical assistance activities organised by the Secretariat have included 36 regional (or sub-regional) and 34 national workshops. Table I provides information about the number of regional/sub-regional and national activities per year between 1999 and 2004. Table II shows the number of Secretariat activities per region in that period.

Since the First Review of the SPS Agreement, the international standard-setting bodies have consistently provided updates about technical assistance activities in their respective areas of work. The OIE and IPPC have developed training programmes, including conferences, seminars and workshops, to enhance national capacities on WTO matters. The IPPC developed a diagnostic tool, the phytosanitary capacity evaluation, to help countries address their current capacity and identify needs for assistance. Similar diagnostic tools have been developed by the Food and Agriculture Organization (FAO)/World Health Organization (WHO) to enhance food safety, and recently by the OIE.

Table I

Number of sanitary and phytosanitary technical assistance activities undertaken by the World Trade Organization Secretariat, 1999 to 2004

	Sanitary and phytosanitary technical assistance activity			
Year	National seminar	Regional/sub-regional workshop	Other*	Total
1999	3	2	1	6
2000	6	3	6	15
2001	4	3	1	8
2002	8	11	3	22
2003	7	10	4	21
2004	6	7	4	17
Total	**34**	**36**	**19**	**89**

* other activities include technical assistance activities not organised by the World Trade Organization Secretariat but in which the Secretariat participated

Table II

Sanitary and phytosanitary technical assistance activities per region undertaken by the World Trade Organization Secretariat, 1999 to 2004

	Sanitary and phytosanitary technical assistance activity			
Region	National seminar	Regional/sub-regional workshop	Other*	Total
Africa	7	12	4	23
Arab and Middle East Countries	8	3	1	12
Asia and the Pacific	8	5	8	21
Central and Eastern Europe and Central Asia	4	4		8
Europe	1	1	3	5
Latin America and the Caribbean	6	11	2	19
North America			1	1
Total	**34**	**36**	**19**	**89**

796

Rev. sci. tech. Off. int. Epiz., **25** (2)

Discussion of technical assistance in the Sanitary and Phytosanitary Committee

In the report of the First Review of the SPS Agreement, the Committee 'stressed the need for enhanced technical assistance and cooperation to developing countries, in particular with regard to human resource development, national capacity building and the transfer of technology and information, particularly by way of concrete, "hands-on" assistance' (4).

During the preparations for the WTO Ministerial Conference in Doha in November 2001, Members also discussed the issue of technical assistance to help developing countries comply with the SPS Agreement. The focus here was twofold: first, on helping developing countries to participate in the standard-setting processes of the Codex, IPPC and OIE, and second, on providing technical assistance to the LDCs. The decision on implementation thus, in Article 3.6:

'i) urges Members to provide, to the extent possible, the financial and technical assistance necessary to enable least-developed countries to respond adequately to the introduction of any new SPS measures which may have significant negative effects on their trade; and

ii) urges Members to ensure that technical assistance is provided to least-developed countries with a view to responding to the special problems faced by them in implementing the [SPS] Agreement.'

On the issue of participation in standard setting, the FAO/WHO (for Codex) and the IPPC have established trust funds to enhance the participation of developing countries in standard-setting meetings and activities, training programmes and regional technical consultations on standards and their implementation. The OIE is establishing a similar trust fund and continues to provide financial support for the participation of Chief Veterinary Officers of its Member Countries in standard-setting activities.

Recent discussions on technical assistance have been focused around five proposals which were referred to the SPS Committee in May 2003 by the Chairman of the General Council (11). These proposals, primarily relating to Articles 9, 10.1 and 10.4 of the SPS Agreement, had originally been put forward in the context of the Doha mandate to review all special and differential treatment provisions with a view to strengthening them and making them more precise, effective and operational.

Proposals to make technical assistance more effective and operational

To make technical assistance more effective and operational, a number of WTO Members proposed to change the clause in Article 9.2 of the SPS Agreement (quoted earlier) from 'shall consider providing' to 'shall provide' technical assistance (11). This group of Members also recommended that: 'if an exporting developing country Member identifies specific problems of inadequate technology and infrastructure in fulfilling the sanitary or phytosanitary requirements of an importing developed country Member, the latter shall provide the former with relevant technology and technical facilities on preferential and non-commercial terms, preferably free of cost, keeping in view the development, financial and trade needs of the exporting developing country' (10) (tabled by Cuba, Dominican Republic, Egypt, Honduras, India, Indonesia, Kenya, Mauritius, Pakistan, Sri Lanka, Tanzania and Zimbabwe).

In the proponents' view, technical assistance should be fully funded and should not entail financial obligations for the exporting developing or least-developed country Members. Furthermore, this group argued that where an importing Member did not actually provide such technical assistance, that Member should withdraw the proposed measures immediately and unconditionally. If not, the importing Member should compensate the exporting developing country Members for loss resulting directly or indirectly from the measures (the actual language of the proposals is 'shall' not 'should'; 'shall' implies a legal obligation in contrast to the best endeavour language of should).

Another proposal was that the WTO should recommend that impact assessments be conducted to determine the likely effect of any proposed standards on the trade of developing and least-developed country Members before such standards were adopted. If the interests of such countries were threatened, the standards would not be applicable until the developing and least-developed country Members that would be affected had acquired the capacity to beneficially comply with them (10). It was also proposed, among other measures, that Members should establish a facility within the WTO's Doha Development Agenda Global Trust Fund to ensure that:

– developing and least-developed country Members have the financial and technical capacity to meet the requirements under the agreement

– delegations from developing and least-developed country Members attend and effectively participate in meetings of the Committee and relevant international standard-setting organisations

– developing and least-developed country Members effectively utilise the flexibility provided by the agreement

– measures adopted under the agreement do not contravene the rights of developing and least-developed country Members (10).

The SPS Committee has to date been unable to develop any clear recommendations for a decision on these proposals. In the discussion of these proposals, concerns have been raised by Members about changing the balance of rights and obligations in the agreement by making Article 9.2 a mandatory obligation, and about the requirement to provide technical assistance cost-free to beneficiaries. Another concern has been the justification for removing SPS measures simply because some Members might have difficulty complying with them. Further discussion of these proposals is expected, and also on further work to assist the Committee to address the concerns identified by Members that underlie the proposals (see WTO document G/SPS/36 for initial elements for this discussion [18]).

The Standards and Trade Development Facility

The Standards and Trade Development Facility (STDF) grew out of a joint communiqué issued by the Heads of the FAO, OIE, World Bank, WHO and WTO at the Doha Ministerial Conference in November 2001. In the communiqué, the five organisations agreed to jointly explore new technical and financial mechanisms for coordination and resource mobilisation, and to build alliances between standard-setting bodies and the implementing and financing agencies so as to ensure the most effective use of technical and financial resources.

The STDF was formally established in mid-2002 as a partnership and a trust fund with three years of start-up financing from the World Bank and WTO. It brings together five partner organisations, each with specific expertise in the domain of SPS standards and trade: the FAO, OIE, World Bank, WHO and WTO.

The STDF is both a financing and a coordinating mechanism. Grant financing is available for private and public organisations in developing countries that are seeking to comply with international SPS standards and hence gain or maintain market access. Applications are particularly encouraged from stakeholders in LDCs.

The STDF maintains a database which provides information on SPS-related technical assistance and capacity-building projects (available online at: http:/stdfdb.wto.org). The STDF database covers national as well as regional projects. It is an ongoing activity and at present the period of coverage is 2001 to 2003 – although data for 2003 is not at present full-year data. Data are reported from the five partner institutions, multilateral agencies, and regional and bilateral donors, and are taken from the existing WTO/Organization for Economic Co-operation and Development (OECD) trade-related technical assistance and capacity-building database.

In the animal health area, there are a total of 27 entries listed for the period 2001 to 2003. The data are reported to the OECD Development assistance Committee and entered into the joint WTO/OECD technical assistance database. Data are subsequently transposed to the STDF database and classified into categories, one of which covers animal health. Table III gives an overview of the entries for animal health.

Table III
Sanitary and phytosanitary technical assistance activities in the animal health sector by donor and recipient undertaken by the World Trade Organization Secretariat, 2001 to 2003

Donor	Number of projects	Beneficiaries
Canada	5	Morocco, the People's Republic of China, South Africa, Caribbean (2)
European Commission	11	Albania, Serbia and Montenegro, Croatia, Cyprus, Slovenia, Latvia, Czech Republic, Bhutan, Cambodia, Laos and developing countries generally
Food and Agriculture Organization	1	Least developed countries
France	5	Morocco, Iran, Russia and Ukraine
Spain	2	Brazil and Uruguay
Switzerland	1	South Africa
United States of America	1	Sub-Saharan Africa

798

Rev. sci. tech. Off. int. Epiz., **25** (2)

Looking in more detail at the individual entries, one discovers that:

– for Canada, it is the technical assistance activities of the Canadian Food Inspection Agency which have been reported. Assistance has been in the form of study tours for Chinese and South African officials and the supply of veterinary experts in Morocco and the Caribbean. The total value of assistance offered cannot be calculated as the monetary value of some projects was not reported;

– in the case of the European Commission, four of the eleven entries deal specifically with animal health (improvement of border veterinary controls in the Czech Republic, and strengthening of veterinary services in Bhutan, Cambodia and Laos). The other entries deal with improving laboratory facilities for all SPS inspections (including for veterinary health as in the cases of projects in Albania, Croatia, Serbia and Montenegro, Latvia and Cyprus) or concern safe trade in animal by-products (Slovenia) or participation in standard setting by developing countries. The total value of assistance reported was US$ 30.8 million;

– the FAO reported one project in the livestock area for the period 2001 to 2003. This concerned strategies for technology transfer in the delivery of veterinary and livestock services. The project benefited LDCs and was valued at US$ 68,000;

– technical assistance offered by France was similar to that offered by Canada, taking the form of specific training for veterinary officials in Russia, funding of seminars on bovine spongiform encephalopathy (BSE) in Iran and Morocco, provision of expertise on foot and mouth disease (FMD) in Iran, and a study tour by Ukrainian officials. The total value of assistance reported was US$ 21,000;

– technical assistance reported by Spain was valued at US$ 120,000 and centred on the creation of a centre of excellence in meat technology in Brazil and testing of meat and food products in Uruguay;

– like France, Swiss technical cooperation activities covered the issue of BSE, with a pilot project on BSE surveillance techniques being funded to a value of US$ 730,000;

– the entry reported by the USA concerns risk-analysis training offered by the Animal and Plant Health Inspection Service (APHIS) to sub-Saharan African countries. The value of the project was US$ 0.5 million.

The data set out above present only a partial picture. For example, projects reported by Canada cover only assistance provided by the Canadian Food Inspection Agency; there are no entries reported for projects funded by the Canadian International Development Agency (CIDA). The same is true of the USA, for which the sole entry covers training offered by APHIS. No entries are reported for projects funded by USAid. Annual overviews of technical assistance circulated by the USA to the SPS Committee also show that there is under-reporting of US technical assistance activities in the database. These overviews reveal a further 39 entries (13, 15, 17) (similar documents have been tabled by New Zealand and Australia):

– in 2001 to 2002, there were nine animal health projects: beef cattle management in Tunisia; US meat and poultry inspection procedures for Colombian officials; tuberculosis eradication in Mexico; animal disease mitigation in former Yugoslavia; FMD training for Turkish officials; training for former Yugolsav officials on meat and poultry inspection and animal quarantine; assessment of brucellosis in Mexico; and assessment of BSE in Vietnam;

– in 2002 to 2003, there were 12 projects in the animal health area. Beneficiaries and training included: veterinary health training in former Yugoslavia; funding for a veterinary quarantine station and epidemiology in Bosnia Herzegovina; an animal epidemiology course in Serbia and Montenegro; training for meat inspectors in Romania; transgenic livestock training for Uzbek officials; two training courses on the SPS laws of the USA for Latin American officials: funding for developing country officials to attend a joint WHO/FAO consultation on campylobacter; and training for Chinese officials in meat inspection and hazard analysis critical control points (HACCP);

– in 2002 to 2003, 18 animal health projects were undertaken. Beneficiaries and training included: meat safety training for Central American countries; HACCP training in meat plants and risk management for the Ministry of Agriculture in Serbia; hands-on training for meat inspectors in Romania; laboratory testing training for meat and poultry inspectors in both Egypt and the USA; training in poultry management and diseases for Nigerian producers; poultry management training in Turkmenistan; meat and poultry inspection training for Central and Latin American officials; beef breeding techniques for Hungarian officials; disease prevention for Polish officials; training in animal inspection and quarantine for Chinese officials; surveillance techniques for veterinary officials in El Salvador; training for veterinarians in Kenya and Uganda; surveillance techniques in Guatemala; poultry processing in Jamaica; meat inspection for Nigerian, Ghanaian and Ugandan officials; US animal health requirements for Thai officials; meat inspection for Korean officials; and risk analysis and epidemiology for Central American officials.

The information in the database and the additional entries listed in the documentation from the USA show that the focus of the technical assistance reported is on the transfer of knowledge. Of the projects reported, only a small minority deal with the strengthening of hard infrastructure such as laboratory facilities. Most of the reported assistance concerns the transfer of knowledge either about a specific disease or measure, or ways to comply with national requirements in importing markets.

Two issues become clear from the discussion thus far:

– first, there is under-reporting of technical cooperation activities in the STDF database in the animal health area. Not only are actions by technical agencies such as APHIS only partially reported, but there are no entries for major bilateral aid programmes such as those of USAid, the CIDA or any of the bilateral programmes of European Union Member States;

– second, the focus of technical cooperation is on the transfer of knowledge about either specific diseases such as BSE and FMD, or specific market entry requirements or general techniques such as risk assessment. Little in the way of the technical cooperation reported is going into the development of new hard infrastructure.

Finally, it is also clear that in terms of the overall number and value of projects, animal health projects lag well behind the food safety sector. Taking the STDF database figures, a total of 27 animal health projects were reported in the period 2001 to 2003 as compared with 93 in the food safety area. Table IV shows reported projects for food safety. It is also worth noting that, as in the animal health area, reporting is incomplete – particularly vis-à-vis technical cooperation activities of the USA (Table V).

Table IV
Technical assistance in the animal health area by category of assistance and donor

Type of assistance	Number of projects
Seminars/study tours	Canada (2), France (1)
Training on a specific disease or measure	France (3), Switzerland (1), USA (6)
Training on how to comply with national sanitary and phytosanitary procedures	USA (6)
Visit by veterinary health expert	Canada (1), France (1)
Risk assessment training	USA (2)
Strengthening laboratory facilities	European Commission (5), USA (1)
Strengthening veterinary services generally	European Commission (3), France (1)

USA: United States of America

Table V
Sanitary and phytosanitary technical assistance activities in the animal health sector by donor and recipient, 2001 to 2003

Donor	Number of projects	Beneficiaries
Australia	2	Indonesia (2)
Canada	19	Cameroon, Morocco (2), Slovakia, Honduras, Chile, Caribbean (2), Thailand, Mexico (2), People's Republic of China (2), Guyana (2), developing countries (2), Korea, Serbia
European Commission	13	Lithuania, Slovenia, Poland (2), Slovenia, least developed countries (2), sub-Saharan Africa (2), People's Republic of China, Latin America, Thailand, Iran
Food and Agriculture Organization	8	Developing countries (3), Maldives, Pakistan, Oceania, Thailand, Turkey
France	7	Morocco, Iran, Argentina (2), Turkey, South Africa, Thailand
International Atomic Energy Agency	9	Malaysia, Nigeria, Senegal, Sri Lanka, developing countries (5)
Italy	2	Lebanon, Tunisia
Netherlands	1	Developing countries
Organization for Economic Co-operation and Development	1	Developing countries
Spain	1	Guatemala
Sweden	2	Developing countries (unallocated)
UNIDO	5	Angola, Ethiopia, Guinea, Lebanon, Ukraine
United States of America	17	Mexico (6), developing countries (5), Uruguay, South America (4), People's Republic of China

USA: United States of America
UNIDO: United Nations Industrial Development Organization

800

Rev. sci. tech. Off. int. Epiz., **25** (2)

Conclusions

The entry into force of the WTO SPS Agreement in 1995 brought to light the need for assistance to developing countries. The SPS Agreement itself has also created new challenges and opportunities for developing countries. One particular task is to harmonise SPS measures on as wide a basis as possible with the standards, guidelines and recommendations developed by the Codex, the OIE and the IPPC. Given the institutional and resource constraints on developing countries, this is a tough challenge. Demand in developing countries for SPS-related assistance is also on the rise due to ever-increasing expectations of higher levels of consumer protection coupled with technological progress.

US$ 70 million annually. For the reasons set out above, this is likely to be an underestimate of the total amount offered annually. One easily reached conclusion is that improvements need to be made to the STDF database to ensure adequate reporting by donors. However, even with the partial data available, it would appear that technical assistance in the animal health sector is running at a level quite some way behind the food safety sectors in terms of the amount of technical assistance offered. Initiatives such as the STDF and the African Livestock Programme (ALive) thus clearly have a role to play.

Veterinary services are a public good, not just at national level but also, as the current concerns about avian influenza have underscored, at global level. Public

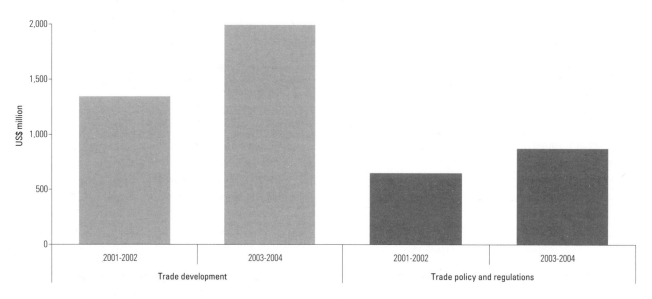

Fig. 1
Donor assistance to trade-capacity building in developing countries (commitments, two-year average, US$ million) (1)

This growing demand for SPS-related technical assistance has been manifested in the SPS Committee in proposals from developing countries to toughen the agreement's requirements for the provision of technical assistance to developing countries. While there is no consensus on these proposals, it is clear that developed countries are more cognizant of the demand from developing countries for trade-related technical assistance. Looking at trade-related technical assistance as a whole, a recent joint study by the WTO and OECD concluded that donor assistance to trade-capacity building in developing countries has increased by 50% between 2001/2002 and 2003/2004 – as illustrated in Figure 1.

Technical assistance in the SPS area is a small slice of this larger cake. The World Bank estimates that annual expenditure by donor agencies on trade-related SPS programmes has been running at some US$ 65 million to

investment in veterinary services thus serves not just the direct beneficiary or the donor but all trading partners: trade becomes safer for all. Furthermore, the technical assistance reported here pales in comparison with the economic losses and dislocation which can be caused by animal health emergencies. One pertinent ongoing example of this is the outbreaks of highly pathogenic avian influenza (HPAI) in several Southeast Asian countries that began in late 2003 and early 2004 and which have caused estimated losses in the Asian poultry sector of around US$ 10 billion. Standard cost–benefit analysis may not necessarily consider the potential gain from avoiding such a situation when decisions are made about allocating government revenues for investment in services. Placing values on such events may be methodologically difficult. However, without consideration of such values, there is a danger that the true value of the public good which is veterinary services may be consistently undervalued. ∎

Rev. sci. tech. Off. int. Epiz., **25** (2)

801

Investissements publics visant à renforcer les Services vétérinaires et les autres instances chargées de la sécurité sanitaires des aliments : problèmes affectant respectivement les pays développés et ceux en développement

M. Roberts

Résumé

Lors des négociations de l'Accord sur l'application des mesures sanitaires et phytosanitaires (Accord SPS) de l'Organisation mondiale du commerce (OMC), les parties prenantes ont pris clairement conscience des difficultés auxquelles les pays en développement seraient inévitablement confrontés avant de pouvoir respecter toutes les exigences de cet Accord. Un certain nombre de clauses ont donc été introduites en bénéfice des pays en développement, relatives à l'assistance technique et au traitement spécial différentiel. Ces deux questions font partie des thèmes régulièrement examinés par le Comité SPS et ont été étudiées avec une grande attention en 1999 et en 2005, lors des deux révisions de l'Accord SPS. De nouvelles propositions visant à mieux définir ces mesures et à les rendre plus efficaces et fonctionnelles sont actuellement en cours d'examen par le Comité SPS.

À la fin du premier semestre 2002, l'Organisation des Nations unies pour l'alimentation et l'agriculture (FAO), l'Organisation mondiale de la santé animale (OIE), la Banque mondiale, l'Organisation mondiale de la santé et l'OMC ont officiellement institué le Mécanisme pour l'élaboration des normes et le développement du commerce (STDF), un nouvel instrument de financement et de coordination. Le mécanisme STDF alimente une base de données, destinée à fournir des informations sur les projets d'assistance technique et de renforcement des capacités dans le cadre des mesures SPS. Il ressort des données, encore assez limitées, recueillies jusqu'à présent que l'assistance technique est restée axée sur le transfert de connaissances. Une très faible proportion de projets portait sur le renforcement d'infrastructures lourdes telles que les installations de laboratoire. En termes de quantité et de montant des projets, il est clair également que le secteur de la santé animale se trouve loin derrière celui de la sécurité sanitaire des aliments. La Banque mondiale estime que les organisations donatrices consacrent chaque année aux programmes SPS relatifs au commerce des sommes allant de 65 à 70 millions de dollars américains. Il convient de noter, cependant, qu'une partie seulement des activités de coopération technique sont notifiées pour figurer dans la base de données STDF.

Mots-clés

Accord sur l'application des mesures sanitaires et phytosanitaires – Assistance technique – Mécanisme pour l'élaboration des normes et le développement du commerce – Protection du consommateur – Santé animale – Sécurité sanitaire des aliments – Système d'inspection des aliments.

■

802

Rev. sci. tech. Off. int. Epiz., **25** (2)

Dificultades de los países desarrollados y en desarrollo en materia de inversiones públicas para reforzar los Servicios Veterinarios y demás autoridades responsables de la seguridad sanitaria de los alimentos

M. Roberts

Resumen

Ya en el curso de las negociaciones relativas al Acuerdo sobre la Aplicación de las Medidas Sanitarias y Fitosanitarias (el Acuerdo MSF) se determinaron claramente las dificultades que habrían de enfrentar los países en desarrollo para cumplir sus cláusulas. Por ello, en el Acuerdo se incluyeron disposiciones sobre asistencia técnica y se establecieron tratos especiales y diferenciados para esos países. Ambos temas figuran permanentemente en el orden del día de las reuniones del Comité MSF. Además, en las dos revisiones del Acuerdo MSF que se efectuaron en 1999 y, más recientemente, en 2005, se los consideró detenidamente. Actualmente, el Comité MSF está estudiando propuestas para mejorar la precisión, la eficiencia y la puesta en práctica de esas disposiciones. El Fondo para la Aplicación de Normas y el Fomento del Comercio (FANFC) fue creado oficialmente a mediados de 2002 por la Organización de las Naciones Unidas para la Agricultura y la Alimentación, la Organización Mundial de Sanidad Animal (OIE), el Banco Mundial, la Organización Mundial de la Salud y la Organización Mundial del Comercio en calidad de mecanismo de financiación y coordinación. El FANFC cuenta con una base de datos sobre los proyectos de asistencia técnica y creación de capacidades en relación con el Acuerdo MSF. De los limitados datos reunidos se desprende que, hasta la fecha, la asistencia técnica se ha concentrado fundamentalmente en la transferencia de conocimientos. Sólo una pequeña minoría de los proyectos tenía por objeto reforzar infraestructuras pesadas, tales como laboratorios. Visto el número y montos totales de los proyectos, también queda claro que la seguridad sanitaria de los alimentos ha sido objeto de mucha más atención que la sanidad animal. El Banco Mundial estima que los fondos anuales otorgados por cada uno de los organismos donantes para programas comerciales relacionados con el Acuerdo MSF han oscilado entre 65 y 70 millones de dólares estadounidenses. Sin embargo, la base de datos del FANFC no contiene suficiente información sobre las actividades de cooperación técnica.

Palabras clave

Acuerdo sobre la Aplicación de las Medidas Sanitarias y Fitosanitarias – Asistencia técnica – Fondo para la Aplicación de Normas y el Fomento del Comercio – Protección de los consumidores – Sanidad animal – Seguridad sanitaria de los alimentos – Sistema de inspección de alimentos.

Rev. sci. tech. Off. int. Epiz., **25** (2)

803

References

1. Organization for Economic Co-operation and Development (OECD) (2005). – Development Co-operation Directorate (DAC). *DACNews*, Nov-Dec. Available at http://www.oecd.org/document/34/0,2340,en_2649_33721_35764450_1_1_1_1,00.html.

2. World Trade Organization (WTO) (1994). – Agreement on the application of sanitary and phytosanitary measures. *In* The results of the Uruguay round of multilateral trade negotiations: the legal texts. WTO, Geneva, 69-84.

3. World Trade Organization (WTO) (1999). – Questionnaire on technical assistance (G/SPS/W/101). WTO, Geneva.

4. World Trade Organization (WTO) (1999). – Review of the operation and implementation of the Agreement on the application of sanitary and phytosanitary measures – Report of the Committee on Sanitary and Phytosanitary Measures (G/SPS/12). WTO, Geneva.

5. World Trade Organization (WTO) (2000). – Summary of the replies to the questionnaire on technical assistance: revision 1. G/SPS/GEN/143/Rev.1. WTO, Geneva.

6. World Trade Organization (WTO) (2000). – Technical assistance provided by the United States (G/SPS/181). WTO, Geneva.

7. World Trade Organization (2001). – Questionnaire on technical assistance (G/SPS/W/113). WTO, Geneva.

8. World Trade Organization (WTO) (2001). – Technical assistance provided by the European Communities (G/SPS/GEN/244). WTO, Geneva.

9. World Trade Organization (WTO) (2001). – Technical assistance provided by the United States: addendum 1 (G/SPS/GEN/181/Add.1). WTO, Geneva.

10. World Trade Organization (2002). – Joint Communication from Cuba, Dominican Republic, Egypt, Honduras, India, Indonesia, Kenya, Mauritius, Pakistan, Sri Lanka, Tanzania and Zimbabwe, to the Special Session of the Committee on Trade and Development, 'Special and Differential Treatment Provisions' TN/CTD/W/2. WTO, Geneva.

11. World Trade Organization (WTO) (2002). – Proposals on special and differential treatment referred to the SPS Committee – JOB(03)/100. WTO, Geneva.

12. World Trade Organization (WTO) (2002). – Technical assistance provided by New Zealand (G/SPS/GEN/352). WTO, Geneva.

13. World Trade Organization (WTO) (2002). – Technical assistance provided by the United States: addendum 2 (G/SPS/GEN/181/Add.2). WTO, Geneva.

14. World Trade Organization (WTO) (2002). – Technical assistance – responses to the questionnaire (G/SPS/GEN/295). WTO, Geneva.

15. World Trade Organization (WTO) (2003). – Technical assistance provided by the United States: addendum 3 (G/SPS/GEN/181/Add.3). WTO, Geneva.

16. World Trade Organization (WTO) (2004). – Technical assistance provided by Australia (G/SPS/GEN/472). WTO, Geneva.

17. World Trade Organization (WTO) (2004). – Technical assistance provided by the United States: addendum 4 (G/SPS/GEN/181/Add.4). WTO, Geneva.

18. World Trade Organization (WTO) (2005). – Review of the operation and implementation of the agreement on the application of sanitary and phytosanitary measures. Report adopted by the Committee on Sanitary and Phytosanitary Measures on 30 June (G/SPS/36). WTO, Geneva.

19. World Trade Organization (WTO) (2005). – Technical assistance provided by New Zealand: revision 1 (G/SPS/GEN/352/Rev.1). WTO, Geneva.

Rev. sci. tech. Off. int. Epiz., 2006, **25** (2), 805-812

OIE philosophy, policy and procedures for the development of food safety standards

W.F.G.L. Droppers

World Organisation for Animal Health (OIE), 12 rue de Prony, 75017 Paris, France

Summary
Food safety was identified as a high priority area in the 2001-2005 World Organisation for Animal Health (OIE) Strategic Plan. Member Countries of the OIE considered that the organisation should be more active in issues of public health and consumer protection and that this should include more involvement in the area of diseases or pathogens transmissible through food, whether or not animals are affected by such diseases or pathogens.
A permanent Working Group on Animal Production Food Safety was established in 2002 to coordinate the OIE's activities in food safety. The Working Group was requested to focus on food safety measures applicable at farm level and to monitor the ongoing cooperation between the OIE and Codex Alimentarius.
More emphasis is now placed on the public health aspects of a disease when OIE standards are developed or revised. For example, the revised chapter on bovine tuberculosis in the *Terrestrial Animal Health Code* includes food safety recommendations for meat and meat products and for milk and milk products. The revised chapter was approved by the OIE International Committee of Member Countries at their 73rd General Session in May 2005. More chapters will follow, beginning with a chapter addressing bovine brucellosis.

Keywords
Codex Alimentarius – Food safety – Food-borne disease – International standard – World Organisation for Animal Health – Zoonosis.

Introduction

Emerging diseases will continue to be significant and in most cases they will originate in animals (wild or domestic). There is a strong food safety element in most of these diseases and food safety is an essential public health issue for all countries. Food-borne diseases due to microbial and parasitic pathogens, biotoxins, and chemical contaminants in food represent serious threats to the health of thousands of millions of people. Serious outbreaks of food-borne disease have been documented on every continent in the past few decades, illustrating both the public health and social significance of these diseases (3). Food-borne disease and zoonoses are recognised as important causes of decreased economic productivity in both developed and less developed countries. Transmission of hazards of animal health importance via the feed and food chain and associated by-products can result in highly significant economic loss in animal populations (11).

In developed countries up to one-third of the population can be affected by food-borne illness each year, and the problem is likely to be even more widespread in developing countries. The poor are the most susceptible to ill-health. Food- and water-borne diarrhoeal diseases are leading causes of illness and death in less developed countries, killing an estimated 2.2 million people annually,

806

Rev. sci. tech. Off. int. Epiz., **25** (2)

most of whom are children. The availability of safe food improves the health of people and is a basic human right. Safe food contributes to health and productivity and provides an effective platform for development and poverty alleviation (5).

To ensure that food is safe from the risks presented by zoonoses requires controls along the continuum from farm to fork. To reduce the challenge to food safety management systems further along the food chain, it is important that everything that is reasonable, practical and economically feasible be achieved on the farm, in the pre-harvest phases. The ongoing risk has to be highlighted for management at all stages and any residual risk communicated to the final consumer (2).

This requires the World Organisation for Animal Health (OIE) and the Codex Alimentarius Commission (Codex) to work closely together and collaborate on a permanent basis. In this respect the OIE has renewed its cooperation with the two parent organisations of Codex, namely, the Food and Agriculture Organization (FAO) and the World Health Organization (WHO) by ratifying two new mutual agreements. Within this cooperation FAO and WHO will continue discussions with the OIE on how to foster the relationship between Codex and the OIE.

International standards on food safety are established by Codex, as stated in the Agreement on the Application of Sanitary and Phytosanitary Measures (SPS Agreement) of the World Trade Organization (WTO). The OIE, for its part, is responsible, under the terms of the SPS Agreement and the mandate given to it by its Member Countries, for standards relating to animal health and zoonoses (animal diseases transmissible to humans).

Since many zoonoses can be transmitted to humans through food, OIE standards also apply to animal products for human and animal consumption that could spread pathogens via international trade. For example, when in 1996 a paper by R.G. Will *et al.* indicated that it was likely that bovine spongiform encephalopathy (BSE) was transmissible to humans (4), the OIE had already included standards to prevent the spread of BSE in its *Terrestrial Animal Health Code (Terrestrial Code)* (10).

To ensure that food is safe from farm to fork, Codex is focusing on human health outcomes ('fork') when developing standards and guidelines. In comparison the OIE's role is to develop standards aimed at protecting consumers from food-borne hazards arising from animals at the primary production level of the food chain ('farm').

Food safety was identified as a high priority area in the 2001-2005 OIE Strategic Plan. Member Countries recommended an increased involvement of the OIE in the area of public health and consumer protection and that this should include developing standards to prevent the spread

of diseases and pathogens transmissible to humans through food, whether or not animals are affected by such diseases or pathogens. This contrasts with the historical view that veterinarians (and the OIE) should only be concerned with zoonoses that cause disease in animals.

To coordinate the food safety activities of the OIE and to ensure a seamless cooperation with Codex, a permanent OIE Working Group on Animal Production Food Safety (APFS) was established in 2002, details of which are provided later in this article.

Development of OIE standards

The OIE Specialist Commissions, the members of which are elected by Member Country representatives, continually develop and revise guidelines and recommendations for the OIE *Terrestrial Code* (10), *Aquatic Animal Health Code* (8), *Manual of Diagnostic Tests and Vaccines for Terrestrial Animals* (*Terrestrial Manual*) (7) and *Manual of Diagnostic Tests and Vaccines for Aquatic Animals* (6). To prepare draft texts for new articles in the *Codes* and *Manuals*, or to propose revisions of existing articles, those Commissions use the expertise of well-known specialists, many of whom work in one of the 171 OIE Collaborating Centres and Reference Laboratories.

An OIE Delegate, an OIE Specialist Commission, an independent expert or a partner organisation may identify an issue or problem on the basis of new scientific information or a new approach. The appropriate Specialist Commission would then deal with the issue, seeking advice from an expert, working group, ad hoc group, other Commission or OIE Reference Laboratories/Collaborating Centres.

The OIE circulates initial proposals for comment by experts, Member Countries and organisations. At the General Session of the International Committee, the Delegates discuss proposed texts. After discussion, the proposal may be returned for further work or may be adopted as an international OIE standard. An adopted text is then included in one of the OIE *Codes* or *Manuals* and then recognised by WTO as an international standard.

The OIE Working Group on Animal Production Food Safety

In May 2002 the International Committee of OIE Member Countries recommended the establishment of a permanent working group on food safety to coordinate the OIE's animal production food safety activities, with

Rev. sci. tech. Off. int. Epiz., **25** (2)

807

multidisciplinary membership and balanced regional representation. As a result, the OIE Working Group on APFS was established with a focus on food safety measures applicable at farm level. In this regard, the Working Group saw its role as one of providing advice to the Director General of the OIE on policy and strategic issues related to the OIE's work on animal production food safety. OIE activities in this area have the goal of reducing food-borne risks to human health by preventing, eliminating or controlling the hazards that can arise during the primary processing of animals and animal products. The Working Group would also collaborate in relevant areas with other international organisations, particularly FAO and WHO and their subsidiary bodies (especially Codex), to ensure a seamless interface between the OIE and these other standard-setting organisations.

This is reflected in the membership of the Working Group. The current members are Dr Stuart Slorach – Chair (Past Chairperson, Codex; former Deputy Director-General, National Food Administration, Sweden); Prof. Hassan Aidaros (Professor of Hygiene and Preventive Medicine, Egypt); Dr Carlos Correa Messuti (Ministry of Animal Production, Agriculture and Fisheries, Uruguay); Mr Michael Scannell, (Head of Unit for international food, veterinary and phytosanitary questions and multilateral international relations,, Health and Consumer Protection Directorate-General, European Commission, Belgium); Dr Joseph Domenech (Chief, Animal Health Service, Agriculture, Biosecurity, Nutrition and Consumer Protection Department, FAO, Italy); Dr Andrew McKenzie (Executive Director, New Zealand Food Safety Authority, New Zealand); Dr Kazuaki Miyagishima (Secretary, Codex, Italy); Dr Alan Randell (former Secretary, Codex, Italy); Dr Jørgen Schlundt (Director, Department of Food Safety, Zoonoses and Food-borne Diseases, WHO, Switzerland) and Dr Robert Thwala (Director, Veterinary and Livestock Services, Swaziland).

In 2005 the Working Group reviewed, revised and identified its priorities as (9):

– identifying and addressing gaps, contradictions, duplications and areas where harmonisation is necessary in the work of the OIE and other international/ intergovernmental organisations (in particular Codex) involved in food safety standards

– strengthening the relationship with other relevant standard-setting organisations (in particular Codex), through enhanced informal exchange

– improving coordination between competent authorities with animal health and food safety responsibilities at national and regional levels

– recommending a work programme to address the mandate of the OIE on animal production food safety.

Furthermore the Working Group was established to act in a steering group capacity regarding the work of OIE expert groups so it could advise the Director General on membership, scope and terms of reference for expert groups and review texts arising from these groups for consideration by the relevant Specialist Commission.

Current food safety issues for the OIE

Cooperation between the Codex Alimentarius Commission and the OIE on food safety throughout the food chain

Historically, Veterinary Services were set up to control animal diseases at farm level. At present, in about 70% of OIE Member Countries, Veterinary Services have both public health and animal health objectives. Because effective links between animal health and public health are essential, Member Countries have been asking the OIE to help them reform their administrations in this regard. As a result, the Working Group revised a paper on a production-to-consumption approach to food control throughout the food chain and renamed it: 'Cooperation between the Codex Alimentarius Commission and the OIE on food safety throughout the food chain'. This paper is available on the OIE website in the food safety section (www.oie.int).

As part of this cooperation the Working Group will develop a document for Veterinary Services that will describe their involvement in food safety activities, which have both public and animal health objectives.

Ante- and post-mortem meat inspection

Food-borne diseases are generally recognised as important public health problems and important causes of decreased economic productivity in both developed and developing countries. Similarly, transmission of hazards of animal health importance via the food chain and associated by-products can result in highly significant economic loss in animal populations. Along with this, rapidly increasing trade in food at both local and international level is resulting in increased attention to biosecurity and the potential for the transmission of animal diseases and zoonoses via the food and feed chain. Inspection of slaughter animals can provide a valuable contribution to surveillance for specified diseases of animal and public health importance. To provide more guidance in the use and development of a risk-based approach to ante- and post-mortem meat inspection, the Working Group drafted a chapter for the *Terrestrial Code* on 'Guidelines for the

808

Rev. sci. tech. Off. int. Epiz., **25** (2)

control of biological hazards of public health and animal health importance through ante- and post-mortem meat inspection'. At its 74th General Session in May 2006 the International Committee of OIE Member Countries approved this chapter for inclusion in the *Terrestrial Code* (10). An information document from the Working Group on 'Control of hazards of public health and animal health importance through ante- and post-mortem meat inspection' has been placed on the OIE website in the food safety section.

Identification and traceability of live animals

The need to ensure the safety of food of animal origin in respect of the risk posed by the transmissible spongiform encephalopathies of animals has increased the importance of sound data on the traceability of food for food animals and the dynamics of trade in animals (2). Therefore the Working Group established terms of reference for a new OIE ad hoc group – the Ad hoc Group on Identification and Traceability of Live Animals. This Ad hoc Group has developed a set of principles for animal identification and animal traceability which is broad, valid for all the relevant animal species (although the initial work is on systems for bovines) and takes into account the differences among OIE Member Countries. The International Committee of OIE Member Countries approved this text for inclusion in the *Terrestrial Code* (10) at the 74th General Session in May 2006. Based on these principles, the Ad hoc Group has started work on developing guidelines for animal identification and traceability to provide an instrument for Member Countries to improve animal health and public health, and to contribute to better management of health crises at international and national levels. The final task of the Ad hoc Group will be to develop a set of recommendations for a practical implementation of the system. It will take into account the work of Codex on traceability, so as to create one workable system that combines Codex guidelines on the traceability of animal products with those of the OIE on live animals.

Good farming practices

The Working Group is developing a guide to good farming practices. The guidelines are designed to address public health risks that can arise at farm level during the primary processing stage of animal production. At this stage the guidelines cover the issues in general terms, but there will be the opportunity to add specific references later to address particular situations in specific regions or countries.

The guidelines will be directed at veterinary administrations and other competent authorities as a means of encouraging them to promote and implement good farming practices, as appropriate within their countries, as a component of the overall animal health system. To maximise the usefulness of the guidelines, the OIE will coordinate its work with FAO (in collaboration with WHO and Codex), with the outcome being published as a joint OIE/FAO document.

Feed safety

Some feed safety recommendations are already included in different OIE standards such as those covering BSE and classical swine fever. The OIE recognises that it should establish an overall standard governing feed safety systems for food producing animals, taking into account relevant aspects of animal health and zoonoses, in order to minimise risks to animal and consumer health. The Working Group recommended terms of reference for an ad hoc group to address this subject taking into account Codex work on the food safety aspects of animal feed ('Code of Practice on Good Animal Feeding') (1). This ad hoc group will need to work in close collaboration with the experts working on the guide to good farming practices.

Strengthening public health and animal health through responsible use of reliable, safe and effective veterinary drugs

In 1999 the OIE created an ad hoc group to address the human and animal health risks related to antimicrobial resistance, and to examine the contribution to resistance of antimicrobial use in veterinary medicine. Activities started with the organisation of an international conference in Paris in 2001. In 2003 the OIE adopted four guidelines on antimicrobial resistance. Three guidelines are part of the *Terrestrial Code* (10) and the fourth guideline is part of the *Terrestrial Manual* (7). In 2004 guidelines on risk analysis for antimicrobial resistance were adopted and included in the *Terrestrial Code*.

During 2004 an ad hoc group, including officials from WHO and FAO, revised and updated the OIE standards on antimicrobial resistance taking into account the work done by the Codex Committee on Residues of Veterinary Drugs in Foods. The proposed revisions were endorsed by the Working Group on AFPS and adopted by the OIE in 2005.

The OIE, FAO and WHO organised two joint Expert Workshops on Non-Human Antimicrobial Usage and Antimicrobial Resistance: one in Geneva, Switzerland, in December 2003 (Scientific Assessment) and the other in Oslo, Norway, in March 2004 (Management Options). It was recommended that the OIE develop a list of critically important antimicrobials in veterinary medicine and that the WHO develop such a list for critically important antimicrobials in human medicine.

Rev. sci. tech. Off. int. Epiz., **25** (2)

809

The list of critically important antimicrobials for human medicine was proposed in February 2005 at a WHO working group consultation meeting in Canberra, Australia. In 2005 the OIE Ad hoc Group on Antimicrobial Resistance prepared a questionnaire for OIE Member Countries, to collate proposals on Veterinary Critically Important Antimicrobials (VCIA). In February 2006 the Ad hoc Group compiled a list of VCIA based on the data collected. Once this list has been accepted by OIE Member Countries, the OIE, FAO and WHO will consider convening a joint meeting to give recommendations on the appropriate balance to be struck between animal health needs and public health considerations.

New approaches to zoonoses

To find the most effective approaches to zoonoses the OIE created an ad hoc group on emerging zoonoses in 2004. The terms of reference included the provision of advice on zoonotic disease control strategies at the animal production level and communication with public health agencies on the human impact of emerging and re-emerging zoonoses. The Ad hoc Group recommended that the OIE, in permanent conjunction with FAO and WHO (including Codex), consider a more proactive approach to developing guidelines, standards and codes of practice for animal production to help reduce the risk of the occurrence of emerging and re-emerging food-borne zoonoses.

The Working Group on APFS discussed the principles underpinning the new OIE single list of notifiable terrestrial diseases and the criteria used for determining whether a disease would be listed. It believed that, in reviewing the criteria for the inclusion of zoonoses for compulsory notification by Member Countries, the OIE should take account of all risk management options, including alternatives to listing, e.g. for some human pathogens associated with food-borne illness. If other risk management options prove to be more effective and less trade restrictive, they should be chosen; these risk management options could include measures at the production or processing stages of the food chain, and may lead to additional chapters in appropriate OIE and/or Codex codes. The Working Group recommended that the OIE develop alternative methods for managing such food-borne pathogens for which compulsory reporting may not be the most appropriate risk management strategy.

Disease specific texts

As previously stated, the OIE has revised the *Terrestrial Code* chapter on bovine tuberculosis, placing more emphasis on the food safety aspects of the disease. The revised chapter now contains recommendations for meat and meat products, and milk and milk products. The same emphasis on food safety issues has been given to a revised chapter on bovine brucellosis which has been submitted to the Terrestrial Animal Health Standards Commission.

The risk of human illness from *Salmonella enteritidis* has increased dramatically. During the past two decades, *S. enteritidis* has emerged as a leading cause of human infections in many countries, with hen eggs being a principal source of the pathogen. The Working Group has initiated work on risk reduction for *S. enteritidis* in eggs, taking into account Codex, WHO and FAO work. The Working Group recommended that an ad hoc group be established to develop standards on salmonellosis in poultry to complement the ongoing work of Codex. The standards should address methods for the detection of *Salmonella* spp. in flocks, measures for control and eradication, and risk mitigation measures for affected commodities.

Certificates

The OIE model international certificates for meat and other products of animal origin are being updated, with the aim of having a common certificate for all commodities. The Working Group will work with Codex and other relevant international organisations (such as the International Dairy Federation and the International Plant Protection Convention) to review international standards on certification with a view to maximising harmonisation. The Working Group proposed that an ad hoc group be set up to revise the current OIE work and update certification guidelines and model certificates.

Future OIE work

At its meeting in January-February 2006, the Working Group identified the following priorities:

– finalising some horizontal issues, e.g. updating the current OIE model certificates

– finalising several disease specific texts, including a modification of the chapter on brucellosis in the *Terrestrial Code*

– continuing to strengthen the relationship between the OIE and Codex

– developing new texts such as a document for Veterinary Services describing their role in food safety activities.

Conclusion

Since the appearance of BSE, the OIE has had an increased involvement in the area of public health and consumer

810

Rev. sci. tech. Off. int. Epiz., **25** (2)

protection. Particularly, cooperation with Codex has been intensified to ensure that there are no inconsistencies or gaps in the standards and topics falling within the scope of the OIE and Codex. The OIE's role is to develop standards aimed at protecting consumers from food-borne hazards arising from animals at the primary production level of the food chain. This concept is already visible in the *Terrestrial Code* and will be even more so in the years to come.

Food safety and consumer participation will play an increased role in standard setting. The OIE Working Group on APFS will coordinate future standard-setting activities with Codex as well as serve as a sounding board for consumer sensitive issues. More food safety measures will be incorporated within on-farm production systems in the future. The OIE will play a key role in increasing the awareness of veterinarians and farmers of the importance of incorporating these food safety measures into the first stages of production. Taking such preventive measures is preferable to having to monitor and take action at slaughter and points beyond.

Acknowledgements

The author wishes to thank Alex Thiermann, David Wilson and Francesco Berlingieri for their most helpful support and comments and to express his gratitude to the members of the OIE Working Group on Animal Production and Food Safety.

■

L'élaboration de normes en matière de sécurité sanitaire des aliments : principes, politiques et procédures de l'OIE

W.F.G.L. Droppers

Résumé
Le Plan stratégique 2001-2005 de l'Organisation mondiale de la santé animale (OIE) a fait de la sécurité sanitaire des aliments une priorité. Les Pays membres de l'OIE ont estimé que l'organisation devait s'impliquer davantage dans le domaine de la santé publique et de la protection des consommateurs, notamment en prêtant une attention accrue aux maladies d'origine alimentaire et à leurs agents pathogènes, que ces maladies et agents affectent ou non les animaux.
Un Groupe de travail permanent sur la sécurité sanitaire des aliments d'origine animale en phase de production a été mis en place en 2002 afin de coordonner les activités de l'OIE dans ce domaine. Il a été demandé au Groupe de travail de se concentrer sur les mesures de sécurité sanitaire des aliments applicables au niveau de la ferme et de suivre en permanence la coopération entre l'OIE et le Codex Alimentarius.
Dorénavant, lors de l'élaboration ou de la révision des normes de l'OIE, l'accent est davantage mis sur les conséquences des maladies animales sur la santé publique. Par exemple, le chapitre révisé du *Code sanitaire pour les animaux terrestres* consacré à la tuberculose bovine comporte des recommandations relatives à la sécurité sanitaire de la viande, des produits carnés, du lait et des produits laitiers. Le chapitre révisé a été approuvé en mai 2005 par le Comité international de l'OIE lors de la 73e Session générale. D'autres chapitres suivront, dont en premier lieu celui consacré à la brucellose bovine.

Mots-clés
Codex Alimentarius – Maladie d'origine alimentaire – Norme internationale – Organisation mondiale de la santé animale – Sécurité sanitaire des aliments – Zoonose.

■

Rev. sci. tech. Off. int. Epiz., **25** (2)

811

Criterios, línea de acción y procedimientos de la OIE para la formulación de normas sobre la seguridad sanitaria de los alimentos

W.F.G.L. Droppers

Resumen

En el Plan Estratégico de la Organización Mundial de Sanidad Animal (OIE) para 2001-2005 se confirió una alta prioridad a la seguridad sanitaria de los alimentos. Los Países Miembros de la Organización consideraron que la OIE debería participar más activamente en el ámbito de la salud pública y la protección de los consumidores; en particular, respecto de las zoonosis y agentes patógenos transmisibles a los seres humanos por los alimentos, independientemente de que los animales estén afectados por dichas enfermedades o agentes patógenos.

En 2002 se estableció un Grupo de Trabajo permanente sobre Seguridad Sanitaria de los Alimentos derivados de la Producción Animal para que coordinara las actividades de la OIE en materia de inocuidad alimentaria. Se pidió al Grupo de Trabajo que centrara sus actividades en las medidas relativas a la seguridad sanitaria de los alimentos aplicables en las explotaciones y en la colaboración permanente entre la OIE y el Codex Alimentarius.

Actualmente, a la hora de formular o revisar las normas de la Organización, se le da prioridad a las consecuencias de las enfermedades animales para la salud pública. Por ejemplo, el capítulo revisado del *Código Sanitario para los Animales Terrestres* sobre la tuberculosis bovina comprende recomendaciones acerca de la seguridad sanitaria de la carne, la leche y sus subproductos. El Comité Internacional de los Países Miembros de la OIE aprobó este capítulo revisado en el curso de su 73ª Sesión General, celebrada en mayo de 2005. Se ha previsto proseguir la revisión de los capítulos del *Código Sanitario* y el próximo que se ampliará será el relativo a la brucelosis bovina.

Palabras clave

Codex Alimentarius – Enfermedad transmitida por alimentos – Norma internacional – Organización Mundial de Sanidad Animal – Seguridad sanitaria de los alimentos – Zoonosis.

■

References

1. Codex Alimentarius Commission (CAC) (2004). – Code of practice on good animal feeding. CAC/RCP 54-2004. CAC, Rome.

2. Collins J.D. & Wall P.G. (2004). – Food safety and animal production systems: controlling zoonoses at farm level. *In* Emerging zoonoses and pathogens of public health concern. *Rev. sci .tech. Off. int. Epiz.*, **23** (2), 685-700.

3. Food and Agriculture Organization of the United Nations (FAO) (2003). – Assuring food safety and quality: guidelines for strengthening national food control systems. FAO Food and Nutrition Paper 76. FAO, Rome.

4. Will R.G., Ironside J.W., Zeidler M., Cousens N., Estibeiro K., Alperovitch A., Poser S., Pocchiari M., Hofman A. & Smith P.G. (1996). – A new variant of Creutzfeldt-Jakob disease in the UK. *Lancet*, **347**, 921-925.

5. World Health Organization (WHO) (2002). – WHO global strategy for food safety: safer food for better health. WHO, Geneva.

6. World Organisation for Animal Health (OIE) (2003). – Manual of Diagnostic Tests for Aquatic Animals, 4th Ed. OIE, Paris.

7. World Organisation for Animal Health (OIE) (2004). – Manual of Diagnostic Tests and Vaccines for Terrestrial Animals, 5th Ed. OIE, Paris.

8. World Organisation for Animal Health (OIE) (2005). – Aquatic Animal Health Code, 8th Ed. OIE, Paris.

9. World Organisation for Animal Health (OIE) (2005). – Final Report, 73rd General Session. OIE, Paris.

10. World Organisation for Animal Health (OIE) (2005). – Terrestrial Animal Health Code, 14th Ed. OIE, Paris.

11. World Organisation for Animal Health (OIE) (2006). – Control of hazards of public health and animal health importance through ante- and post-mortem meat inspection. OIE Working Group on Animal Production Food Safety. Available at: www.oie.int.

Rev. sci. tech. Off. int. Epiz., 2006, **25** (2), 813-821

Assuring food safety: the complementary tasks and standards of the World Organisation for Animal Health and the Codex Alimentarius Commission

S.A. Slorach

Chairperson of Codex Alimentarius Commission (2003-2005); Chairman of the OIE Working Group on Animal Production Food Safety
Stubbängsvägen 9A, SE-12553 Älvsjö, Sweden

Summary

The Agreement on the Application of Sanitary and Phytosanitary Measures of the World Trade Organization specifically recognises the international standards developed by the World Organisation for Animal Health (OIE) and the Codex Alimentarius Commission (CAC). OIE standards focus on animal health and zoonoses and those of the CAC on food safety, but since zoonoses can affect food safety, it is vital that the two organisations cooperate closely to avoid duplication of effort, gaps and conflicting standards. The OIE has established an Animal Production Food Safety Working Group to promote cooperation with the CAC and to act as a steering committee for the OIE's work programme on the development of standards aimed at protecting consumers from foodborne hazards arising from animals at the production level of the food chain. This paper describes briefly how standards are developed by the OIE and the CAC and gives examples of how the tasks and standards of the two organisations complement each other in helping to assure food safety. The areas covered include meat hygiene, the identification and traceability of live animals, model certificates for international trade, antimicrobial resistance, veterinary drugs, animal feed, and salmonellosis.

Keywords

Codex Alimentarius Commission – Cooperation – Food safety – International standards – World Organisation for Animal Health – Zoonoses.

The OIE and the Codex Alimentarius Commission – two of the three 'SPS Sisters'

The Agreement on the Application of Sanitary and Phytosanitary Measures (the 'SPS Agreement') of the World Trade Organization (WTO) specifically recognises the standards developed by the World Organisation for Animal Health (OIE) for animal health and zoonoses, the Codex Alimentarius Commission (CAC) for food safety, and the International Plant Protection Convention (IPPC) for plant health. Measures based on the standards of these three 'SPS Sisters' are considered to fulfil international requirements for the protection of animal health, human health and plant health.

In order to ensure food safety and quality it is necessary to consider the whole of the food production, distribution and consumption chain from 'farm to fork' as hazards arising in primary production can often impair the safety of the final food product. Under the SPS Agreement, the OIE has responsibility for developing international standards

814

Rev. sci. tech. Off. int. Epiz., **25** (2)

related to animal health and zoonoses; it should be noted that zoonoses can affect food safety, the CAC area of responsibility under the SPS Agreement. Thus it is vital that the OIE and the CAC cooperate closely to avoid duplication of effort, gaps and conflicting standards.

Founded in 1924, the OIE is a much older organisation than the CAC, which was established in 1964. The OIE currently has 167 Member Countries and the CAC has 173 member countries and one member organisation (the European Community). Although most countries are members of both organisations, the membership of the OIE and the CAC differs somewhat. The OIE is an intergovernmental organisation, but not a United Nations agency. The CAC is an intergovernmental body operating under the auspices of the Food and Agriculture Organization of the United Nations (FAO) and the World Health Organization (WHO) (also a United Nations agency). Membership of the CAC is open to all countries that are members of FAO or WHO.

Development of OIE standards

The philosophy, policy and procedures of the OIE for the development of its standards are described by Willem Droppers in another paper in this volume of the OIE *Scientific and Technical Review*. OIE standards are prepared by elected Specialist Commissions and by Working Groups bringing together internationally renowned scientists, most of whom are experts within the network of 181 OIE Collaborating Centres and Reference Laboratories that contribute towards the scientific objectives of the OIE. These standards are adopted by the International Committee, which is composed of the 167 OIE Delegates nominated by their governments. The OIE *Terrestrial Animal Health Code* (the *Terrestrial Code*) (12) contains the OIE international standards for terrestrial animals and their products.

Development of Codex standards

The CAC was established by FAO and WHO to develop international food standards, guidelines and recommendations for a dual purpose – to protect the health of consumers and ensure fair practices in the food trade. This collection of standards and related texts, called the '*Codex Alimentarius*', or the food code, has become the global reference point for consumers, food producers and processors, national food control agencies and the international food trade.

Responsibility for developing the standards that are adopted into the *Codex Alimentarius* rests with the CAC and its subsidiary bodies. These standards are science-based and are developed taking into account the expert advice provided by joint expert bodies established by FAO and WHO, such as the Joint FAO/WHO Expert Committee on Food Additives (JECFA), the Joint FAO/WHO Meeting on Pesticide Residues (JMPR) and the Joint FAO/WHO Expert Meetings on Microbiological Risk Assessment (JEMRA), or by *ad hoc* expert consultations.

The standards contained within the *Codex Alimentarius* are developed through a sometimes lengthy, eight-step process or an accelerated five-step process, as described in the *Procedural Manual* of the CAC (10). Most of the work is carried out by subsidiary bodies (Codex Committees or Task Forces), which submit draft standards to the CAC for adoption at steps 5 and 8 of the elaboration procedure. Draft texts are sent to governments and international organisations for comment twice (at steps 3 and 6) in the eight-step procedure and at step 3 in the accelerated procedure. These members and observers can also participate in meetings of the subsidiary bodies to voice their position and negotiate solutions with other delegations at steps 4 and 7. As one of the recognised international governmental organisations, the OIE participates actively in the development of Codex standards in relevant areas, both by submitting comments on draft standards and participation in the meetings of the CAC and its subsidiary bodies.

Information about the CAC, its membership, subsidiary bodies, organisation and working procedures and the standards it develops (i.e. the *Codex Alimentarius*) can be accessed via the Codex website (www.codexalimentarius.net).

Cooperation between the OIE and the Codex Alimentarius Commission

The OIE is keen to formalise its collaboration with the CAC and has already renewed its cooperation with the parent organisations of the CAC, i.e. FAO and WHO, by ratifying two new mutual agreements. Within this cooperation and at the request of the Executive Committee of the CAC, FAO and WHO will continue discussions with the OIE on how to foster relationship between the CAC and the OIE. The resulting synergies will benefit both organisations. This collaboration should be facilitated by the fact that almost all OIE Member Countries are also CAC Member Countries. The OIE encourages national representatives participating in the CAC and its subsidiary

Rev. sci. tech. Off. int. Epiz., **25** (2)

815

bodies to coordinate points of common interest in the fields of animal health and food safety with their national counterparts, the OIE Delegates. A framework paper on the 'Cooperation between the Codex Alimentarius Commission and the OIE on food safety throughout the food chain' developed by the OIE Animal Production Food Safety Working Group (see below) was provided to those attending the CAC meeting in July 2006 (13) and is also available on the OIE website (www.oie.int).

The 28th Session of the CAC, meeting in Rome in July 2005, expressed its appreciation for the active participation of the OIE in the work of the CAC and its subsidiary bodies and reiterated its interest in strengthening this cooperation. The CAC endorsed the following recommendations related to the cooperation between the CAC and the OIE:

– the OIE should be encouraged to participate actively in the standard-setting work of the CAC, namely through the work of relevant subsidiary bodies of the CAC

– the OIE should be invited to regularly submit, to relevant Codex subsidiary bodies, reports on its activities relevant to the work of these subsidiary bodies, while these subsidiary bodies continue to seek ways to improve cooperation with the OIE in their respective areas of work and inform the Executive Committee of the CAC of their decisions/recommendations accordingly

– the OIE should be invited to submit a summary report to the regular sessions of the CAC on its activities of relevance to the work of the CAC, including the outcome of the OIE Animal Production Food Safety Working Group (see below).

In accordance with the above, the Director General of the OIE presented such a summary report at the CAC meeting in July 2006. The CAC is also expected to review the effectiveness of the current cooperative arrangements by 2007, with a view to considering if further arrangements will be necessary or desirable.

OIE Animal Production Food Safety Working Group

To help coordination between the CAC and the OIE, the OIE Member Countries gave the Director General a mandate to establish the OIE Animal Production Food Safety Working Group (APFSWG). Its current membership includes high-level current and former CAC office holders; the Director of the Department of Food Safety, Zoonoses and Foodborne Diseases of the WHO; the Chief of the Animal Health Service of the FAO and experts from OIE Member Countries in all regions. The Working Group's

primary role is to act as a steering committee for the OIE's work programme on the development of standards aimed at protecting consumers from food-borne hazards arising from animals at the production level of the food chain and to promote cooperation with the CAC. The APFSWG held its 5th meeting in January 2006 and a report of its activities was presented to the General Session of the OIE International Committee in May 2006. Through this Working Group, the OIE has been working on several topics of interest for the CAC.

Areas where the tasks and standards of the OIE and the Codex Alimentarius Commission complement each other

As previously mentioned, the APFSWG has developed a document on the 'Cooperation between the Codex Alimentarius Commission and the OIE on food safety throughout the food chain' (13). This document provides an introduction on how to address the 'production-to-consumption' continuum from a regulatory point of view and constitutes a framework for subsequent documents on *inter alia* the roles and functions of Veterinary Services in food safety.

Meat hygiene

Following the drafting of the framework document and the parallel work then underway in the Codex Committee on Meat Hygiene (CCMH), the APFSWG prepared an appendix for the OIE *Terrestrial Code* on 'Guidelines for the Control of Biological Hazards of Animal Health and Public Health Importance through *Ante-* and *Post-Mortem* Meat Inspection'. This appendix complements and refers to the 'Code of Hygienic Practice for Meat' adopted by the CAC in 2005 (7). This appendix was adopted as an international standard by the OIE International Committee in May 2006. The Codex Code, in turn, includes references to the OIE *Terrestrial Code*.

Identification and traceability of live animals

The APFSWG guided the drafting of a chapter for the OIE *Terrestrial Code* on 'Identification and Traceability of Live Animals'. This chapter was adopted as an international standard by the OIE International Committee in May 2006. The OIE is now putting together the main points that constitute a system for identification and traceability for live animals to guide Member Countries in setting up a proper animal identification and traceability system. The

816

Rev. sci. tech. Off. int. Epiz., **25** (2)

OIE welcomed the finalisation of the 'Proposed Draft Principles for Traceability/Product Tracing as a Tool within a Food Inspection and Certification System' (prepared by the Codex Committee on Food Import and Export Inspection and Certification Systems [CCFICS]), which were adopted by the CAC in July 2006 at step 5/8 of the elaboration procedure. The OIE has coordinated its work with the CAC in order to minimise gaps and duplication.

Model certificates for international trade

To better address the needs of its Member Countries, the OIE is updating its standards on certification. Considering the relevant work already done by the CAC, cooperation with this organisation is necessary to obtain, when possible, combined certificates in order to promote harmonisation and avoid contradictory standards for both CAC and OIE Member Countries.

The OIE *Terrestrial Code* includes several appendices on certificates for international trade and the procedures related to certification. Those model certificates address trade in animals and their products among OIE Member Countries. The OIE is concerned by the increasing administrative burden that trading partners have to undertake; this is especially relevant for developing countries. Therefore, an effort has to be made to reduce redundant or duplicative certificates. The OIE intends to start the revision of its model certificates, through the setting up of a specific expert group.

As suggested by the APFSWG, the OIE intends to provide its input to the ongoing work of the CCFICS, including participation in the working group established by the CCFICS on the revision of the Codex 'Guidelines for Generic Certificate Formats and the Production and Issuance of Certificates' (3), outlining its proposal for a combined certificate. The OIE agrees with the CCFICS recommendation to the CAC on the need for harmonised attestations for similar certification needs (to minimise misunderstandings and errors) and for specific attestation examples for common types of certification.

Certificate for milk and milk products

The OIE participated to the 7th Session of the Codex Committee on Milk and Milk Products (CCMMP) and contributed to the development of the 'Proposed Draft Model Export Certificate for Milk and Milk Products'. The intent was to provide the basis for allowing OIE and CAC Member Countries to draw up a single certificate per commodity (in this case milk and milk products) that addresses both the animal health and public health aspects relevant to international trade. Therefore, the OIE proposed the inclusion of an animal health attestation in the proposed draft model certificate. The CCMMP did not

take on board the proposal to include an animal health attestation in the model certificate itself but they acknowledged the need to link animal and public health when they are related to food safety and consequently amended the introductory part of the proposed certificate. This amended document now explicitly gives countries the option, if applicable, of including both animal and public health attestations on the same certificate. The OIE is satisfied with this amendment to the text, which was adopted by the CAC at step 5 in July 2006. In order to harmonise the work of the CAC and the OIE on certification, both organisations should revise their standards in close collaboration. The final goal will be to give Member Countries the means to set up a single certificate per product (addressing both public health and animal health) and to simplify the exporting/importing procedures.

Antimicrobial resistance and veterinary drugs

Existing OIE standards

Because of the demand from Member Countries and the impact on animal and human health, antimicrobial resistance is a priority topic for the OIE in its standardisation work. The OIE started to address the matter in 1998 through an expert meeting, which was followed by an international conference in Paris in October 2001. Four guidelines were adopted by the OIE International Committee in May 2003 on the basis of the conclusions of the Conference. Three of them were incorporated into the *Terrestrial Code* (12) as appendices 3.9.1, 3.9.2 and 3.9.3 respectively, and the fourth was included in the OIE *Manual of Diagnostic Tests and Vaccines for Terrestrial Animals* (the *Terrestrial Manual* [11]). The 'Guidelines on Risk Analysis for Antimicrobial Resistance', a companion appendix (3.9.4) for the three guidelines adopted in 2003, were adopted in May 2004. During 2004, the OIE convened two meetings of a new *ad hoc* group, the *Ad hoc* Group on Antimicrobial Resistance. The *Ad hoc* Group updated the OIE standards on antimicrobial resistance (appendices 3.9.4. and 3.9.3. of the *Terrestrial Code*) taking into account the latest scientific knowledge and the work done during the October 2004 meeting of the Codex Committee on Residues of Veterinary Drugs in Foods (CCRVDF). The updates proposed by the *Ad hoc* Group were endorsed by the APFSWG and subsequently by the OIE International Committee in May 2005. The *Ad hoc* Group has also established a list of critically important antimicrobials for veterinary use which the OIE International Committee has endorsed.

Codex standards

The CCRVDF, hosted by the United States of America (USA), recommends maximum levels for residues (MRLs) of veterinary drugs in foods, develops codes of practice and

Rev. sci. tech. Off. int. Epiz., **25** (2)

817

considers methods of sampling and analysis for the determination of residues of veterinary drugs in foods. The MRLs for a large number of veterinary drugs in a variety of foods of animal origin, as well as a 'Recommended International Code of Practice for the Control of the Use of Veterinary Drugs' (2) and 'Guidelines for the Establishment of a Regulatory Programme for Control of Veterinary Drug Residues in Foods' (1) are to be found in Volume 3 of the *Codex Alimentarius*. The CCRVDF has also developed, taking into account the relevant OIE work, a 'Code of Practice to Minimize and Contain Antimicrobial Resistance', which was adopted by the CAC in July 2005 (9). Scientific advice on MRLs for veterinary drugs is provided by JECFA (which, despite its name, deals with issues other than food additives, e.g. veterinary drug residues, mycotoxins and heavy metals).

Cooperation and future work

Progress in the area of antimicrobial resistance can best be achieved by close cooperation between all organisations working on this important issue, including the OIE, FAO, WHO, the CAC and national governments. The OIE, FAO and the WHO have actively cooperated in this area through joint activities and by participating in the activities of the International Cooperation on Harmonisation of Technical Requirements for Registration of Veterinary Products (VICH). Following a suggestion of the WHO and the CAC, consultations of experts were organised in Geneva (2003), Oslo (2004) and Seoul (2006) by WHO, FAO and the OIE with the aim of gathering all available scientific data and preparing a common action plan for the future.

The first Workshop on Non-Human Antimicrobial Usage, held in December 2003 in Geneva, included a preliminary scientific assessment of all non-human uses of antimicrobials in animals and plants, and their role in antimicrobial resistance, based on the available scientific information. Based on the outcome of the first workshop in Geneva, as well as other relevant input (e.g. reports of previous WHO and OIE workshops), the second workshop, held in Oslo in February 2004, considered the broad range of possible risk management options for antimicrobial resistance from non-human use of antimicrobials. In particular, this second workshop focused on potential directions of future CAC, FAO, WHO and OIE work in this area, in order to prevent and minimise antimicrobial resistance at global level. To ensure that the conclusions of the second workshop reflected the perspectives of interested parties, the major stakeholder groups (e.g. members of the pharmaceutical industry, farmers, food processors, consumers, regulatory agencies, and veterinarians) participated in the meeting. The aim of these two workshops was to enable decision-makers in Member Countries to identify risk management options in the field of antimicrobial resistance.

Following these two Expert Workshops on Non-Human Antimicrobial Usage organised by FAO, the OIE and WHO, it was recommended that the concept of 'critically important' classes of antimicrobials for human and animal usage be developed by WHO and the OIE, respectively. The list of Critically Important Antibacterial Agents for Human Medicine was proposed in February 2005 at a WHO working group consultation meeting in Canberra, Australia. In January 2005, the OIE *Ad hoc* Group on Antimicrobial Resistance proposed to define and designate Veterinary Critically Important Antimicrobials (VCIA). This concept was endorsed by the OIE Biological Standards Commission and adopted by the OIE International Committee in May 2005. The OIE referred the task of establishing a list of VCIA to the OIE *Ad hoc* Group on Antimicrobial Resistance. This *ad hoc* group prepared a questionnaire to collect proposals on VCIA as well as comments regarding the definition and aim of the list. The questionnaire was sent to the 167 OIE Member Countries and to International Organisations with a cooperation agreement with the OIE in order to establish a list of VCIA. All proposals to include antimicrobials needed to be scientifically justified. The results were reviewed in January 2006. A general agreement was expressed by respondents on the criteria proposed by the OIE and the list of proposed VCIA was compiled. The report and the executive summary were endorsed by the OIE Biological Standards Commission and subsequently endorsed by the OIE International Committee in May 2006 with the proviso that the conditions of use of all the antibiotics mentioned in the list should also be included (e.g. for animals destined for consumption).

A joint FAO/WHO/OIE Expert Consultation on antimicrobial use in aquaculture and antimicrobial resistance was held in June 2006 in Seoul. Using the complementary expertise of the OIE, FAO and WHO, the Consultation analysed all the available information on antimicrobial use in aquaculture and its consequences for public health. The overall objective of this meeting was to develop strategies and recommendations to minimise the risks related to antimicrobial use in aquaculture and its consequences for human public health and animal health, based on scientific assessment. Another joint expert consultation on critically important antimicrobials for human and animal use is currently being planned.

Moreover, following the recommendations of the workshop held in Oslo endorsed by the OIE, WHO, FAO, and all participants, the OIE supported the proposal to create a joint Codex/OIE task force on the issue of antimicrobial resistance and stated that it was prepared to support such a task force financially. A proposal to establish procedures enabling the establishment of task forces jointly with other intergovernmental organisations, which could have paved the way for establishing a joint Codex/OIE task force on antimicrobial resistance has been

818

Rev. sci. tech. Off. int. Epiz., **25** (2)

discussed within the CAC and its subsidiary bodies but has not yet been supported. Instead, a proposal to establish a Codex *ad hoc* Intergovernmental Task Force on this subject has been made and this proposal was approved at the CAC meeting in July 2006. The Codex *ad hoc* Intergovernmental Task Force on Antimicrobial Resistance (TFAMR) is expected to develop guidance on methodology and processes for risk assessment, its application to the antimicrobials used in human and veterinary medicine as provided by FAO/WHO through JEMRA, and in close cooperation with the OIE, with subsequent considerations of risk management options.

Animal feed

The Codex *ad hoc* Intergovernmental Task Force on Animal Feeding (TFAF), which was hosted by Denmark, developed a 'Recommended Code of Practice on Good Animal Feeding', which was adopted by the CAC in 2004 (6). The Task Force had then completed the work that had been assigned to it by the CAC. However, discussions about the need for new work on animal feed are ongoing in the CAC. The OIE is further developing its standards on animal feeding by setting up an expert group that will take into account what is already present in the *Terrestrial Code*. The APFSWG has emphasised that in doing this the expert group must consider the Codex 'Recommended Code of Practice on Good Animal Feeding' in order to make the standards complementary.

Food hygiene

The Codex Committee on Food Hygiene (CCFH), hosted by the USA, develops basic provisions on food hygiene and considers, amends (if necessary) and endorses provisions on hygiene prepared by Codex commodity committees and contained in Codex commodity standards and codes of practice; it also considers specific hygiene problems assigned to it by the CAC. An example of a text developed by the CCFH is the 'Recommended International Code of Practice: General Principles of Food Hygiene' (4) including its Annex 'Hazard Analysis and Critical Control Point (HACCP): System and Guidelines for its Application'. At its meeting in early 2006, the APFSWG addressed the issue of salmonellosis, taking into account CCFH and WHO work on risk reduction for salmonellosis (initially *Salmonella enteritidis* in eggs) and focusing on the draft 'Code of Hygienic Practice for Eggs and Egg Products' prepared by the CCFH. The Working Group considered the draft Code as an important tool for Member Countries to ensure safe and suitable eggs and egg products. While the Codex draft Code encompasses the whole food chain, the Working Group considered that the provisions contained in the draft section on 'Flock Management and Animal Health' could be expanded from the viewpoint of the OIE

recommendations for controlling and eradicating animal diseases, including zoonoses. The APFSWG recommended that the Director General of the OIE appoint an *ad hoc* group to develop draft standards on salmonellosis in poultry to complement the ongoing work of the CAC. The standards should address methods for the detection of *Salmonella* spp. in flocks, measures for control and eradication, as well as risk mitigation measures for affected commodities. This recommendation has been accepted.

Other areas for cooperation between the OIE and the Codex Alimentarius Commission

In addition to the above important areas for cooperation between the OIE and the CAC in matters related to the safety of foods of animal origin, the two organisations have a common interest in several other areas (all of which are discussed in more detail below), for example:

– foods derived from biotechnology

– pesticide residues

– fish and fishery products

– general principles for risk analysis.

Foods derived from biotechnology

The first Codex *ad hoc* Intergovernmental Task Force on Foods Derived from Biotechnology (TFFBT), hosted by Japan, began developing basic texts on the risk analysis and food safety assessment of foods derived from transgenic plants and transgenic microorganisms in 2000 and completed its work in 2003. A new Task Force was established in 2005 and it will deal with foods of animal origin, among others. In 2005 the OIE International Committee adopted a resolution on 'Applications of Genetic Engineering for Livestock and Biotechnology Products' and terms of reference for an *ad hoc* group on biotechnology were drawn up by the Biological Standards Commission according to that resolution. The *ad hoc* group will be working on two main topics in relation to biotechnology: on the one hand vaccines and diagnostic tests and on the other cloning of animals. The APFSWG discussed the terms of reference in light of the current work of the CAC on the use of modern biotechnology and made several recommendations to the OIE and to the Biological Standards Commission on the ongoing work. The active participation of the two organisations in relevant aspects of each other's work was emphasised.

Pesticide residues

The Codex Committee on Pesticide Residues (CCPR) establishes maximum limits for pesticide residues in foods (including foods of animal origin) and animal feed. Scientific advice is provided by the JMPR.

Rev. sci. tech. Off. int. Epiz., **25** (2)

819

Fish and fishery products

The Codex Committee on Fish and Fishery Products (CCFFP), hosted by Norway, elaborates worldwide standards for fresh, frozen or otherwise processed fish, crustaceans and molluscs and also develops codes of practice, including codes on hygienic aspects of producing and processing fish and fish products. The Committee developed a 'Code of Practice for Fish and Fishery Products' the latest amendments to which (section on aquaculture) were adopted by the CAC in July 2005 (8).

General principles for risk analysis

The Codex Committee on General Principles has developed the 'Working Principles for Risk Analysis for Application in the Framework of the Codex Alimentarius' (5) and is pursuing its work on the development of a risk analysis guidance document for use by governments. The Committee has also dealt with the procedural texts governing the relations between the CAC and other organisations, including international intergovernmental organisations, such as the OIE.

Prospects for future cooperation between the OIE and the Codex Alimentarius Commission

Although there is still no formal agreement between the OIE and the CAC, the prospects for future cooperation between these two 'SPS Sisters' in developing food standards and related work are good. As discussed earlier in this paper, the CAC has reaffirmed its desire for close cooperation with the OIE.

The OIE established the APFSWG in 2002 and the Working Group has held five meetings to date; the next meeting is planned for November 2006. The 74th General Session of the OIE International Committee, held in May 2006, unanimously adopted Resolution No. XXII on Animal Production Food Safety which describes the future work of the OIE in this field in the short term (14). In the Resolution the Committee recommends that:

1. The Director General continue to rely on the Working Group on Animal Production Food Safety to advise him as well as the relevant OIE Specialist Commissions on OIE activities in the area of animal production food safety,

2. The participation of FAO and WHO experts as members of this Working Group be continued to further strengthen the collaboration between OIE and Codex,

3. The Working Group's 2006/2007 work programme be a guide for the OIE's activities on animal production food safety for the next year, and the Working Group be provided with the necessary resources to address the priorities listed,

4. The Working Group give special attention to its work on animal identification and traceability, and to drafting texts dealing with food-borne zoonoses and animal feeding, complementing relevant *Codex Alimentarius* texts, for consideration by the Terrestrial Animal Health Standards Commission,

5. An *ad hoc* group be established to revise the current OIE model certificates, bearing in mind the need for a common approach with the other international standards and requirements, and the use of electronic certification. The development of the certificates addressing animal health and food safety be established to minimise the administrative load before product export,

6. The OIE develop a new document on the role and functionality of Veterinary Services in food safety, in order to describe the involvement of Veterinary Services in food safety activities which encompass both public and animal health objectives.

From the above it can be seen that the OIE is firmly committed to cooperation with the CAC and its subsidiary bodies in the development of international standards for food safety and to ensure that the activities of the two organisations in this area complement each other.

■

820

Rev. sci. tech. Off. int. Epiz., **25** (2)

Assurer la sécurité sanitaire des aliments : la complémentarité des tâches et des normes de l'Organisation mondiale de la santé animale et de la Commission du Codex alimentarius

S.A. Slorach

Résumé
Les normes internationales élaborées par l'Organisation mondiale de la santé animale (OIE) et par la Commission du Codex alimentarius (CCA) sont reconnues aux termes de l'Accord sur l'application des mesures sanitaires et phytosanitaires de l'Organisation mondiale du commerce en tant que références internationales dans les domaines de compétence de ces deux organisations, à savoir, la santé animale et les zoonoses pour l'OIE et la sécurité sanitaire des aliments pour la CCA. Néanmoins, dans la mesure où les zoonoses ont un impact sur la sécurité sanitaire des aliments, il est essentiel que les deux organisations travaillent de concert afin d'éviter les chevauchements d'activités, les lacunes et les divergences entre les normes. L'OIE a mis en place un Groupe de travail permanent sur la sécurité sanitaire des aliments d'origine animale en phase de production, chargé de promouvoir la collaboration avec la CCA et d'orienter le programme de travail de l'OIE sur l'élaboration de normes visant à protéger les consommateurs contre les risques alimentaires associés aux animaux au niveau de la production. L'auteur décrit brièvement les procédures d'élaboration des normes par l'OIE et la CCA et fournit quelques exemples de la complémentarité des tâches et des normes produites par ces deux organisations dans le domaine de la sécurité sanitaire des aliments. L'hygiène des viandes, l'identification et la traçabilité des animaux sur pied, les modèles de certificats pour le commerce international, la résistance aux agents antimicrobiens, les médicaments vétérinaires, l'alimentation animale et la salmonellose figurent parmi les sujets traités.

Mots-clés
Commission du Codex alimentarius – Coopération – Norme internationale – Organisation mondiale de la santé animale – Sécurité sanitaire des aliments – Zoonose.

■

Complementariedad de las tareas y normas de la Organización Mundial de Sanidad Animal y la Comisión del Codex Alimentarius para garantizar la inocuidad de los alimentos

S.A. Slorach

Resumen
En el Acuerdo sobre la Aplicación de las Medidas Sanitarias y Fitosanitarias de la Organización Mundial del Comercio se reconocen específicamente las normas internacionales formuladas por la Organización Mundial de Sanidad Animal (OIE) y la Comisión del Codex Alimentarius (CCA). Las normas de la OIE se centran en la sanidad animal y las zoonosis; a su vez, las normas de la CCA se refieren a la inocuidad de los alimentos. Pero puesto que las zoonosis pueden afectar la inocuidad de los alimentos, ambas organizaciones deben trabajar en

Rev. sci. tech. Off. int. Epiz., **25** (2)

estrecha colaboración para evitar las duplicaciones y lagunas así como, en particular, la formulación de normas contradictorias. La OIE estableció un Grupo de Trabajo sobre Seguridad Sanitaria de los Alimentos derivados de la Producción Animal. Su mandato incluye el fomento de la cooperación con la CCA. También le atribuye las funciones de comité de dirección del programa de trabajo de la OIE sobre la formulación de normas destinadas a proteger a los consumidores de las enfermedades transmitidas por los alimentos de origen animal que puedan originarse en la etapa de producción de la cadena alimentaria. En este artículo se describe brevemente la labor de formulación de normas de la OIE y la CCA y se presentan ejemplos de la complementariedad de las tareas y normas de ambas organizaciones para garantizar la inocuidad de los alimentos. Esas normas cubren los ámbitos de la higiene de la carne, la identificación y la trazabilidad de los animales vivos, los modelos de certificados para el comercio internacional, la resistencia a los antimicrobianos, los medicamentos veterinarios, los piensos y la salmonelosis.

Palabras clave

Comisión del Codex Alimentarius – Cooperación – Inocuidad de los alimentos – Normas internacionales – Organización Mundial de Sanidad Animal – Zoonosis.

■

References

1. Codex Alimentarius Commission (CAC) (1993). – Guidelines for the Establishment of a Regulatory Programme for Control of Veterinary Drug Residues in Foods, CAC/GL-16. Joint FAO/WHO Food Standards Programme, Rome.

2. Codex Alimentarius Commission (CAC) (1993). – Recommended International Code of Practice for the Control of the Use of Veterinary Drugs, CAC/RCP-38. Joint FAO/WHO Food Standards Programme, Rome.

3. Codex Alimentarius Commission (CAC) (2001). – Guidelines for Generic Official Certificate Formats and the Production and Issuance of Certificates, CAC/GL-38. Joint FAO/WHO Food Standards Programme, Rome.

4. Codex Alimentarius Commission (CAC) (2001). – Recommended International Code of Practice: general principles of food hygiene, CAC/RCP 1-1969, Rev. 4. *In* Food hygiene: basic texts. Joint FAO/WHO Food Standards Programme, Rome.

5. Codex Alimentarius Commission (CAC) (2003). – Working Principles for Risk Analysis for Application in the Framework of the Codex Alimentarius (adopted by the 26th Session of the Codex Alimentarius Commission, 30 June-7 July, Rome). *In* Codex Alimentarius Commission Procedural Manual, 15th Ed. Joint FAO/WHO Food Standards Programme, Rome, 101-107.

6. Codex Alimentarius Commission (CAC) (2004). – Recommended Code of Practice on Good Animal Feeding, CAC/RCP-54. Joint FAO/WHO Food Standards Programme, Rome.

7. Codex Alimentarius Commission (CAC) (2005). – Code of Hygienic Practice for Meat, CAC/RCP-58. Joint FAO/WHO Food Standards Programme, Rome.

8. Codex Alimentarius Commission (CAC) (2005). – Code of Practice for Fish and Fishery Products, CAC/RCP-52, Rev. 2. Joint FAO/WHO Food Standards Programme, Rome.

9. Codex Alimentarius Commission (CAC) (2005). – Code of Practice to Minimize and Contain Antimicrobial Resistance, CAC/RCP-61. Joint FAO/WHO Food Standards Programme, Rome.

10. Codex Alimentarius Commission (CAC) (2005). – Procedural Manual, 15th Ed. Joint FAO/WHO Food Standards Programme, Rome.

11. World Organisation for Animal Health (OIE) (2004). – Manual of Diagnostic Tests and Vaccines for Terrestrial Animals, 5th Ed. OIE, Paris.

12. World Organisation for Animal Health (OIE) (2005). – Terrestrial Animal Health Code, 14th Ed. OIE, Paris.

13. World Organisation for Animal Health (OIE) (2006). – Cooperation between the Codex Alimentarius Commission and the OIE on food safety throughout the food chain. Available from the food safety section of the OIE website (www.oie.int).

14. World Organisation for Animal Health (OIE) (2006). – Resolution No. XXII: Animal production food safety. *In* Final Report of the 74th General Session, 21-26 May, Paris. OIE, Paris, 138-139.

Rev. sci. tech. Off. int. Epiz., 2006, **25** (2), 823-836

Guide to good farming practices for animal production food safety

OIE Animal Production Food Safety Working Group

World Organisation for Animal Health (OIE), 12 rue de Prony, 75017 Paris, France

This draft guide to good farming practices for animal production food safety was taken from the Report of the Meeting of the OIE Terrestrial Animal Health Standards Commission (Paris, 17-28 January 2005).

Summary
Food safety is now universally recognised as a public health priority. It requires a global approach, from production to consumption. This article addresses the first stage of the food chain and the steps farmers can take to optimise the food safety control of products of animal origin. This inevitably means controlling the health status of the animals from which food products are derived. The present article addresses all those hazards whose control at farm level can have a beneficial or even decisive effect on the food safety of products of animal origin (including: milk and milk products, meat and meat products, eggs and egg products, honey and apiculture products). It is organised in eight sections: buildings and other facilities; health conditions for introduction of animals into the farm; animal feeding; animal watering; veterinary drugs; farm management; preparation of animals for slaughter; and common measures for record keeping and traceability.

Keywords
Animal production – Farm management – Farming practices – Food safety – Production level – Rearing.

Foreword

Following a request by the World Organisation for Animal Health (OIE) International Committee to strengthen activities in the food safety area, and desiring to further develop collaboration with the Codex Alimentarius Commission (CAC), a permanent 'OIE Working Group on Animal Production Food Safety' was established in 2002. The Working Group's role is to coordinate OIE activities related to animal production food safety and to provide advice to the Director General of the OIE and relevant Specialist Commissions in these areas.

The draft guide to good farming practices presented in this article has been produced by the Working Group. The Working Group is further developing this guide, so this article cannot be considered as a definitive version. The version reported here was included in the report of the third meeting of the OIE Working Group, which was published in the report of the meeting of the OIE Terrestrial Animal Health Standards Commission (January 2005). Other international standards and recommendations are included in the Appendix.

At its fifth meeting (February 2006), the Working Group recommended a joint OIE/Food and Agriculture Organization (FAO) revision of this draft guide to good farming practices; in this work, a contribution from the World Health Organization and the CAC Secretariat would be sought. The outcome would be published as a joint OIE/FAO guide.

Introduction

These guidelines are intended to help competent authorities and stakeholders, especially farmers, to fully assume their responsibilities at the first stage of the food

824

Rev. sci. tech. Off. int. Epiz., **25** (2)

chain to optimise the food safety control of products of animal origin offered to consumers.

The recommendations in these guidelines serve as a tool to help competent authorities at the farm level, particularly Veterinary Services, to fulfil their responsibilities.

Food safety is now universally recognised as a public health priority. It requires a global approach, from production to consumption, which is so aptly conveyed by the expressions 'from the stable to the table' and 'from the field to the plate'.

As far as animal products and products of animal origin are concerned, this inevitably means controlling the health status of the animals from which these food products are derived. Animal health status must be assessed with regard to any infectious (bacterial and viral) or parasitic agents, and especially zoonotic agents, that they could be carrying at the primary production stage. The possibility of the animals having ingested and possibly accumulated chemical (drug residues, pesticides, heavy metals, etc.) or physical contaminants (radioactive elements, foreign bodies, etc.) during their lifetime must also be addressed.

Any such biological, chemical and physical agents present in the body of the live animal may contaminate animal products (milk, meat, fish, eggs, etc.) at levels that are unacceptable in terms of public health. Controlling the safety of food of animal origin at the primary production stage therefore involves all the measures (implemented at the farm or production unit level) necessary to ensure that these contaminants do not end up in animal products, or, if they do, that their levels do not exceed the maximum permissible levels, notably the maximum residue limits and microbiological criteria set by the CAC.

The tools for controlling food safety, namely the codes of hygienic practice and the hazard analysis and critical control point system, have proved their effectiveness at the secondary production and distribution stages. It is clearly appropriate to try to apply them wherever possible at the primary production stage of animal products, in other words at the farm or production unit level, whenever an appreciable improvement in the level of the control of food safety may result.

The guidelines presented here cover eight areas of primary production in which preventive actions can usefully be implemented; they are, as follows:

a) buildings and other facilities: surroundings and environmental control

b) health conditions for introduction of animals into the farm

c) animal feeding

d) animal watering

e) veterinary drugs

f) farm management

g) preparation of animals for slaughter

h) common measures for record keeping and traceability.

Scope of this Guide

The present document addresses all those hazards whose control at farm level can have a beneficial or even decisive effect on the food safety of products of animal origin (including: milk and milk products, meat and meat products, eggs and egg products, honey and apiculture products).

It does not address the processing of products at the farm level which comes within the scope of specific standards in the Codex Alimentarius.

It does not address animal welfare aspects of farm production.

Hazards considered within this Guide

Biological hazards

The biological agents of the most common and/or dangerous diseases that can be transmitted to humans via foodstuffs of animal origin are as follows:

– *Salmonella*

– *Campylobacter*

– verotoxinogenic *Escherichia coli*, including *Escherichia coli* O157:H7

– *Listeria monocytogenes*

– *Toxoplasma*

– *Leptospira*

– *Coxiella burnetii* (Q fever)

– *Brucella*

– *Mycobacterium* (tuberculosis)

– *Yersinia enterocolitica*

– prions (bovine spongiform encephalopathy agent, etc.)

– parasites such as *Taenia solium*, *Taenia saginata* and *Trichinella spiralis*.

While these pathogens arouse the greatest concern among consumers and governments in terms of food safety, the diseases they cause are also the most difficult to prevent at

Rev. sci. tech. Off. int. Epiz., **25** (2)

825

the farm level as they can also be transmitted by warm-blooded animals, such as birds, crawling or flying insects and even by water or the soil.

Chemical and physical hazards

These hazards chiefly consist of the following:

– drug residues (notably antibiotics)

– growth promoters (some unauthorised hormones, substances having a thyrostatic action and anabolic substances)

– residues of chemical products used on the farm (pesticides, disinfectants, etc.)

– environmental contaminants (dioxins, polychlorinated biphenyls [PCBs], polyaromatic hydrocarbons [PAHs], heavy metals, radioactive isotopes, etc.)

– foreign bodies (needles, fragments of glass, pieces of plastic or metal, etc.).

In the majority of cases, the action needed at the farm level to reduce or eliminate the risk presented by these chemical and physical contaminants is, in comparison to that needed to control biological risks, easier to implement.

The remainder of this document recommends actions to reduce the risks that the occurrence of these hazards at farm level poses for public health.

Buildings and other farm facilities: surroundings and environmental control

Hazards

These consist of pathogenic biological agents (e.g. certain species of *Leptospira*, *Salmonella*, *Trichinella*, *Legionella*, etc.), chemical agents (e.g. dioxins, pesticides, hydrocarbons, etc.) or physical agents (e.g. radioisotopes) which can be a direct (air-borne or feed-borne) or indirect (notably via water and feedstuffs) source of contamination for animals. Problems can occur as a result of hazards found in the farm's immediate surroundings or as a result of a failure to control the environment in livestock buildings.

Recommendations

To minimise hazards coming from the farm's immediate surroundings the following steps should be taken:

– avoid conducting farming activities close to industrial plants likely to be a source of pollution (e.g. domestic waste incineration plant releasing dioxins, surface processing plant releasing solvents or heavy metals, etc.) or in an environment susceptible to air-borne pollution (e.g. near a road with heavy motor traffic – emissions of lead and hydrocarbons), soil pollution (former industrial site or site where dumping of toxic substances has taken place) or the proliferation of pests (e.g. open municipal rubbish tip);

– site farm buildings or other facilities (e.g. in the case of extensive husbandry) so that they are independent of private buildings (residential accommodation), sufficiently far away from areas where waste materials are stored, and so that access by visitors can be effectively controlled (direction signs or 'access prohibited' signs where necessary);

– site farm buildings or other facilities away from buildings on neighbouring farms that are used for purposes which could increase the risk of disease transfer;

– if necessary, seek the advice of the relevant competent authorities (e.g. Veterinary Services, Environmental Services, etc.).

To minimise hazards arising from a failure to control the environment in livestock buildings such buildings should be designed as follows:

– adequate in size and correctly ventilated

– with a rational arrangement of the premises (separation of clean and soiled areas, absence of any intersection of production chains, separation of working areas and storage areas from animal production areas)

– allowing animals to be dealt with in single groups (poultry, pigs) and newly arrived (quarantine) or sick animals (observation pen) to be satisfactorily isolated

– allowing easy, complete and effective cleaning and disinfection

– correctly isolated from pests and from wild or stray animals, and from other domestic animals as appropriate

– allowing easy, rational and effective evacuation of excreta

– suitably equipped for the collection of farm effluents and wastewater

– keeping the immediate surroundings clear and free from stagnant water and anywhere that could harbour pests, and arranged so as to allow easy disinfection of areas used by professional visitors (veterinarian, animal or feed deliverers, milk or egg collectors, carcass disposal agents, etc.)

– so as to make access difficult for unauthorised persons or vehicles (barriers, fences, signs)

826

Rev. sci. tech. Off. int. Epiz., **25** (2)

– taking into account the risk of natural disasters (flooding, landslides, heat waves, prolonged freezing conditions, earthquake, etc.)

– using inert construction and surface materials that cannot be a potential source of contamination (e.g. prohibit the use of lead paint)

– if necessary, seek the advice of a veterinarian, para-veterinarian or an official with the relevant competent authority.

Health conditions for introduction of animals into the farm

Hazards

These consist of biological agents (pathogenic bacteria, viruses, parasites, etc.) that can be introduced into herds and flocks by animals that do not have all the necessary health guarantees.

Recommendations

– Introduce into the farm only animals from farms at which this guide has been implemented

– introduce only animals of known health status (for example regarding tuberculosis, brucellosis, leptospirosis, vibriosis, salmonelloses and cryptosporidiosis), in accordance with the provisions adopted by the competent authority (Veterinary Services)

– ensure that all the animals introduced are correctly identified (tagged or marked) and that their identification does indeed correspond to the accompanying health documents

– obtain from the seller full details of the route taken by the animals being introduced, from the hatchery, apiary, herd or flock of origin to their destination

– control the sanitary conditions under which the introduced animals are transported: ensure that the deliverer has a suitable vehicle and implements an effective cleaning and disinfection programme for the vehicle, so as to reduce the risk of transmitting pathogens between production units or farms

– obtain a declaration from the seller regarding any chemical residues that might be present due to the introduced animal's having recently been treated

– refuse any introduction of animals presenting suspicious clinical signs on delivery and, if necessary,

inform the competent authority (Veterinary Services) if a contagious disease is suspected

– record full details of the purchased animals: description, identification, sex, age, health status, date of introduction, name and address of the seller and of the attending veterinarian, etc.

– isolate the newly introduced animal(s) for a suitable surveillance and acclimatisation period

– arrange for a veterinarian or para-veterinarian to perform any necessary biological tests when the animals are introduced and isolated, and do not bring these animals into contact with other animals on the farm until the results of these tests are known and have proved satisfactory.

Animal feeding

Hazards

These consist of biological agents (bacteria, viruses, prions, parasites, antibiotics, promoters, phytotoxins or mould toxins), chemical agents (farm chemicals [pesticides], dioxins, heavy metals, environmental contaminants, etc.) or physical agents (foreign bodies, etc.) which could be present in animal feed and, consequently, in animal products (milk, meat, fish, egg products, etc.). Risks may also result from an overdosage of certain components, notably medication, in animal feed.

Recommendations

The use of veterinary drugs as supplements in animal feeding is discussed in the section below entitled 'Veterinary drugs'.

Grassland and pasture

– Carry out a risk assessment when livestock are put out to pasture outside the farm: in particular, ensure that the land where the animals are put out to pasture is not exposed to potential sources of chronic contamination (e.g. main road with heavy traffic, domestic waste incineration plant), is not polluted with chemical residues (e.g. pesticides, dioxins, heavy metals) at an unacceptable level and is not known to harbour animal pathogens (bacteria, e.g. anthrax spores; parasites, e.g. flukes);

– ensure that the fields surrounding the pasture are not sprayed with substances that have not been shown to be safe, and that the animals cannot have access to potentially contaminating material on the perimeter of the pasture (e.g. unauthorised dumping, stocks of herbicides, posts coated with aluminium paint);

Rev. sci. tech. Off. int. Epiz., **25** (2)

827

– carefully follow the manufacturer's instructions shown on the label before spreading any chemical product on fields, pastures or in grain silos;

– respect the recommended waiting times before animals are put out to pasture after the pasture or neighbouring pieces of land have been treated with agricultural chemicals;

– comply with recommendations for the use of animal by-products for agricultural reclamation/spreading;

– prevent livestock entering pastures containing toxic plants;

– when purchasing pasture or other land, require certification for the land in question regarding previous use of agricultural inputs or any chemical pollution (e.g. resulting from the dumping of industrial waste). Where necessary, have a soil study carried out to detect the presence of any toxic chemicals.

Use of commercial feed

– Require that all the animal feed purchased is free of chemical residues and complies with regulatory requirements (obtain, if this is not stated on the label, a certificate guaranteeing that it complies with the regulations)

– check that the feed delivered is correctly labelled (manufacturer's name, composition, manufacturing date, use-by date, instructions for use and precautionary measures to be followed, batch number, etc.) and that the packaging is intact and without any defect that might have affected the contents

– check the quality of the feed delivered in terms of appearance (visual examination) and keep a written record of the results

– refuse, treat appropriately or destroy any feed presenting traces of contamination by mould

– ensure that feed for ruminants is free from any trace of animal by-products prohibited by the regulations and eliminate any risk of accidental cross-contamination

– keep samples of purchased feed for any subsequent analytical testing should a problem of residues be identified at the farm production level

– store feed in a clean area, protected from humidity and pests (insects and rodents)

– if storage conditions are not optimal, prefer more frequent deliveries of smaller quantities

– keep an up-to-date register of feed delivered and used (batch numbers, date used and destination)

– seek advice if there is the slightest doubt as to the quality of the feed given to animals

– when a problem exists, immediately inform the supplier and, if necessary, the competent authorities.

Manufacture of animal feed on the farm

– Check the quality of the raw materials delivered in terms of their appearance (visual examination, to rule out any risk of macroscopic contamination) and keep a record of the findings

– ensure that all the raw materials of plant origin used as ingredients for animal feed have been grown, stored and treated using validated procedures

– keep an up-to-date register of the raw materials delivered and used (batch numbers, dates used, batch numbers of the feed in which they were used)

– store the raw materials in a clean area, protected from humidity and pests (insects and rodents)

– eliminate raw materials presenting traces of contamination with mould

– ensure that the water used is potable

– comply with the recommendations regarding storage (in a safe place) and the use of additives and feed supplements (always follow the recommendations on the label regarding dosage and withdrawal periods)

– ensure uniform mixing of the different components

– eliminate any risk of cross-contamination, at all stages (production, storage and distribution)

– have clearly defined written procedures for the manufacture of feed, fixing precisely the formulation and production stages, and, in particular, making provision for mixers to be purged between the production of two types of feed with different ingredients

– regularly check and calibrate weighing machines

– plan corrective actions to be implemented in the event of a formulation error and actions to deal with substandard batches that might constitute a hazard

– keep, and file for as long as necessary, up-to-date manufacturing records specifying the dosage and batch number(s) of each of the raw materials used

– keep samples of manufactured feed for subsequent analytical testing should a problem of residues be identified at the farm production level

– set a use-by date for each batch of manufactured feed, taking into account the use-by dates of each of the ingredients and the packaging and storage conditions

– correctly label the sacks or hoppers containing the manufactured feed (date of manufacture, feed type, batch number, use-by date)

– store the manufactured feed in a clean place, protected from humidity and pests (insects and rodents)

– in the case of bulk feed, do not mix two batches of feed in the same container (separate hoppers)

– have the composition of the manufactured feed checked at least once a year (correct dosages of the various ingredients, presence of any contaminants)

– keep an up-to-date register of feed delivered and used (batch numbers and dates of use)

– seek advice if there is the slightest doubt as to the quality of the manufactured feed

– when a problem occurs that could affect the safety of animal products, inform the competent authorities immediately.

General recommendations on animal feeding

– Avoid overfilling the animals' feeding troughs (fill them twice rather than once, adapt the quantity of feed to the specific requirements of the animals)

– remove any unused feed from the troughs before refilling

– clean the troughs and automatic feeders regularly

– ensure animals are fed with feed suitable for the species.

Animal watering

Hazards

These are basically of two types: microbiological and chemical.

Microbiological hazards

These consist of:
– pathogenic bacteria, e.g. toxic strains of *Escherichia coli* (e.g. *E. coli* O157:H7), *Salmonella* spp., *Vibrio cholerae* and *Shigella* spp.

– viruses, e.g. small round structured viruses (Norwalk virus) and the hepatitis A virus

– parasites, e.g. pathogenic protozoa such as *Cryptosporidium parvum, Giardia lamblia* and *Cyclospora cayetanesis*, and eggs and larvae of nematoda, cestoda and trematoda.

Microbiological hazards are most frequently caused by human waste and animal excreta, which may contaminate the water supply used for livestock.

Chemical hazards

These consist of farm chemicals (e.g. pesticides, nitrates/nitrites), industrial contaminants (e.g. dioxins, PAHs, heavy metals), or the water supply network itself (e.g. lead piping).

These chemical agents may eventually be found in animal products (milk, meat, egg products, aquaculture products, apiculture products, etc.) as a result of the animals drinking this water.

Recommendations

– Veterinary drugs as supplements in animal watering should be administered in accordance with the next section – 'Veterinary drugs'

– prevent, by means of barriers or fences, domestic or wild animals approaching safe water reserves or watering points and polluting them

– prevent, by means of barriers or fences, livestock approaching polluted water reserves or watering points and contaminating themselves

– protect water reserves from contamination by undesirable substances, and specifically:

a) use chemicals and organic substances with great care (comply with doses and minimum distance requirements), notably near water collection points, streams and ditches

b) always follow the manufacturer's instructions (see label) for the use of any chemical product for spraying or fumigating (how to apply, dosage and waiting time)

c) avoid using pesticides and herbicides anywhere where there is a possibility of contaminating the water table or nearby water collection points

d) avoid cleaning spraying equipment or chemical product containers in places where any remaining substances and the flushing water can re-enter the water supply network

e) avoid spreading slurry, manure or dairy effluents where there is any possibility of their contaminating the water table or nearby water collection points

f) avoid human and animal effluent being a source of contamination

– monitor compliance of, maintain and regularly clean water distribution systems. Use closed-circuit systems whenever possible, so as to reduce access by other animals

– have the bacteriological and physico-chemical quality of water regularly tested, where appropriate (e.g. bore-hole), and ask to receive the results of analyses conducted on water in the local water supply network

– seek advice and test the water resources if there is the slightest doubt about the safety of water used for animals.

Rev. sci. tech. Off. int. Epiz., **25** (2)

829

Veterinary drugs

Hazards

These consist of the inappropriate use of both veterinary drugs (which may induce the presence of residues in food products) and antibiotics (which may induce the creation of multi-resistant bacterial strains, which can pose a major threat to public health).

Recommendations

– Any therapeutic treatment should only be undertaken when the diagnosis is precise and certain, and should be based on the dual principle of maximum efficacy and minimum risk;

– use only drugs that are authorised for the treatment of the particular species, and use antimicrobials only on veterinary prescription and as prescribed;

– use drugs in accordance with the species, uses and doses indicated on the label, and in accordance with the instructions on the label or on the advice of a veterinarian well acquainted with the animals and the production site;

– use only drugs that are known to be effective for the intended use and in strict compliance with the recommendations on the label or the veterinarian's prescription;

– do not use veterinary drugs beyond their expiry date;

– use weighing machines, animal measuring tape or other suitable measuring instruments to evaluate the weight of the animals and adjust the dose to be administered (avoid any overdosage);

– wherever possible, isolate sick animals from healthy animals, so as to avoid the transfer of resistant bacteria, and treat animals individually;

– strictly observe the recommended withdrawal periods so as to guarantee that residue levels in food of animal origin do not present any risk to the consumer, on the understanding that any drug likely to result in residues must be prescribed by a veterinarian;

– use the appropriate techniques and equipment to administer drugs, and avoid any accidental contamination of the product by thoroughly cleaning equipment, such as buckets. Change the syringe for each new drug and, if appropriate, the needle for each animal;

– in the event of the injection needle breaking in the animal's muscle tissue, place an indelible mark on the injection site, note the identification number of the animal and record the problem in a written document which will accompany the animal to the abattoir;

– keep a written record of all treatments dispensed to the animals, and keep all the laboratory reports, including bacteriological tests and sensitivity tests;

– keep up-to-date records of the use made of veterinary drugs on the farm, including the following information (all of which should be placed at the disposal of the competent authority [Veterinary Services]):

a) name of the product or active substance, and the batch number

b) supplier's name

c) dates of administration and date of end of treatment

d) identification of the animal (or group of animals) to which the drug was administered

e) diagnosis or clinical signs treated

f) quantity of the drug administered and the administration route (if transcutaneous, state the injection site)

g) withdrawal periods (dates from which milk, meat or any other animal product can be offered for human consumption)

h) results of laboratory tests

i) effectiveness of the therapy

– develop rational stock management procedures for drugs, in particular vaccines and medicated premixes (keep an up-to-date record of stock movements);

– ensure that the conditions under which antimicrobials and other veterinary drugs are stored on the farm comply with the label and insert instructions (in particular provide a safe place [cabinet in a locked room], where they can be stored in the dark and at the recommended temperature);

– safely dispose of all veterinary drugs past their expiry date, instruments and empty containers in an environmentally friendly manner.

Farm management

Hazards

These consist of pathogenic biological agents which can be introduced onto a farm and proliferate due to lack of respect for basic farm management rules. These can also consist of chemical contaminants. Both biological agents and chemical contaminants can induce subsequent contamination of animals and their products.

Rev. sci. tech. Off. int. Epiz., **25** (2)

Recommendations

Training, conduct and health status of staff

– Provide suitable training for staff required to handle farm chemical inputs, manufacture feed on the farm, clean and disinfect premises and equipment and treat animals. Appropriate training will give them a good knowledge of hazards present on the farm and methods of managing risks so as to guarantee the safety of food products of animal origin;

– train staff in basic biosecurity principles and practices to minimise the likelihood of introducing or spreading pathogens;

– insist that staff wear suitable working attire (clothing and boots that are kept clean or changed as often as necessary) and respect sanitary measures (e.g. changing clothes, washing hands or showering) before they enter controlled areas;

– ensure that staff are regularly monitored to detect any healthy carriers of bacterial or parasitic agents that could be transmitted to animals.

Maintenance, cleaning and disinfection of equipment, premises and immediate surroundings

– Develop and implement the appropriate procedures to maintain, clean and disinfect farm equipment, premises and immediate surroundings, respecting the manufacturer's instructions regarding the use of detergents and disinfectants (preparation of surfaces, dilution, contact period)

– ensure that the procedures in place are effective (visual self-inspections with, if necessary, recourse to bacteriological analysis) and take any corrective measures that may be required

– use clean instruments so as to avoid spreading diseases.

Measures to control pests and stray animals and prevent unauthorised access

– Develop and implement a global plan to control pests (rodents, insects, spiders) within the farm, using licensed products in the appropriate manner

– ensure the effectiveness of this control plan (visual self-inspections) and take any corrective measures that may be required

– prevent domestic animals (cats and dogs) from roaming in and around livestock buildings

– put in place all the appropriate prevention and control measures, respecting the regulations currently in force in terms of protection of biodiversity, so as to minimise contact between livestock and wild animals

– ensure that no unauthorised person can enter the livestock buildings.

Stock management (feed, drugs)

– Ensure that there is a satisfactory turnover of stock, applying the first in first out method, and disposing of any product that has passed its expiry date

– ensure that all containers (sacks or cans) are hermetically sealed

– ensure that storage conditions are appropriate and in particular that the recommended temperatures are respected.

Management of waste materials, effluents and expired products

– Ensure that the waste materials generated by the farm (excreta, feed remains, etc.) are regularly removed, in such a way that neither their transport to the storage site nor the conditions under which they are stored can be either a source of environmental contamination for the farm and its immediate surroundings or conducive to the proliferation of pests (rodents, insects)

– ensure that products that have passed their expiry date (farm chemical inputs, veterinary drugs) and their packaging are disposed of, and effluents (wastewater, washing water) treated, in such a way that they cannot be a source of environmental pollution, and, indirectly, of contamination for the animals.

Storage of chemical products

Store chemical products and equipment that may contain them safely out of reach of the animals.

Production monitoring of animals

– Ensure that the animals or groups of animals present on the farm are permanently identified and keep the farm records up-to-date

– minimise mixing of animals of different species

– conduct daily surveillance of the animals to detect any anomaly or suspicious symptom

– set up a system for monitoring the production performance of the animals and identify indicators that will allow the early detection of any anomaly.

Health monitoring of animals and disease prevention programmes

– Develop, in conjunction with the veterinarian in charge of the animals, an animal health and welfare plan that includes disease prevention measures (e.g. mastitis programme, vaccination and deworming programmes, etc.)

– implement this health plan, following the guidelines issued by the competent authority for animal disease control (Veterinary Services), with the advice of a veterinarian or para-veterinarian

– treat animals regularly against gastrointestinal parasites

– seek professional advice in the event of unusual clinical signs suggestive of a disease in the herd/flock or if there is an unexpected drop in the yield or quality of animal products

– establish written standardised operational procedures for the detection and management of animal diseases and for the use of veterinary products

– inform the veterinarian responsible for monitoring the health of the animals of any problems of disease recurrence or relapses

– take advantage of all the information obtained at the abattoir during ante-mortem inspections of animals and post-mortem inspection of meat and offal by official veterinarians relating to specific pathologies for which corrective measures can be taken at the farm level (parasitism, muscular degeneration, melanosis, presence of foreign bodies [e.g. cactus spines], etc.)

– determine whether fallen stock and dead animals need to be tested as part of an official surveillance programme.

Animal movements

Ensure that any isolated or seasonal movement of animals outside the farm (transhumance, grazing on mountain pasture, etc.) does not expose them to an excessive risk of chemical or microbiological contamination, whether by air-borne route, digestive route or direct or indirect contact with wild animals.

Isolation of sick animals and their products

– Separate sick or potentially sick animals from healthy animals so as to avoid the transfer of pathogenic agents and resistant bacteria

– comply with hygiene regulations relating to contacts between persons (veterinarians, livestock producers, owners, children) and animals undergoing treatment

– ensure that products from sick animals cannot be used for human consumption or for animal feed.

Storage and disposal of dead animals

– Isolate the dead animals prior to their collection or destruction, and store them in a suitable place (easy access and disinfection) so as to avoid any contact with livestock or their environment

– ensure that the dead animals that have died on the farm are rapidly disposed of and ensure that their removal by a carcass disposal firm cannot be a source of pathogens for the farm.

Preparation of animals for slaughter

Hazards

These consist of numerous potentially dangerous agents for humans which are present in the digestive tube or excreta, and on the hides and skins of cattle and sheep or the plumage of birds in good health. These agents include *E. coli*, *Salmonella* and *Campylobacter*, which can cause food poisoning in humans.

Stress caused by grouping animals together, loading them and transporting them to the abattoir can promote the passage of these pathogenic bacteria from the intestine into muscle tissue.

Moreover, the greater the faecal soiling of hides, skins and feathers, the higher the risk of any pathogenic bacteria they may contain contaminating meat during the dressing or defeathering of carcasses at the abattoir.

Recommendations

General measures

– Ensure that animals are fit for slaughter

– prevent animals from becoming soiled by keeping the enclosures, gangways, and loading and unloading areas clean, avoiding overcrowding, increasing the quantity of litter and resolving any problems of effluent disposal

– give animals raised in livestock buildings free access to straw, hay and silage with a high dry matter content for 48 h prior to slaughter

– avoid any abrupt changes in diet at the end of the production cycle

– give animals free access to watering points up to their departure for the abattoir and withdraw feed from animals for the 24 h prior to slaughter

– handle animals humanely and do not subject them to undue stress, given that stressed animals are more likely to release pathogenic bacteria, especially *E. coli* O157:H7, in their excreta

– check the state of the animals' identification marks and bands several days before they are due to leave so as to avoid having to tag the animals immediately before they are transported to the abattoir

– ensure that the conditions under which the animals are transported to the abattoir are not a source of stress and are not conducive to substantial soiling of their hides, skins or plumage.

Extensively grazed livestock

Weather conditions prior to departure (e.g. heavy rainfall) and the absence of any special measures to avoid watering points becoming a quagmire can lead to considerable soiling of ruminants (cattle, sheep, goats) and omnivores (pigs) before their departure to the abattoir. Furthermore, gathering animals together prior to their transport is an operation that causes stress, especially for animals that have ranged freely all year round in the open and are unused to the presence of humans.

It is therefore important to ensure that:

– animals at the end of the fattening phase are placed in pastures that are the least prone to the effects of inclement weather, with watering points that are sufficient in number and arranged in such as way as to avoid the animals becoming soiled with mud

– the animals are brought together a sufficient length of time before their departure to the abattoir, in an enclosure, preferably covered, or other suitable area, so as to minimise the risk of major soiling of their hides, skins, wool or plumage.

Livestock housed on slatted flooring

The correct stocking density of feedlots and enclosures (density per square metre) throughout the fattening phase is an important consideration, as overcrowding, like under-population, prevents the satisfactory evacuation of excreta between the slats.

It is therefore important to ensure that:

– the correct stocking density is maintained for as long as possible during the fattening phase (the density depends on the size and nature of the stalls, as well as on the age of the animals)

– the slatted flooring is kept satisfactorily clean and that the housing is correctly ventilated

– particular attention is given to the cleaning operations conducted just before the departure of the animals for the abattoir

– wherever possible, cattle are kept on straw bedding for 1 to 20 days before slaughter.

Livestock housed on litter

The density of animals housed on litter has a significant effect on the cleanliness of the hides. The addition of extra litter will not counteract the adverse effects of over-stocking. The amount of litter required depends on factors such as the density of animals, their weight and the design of the building.

It is therefore important:

– to avoid over-stocking

– to provide an adequate supply of clean litter as often as is necessary

– to ensure that the premises are adequately ventilated and correctly arranged for the evacuation of effluent and cleaning water.

Health measures

– Isolate sick animal in suitable premises, treat them and wait until they have fully recovered before sending them to the abattoir

– check the treatment records of all the animals before they leave so as to ensure that the withdrawal periods or pre-slaughter confinement periods have indeed been respected

– withdraw from the batch being sent to the abattoir any animal whose health status is in doubt and any animal that is still in the withdrawal period following the administration of medication.

Common measures for record keeping and traceability

An identification and traceability system for animals, their feed and products leaving the farm can help:

– to identify the true source of a problem of contamination of products of animal origin

– to implement measures to eliminate, or at least limit, any harmful consequences (such as by the targeted withdrawal of the products in question).

A complete and reliable system of recording procedures, actions and controls implemented on the farm can assist the genuine and effective control of the risks that primary production represents for food safety. It can also assist livestock owners to prove that they have fully carried out their public health responsibilities.

Rev. sci. tech. Off. int. Epiz., **25** (2)

Recommendations

Traceability of animals, animal feed and animal products

– For each animal or group of animals, require and keep all commercial and health documents enabling their exact itinerary to be traced from their farm or establishment of origin to their final destination (other farm or abattoir)

– establish a data-recording system that can be used to ascertain exactly which batches of commercial feed the farm's livestock were fed with and what raw materials were used in feed manufactured on the farm and given to the animals. Keep samples of all the feed used

– establish a data-recording system that can be used to ascertain the exact origin (animal batch) and destination of animal products produced by the farm

– keep all these documents and records and place them at the disposal of the competent authority (Veterinary Services).

Record keeping

– Keep a record of all persons entering the farm: visitors, service staff and farm professionals (veterinarian, milk tester, inseminator, feed deliverer, carcass disposal agent, etc.)

– keep the medical certificates of persons working in contact with animals and any document certifying their qualifications and training

– keep, for each animal or group of animals, all documents relating to the treatment and veterinary actions it has undergone (castration, calving, caesarean section, dehorning, debeaking, administration of medication, etc.)

– keep all laboratory reports, including bacteriological tests and sensitivity tests (data to be placed at the disposal of the veterinarian responsible for treating the animals)

– keep all documents proving that the bacteriological and physico-chemical quality of the water given to the animals is regularly tested

– keep all records of all feed manufacture procedures and manufacturing records for each batch of feed

– keep detailed records of any application of chemical products to fields, pastures and grain silos, as well as the dates that animals are put out to grass and on which plots of land

– keep all the records relating to the cleaning and disinfection procedures used in the farm (including data sheets for each detergent or disinfectant used) as well as all the records showing that these procedures have effectively been implemented (job sheets, self-inspection checks on the effectiveness of the operations)

– keep documents relating to the pest control plan (including the data sheets for each raticide and insecticide used) as well as all the records showing that the control plan has effectively been implemented (plan showing the location of baits and insecticide diffusers, self-inspection checks on the effectiveness of the plan)

– keep all the documents relating to self-inspections (by the livestock producer) and controls (by the authorities and other official bodies) relating to the proper management of the farm and the sanitary and hygienic quality of the animal products leaving it

– keep all documents sent by the official inspection services (distributors or the quality control departments of food-processing firms) relating to anomalies detected at the abattoir, dairy, processing plant or during the distribution of products (meat, eggs, milk, fish, etc.) derived from the farm's animals

– ensure that all these documents are kept long enough to enable any subsequent investigations to be carried out to determine whether contamination of food products detected at the secondary production or distribution stage was due to a dysfunction at the primary production level

– place all these documents and records at the disposal of the competent authority (Veterinary Services) when it conducts farm visits.

Acknowledgements

The Working Group would like to thank the French Ministry of Fisheries and Agriculture (Direction générale de l'alimentation – Ministère de l'agriculture et de la pêche) for its initial contribution to the development of this document. The Working Group also wishes to thank the OIE International Trade Department for their assistance in the development of this guide. The department can be contacted for further information (email: trade.dept@ oie.int).

834

Rev. sci. tech. Off. int. Epiz., **25** (2)

Guide des bonnes pratiques d'élevage pour la sécurité sanitaire des aliments d'origine animale en phase de production

Groupe de travail de l'OIE sur la sécurité sanitaire des aliments d'origine animale en phase de production

Résumé

Il est désormais admis que la sécurité sanitaire des aliments est l'une des priorités de la santé publique. Elle requiert une approche globale, allant de la ferme à l'assiette. Cet article aborde la première phase de la chaîne alimentaire et les mesures que les éleveurs peuvent adopter pour mieux contrôler la sécurité sanitaire des produits d'origine animale. Cela implique, bien évidemment, de contrôler le statut sanitaire des animaux dont sont issus ces produits. L'article examine l'ensemble des risques qu'un contrôle efficace au niveau de la ferme peut parvenir à maîtriser, avec un effet bénéfique, voire décisif sur la sécurité sanitaire des produits alimentaires d'origine animale (incluant le lait et les produits laitiers, la viande et les produits carnés, les œufs et les produits dérivés, le miel et les produits de l'apiculture). L'article comprend huit sections, consacrées respectivement aux bâtiments et aux installations, aux conditions sanitaires de l'accès des animaux à la ferme, à l'alimentation animale, à l'abreuvement, aux médicaments vétérinaires, à la gestion de l'exploitation, à la préparation des animaux avant l'abattage et aux mesures relatives à la tenue de registres et à la traçabilité.

Mots-clés

Élevage – Gestion de l'exploitation – Phase de production – Pratique d'élevage – Production animale – Sécurité sanitaire des aliments.

■

Guía de buenas prácticas ganaderas para la seguridad sanitaria de los alimentos derivados de la producción animal

Grupo de Trabajo de la OIE sobre Seguridad Sanitaria de los Alimentos Derivados de la Producción Animal

Resumen

En todas partes del mundo, la seguridad sanitaria de los alimentos se ha convertido en una de las prioridades de la salud pública. Para garantizarla es preciso utilizar un método global, aplicable desde la granja hasta la mesa. En este artículo se examinan la primera etapa de la cadena alimentaria y las medidas que pueden tomarse para mejorar al máximo posible el control sanitario de los productos de origen animal. Estas incluyen, forzosamente, el control del estado sanitario de los animales destinados a la producción de alimentos. También se analizan todos los peligros cuyo control en los criaderos puede ser

Rev. sci. tech. Off. int. Epiz., **25** (2)

835

beneficioso, e incluso decisivo, para la seguridad sanitaria de los alimentos de origen animal (incluidos la leche, la carne, los huevos, la miel y sus subproductos). La Guía comprende ocho secciones dedicadas a los locales y demás instalaciones, las condiciones sanitarias de los animales para introducirlos en un criadero, la alimentación animal, los abrevaderos, los medicamentos veterinarios, la gestión de las explotaciones, la preparación de los animales para la matanza y las medidas usuales relativas a los registros y la trazabilidad.

Palabras clave

Cría – Gestión de las explotaciones – Nivel de producción – Práctica pecuaria – Producción animal – Seguridad sanitaria de los alimentos.

■

Appendix

Other material related to international food safety standards

Codex Alimentarius Commission (1933). – Recommended international code of practice for the control of the use of veterinary drugs (CAC/RCP 38-1993). World Health Organization and Food and Agriculture Organization of the United Nations, Rome. Available at: http://www.codex alimentarius.net/web/standard_list.do?lang=en (accessed on 2 January 2006).

Codex Alimentarius Commission (1985). – Recommended code of hygienic practice for egg products (CAC/RCP 15-1976 Amendemnt 2-1985). World Health Organization and Food and Agriculture Organization of the United Nations, Rome. Available at: http://www.codexalimentarius.net/web/standard_list.do?lang= en (accessed on 2 January 2006).

Codex Alimentarius Commission (1993). – Guidelines for the establishment of a regulatory programme for control of veterinary drug residues in foods (CAC/GL 16-1993). World Health Organization and Food and Agriculture Organization of the United Nations, Rome. Available at: http://www.codexalimentarius.net/ web/standard_list.do?lang=en (accessed on 2 January 2006).

Codex Alimentarius Commission (1997). – Code of practice for the reduction of aflatoxin B1 in raw materials and supplemental feeding stuffs for milk-producing animals (CAC/RCP 45-1997). World Health Organization and Food and Agriculture Organization of the United Nations, Rome. Available at: http://www.codexalimentarius.net/web/standard_list.do?lang=en (accessed on 2 January 2006).

Codex Alimentarius Commission (1997). – General standard for contaminants and toxins in foods (CAC/STAN 193-1995, Rev. 1-1997). World Health Organization and Food and Agriculture Organization of the United Nations, Rome. Available at: http://www.codexalimentarius.net/web/standard_list.do?lang=en (accessed on 2 January 2006).

Codex Alimentarius Commission (2001). – Code of practice concerning source directed measures to reduce contamination of food with chemicals (CAC/RCP 49/2001). World Health Organization and Food and Agriculture Organization of the United Nations, Rome. Available at: http://www.codexalimentarius.net/ web/standard_list.do?lang=en (accessed on 2 January 2006).

Codex Alimentarius Commission (2001). – Extraneous maximum residue limits (CAC/MRL 3-2001). World Health Organization and Food and Agriculture Organization of the United Nations, Rome. Available at: http://www.codexalimentarius.net/web/standard_ list.do?lang=en (accessed on 2 January 2006).

Codex Alimentarius Commission (2003). – General principles of food hygiene (CAC/RCP 1-1969, Rev. 4-2003). [Incorporates hazard analysis and critical control point (HACCP) system and guidelines for its application.] World Health Organization and Food and Agriculture Organization of the United Nations, Rome. Available at: http://www.codexalimentarius.net/web/standard_ list.do?lang=en (accessed on 2 January 2006).

Codex Alimentarius Commission (2004). – Code of hygienic practice for milk and milk products (CAC/RCP 57-2004). World Health Organization and Food and Agriculture Organization of the United Nations, Rome. Available at: http://www.codex alimentarius.net/web/standard_list.do?lang=en (accessed on 2 January 2006).

Codex Alimentarius Commission (2004). – Code of practice for fish and fishery products (CAC/RCP 52-2003, Rev. 1-2004). World Health Organization and Food and Agriculture Organization of the United Nations, Rome. Available at: http://www.codexalimentarius.net/web/standard_list.do?lang=en (accessed on 2 January 2006).

836

Rev. sci. tech. Off. int. Epiz., **25** (2)

Codex Alimentarius Commission (2004). – Code of practice for the prevention and reduction of lead contamination in foods (CAC/RCP 56-2004). World Health Organization and Food and Agriculture Organization of the United Nations, Rome. Available at: http://www.codexalimentarius.net/web/standard_list.do?lang=en (accessed on 2 January 2006).

Codex Alimentarius Commission (2004). – Recommended code of practice on good animal feeding (CAC/RCP 54-2004). World Health Organization and Food and Agriculture Organization of the United Nations, Rome. Available at: http://www.codex alimentarius.net/web/standard_list.do?lang=en (accessed on 2 January 2006).

Codex Alimentarius Commission (2005). – Code of hygienic practice for meat (CAC/RCP 58-2005). World Health Organization and Food and Agriculture Organization of the United Nations, Rome. Available at: http://www.codex alimentarius.net/web/standard_list.do?lang=en (accessed on 2 January 2006).

Codex Alimentarius Commission (2005). – Code of practice to minimize and contain antimicrobial resistance (CAC/RCP 61-2005). World Health Organization and Food and Agriculture Organization of the United Nations, Rome. Available at: http://www.codexalimentarius.net/web/standard_list.do?lang=en (accessed on 2 January 2006).

Codex Alimentarius Commission (2005). – Maximum residue limits for veterinary drugs in food (CAC/MRL 2-2005). World Health Organization and Food and Agriculture Organization of the United Nations, Rome. Available at: http://www.codex alimentarius.net/web/standard_list.do?lang=en (accessed on 2 January 2006).

Food and Agriculture Organization of the United Nations (FAO) (1991). – FAO guidelines for slaughtering, meat cutting and further processing. FAO Animal Production and Health Paper 91. FAO, Rome. Available at: http://www.fao.org/documents/index.asp (accessed on 2 January 2006).

Food and Agriculture Organization of the United Nations (FAO) (1998). – A training manual on food hygiene and the hazard analysis and critical control point (HACCP) system. FAO, Rome. Available at: http://www.fao.org/documents/index.asp (accessed on 2 January 2006).

Food and Agriculture Organization of the United Nations (FAO) (2001). – Guidelines for humane handling, transport and slaughter of livestock. FAO, Rome. Available at: http://www.fao.org/documents/index.asp (accessed on 2 January 2006).

Food and Agriculture Organization of the United Nations (FAO) (2004). – Good practices for the meat industry. FAO, Rome. Available at: http://www.fao.org/documents/index.asp (accessed on 2 January 2006).

Food and Agriculture Organization of the United Nations (FAO) (2004). – Guide to good dairy farming practice. International Dairy Foundation/FAO, Rome. Available at: http://www.fao.org/documents/index.asp (accessed on 2 January 2006).

World Organisation for Animal Health (OIE) (2005). – Terrestrial Animal Health Code, 14th Ed. OIE, Paris. Available at: http://www.oie.int/eng/normes/en_mcode.htm (accessed on 2 January 2006). In particular the following chapters and appendices:

– Chapter 1.1.1. General definitions

– Chapter 1.3.3. Evaluation of Veterinary Services

– Chapter 1.3.4. Guidelines for the evaluation of Veterinary Services

– Appendix 3.4.1. Hygiene and disease security procedures in poultry breeding flocks and hatcheries

– Appendix 3.4.2. Hygiene and disease security procedures in apiaries

– Appendix 3.4.3. Hygiene precautions, identification, blood sampling and vaccination

– Appendix 3.6.1. General recommendations on disinfection and disinsectisation

– Appendix 3.7.2. Guidelines for the transport of animals by sea

– Appendix 3.7.3. Guidelines for the transport of animals by land

– Appendix 3.7.4. Guidelines for the transport of animals by air

– Appendix 3.9.1. Guidelines for the harmonisation of national antimicrobial resistance surveillance and monitoring programmes

– Appendix 3.9.2. Guidelines for the monitoring of the quantities of antimicrobials used in animal husbandry

– Appendix 3.9.3. Guidelines for the responsible and prudent use of antimicrobial agents in veterinary medicine

– Appendix 3.9.4. Risk assessment for antimicrobial resistance arising from the use of antimicrobials in animals.

Rev. sci. tech. Off. int. Epiz., 2006, **25** (2), 837-848

The role and functionality of Veterinary Services in food safety throughout the food chain

A.I. McKenzie & S.C. Hathaway

New Zealand Food Safety Authority, P.O. Box 2835, Wellington, New Zealand

Summary
Both national Veterinary Services and international standard-setting organisations have now embraced risk assessment as an essential tool for achieving their goals. Veterinarians have key roles in all aspects of the control of food-borne hazards of animal origin, but additional specialist skills are necessary for assessing, managing and communicating risk. Further, the deployment of Veterinary Services must reflect the multi-functional aspects of public and animal health activities.

A generic risk management framework provides a systematic process whereby food safety standards and other measures are chosen and implemented on the basis of knowledge of risk and evaluation of other factors relevant to protecting human health and promoting non-discriminatory trade practices. In this context, a number of countries are exploring new administrative and structural arrangements for competent authorities.

The traditional focus of veterinary involvement in food safety has been in meat hygiene at the level of the slaughterhouse. While this role continues, the emerging 'risk-based' approach to food control requires increased involvement in other segments of the meat food chain, as well as other areas such as production of milk and fish. This more extensive role requires a wider skill base and establishment of effective networks with a different range of stakeholders.

Keywords
Competent authority – Food chain – Food safety – Food standard – Risk-based approach – Veterinary Services.

Introduction

In a contemporary food safety environment, veterinarians play an essential role in the prevention and control of food-borne zoonoses (diseases and/or infections which are likely to be naturally transmitted from animals to man) and other sources of food-borne disease. Food vehicles include meat and meat products, milk and milk products, eggs and egg products, fish and fish products, and honey and apiculture products.

Risk analysis processes and methodologies are at the heart of modern approaches to food safety and Veterinary Services must adopt new approaches to decision-making and standard setting if they are to be successful risk managers. (For the purposes of this paper, 'Veterinary Services' refers to veterinary public and animal health activities, irrespective of the organisational arrangements of competent authorities at the national level.) While Veterinary Services operate predominantly at the national level in contributing to public health, food is a significant part of the import and export trade profile of most countries. Thus there is an increasing need for involvement of Veterinary Services in risk-based standard setting at the international level.

Where zoonoses are concerned, it is clear that there is a functional overlap between public and animal health activities. Veterinary competence can be shared in these circumstances, even when public health and animal health objectives are separate and distinct. A number of countries are exploring such synergies in the reform of regulatory systems and structures.

838

Rev. sci. tech. Off. int. Epiz., **25** (2)

Veterinary roles

Food safety

Veterinary involvement in food safety activities throughout the food chain may encompass food safety, zoonoses and animal health. Risk management activities in these areas will contribute in various ways to reducing food-borne risks to human health by preventing, eliminating or controlling hazards transmitted by food (16). Most veterinary involvement is currently focused on meat hygiene (defined by the Codex Committee on Meat Hygiene as 'all conditions and measures necessary to ensure the safety and suitability of meat at all stages of the food chain', noting that meat includes poultry and game meat (6, 11). However, generic areas of veterinary activity also include:

– development of the public health policy of the competent authority

– scientific evaluation of food-borne hazards and risk assessment

– design, implementation and verification of food controls at appropriate points in the food chain, including primary production

– monitoring of biological and chemical hazards at appropriate points in the food chain

– specialised veterinary inputs, e.g. evaluation and control of antimicrobial-resistant zoonotic bacteria that may be transmitted by food

– risk communication.

Although the primary responsibility for food safety in contemporary food control systems lies with food producers and food processors, veterinarians employed by Veterinary Services, agri-businesses and the practitioner sector will all play a part in ensuring safe food. Furthermore, food safety regulatory reform in a number of countries is changing the traditional roles of each sector. In many countries, industry now has a leading role in implementing food hygiene programmes, and competent authorities are increasingly moving towards verification and audit of outcome-based regulatory requirements. This provides new opportunities and responsibilities for veterinarians.

Food suitability

Food hygiene is regarded as all conditions and measures necessary to ensure the safety and suitability of food at all stages of the food chain. Suitability is regarded as the assurance that food is acceptable for human consumption according to its intended use. It is clear that in the case of

meat hygiene, a major component of suitability is related to detection and removal of abnormalities in meat that are not of public health significance. Other aspects of suitability relating to consumer expectations include certification requirements such as the Codex *General Guidelines for Use of the Term 'Halal'* (5).

Animal health and animal welfare

In parallel to food hygiene, functionality aspects of Veterinary Services must be considered in relation to other activities that require veterinary competence, such as animal health and animal welfare (see section below – Multi-functionality of Veterinary Services).

A risk-based approach to food safety

Veterinary Services involved in food safety must have a clear understanding of risk analysis processes and methodologies if they are to maximise their contribution to improving public health while ensuring that the food industry operates efficiently and effectively.

In this respect, three waves of change in approaches to food safety have been seen in recent years (Fig. 1). The early 1990s saw more rigorous science being applied in review of traditional controls based on good hygienic practice (GHP). The mid-1990s brought more targeted food safety systems – particularly those based on hazard analysis critical control point systems – and challenging of standards based on reducing hazards to levels that were 'as-low-as-reasonably-achievable'. The late 1990s saw the need for risk-based controls emerge as a global goal.

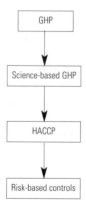

GHP: good hygienic practice
HACCP: hazard analysis critical control point

Fig. 1
Changes in approach to food safety in the last two decades

Rev. sci. tech. Off. int. Epiz., **25** (2)

839

Good hygienic practice

Good hygienic practice throughout the food chain is a prerequisite to a risk-based approach to food safety. Regulatory GHP requirements generally apply during primary and secondary processing, are prescriptive, and describe process requirements rather than outcomes. Some quantitative specifications may be included, such as chlorine levels for potable water or acceptable defect rates for visible contamination on chilled carcasses. Requirements for GHP may be also mandated during primary production of food: good veterinary practice in the use of veterinary drugs, for example.

Implementation of GHP in all segments of the food chain is a responsibility that is shared by all stakeholders. For example, non-regulatory codes of hygienic practice are often part of quality assurance (QA) schemes administered by farmer groups at the level of primary production, and GHP in the home is often the subject of public education programmes formulated by competent authorities and consumer advocate groups.

Risk-based approaches

The emergence of risk-based approaches to food hygiene at both the national and international level has been highly influenced by the signing of the World Trade Organization (WTO) Agreement on the Application of Sanitary and Phytosanitary Measures (SPS Agreement). A risk-based approach to food safety requires decisions, standards and actions to be based on specific knowledge of risks. Risk-based standards formulated according to quantitative or qualitative information about risks are designed to achieve an established level of health protection, and should be able to be explained and validated in these terms.

Risk management frameworks

A generic risk management framework (RMF) provides a systematic process whereby food safety standards and other measures are chosen and implemented on the basis of knowledge of risk and evaluation of other factors relevant to protecting human health and the promotion of non-discriminatory and least trade-restrictive practices.

Veterinary Services have essential roles in the application of the RMF process. Some activities draw almost exclusively on Veterinary Services, whereas others require multidisciplinary inputs. The four steps in applying an RMF (Fig. 2) are outlined in the sections below.

Preliminary risk management activities

Once a food safety issue has been identified, the initial process includes the establishment of a risk profile to place

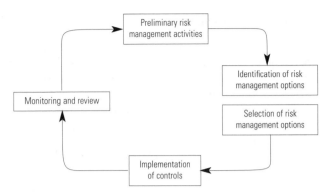

Fig. 2
The risk management framework

the issue within a particular context and provide as much information as possible to guide further action. Risk profiling may also be used for ranking or prioritising different food safety issues. Although a detailed risk assessment is not necessary in many cases, the risk manager may commission one as an independent scientific process to inform decision-making.

Identification and selection of risk management options

This is the process whereby potential risk management options are identified, and then selected according to appropriate decision-making criteria. This will usually involve balancing expectations in terms of minimising risks against available food control measures, and may include reaching a decision about an appropriate level of protection (ALOP). Although this process is facilitated by Veterinary Services, both industry and consumers have critical inputs to such decisions.

Food controls should be implemented by industry at those steps in the food chain where there is maximum reduction of risk for the effort required. Various food safety controls can be simulated in a risk assessment model to determine their individual impact on minimising risks to consumers.

Implementation of controls

Implementation of food controls by industry will usually be by means of a tailor-made programme that is based on GHP and may contain one or more critical control points. Regulatory limits or procedures derived from risk assessment may also be present. The final responsibility for verification of the food safety programme on an ongoing basis lies with the Veterinary Services.

For some hazards, it may not be practical or cost-effective for industry to implement food controls on an individual premises basis; an example is testing for chemical residues of one sort or another. National chemical residue programmes can usually provide risk-based food safety assurances in such circumstances.

840

Rev. sci. tech. Off. int. Epiz., **25** (2)

Monitoring and review

Processes are monitored and reviewed by the gathering and analysing of data on human health so as to give an overview of food safety and consumer health. Monitoring (which includes surveillance) is usually carried out by national public health authorities and should identify new food safety problems as they emerge. Where there is evidence that food safety goals are not being achieved, food safety controls will need to be redesigned. Both Veterinary Services and industry will be involved in this task.

Effective risk management relies on appropriate risk communication and stakeholder representation at all steps.

The wider food safety and biosecurity environment

Application of an RMF to food safety issues is increasingly being recognised as an optimal means to bring about a reduction in health risks across all food safety and biosecurity sectors: public, animal, plant and environmental health (9). Activities involved in the four steps of the RMF differ somewhat across these sectors, but harmonised application allows:

– decisions to be taken in all sectors that are proportionate to the risks involved

– systematic evaluation of the likely impact of specific standards in managing identified risks

– due regard to be taken of costs as well as benefits

– cross-sector risk management decisions that take into account competing health risks.

The role of Veterinary Services in the application of a risk management framework

Legislation and infrastructure

Establishment of a legislative framework and an institutional structure is a prerequisite for the proper functioning of a food hygiene programme, and Veterinary Services contribute to this in various ways. Legislation includes acts, regulations, requirements and procedures that cover protection of human (and animal) health, and protection of consumer rights and fair trading conditions. Institutional structures must successfully interface with non-governmental and private sectors and also facilitate a range of professional inputs, for example from human health specialists, food technologists and agricultural scientists.

In recent years, several approaches have emerged in the organisation of veterinary public health, veterinary animal health and public health services within national competent authorities (13, 14, 15, 17). Integrating all nationally mandated food inspection systems under a single competent authority is promoted as having several advantages, including a reduction in overlap and improvement in service delivery (6).

Whatever the structural arrangements, a primary driver in the re-organisation of the role of government has been the need for clearer delineation of responsibilities between the part of government that deals with economic issues of food production and trade, and the part concerned with public health and consumer protection (7). A consolidation of multiple legislative and functional activities that were previously spread over several legislative jurisdictions gives practical meaning to multidisciplinary approaches to food hygiene and implementation of a 'production-to-consumption' approach.

While organisational structure will inevitably vary from country to country, it is essential that coverage, resources and technical capabilities deliver a continuously high standard of service. Not only is this important at the national level, but credible public and animal health assurances are essential for access of animal products to international markets.

Key food hygiene legislative responsibilities of Veterinary Services include:

– establishment of policies and standards

– design and management of inspection programmes

– scientific evaluation and risk assessment

– assurance and certification that inspection and compliance activities are appropriately delivered

– dissemination of information throughout the food chain

– conformance with WTO obligations

– negotiation of mutual recognition and equivalence agreements with trading partners.

Implementing risk-based food hygiene programmes presents particular challenges in developing countries, which are often under-resourced in terms of regulatory systems and scientific capacity. Development of risk-based standards based on an integrated production-to-consumption approach to food hygiene ideally requires application of an RMF. This, however, is likely to be difficult where there is limited communication between veterinary public health, animal health and medical professionals, and poor monitoring and feedback of information about zoonoses and other food-borne diseases.

Rev. sci. tech. Off. int. Epiz., **25** (2)

841

Preliminary risk management activities

The initial step in the RMF involves key veterinary competencies. Consideration of all food-borne hazards and their significance in terms of risks to human health is an essential food hygiene activity. Hazards arising from animals can be grouped into several categories, including:

– zoonoses (resulting from clinical disease in animals or from asymptomatic carriage)

– microbiological contaminants arising from the food processing environment

– chemical residues in live animals.

Emerging food safety issues often involve zoonoses that have newly appeared in a population or are rapidly increasing in incidence and/or range, and risk profiling will be heavily reliant on a production-to-consumption approach. Recent examples are bovine spongiform encephalopathy, haemolytic uraemic syndrome caused by *Escherichia coli* O157:H7 and acute diarrhoea caused by *Campylobacter* spp.

Ante- and post-mortem meat inspection programmes are ongoing responsibilities of national Veterinary Services. Wherever possible, inspection procedures should be designed according to a risk-based approach and management systems should reflect international norms. This requires that, as part of preliminary risk management activities, Veterinary Services should be constantly aware of changing hazard profiles associated with slaughter animal populations.

Where necessary and practicable, risk assessments focused on a specific hazard/food combination will be commissioned by Veterinary Services. This scientific work is often carried out by other branches of government or external science providers, as multidisciplinary skills are required. However, Veterinary Services will probably have the in-house expertise to carry out qualitative risk assessments, and may also embark on quantitative risk assessments when time and resources allow.

While focusing on reducing food-borne risks to human health, Veterinary Services must also strive to implement food safety standards in ways that do not incur unnecessary costs or rigidities for the industry. 'Traditional' meat inspection procedures, for example, are complex and resource-intensive, and so a number of recent studies have used a risk assessment approach to determine their relative value in minimising meat-borne risks (10). In contrast to quantitative risk assessments focused on a specific hazard/food combination, scientific studies of this kind are usually carried out by Veterinary Services. Risk-based post-mortem inspection standards that are tailored to the particular type and geographical origin of slaughtered animals should achieve at least the same level of consumer protection as 'traditional' procedures.

The need for safe transfer, handling and use of living organisms genetically modified by modern biotechnology has created a new focal point for regulatory requirements. Food may be derived from (or traits introduced by) modern biotechnology, and although international guidelines for safety assessment of foods containing genetically modified organisms are being developed, the adequacy of current processes is a continuing issue of public concern.

Identification and selection of risk management options

The identification and selection of risk management options should be based on science and risk assessment wherever possible. Science-based standards are formulated according to objective and verifiable information about relevant hazards, and are designed to eliminate or reduce exposure to hazards, with the expectation that there will be a reduction in risk. Risk-based standards are more demanding; they are formulated according to specific knowledge, whether quantitative or qualitative, of actual risks. They are designed to achieve a specified level of health protection and should be able to be explained and validated in these terms.

It should be noted that, after evaluation, risk management options may not always lead to regulatory standards. Measures implemented by stakeholders other than Veterinary Services may be deemed to be more effective in some cases; examples include farmer-driven QA schemes, and public education programmes to encourage a higher level of food hygiene in the home.

Selection of risk management options must combine available knowledge about risk with other factors relevant to protecting human health. These factors include cost–benefit considerations and the technical feasibility of controls. Where food is exported or imported, the selection process should also promote adoption of non-discriminatory and least trade-restrictive practices. In the case of meat hygiene, application of this step in the RMF has led to the removal of many resource-intensive post-mortem inspection procedures where they have been shown to be of negligible value.

The practicality of standards also relies on Veterinary Service inputs, as does establishment of the competencies of inspection personnel and training requirements. The national competent authority must also provide an appropriate institutional environment for Veterinary Services to develop competency and training requirements.

842

Rev. sci. tech. Off. int. Epiz., **25** (2)

In meat hygiene, it is now well established that general attention to proper livestock management, environmental hygiene and transport will limit the numbers of live animals shedding and/or being contaminated with enteric pathogens such as *Salmonella, Campylobacter* and *E. coli* O157:H7. This will result in a commensurate decrease in pathogen numbers on dressed carcasses. A number of recent studies indicate that minimising the level of inadvertent microbiological contamination with enteric pathogens during processing will significantly reduce meat-borne risks in most situations.

Evaluation of the outputs of specific risk assessment models is also leading to 'whole food chain' changes in food hygiene. For example, an international Food and Agriculture Organization/World Health Organization risk assessment of *Campylobacter* spp. in broiler chickens used modular modelling of the production-to-consumption food pathway to estimate risks to consumers and evaluate the impact of different interventions in each module (2). The model indicated that any intervention that significantly reduces flock prevalence will be of measurable benefit in reducing risks to consumers. The challenge from this work is for regulators to facilitate decisions on an ALOP for this food-borne disease, with industry finding practical and cost-effective ways to implement the necessary interventions at the farm level.

Another expression of the 'whole food chain' approach to food safety is the establishment of controls that prevent the introduction of unacceptable levels of chemical hazards such as residues of veterinary drugs and pesticides at the time of primary production. This involves multidisciplinary inputs. Veterinary Services, for example, are involved in ensuring good practice in the use of veterinary drugs and food monitoring programmes. Other tasks, such as toxicological evaluation, registration and establishment of maximum residue levels, are generally assigned to technical specialists in these areas. The competent authority will be likely to employ specialist policy analysts and risk communicators to bring wider aspects of the risk management of veterinary drug residues in foods to the various stakeholder groups involved.

Implementation of controls

A range of stakeholders may be involved in the implementation step of the RMF, including regulatory authorities, industry and the public. The controls that have been selected may not necessarily be mandated by regulations but rather take effect through, for example, consumer education in safe food handling practices.

Meat hygiene activities are usually undertaken by Veterinary Services, and these must have sufficient numbers of qualified personnel to perform the allocated tasks. The resources required to support those tasks include equipment, transport, laboratories and training programmes. All inspection procedures and judgements must be performed by personnel who have the appropriate competence.

Veterinary Services also must ensure compliance with regulatory requirements by applying a systematic and functionally independent verification and audit programme. Legislation must provide for the ability to enforce regulatory requirements and impose sanctions in cases of non-compliance.

The provision of written (or equivalent) assurances that food hygiene systems conform to regulatory requirements is a vital function of Veterinary Services. Such assurances can be provided by a competent authority (a government agency having official jurisdiction) or by a 'competent body' (a body officially recognised and overseen by the competent authority to undertake specified food hygiene activities).

International health certificates providing official assurances for trading of food should give full confidence to the country of importation. Importing countries will take commensurate measures to verify certification assurances, including documentary and physical checks at the port of entry, and third-party audits of food hygiene systems in the exporting country (4).

A QA system includes the organisational structure, procedures, processes and resources needed to implement QA. Food industries are increasingly committing themselves to such systems due to demand from their customers (8). Inputs to QA systems can be provided by veterinarians employed by industry; for example, industry-led programmes at the level of primary production may involve veterinary supervision and slaughterhouse information servicing. Individual health certification of groups of slaughter animals is a common practice in a number of countries, for zoonotic diseases, veterinary drug residues and vaccination regimes for example.

In the case of ante- and post-mortem inspection, QA systems can be extended to 'co-regulatory' systems that integrate industry and Veterinary Service activities (3). In Australia, the official Veterinary Service is responsible for the broad design of the inspection system and its audits and sanctions, while industry is responsible for further developing, implementing and maintaining the system. The veterinarian responsible for a specific slaughterhouse ensures that the meat safety QA programme implemented by industry meets regulatory requirements on an ongoing basis.

Use of private or public non-veterinary personnel to carry out ante- and post-mortem inspection activities is now well established within many national programmes. However, all ante- and post-mortem inspection arrangements should

Rev. sci. tech. Off. int. Epiz., **25** (2)

843

satisfy the principles of independence, competence of inspectors and impartiality, and must be carried out under the overall supervision and responsibility of the official Veterinary Services.

A number of institutional models are emerging for the audit and enforcement of regulatory requirements in food hygiene. It is generally recognised that the effectiveness and consistency of audit and enforcement must be demonstrably improved, especially if consumers are to have ongoing confidence in the safety of the food supply.

The auditing and enforcing standards of Veterinary Services may be separate from, or included in, the remit of the centralised competent authority promulgating food hygiene policy and standards. Notwithstanding this, audit and enforcement remain decentralised in some countries and are undertaken by regional or local governments. Whatever the organisational structure, the theme of greater centralisation of responsibility and 'checking-the-checker' is becoming standard audit practice. Risk-based procedures and sanctions are becoming more common, and private third parties are emerging as independent auditing bodies.

Monitoring and review

Most Veterinary Services apply regulatory programmes at various points in the food chain to monitor the presence of specific hazards; examples include statutory veterinary reporting of food-borne infectious diseases and chemical intoxications of animals at the level of livestock production, and national residue surveys. Even though these programmes may not be integrated components of an overall risk-based system, they provide valuable information on the prevalence of hazards over time and the level of regulatory compliance.

Notwithstanding this, the final step in the RMF primarily relies on human health surveillance to complete the RMF process. This function is outside the jurisdiction of Veterinary Services but may be a function of an overarching competent authority. Monitoring and review activities should be specifically designed to service management of food-borne risks, and provide a good example of the multidisciplinary needs of a risk-based approach to food safety. Food-borne disease investigations and strain typing of bacterial hazards can provide a valuable adjunct to human surveillance data.

Contribution to international standards

National Veterinary Services should have an ongoing commitment to the establishment and review of international standards. The Codex Alimentarius Commission (CAC) elaborates standards and related texts for both safety and suitability aspects of food control, while the World Organisation for Animal Health (OIE) elaborates standards and related texts for the prevention, control and eradication of zoonoses. The OIE has a parallel responsibility for developing standards and related texts for animal health. Both organisations are committed to working together to enhance the scope and scientific quality of international standards, guidelines and related texts, especially in regard to food safety measures applicable at the farm level.

It is essential that all countries contribute to the continuing development of the Codex Alimentarius if they are to optimise food production in terms of food hygiene and access to international markets. As well as protecting consumers' health, food standards reduce the costs of doing business by, for example, reducing the risk of international fraud and the costs of finding reliable trading partners. Consumers are also protected from buying inferior food. In providing benefits to both producers and consumers, Codex standards promote economic welfare and are a prerequisite to the operation of a well-functioning market. If standards are harmonised between countries, they further facilitate trade (1).

National Veterinary Services obviously have a key role in providing the scientific underpinning for international standards, as well as bringing forward national views on 'other legitimate factors' that should be taken into account. In implementing the provisions of the SPS and Technical Barriers to Trade (TBT) agreements of the WTO, Veterinary Services also have an increasing role in developing mutual recognition and equivalence agreements among trading partners. At the national level, differences often occur in food production systems, technological capacity, and regulatory controls themselves. Such situations illustrate the importance of the concept of equivalence. If risk assessment can demonstrate that different practices in different countries can still provide the same level of consumer protection, there should be no impediment to international trade in the food concerned. Application of a risk-based approach to demonstrate the equivalence of new procedures and technologies also facilitates industry efficiency and innovation.

Multi-functionality of Veterinary Services

In meeting veterinary public health and animal health objectives prescribed in national legislation or required by importing countries, Veterinary Services contribute in various ways 'from the direct performance of necessary veterinary tasks to the evaluation of veterinary activities conducted by operators in the agro-industrial chain' (12). It should be noted that 'Veterinary Services are no longer the sole managers of animal health protection and disease control, but rather guarantors that all parties involved in food production fulfil their respective obligations to guarantee safe food for the consumer' (12).

Animal health

Transmission via the food chain of hazards that may seriously affect animal health can result in very significant economic loss in animal populations; such hazards include transmission of exotic diseases by feeding of meat scraps to animals, or transmission via meat with a designated non-human end-use, such as uncooked petfood. Consequently, control and/or reduction of hazards of animal health importance during ante- and post-mortem meat inspection is a core function of Veterinary Services. Inspection of slaughter animals can also make a valuable contribution to surveillance for specified diseases of animal health importance, particularly exotic diseases.

The extent to which animal health functions should be carried out by veterinarians whose primary focus is food control is a matter of national jurisdiction. In the past, Veterinary Services were generally the sole competent authority responsible for animal health, and in many cases they were also responsible for food safety aspects of slaughter animals up until the end of primary processing. These legislative arrangements have now been broadened in a number of countries.

The OIE *Terrestrial Animal Health Code*, 2004, describes animal health surveillance as the 'continuous investigation of a given population to detect the occurrence of disease for control purposes', and defines monitoring as 'ongoing programmes directed at detection of changes in the prevalence of disease in a given population' (18). In this context, inspection of slaughter animals can provide an important sentinel function for zoonoses and diseases solely of animal health importance. Further diagnostic tests can be applied in the case of suspect animals.

Animal health surveillance and monitoring allow Veterinary Services to identify and control significant endemic or exotic diseases within their territory, and substantiate reports on the animal health situation in their country. Both functions provide essential inputs to animal health import risk analysis. As in the case of meat hygiene, policies and standards applied at ante- and post-mortem inspection for the purposes of animal health surveillance and monitoring should be risk based and should be feasible and practical in the slaughterhouse environment.

Irrespective of the jurisdiction of the competent authorities involved, it is obvious that Veterinary Services should

integrate their activities to the maximum extent possible and practicable so as to prevent duplication of effort and unnecessary costs. In addition to sharing of routine inspection activities to achieve both public health and animal health objectives, other opportunities that arise are:

- collection and integration of monitoring data, sharing of diagnostic facilities and methodologies

- verification and enforcement of inspection requirements in an integrated manner

- pooling of technical expertise.

Whatever the activity, Veterinary Services must be able to demonstrate that no conflict of interest exists between public and/or animal health objectives on the one hand, and economic support for the food production and processing industries on the other.

Animal welfare

The importance of welfare standards for food-producing animals is widely recognised by Veterinary Services. Animal welfare on the farm, during transport and at the time of slaughter can have an impact on food safety, and is also of increasing concern to consumers in terms of the 'acceptability' of foods of animal origin. Although it is generally agreed that international trade measures based on animal welfare objectives are not permitted under the SPS and TBT agreements, science-based regulatory requirements have been implemented in some WTO Member countries. Industry-led QA programmes for ensuring animal welfare are now well established.

Convergence of food safety and biosecurity

Animal health biosecurity is concerned with import, domestic and export health controls. Import controls are primarily designed to prevent the introduction of hazards pathogenic to animals during trade in animals, animal genetic material, animal products, feedstuffs and biological products. However, trade in animal commodities crossing borders is rapidly changing, especially in terms of the volume, range and complexity of animal products. The increasing availability of animal genetic material has meant a decrease in the international trading of breeding animals; however, the economics of the global food supply is driving an increasing trade in export of live animals for slaughter. Consumption of animal products is rising rapidly in developing countries, especially in Asia. Livestock production is increasing to meet this need, and there is a commensurate increase in animal health risks. The closer proximity of people and animals, especially poultry, adds to these risks.

Within this broad context, emerging zoonoses illustrate the recent convergence of food safety and biosecurity aspects

Rev. sci. tech. Off. int. Epiz., **25** (2)

845

of human and animal health, and this is likely to lead to significant changes in the roles, partnerships and regulatory activities of Veterinary Services collectively involved in their control. New and emerging diseases of animal health importance are increasing in incidence and geographical range. Where zoonoses are concerned, it is clear that there is often an overlap between public health and animal health objectives. Veterinary competence can be shared in these circumstances and a number of countries are exploring such synergies in the reform of legislative systems.

As with plant biotechnology in the early 1990s, animal biotechnology has reached a point where developers are beginning to market products derived in this manner. This may, in the near future, include agri-food applications. As an example, transgenic animals are derived from recombinant DNA technology or by cloning (somatic cell nuclear transfer), which is a means to generate animals with preferred traits. These animals and/or their products are likely to trigger food safety regulatory requirements in most countries, but guidance on risk assessment is still at the developmental stage.

Other functions

Increasingly, veterinarians are developing multidisciplinary skills that extend their activities well beyond the farm and initial processing of food. Preventing degradation of the environment by contamination with animal wastes and animal products is one example.

The SPS Agreement and the standards developed by the CAC and OIE all refer to the need for a systematic process to gather, evaluate and document scientific and other information as the basis for public health and animal health controls. This has long been recognised by Veterinary Services at the national level. The organisation and dissemination of information throughout the food chain involve multidisciplinary activities; for example, animal identification and traceback systems, either for individuals or groups, are necessary to achieve both public health and animal health objectives.

Governments are increasingly aware that the food chain is a potential vehicle for bioterrorism. Strategic responses to the risks of bio-terrorism are well advanced in the United States, and the impact of new food standards to prevent such acts is being felt around the world.

Conclusion

A commitment to risk assessment as the basis for establishing food safety controls has placed new responsibilities and accountabilities on Veterinary Service components of competent authorities. While developing technical capability to assess risks, Veterinary Services must also properly employ other aspects of risk analysis, particularly risk management and risk communication, if they are to effectively protect human health.

The emerging 'risk-based' approach to food control demands increased involvement of Veterinary Services throughout the food chain and systematic application of an RMF when making decisions and taking regulatory action. Harmonised application of an RMF as an optimal means of reducing health risks across all food safety and biosecurity sectors – public, animal, plant and environmental health – will allow decisions to be taken that are proportionate in nature and which take into account competing risks.

In some countries, the organisation of food control at the national level is now falling under a single competent authority that has responsibility for the entire food chain. Concrete benefits have already been reported, particularly in respect of:

– clarifying roles and responsibilities

– reducing overlap and duplication of programme functions

– improving service delivery

– facilitating federal/provincial collaboration.

■

846

Rev. sci. tech. Off. int. Epiz., **25** (2)

Le rôle et les capacités opérationnelles des Services vétérinaires en matière de sécurité sanitaire tout au long de la chaîne alimentaire

A.I. McKenzie & S.C. Hathaway

Résumé
Pour atteindre leurs objectifs, les Services vétérinaires nationaux, tout comme les organisations en charge de l'élaboration des normes internationales, recourent désormais à cet outil fondamental qu'est l'évaluation des risques. Si les vétérinaires jouent un rôle clé pour tout ce qui concerne la maîtrise des risques d'altération des denrées alimentaires d'origine animale, l'évaluation de ces risques, leur gestion et la communication à leur sujet requièrent une expertise spécifique. En outre, les interventions des Services vétérinaires doivent refléter la diversité opérationnelle des activités de santé publique et de santé animale.
Un cadre générique de gestion des risques doit fournir un processus systématique permettant de choisir et de mettre en œuvre les normes appropriées, notamment de sécurité sanitaire des aliments, en partant de la connaissance du risque et de l'évaluation de tous les facteurs pertinents pour la protection de la santé humaine et la promotion de pratiques commerciales non discriminatoires. À cet égard, de nouveaux dispositifs administratifs et structurels applicables par les autorités compétentes sont actuellement à l'étude dans plusieurs pays.
Traditionnellement, les activités des Services vétérinaires relatives à la sécurité sanitaire des aliments étaient axées sur l'hygiène des viandes et leur inspection à l'abattoir. Certes, ce rôle leur est toujours dévolu, mais avec le développement des approches basées sur le risque, les vétérinaires sont invités à s'investir davantage dans d'autres segments de la chaîne de production alimentaire, ainsi que dans des secteurs tels que les laiteries ou la production de poisson. Cette extension de leur rôle exige des vétérinaires qu'ils élargissent leur champ de compétences et travaillent en réseaux avec les différentes parties prenantes.

Mots-clés
Approche fondée sur le risque – Autorité compétente – Chaîne alimentaire – Norme alimentaire – Sécurité sanitaire des aliments – Service vétérinaire.

■

Papel y actuaciones de los Servicios Veterinarios respecto de la inocuidad de los alimentos en toda la cadena alimentaria

A.I. McKenzie & S.C. Hathaway

Resumen
La evaluación de riesgos se ha convertido en un instrumento fundamental para el logro de los objetivos de los Servicios Veterinarios nacionales y las organizaciones normativas. Si bien los veterinarios desempeñan un papel clave en todos los ámbitos del control del riesgo de toxi-infecciones alimentarias de

Rev. sci. tech. Off. int. Epiz., **25** (2)

847

origen animal, para evaluar y manejar el peligro, así como para informar sobre el mismo, se necesitan competencias adicionales. Además, los Servicios Veterinarios deben estar preparados para asumir las múltiples actuaciones que implican las actividades relacionadas con la salud pública y la sanidad animal.

La gestión genérica de riesgos es un proceso sistemático que comprende normas sobre inocuidad de los alimentos y otras medidas que se eligen y aplican basándose en los conocimientos sobre los peligros y la evaluación de otros factores pertinentes a fin de proteger la salud pública y fomentar prácticas comerciales no discriminatorias. A este respecto, varios países están estudiando actualmente nuevos acuerdos administrativos y estructurales para las autoridades competentes.

Tradicionalmente, la actuación de los veterinarios en materia de inocuidad de los alimentos consistía en controlar la higiene de la carne en los mataderos. Si bien siguen desempeñando esa función, los nuevos métodos de control de los alimentos basados en el riesgo los llevan a participar activamente en otros segmentos de la cadena de producción de productos cárnicos, así como en otras esferas alimentarias como, por ejemplo, la producción de leche y peces. Estas actuaciones más amplias requieren mayores competencias y la creación de redes eficientes con nuevos interlocutores.

Palabras clave

Autoridad competente – Cadena alimentaria – Inocuidad de los alimentos – Método basado en los riesgos – Norma alimentaria – Servicio Veterinario.

■

References

1. Anon. (2002). – Report of the Evaluation of the Codex Alimentarius and other FAO and WHO Food Standards Work. Food and Agriculture Organization, Rome/World Health Organization, Geneva.

2. Anon. (2002). – Risk assessment of *Campylobacter* spp. in broiler chickens and *Vibrio* spp. in seafood, a joint FAO/WHO consultation, Bangkok, Thailand, 5-9 August. World Health Organization (WHO), Geneva.

3. Butler R.J., Murray J.G. & Tidswell S. (2003). – Quality assurance and meat inspection in Australia. *In* Veterinary Services: organisation, quality assurance, evaluation (E. Correa Melo & F. Gerster, eds). *Rev. sci. tech. Off. int. Epiz.*, **22** (2), 629-659.

4. Codex Alimentarius Commission (CAC) (1995). – Principles for food import and export inspection and certification (CAC/GL 20). CAC, Rome.

5. Codex Alimentarius Commission (CAC) (1997). – General guidelines for use of the term 'halal' (CAC/GL 24-1997). CAC, Rome.

6. Codex Alimentarius Commission (CAC) (2005). – Code of hygienic practice for meat (CAC/RCP 58-2005). CAC, Rome.

7. Evans B.R., Doering R.L., Clarke R.C. & Ranger R. (2003). – The organisation of federal Veterinary Services in Canada: the Canadian Food Inspection Agency. *In* Veterinary Services: organisation, quality assurance, evaluation (E. Correa Melo & F. Gerster, eds). *Rev. sci. tech. Off. int. Epiz.*, **22** (2), 409-421.

8. Gary F. (2003). – Accreditation of veterinary inspection systems. *In* Veterinary Services: organisation, quality assurance, evaluation (E. Correa Melo & F. Gerster, eds). *Rev. sci. tech. Off. int. Epiz.*, **22** (2), 761-768.

9. Hathaway S.C. (2002). – Risk analysis in biosecurity for food and agriculture. *In* Report of an Expert Consultation on biosecurity in food and agriculture, 10-13 September, Food and Agriculture Organization (FAO), Rome. FAO, Rome.

848

Rev. sci. tech. Off. int. Epiz., **25** (2)

10. Hathaway S.C. (2004). – Codex Committee on meat and poultry hygiene. *In* Proc. World Meat Hygiene and Inspection Congress, 6-8 July, Downing College, Cambridge. (Proceedings were sent to all delegates on a CD-rom produced by the United Kingdom Food Standards Agency.)

11. McKenzie A.I. & Hathaway S.C. (2003). – The role of veterinarians in the prevention and management of food-borne diseases, in particular at the level of livestock producers. Technical item I. 70th General Session of the World Organisation for Animal Health (OIE), 26-31 May, Paris (Doc. 70 SG/9). OIE, Paris.

12. Marabelli R. (2003). – The role of official Veterinary Services in dealing with new social challenges: animal health and protection, food safety and the environment. *In* Veterinary Services: organisation, quality assurance, evaluation (E. Correa Melo & F. Gerster, eds). *Rev. sci. tech. Off. int. Epiz.,* **22** (2), 363-371.

13. World Health Organization (WHO) (2002). – Future trends in veterinary public health. Report of a WHO Study Group. WHO Technical Report Series No. 907. WHO, Geneva.

14. World Organisation for Animal Health (OIE) (1991). – Veterinary public health: part one. *Rev. sci. tech. Off. int. Epiz.,* **10** (4).

15. World Organisation for Animal Health (OIE) (1992). – Veterinary public health: part two. *Rev. sci. tech. Off. int. Epiz.,* **11** (1).

16. World Organisation for Animal Health (OIE). (2002). – Report of the Meeting of the OIE Working Group on animal production food safety, 18-20 November, Paris. OIE, Paris.

17. World Organisation for Animal Health (OIE) (2003). – Veterinary Services: organisation, quality, evaluation. *Rev. sci. tech. Off. int. Epiz.,* **22** (2).

18. World Organisation for Animal Health (OIE) (2004). – Terrestrial Animal Health Code, 13th Ed. Chapter 1.3.6. Surveillance and monitoring of animal health. OIE, Paris, 52.

Rev. sci. tech. Off. int. Epiz., 2006, **25** (2), 849-860

Pautas para los procedimientos de inspección en animales y carnes en un matadero

A. Schnöller

Director de Fiscalización de Productos de Origen Animal, Servicio Nacional de Sanidad y Calidad Agroalimentaria (SENASA), Paseo Colón 367 – 6º Piso, 1063 Buenos Aires, Argentina

Resumen

En las últimas décadas hemos asistido a grandes transformaciones en los sistemas de inspección del ganado y de la carne en los mataderos.

La legislación de los países más desarrollados ha liderado estos cambios y el Codex Alimentarius los ha reflejado en sus Códigos recomendados de prácticas, que sirven para armonizar los intercambios internacionales de alimentos.

En este trabajo se definen las diferentes áreas que se deben considerar en los mataderos para efectuar la inspección veterinaria de los animales y de sus productos, teniendo en cuenta la salud pública y la sanidad animal. A pesar de que sólo se refieren a la especie bovina, gran parte de los criterios expuestos por el autor pueden aplicarse a las demás especies ganaderas.

La información obtenida en el matadero es interesante para la producción primaria; recíprocamente, la información recopilada durante la producción primaria permite hacer más eficiente la utilización de recursos en el matadero.

Esta nueva concepción permite realizar procedimientos de inspección basados en el riesgo, que irán reemplazando a los sistemas tradicionales, a menudo demasiado rígidos y mecánicos, e incapaces de medir la gravedad de los peligros.

Los peligros emergentes, biológicos, físicos o químicos y la utilización de nuevas tecnologías no autorizan acciones meramente rutinarias y obligan a guardar una actitud de alerta, adaptada a los cambios permanentes que ofrecen las ciencias dedicadas a la inocuidad de los alimentos.

Otra tendencia es la participación activa de los operadores, que deben asumir la responsabilidad primaria en relación con la seguridad sanitaria de los alimentos que están elaborando.

La inspección veterinaria oficial que opera en el matadero como parte de la denominada Autoridad Competente juega varios roles: detectar las enfermedades de los animales, ejercer el control de las carnes y productos cárnicos, y verificar los sistemas de auditoría desarrollados en las empresas.

Recientemente, las crisis debidas a la encefalopatía espongiforme bovina y a las intoxicaciones por dioxinas pusieron en evidencia la necesidad de implementar la rastreabilidad (o trazabilidad) de los alimentos, es decir, de ofrecer a los consumidores la posibilidad de conocer el origen de los productos alimentarios, siguiendo la cadena habitualmente denominada "del campo al plato".

Por último, otra responsabilidad que tiene el veterinario del matadero es asegurar el bienestar animal, para el que tiene una obligación ética indelegable como profesional dedicado al cuidado de los animales.

Palabras clave

Análisis de peligros y puntos críticos de control – Buena práctica de manufactura – Directriz – Higiene – Inspección veterinaria – Matadero – Seguridad sanitaria de los alimentos – Toxiinfección alimentaria.

850

Rev. sci. tech. Off. int. Epiz., **25** (2)

Introducción

Sistemas de seguridad sanitaria de los alimentos

Los métodos ideados para garantizar la inocuidad de los alimentos siguen una tendencia mundial, basada en sistemas que abarcan la participación de organismos oficiales gubernamentales y los controles efectuados por los operadores, que son los primeros responsables ante los consumidores.

En la base de la pirámide se hallan los denominados autocontroles, es decir los sistemas de autogestión de la calidad y de la inocuidad basados en "buenas prácticas de manufactura" (GMP), "procedimientos operativos estándar de saneamiento" (SSOP) y "análisis de peligros y puntos críticos de control" (HACCP).

La Autoridad Competente mantiene personal permanente en los mataderos y salas de despiece, que cumplen funciones de control de las patologías de los animales al realizar la inspección antemortem, postmortem, de la higiene de los productos y de las instalaciones, además de otros factores como el bienestar de los animales, el manejo de materiales de riesgo para la encefalopatía espongiforme transmisible de los animales, etc. Este personal oficial se denomina Servicio de Inspección Veterinaria (SIV).

En todos los casos, el sistema debe ser supervisado, lo que generalmente se realiza en los niveles regional, provincial o estatal. A su vez esta estructura está situada bajo el mando de la Autoridad Competente Central que elabora la legislación sanitaria, las políticas y la auditoría del sistema, incluyendo los mencionados subsistemas.

La Figura 1 da un ejemplo de este tipo de organización, a pesar de existir diferencias de un país a otro (19): algunos países son más extensos, otros más pequeños, unos son muy centralizados, otros más federativos; todos presentan pequeñas diferencias, pero en general comparten el tipo de estructura señalada.

Inspección antemortem

Análisis de los documentos

Los animales que llegan al establecimiento deben venir acompañados de un documento en el que se describen su origen y condición sanitaria (7).

El origen exacto permite asegurar la rastreabilidad (o trazabilidad), que se ha convertido en una información imprescindible para los consumidores; por otra parte, la información procedente de la fase de producción primaria

ACC: Autoridad Competente Central

Fig. 1
Estructura del sistema de seguridad sanitaria de los alimentos en los mataderos

permite conocer los peligros que deben atenderse en el matadero. Por lo tanto, la inspección veterinaria antemortem y postmortem se basará en el riesgo deducido del análisis de la información recopilada durante la fase de producción primaria (9).

Hoy se sabe que las prácticas de producción y de alimentación pueden incrementar el riesgo de presencia de *Escherichia coli* O157:H7, *Salmonella* spp., *Campylobacter* (15), etc., así como otros peligros físicos y químicos (6, 7, 9, 12, 20, 21).

La provisión de información relevante permite desarrollar programas de higiene de la carne basados en el riesgo (7), lo que se traduce en una mejor eficiencia de recursos. En algunas situaciones, por ejemplo en caso de zoonosis como la cisticercosis, el conocimiento de las áreas afectadas permite tomar medidas específicas.

La Autoridad Competente debe considerar los sistemas de gestión de la calidad llevados a cabo por los productores primarios, entre ellos el sistema de buenas prácticas de higiene (5).

Otro factor esencial es la identificación de los animales con miras a la trazabilidad; como lo veremos más adelante, éste es un factor pertinente a lo largo de la cadena de transformación de productos alimenticios (6).

Examen de los animales

El examen veterinario de los animales cumple la doble función de prevenir la introducción de alteraciones que puedan significar un peligro para la salud humana, y de dar fundamento a las medidas que se han de tomar en caso de constatarse una enfermedad animal. Esta información será de suma utilidad en los establecimientos de origen (producción primaria).

Rev. sci. tech. Off. int. Epiz., **25** (2)

851

Se debe prestar especial atención a las zoonosis y enfermedades listadas por la Organización Mundial de Sanidad Animal (OIE).

Una vez controlados sus documentos de transporte, los animales son examinados, en conjunto e individualmente, para buscar cualquier anormalidad o defecto que haga presumir la presencia de enfermedad.

Los animales sospechosos deben ser llevados a una manga o cajón para realizar su examen clínico y comprobar los parámetros fisiológicos (temperatura, estado de las mucosas, respiración, estado sensorial, etc.), además de las lesiones o anormalidades que puedan presentarse. En el caso de requerirse mayor información se procederá a la necropsia del animal, actuando de la misma manera con el resto del lote. Todas las observaciones deben registrarse en un sistema de fichas que a tal efecto llevará el Servicio de Inspección Veterinaria.

Identificación de lote

Se designa por "lote" un grupo de animales provenientes del mismo origen y conducidos en el mismo transporte. Deben ser alojados en el mismo corral, comportando una ficha en la que se describen los datos del lote, la identificación y los eventos sanitarios.

Permanencia en corrales

Es aconsejable el descanso de los animales por un período de al menos seis horas, teniendo en cuenta que el examen antemortem en animales excitados por el viaje resulta bastante dificultoso y puede enmascarar enfermedades febriles.

Los animales que permanezcan en los corrales por más de 6 horas serán examinados al menos una vez cada 24 horas. Asimismo, no se aconseja que permanezcan en los corrales más de 72 horas. Mientras se hallan alojados, se les debe suministrar suficiente heno y agua.

Inspección de los animales conducidos a faena

Para examinar los animales que son conducidos a la faena es necesario tenerlos en buena condición de higiene de manera a poder observarlos correctamente. La intensidad de la limpieza depende del estado de los animales en el momento de su llegada (7).

Es conveniente realizar una limpieza con agua a presión y, si necesario, con detergentes para eliminar la suciedad, sobre todo en los animales cuyo pelambre se encuentra en un estado que requiere especial atención, al provenir de predios que por razones de producción (tener en cuenta especialmente los *feed lots*), área geográfica y otras, ofrecen condiciones de higiene mediocres.

Es aconsejable que esta tarea sea seguida de un tiempo de escurrimiento lo suficientemente prolongado para evitar que los animales entren demasiado mojados en el cajón de noqueo, lo cual facilita la contaminación durante las operaciones de cuereado.

Sin embargo, es conveniente mantener un cierto nivel de humedad de los pelambres, pues cuando están demasiado secos hay un riesgo de formación de polvillo muy contaminante.

Las intervenciones anteriores a la faena de los animales, destinadas a reducir la presencia de bacterias patógenas en éstos, y por ende en las carnes, son muy numerosas y consisten en aplicar, entre otros, elementos biológicos que actúan por competencia (3).

En esta etapa debe restringirse el uso de elementos que afecten el bienestar de los animales, especialmente rebenques y picanas eléctricas, y es aquí donde entra en juego el nivel de entrenamiento del personal afectado a estas tareas.

Rastreabilidad

En los mataderos, las primeras tareas y registros referidos a la rastreabilidad empiezan en el momento en que los animales entran en el establecimiento. Cualquier error en este punto automáticamente se traslada a lo largo de la cadena hasta el consumidor.

La rastreabilidad (o trazabilidad) se define de la manera siguiente:

– según el Codex Alimentarius, la "trazabilidad es la capacidad para seguir el movimiento de un alimento a través de la(s) etapa(s) especificada(s) de la producción, transformación y distribución" (6);

– según la Unión Europea, en su Reglamento 2002/178, Artículo 3, es "la posibilidad de encontrar y seguir el rastro, a través de todas las etapas de producción, transformación y distribución, de un alimento, un pienso, un animal destinado a la producción de alimentos o una sustancia destinados a ser incorporados en alimentos o piensos o con probabilidades de serlo" (10).

Bienestar de los animales

Durante la estadía de los animales en los corrales hasta su sacrificio, es función imprescindible del Servicio de Inspección Veterinaria velar por su bienestar.

852

Rev. sci. tech. Off. int. Epiz., **25** (2)

El operador debe poseer un "manual de procedimientos" donde se indique el tratamiento dado a los animales en las diferentes etapas, desde su llegada a la planta hasta su sacrificio, incluyendo su estadía en los corrales, movimiento, entrenamiento del personal encargado de esta tarea, diseño de las instalaciones, método de eutanasia (insensibilización y sangrado), etc.

La Autoridad Competente deberá auditar y verificar las actividades realizadas por el operador. Un soporte legal permitirá, en situaciones de no conformidad, tomar las medidas correctivas necesarias y suspender las actividades cuando corresponda (13, 14).

Inspección postmortem

Aturdimiento y sangrado

La primera observación que se debe realizar en la manga de ingreso a la playa de faena y antes de entrar al cajón de noqueo, es el estado de limpieza de los animales. Si se aplicó un baño previo, como lo exigen la mayoría de las legislaciones nacionales, el tiempo de escurrido debe ser suficiente, pues los animales deben estar apenas húmedos para evitar que el agua contaminada salpique la carne durante las operaciones de cuereado.

La segunda observación es verificar que la insensibilización se efectúe respetando los criterios del bienestar animal (13, 14). Los diferentes sistemas de aturdimiento deben ser validados por la Autoridad Competente (13, 14) y verificados periódicamente por el Servicio Veterinario Oficial.

La operación del sangrado también será verificada periódicamente por el Servicio de Inspección Veterinaria. El sangrado debe realizarse con dos cuchillos, uno para rajar el cuero y el otro para incidir los grandes vasos, evitando seccionar el esófago o la tráquea. El tiempo del sangrado debe ser suficiente; para obtener un sangrado más eficiente se puede usar la electroestimulación.

Este sector debe estar aislado del resto de la playa de faena y tanto su diseño sanitario como sus instalaciones deben impedir la contaminación.

Cuereado

El sector siguiente es la zona intermedia donde se realiza la operación del cuereado. En esa fase el Servicio de Inspección Veterinaria debe verificar que los operarios de la empresa aplican correctamente las buenas prácticas de higiene, y verificar los controles realizados por el operador (control de calidad) y los controles de autogestión.

La prevención de la contaminación de la carne en la etapa del cuereado es decisiva para prevenir las toxiinfecciones transmitidas por los alimentos que más frecuentemente se describen en la literatura mundial. El área del cuereado debe estar separada de la zona limpia, pero lo más importante que se ha de verificar es el flujo de aire, que debe conservar constantemente una presión positiva desde las zonas limpias hacia las más contaminadas.

Eviscerado

La etapa siguiente es la evisceración, que constituye la segunda gran posibilidad de contaminación de la carne por ingesta o materia fecal, peligro de igual gravedad que la etapa del cuereado descrita anteriormente.

Aquí la inspección debe analizar las buenas prácticas de manipulación de las menudencias y de ligadura del esófago, intestino delgado, recto y vejiga, para impedir la evacuación de sus contenidos.

La separación de la cabeza, su perfecto lavado por dentro y por fuera, por los ollares y por la garganta, en ese orden, también deben ser controlados y verificados.

Inspección veterinaria

La etapa siguiente, que se realiza dentro del área limpia, es la inspección veterinaria de los animales faenados.

El Servicio de Inspección Veterinaria llevará una lista de matanza con toda la información sobre el origen de los animales. Esta información permitirá que la inspección siga procedimientos basados en el riesgo más bien que en sistemas rutinarios tradicionales, tal como lo recomienda el Comité de Higiene del Codex Alimentarius en su reciente *Código de prácticas de higiene para la carne* (7).

Para las vísceras, se dispondrá de mesas de inspección, donde las rojas queden separadas de las verdes. Se realizará la inspección visual de cada víscera y se incidirán las linfoglándulas según lo especifique la Autoridad Competente. Algunas vísceras, como el pulmón, deben ser incididas transversalmente para visualizar los parénquimas y el hígado a nivel de los conductos biliares, para la detección de *Fasciola hepatica* si corresponde. Las mesas o bandejas de inspección deben ser diseñadas de manera a evitar la contaminación cruzada.

La inspección de la cabeza debe realizarse una vez separada la lengua, incididas las linfoglándulas – submaxilar, parotídea y retrofaríngea – y/o las que correspondan, e inspeccionadas y desechadas las amígdalas. Se procede luego a incidir los músculos pterigoideos internos y externos para el diagnóstico de la cisticercosis.

Rev. sci. tech. Off. int. Epiz., **25** (2)

853

Se observarán las canales y medias canales y se incidirán todas aquellas linfoglándulas que ordena la Autoridad Competente. La iluminación en todas las áreas de inspección será de 300 o 500 unidades lux, según la regulación que se aplique.

La inspección veterinaria oficial realizará todos los análisis microbiológicos, pruebas complementarias y pruebas serológicas que considere necesarios a los fines de completar un diagnóstico.

El descarte y la posterior destrucción del material de riesgo también deben ser controlados por el Servicio de Inspección Veterinaria, por lo menos en lo que se refiere al encéfalo y médula espinal, según el riesgo específico de cada país en relación con las encefalopatías espongiformes transmisibles.

La información sobre los hallazgos de patologías, parasitosis, neoplasias y otras alteraciones debe apuntarse en el formulario que a tal efecto lleva el Servicio de Inspección Veterinaria. Esta información será integralmente remitida a la Autoridad Competente así como al operador de la producción primaria.

La difusión a los sectores productivos de los informes sobre los hallazgos realizados en el matadero permite planificar acciones preventivas, lo que se traduce en una mejora de la eficiencia.

Cuando los animales que entran en el matadero son objeto de un plan nacional o regional de control de una enfermedad o de un plan de contingencia o de sacrificio por motivos sanitarios, el Servicio de Inspección Veterinaria debe tomar las precauciones necesarias para el examen de los animales, pero también para proteger la salud de los operarios y especialmente para prevenir la contaminación cruzada.

Las enfermedades trasmitidas por alimentos que han provocado la mayor cantidad de brotes en los últimos años son las bacterianas, por ejemplo causadas por *E. coli* O157 (12), *Salmonella, Campylobacter*, etc. Todas estas bacterias se encuentran frecuentemente en el tubo intestinal (1, 12, 15, 18, 20).

Esto justifica la creación de un punto de control para la detección de contaminaciones, denominado "cero contaminación de ingesta o fecal visible", que debe hacer parte del sistema de autogestión de la empresa y del sistema de inspección oficial.

En las regulaciones el lavado de las canales con agua a presión suele ser obligatorio (agua potable) y en muchos casos se aplican diversos tipos de sustancias inhibitorias de las bacterias, tales como ácidos orgánicos, vapor de agua a altas temperaturas con vacío, etc.

Es frecuente aplicar ácidos como ácido acético, láctico, etc., para disminuir el riesgo de *E. coli* O157:H7. Algunos países tienen regulaciones al respecto. Sin embargo, debería analizarse con mayor detenimiento este procedimiento, pues existen indicios de desarrollo en pH ácido (2, 11, 16, 22, 23).

Además, por la propia definición de "carne fresca", sólo se admite "el frío" como medio de conservación, tanto en las regulaciones de la Unión Europea como en las del Mercado Común del Sur (Argentina-Brasil-Paraguay-Uruguay) y de muchos otros países.

Marca sanitaria

Todas las canales y vísceras deben ser selladas con una marca que indica su aptitud para el consumo. Este sello se aplica con tinta o marca térmica, generalmente indicando el país y el número oficial del establecimiento. En el mismo palco se aplican otros sellos o tarjetas, relacionados con la trazabilidad y con la calidad de las canales.

Oreado

Esta etapa tiene como objetivo secar la superficie y bajar la temperatura de las canales antes de llevarlas a las cámaras frigoríficas. La inspección prestará especial atención a los sistemas utilizados, que deberán evitar la condensación.

Enfriado, cámaras frigoríficas

En esta etapa es esencial controlar la temperatura y los tiempos de enfriamiento, según los peligros biológicos que se consideren, es decir en función del riesgo de que se desarrollen bacterias capaces de deteriorar el producto y de afectar la salud de los consumidores.

La inspección veterinaria de los establecimientos y los controles propios de la empresa deben llevar registros de temperatura durante todo el proceso de enfriamiento y también en las etapas posteriores de transformación, depósito y transporte. Los registros deben guardarse durante un tiempo suficiente a disposición de la Autoridad Competente o en vistas de posibles reclamaciones por parte de los consumidores.

En los sistemas de HACCP esta etapa puede constituir un punto crítico de control.

El inspector oficial debe prestar especial atención a la higiene de las cámaras frigoríficas, y controlar la forma en que se halla dispuesta la carga, que debe permitir la circulación del aire y sobretodo el funcionamiento y disposición de los equipos de frío, evitando la condensación y la contaminación consiguiente de las canales.

854

Rev. sci. tech. Off. int. Epiz., **25** (2)

Corte y desosado

Como se explicó anteriormente, el control de la temperatura de la carne y de las salas es esencial en esta etapa. Para cuartear y desosar las canales se considera como óptima una temperatura de la carne comprendida entre 4°C y 7°C y una temperatura ambiental de 10°C a 12°C.

Las buenas prácticas de manufactura (5) incluyen el entrenamiento, la capacitación, la higiene y la salud del personal; el diseño, la limpieza y desinfección de las instalaciones, utensilios, entre otros componentes esenciales. La inspección veterinaria debe controlar el cumplimiento de estos requisitos en las salas de corte y despostado (7).

Etiquetado y empacado

El etiquetado constituye una importante etapa de control por parte de los servicios oficiales de inspección, pues produce la información que llegará al consumidor final, la trazabilidad para determinar el origen, así como los demás datos referentes a la calidad. La fecha de vencimiento, las propiedades y las indicaciones de uso deben ser exactas y no fraudulentas.

El empacado también debe ser controlado. Los materiales usados, las buenas prácticas de fabricación, el uso adecuado del vacío o de las atmósferas controladas resultan sumamente importantes, así como los procesos para evitar la contaminación cruzada con los materiales de empaque secundarios, como cartones.

También conviene asegurarse de que esta etapa dure lo menos posible, para que la temperatura de los cortes de carne no tenga tiempo de subir.

Depósito

Los depósitos frigoríficos deben estar provistos de termógrafos. Los registros deben ser archivados durante un tiempo suficiente, y quedar a la disposición de los servicios oficiales de inspección.

La higiene de los depósitos debe respetar los criterios de orden y de higiene que hemos descrito para las cámaras de medias reses, evitando en todo momento la condensación y la contaminación.

Certificación

La certificación de los productos por parte de los Servicios Oficiales difiere según los países, y está relacionada con el precinto de los medios de transporte. Existen diferentes sistemas para garantizar la autenticidad de los productos transportados, así como la conservación de la cadena de frío.

La certificación para el tráfico internacional también supone requisitos específicos para cada país o región.

Transporte

Los medios de transporte serán diseñados para evitar toda contaminación y asegurar la conservación de la temperatura del producto transportado (7).

Las superficies internas del contenedor deben ser lisas, inoxidables y lavables.

El Servicio de Inspección Veterinaria debe verificar que los contenedores han sido lavados y desinfectados antes de la carga, y que los equipos de enfriamiento están en buen estado de funcionamiento. La cadena de frío no debe interrumpirse bajo ninguna circunstancia, por lo que se aconseja el uso de termo-registros que permitan el control de la temperatura durante todo el tiempo que dure el transporte.

Sistemas de autogestión de la inocuidad

En la introducción se ha explicado la importancia del rol que cumple el operador. En este sentido, las herramientas pertinentes son las buenas prácticas de manufactura, que incluyen los prerrequisitos y procedimientos operativos estándar de saneamiento.

Estos aspectos se hallan en el *Código internacional de prácticas recomendado para principios generales de higiene de los alimentos* del Codex Alimentarius (5) e incluyen requisitos que van desde la producción primaria hasta el transporte y comercialización.

Las buenas prácticas de manufactura son las prácticas y procedimientos recomendados para la manipulación de alimentos, teniendo en cuenta su identidad, calidad e inocuidad (5).

El Codex recomienda que las buenas prácticas de manufactura sean parte integrante de las políticas de los gobiernos. El compromiso suscrito por las empresas de aplicar estas buenas prácticas de manufactura debe constar explícitamente en un documento, y concretarse mediante programas y procedimientos a tal efecto.

Los prerrequisitos operativos y el sistema HACCP son las herramientas que debe usar el operador, primer responsable de la inocuidad de los alimentos que fabrica.

Más adelante veremos el papel que aquí desempeña la Autoridad Competente.

Prerrequisitos

Las actividades que deben llevarse a cabo para hacer funcionar el sistema HACCP son varias.

Las condiciones previas son imprescindibles y sin ellas no se puede construir un sistema de autogestión de la inocuidad en apoyo a la competitividad de las industrias, particularmente las que desean comerciar con otros países.

Estos prerrequisitos son condiciones básicas para el funcionamiento de los mataderos, y deben ser considerados por los operadores de los mataderos, por un lado, y por la Autoridad Competente, por el otro.

Los más importantes son los siguientes:

– el emplazamiento de la planta: el matadero debe estar ubicado en un terreno no inundable, con abastecimiento de agua potable en abundancia, alejado de actividades que generen contaminación ambiental;

– el diseño higiénico de las instalaciones: las salas deben ser fáciles de limpiar, las superficies han de ser lisas e impermeables, los encuentros entre pisos y paredes redondeados para permitir la eliminación de la materia orgánica. El aire debe circular de las zonas más limpias hacia las más contaminadas. Los drenajes deben estar dotados de sifones con válvulas de reflujo para los afluentes;

– el diseño del flujo operacional: el diagrama de flujo (*flow chart*) debe ser lineal y sin retrocesos, con el fin de evitar la contaminación cruzada;

– el mantenimiento de las instalaciones: debe existir un plan de mantenimiento preventivo de las instalaciones, diseñado por los servicios de control de calidad de la empresa de común acuerdo con el Servicio de Inspección Veterinaria;

– el diseño y mantenimiento higiénico de los equipos: de la misma forma que las instalaciones, los equipos deben estar diseñados para permitir su saneamiento y mantenimiento permanentes;

– la provisión de agua potable: el matadero debe contar con una provisión suficiente y se realizarán análisis microbiológicos y físico-químicos con una periodicidad basada en el riesgo, por lo menos una vez al mes;

– la higiene de los operarios: este aspecto está directamente relacionado con la capacitación del personal. Los operadores deben llevar ropa limpia, cambiada a diario o con mayor frecuencia cuando lo determine el Servicio de Inspección Veterinaria;

– la higiene durante el transporte;

– la eliminación adecuada de los desechos: las diferentes categorías de deshechos orgánicos deben eliminarse permanentemente para evitar la proliferación de fuentes contaminantes. Los mataderos deben poseer dispositivos para la esterilización de determinados tipos de tejidos patógenos, así como manómetros, termómetros y registros. El material de riesgo con relación a las encefalopatías espongiformes transmisibles debe ser tratado en función de la situación particular de cada país;

– el control de plagas: este control lo debe llevar a cabo el propio establecimiento, bajo la supervisión del Servicio de Inspección Veterinaria. Comprende la lucha contra los insectos y roedores. Deben existir registros de seguimiento de esta actividad;

– el manejo de sustancias tóxicas y productos químicos: estas sustancias, entre las que se incluyen los productos para la limpieza y desinfección, deben depositarse y prepararse en salas independientes;

– la capacitación del personal a todos los niveles: el entrenamiento adecuado del personal es necesario en todos los niveles y el Servicio oficial de inspección debe participar a las actividades de formación;

– el etiquetado del producto y la información del consumidor: existen al respecto regulaciones oficiales que deben ser respetadas por los operadores y controladas por la Autoridad Competente.

Procedimientos operativos estándar de saneamiento

Son procedimientos escritos, que se relacionan con:

– el mantenimiento general,

– las sustancias utilizadas para la limpieza y la desinfección,

– el almacenamiento de sustancias tóxicas,

– el control de plagas,

– la higiene de las superficies que están en contacto con la carne,

– el almacenamiento y la manipulación de equipos y utensilios limpios,

– el depósito de los sacos de basura y su eliminación.

Estos procedimientos deben aplicarse de manera permanente, en particular en lo que se refiere a la higiene de las superficies en contacto con la carne, e incluir:

– el monitoreo,

– las acciones correctivas,

856

Rev. sci. tech. Off. int. Epiz., **25** (2)

– la verificación,

– el registro.

Es esencial mantener registros donde se notifiquen las operaciones de limpieza y desinfección de las superficies en contacto con la carne, controladas por los servicios de supervisión del establecimiento. Uno de los controles debe realizarse fuera de los horarios de actividad (pre-operacional) y otro durante los horarios de actividad (operacional).

Cuando existan diferencias, los registros deben describir las acciones correctivas llevadas a cabo. El personal designado para manejar el sistema de autocontrol de la empresa debe verificar y validar las actividades realizadas sobre estos registros, dentro de plazos predeterminados en los procedimientos escritos.

La Autoridad Competente también debe verificar la eficacia con que se lleva a cabo esta actividad, controlando los registros, las instalaciones, las tareas, y efectuando verificaciones microbiológicas o de otro tipo cuando lo considere necesario.

Análisis de peligros y puntos críticos de control

En tan solo quince años, desde que empezó a aplicarse en la industria alimenticia, el sistema HACCP se ha ido generalizando en todos los países del mundo.

Se trata de un sistema "auditable" de orientación preventiva, basado sobre el concepto del análisis de peligro o de riesgo a través de todas las etapas de la cadena alimentaria. En 1997 fue editada la versión final de *Sistema de análisis de peligros y de puntos críticos de control (HACCP) y directrices para su aplicación* por el Codex Alimentarius, anexada al *Código internacional recomendado de prácticas* (4).

Algunos requisitos indispensables para la aplicación del HACCP son los siguientes:

– el compromiso de la dirección de la empresa y sus responsables de aplicar e implementar el sistema;

– la construcción de vínculos con proveedores, autoridades y clientes;

– el estudio y el conocimiento del sistema de gestión de inocuidad;

– la elaboración del plan como resultado de este estudio;

– la capacitación del personal en sus funciones y de la forma estipulada en el plan;

– la implementación del plan;

– el monitoreo, las acciones correctivas, la verificación y la mejora continua.

Generalmente se considera que la decisión de implementar un sistema HACCP pertenece a las máximas autoridades de la empresa; sin embargo, en varios países se han desarrollado guías o sistemas HACCP genéricos, sobre todo en pequeñas o medianas empresas, pero sin dotar a éstas de los medios financieros suficientes para hacer frente a su costo.

Sin pretender redactar un manual o guía de HACCP, pues existen muchos y muy buenos, se da a continuación una breve descripción de lo que debe ser un sistema HACCP, mostrando algunas pautas que deben tenerse en cuenta.

En los mataderos el primer paso es la constitución del equipo de personas responsables del sistema en los diferentes sectores y dirigido por un líder. Es muy importante que participen los encargados de: producción, mantenimiento, limpieza, etc., formando lo que se denomina un equipo multidisciplinario.

Entre los pasos que siguen, es de suma importancia elaborar el diagrama de flujo sobre el que se desarrollará el plan HACCP, que consta de los "7 principios" que se exponen a continuación.

a) el primero es el análisis de peligros: éste es sin duda el que requiere más conocimientos, experiencia y sobre todo información científica y epidemiológica. Se realiza a partir del diagrama de flujo que permite seguir una secuencia ordenada con los diferentes pasos en la producción del alimento. Interesa definir aquí la posibilidad y la probabilidad de que un determinado peligro ocurra;

b) el segundo es la determinación de los puntos críticos de control, siguiendo una secuencia de decisiones, para definir, en determinadas etapas de la cadena, qué medida de control existe para prevenir, eliminar o reducir un peligro a niveles aceptables;

c) luego se fijarán los límites críticos, es decir el valor o criterio que separa lo aceptable de lo inaceptable;

d) la vigilancia o monitoreo es el cuarto principio y consiste en una secuencia planeada de observaciones o mediciones con el fin de verificar que se está respetando el límite fijado;

e) establecer acciones correctivas cuando ocurren desviaciones fuera de los límites críticos;

f) establecer procedimientos de verificación: aplicación de métodos, procedimientos, pruebas, auditorías que permiten asegurar que el plan HACCP cumple con todos los requisitos prefijados. La validación, que frecuentemente se incluye dentro de la verificación, consiste en obtener

Rev. sci. tech. Off. int. Epiz., **25** (2)

857

pruebas que demuestren que los elementos del plan son efectivos para alcanzar las metas propuestas. En general, se acepta la idea de que la validación debe realizarse en el momento de iniciar el plan HACCP (validación inicial), y luego una vez por año o cuando varíen algunos elementos o aspectos de los alimentos, equipos o instalaciones;

g) El último principio consiste en establecer un sistema de registro y documentación que recopile las pruebas documentales u objetivas de que los límites críticos funcionan dentro de lo establecido, así como las acciones correctivas tomadas en caso de desviaciones. En los registros también deben figurar la verificación realizada sobre los puntos críticos, las calibraciones de los equipos de medición y otros controles, entre ellos los análisis microbiológicos.

Los planes HACCP son realizados por las propias empresas elaboradoras de alimentos, como por ejemplo los mataderos, pero los Servicios Veterinarios que operan en las plantas, tal como lo prevén los sistemas de inocuidad en la mayoría de los países y especialmente en los desarrollados, deben ejercer controles para verificar y validar el correcto cumplimiento de los planes HACCP.

Generalmente estos planes vienen acompañados de un control del proceso de higiene de la carne, mediante pruebas microbiológicas (9).

El objetivo es establecer el criterio de rendimiento microbiológico, fijado en general por las legislaciones de los organismos oficiales. Así, suelen utilizarse bacterias indicadoras de contaminación, como *E. coli* genérico, recuento de mesófilos totales, enterobacterias, o *Salmonella* (9).

En la playa de faena es muy frecuente la elección de un punto crítico de control relativo a la contaminación fecal o ingesta. El límite crítico que se busca es "cero contaminación fecal". Las medidas correctivas, cuando se producen desviaciones, varían entre las plantas en función de determinados criterios. El peligro biológico que se pretende eliminar, o al menos minimizar, es el de la presencia de *E. coli* O157:H7 y *Salmonella*, entre otros patógenos.

Otro ejemplo que resulta muy frecuente en los mataderos es el de los puntos críticos relativos al tiempo y a la temperatura de enfriamiento de las canales.

¿Cuál será entonces el rol del Servicio de Inspección Veterinaria o de la Autoridad Competente? Será sin duda de verificar que los prerrequisitos, el plan HACCP y todos sus requerimientos han sido implementados correctamente. Deberá controlar, entre otras cosas, los registros de monitoreo de los puntos críticos, las eventuales acciones correctivas y preventivas, constatar las desviaciones y controlar las verificaciones realizadas por los servicios de control de calidad de las empresas.

Además, la Autoridad Competente debe llevar a cabo auditorías de conformidad que demuestren y confirmen que el sistema es efectivo, que se han tenido en cuenta en el análisis todos los peligros/riesgos y que efectivamente éstos últimos se encuentran bajo control.

Plan Nacional de Control de Residuos y Medicamentos

Después de las crisis debidas a la contaminación por dioxinas y a la encefalopatía espongiforme bovina en la década de los 90, la idea de que los avances de la biotecnología podían representar a la vez graves peligros para la salud fue ganando terreno en la percepción de los consumidores.

Actualmente, la Autoridad Competente Central debe llevar a cabo sistemáticamente un plan de control de residuos en carnes y realizar actividades de control sobre los animales vivos, las carnes y determinados órganos con el fin de investigar la presencia de los elementos que se deben analizar.

La Autoridad Competente debe realizar un análisis de riesgos, evaluando inicialmente el uso de los antibióticos, antiparasitarios y otros medicamentos o productos usados en medicina veterinaria.

Recientemente la resistencia bacteriana como consecuencia del uso indiscriminado de productos antimicrobianos en la alimentación y en terapéutica animal y humana, es motivo de preocupación en todos los ámbitos científicos (8, 17).

El plan de vigilancia de residuos debe considerar la posibilidad de metales pesados, toxinas o mico-toxinas y cualquier tipo de residuos.

En los mataderos el Servicio de Inspección Veterinaria debe saber de dónde vienen los animales para conocer los antecedentes y características de los animales, y orientar el muestreo hacia aquellos que puedan resultar sospechosos.

La Autoridad Competente debe establecer los límites máximos de residuos (LMR) para los residuos que se consideran permitidos. Los que están prohibidos deben figurar en la categoría de los residuos para los cuales no se admiten límites.

Para poner en práctica un plan de control de residuos, se debe disponer de personal capacitado para la toma de muestras, su acondicionamiento y entrega, y contar con una red de laboratorios acreditados por la Autoridad Competente para realizar los análisis.

858

Rev. sci. tech. Off. int. Epiz., **25** (2)

Guidelines for animal and meat inspection procedures in the slaughterhouse

A. Schnöller

Summary

Over the last few decades there have been significant developments in livestock and meat inspection systems in slaughterhouses.

The most highly developed countries have taken the lead in bringing about these changes by enacting new legislation. These new national laws have been reflected by the Codex Alimentarius in its Codes of Good Practice and this has served to harmonise world trade in foodstuffs.

The author identifies the different aspects to be considered when carrying out a veterinary inspection of animals and animal products in the slaughterhouse, bearing in mind the need to protect public and animal health. Although this article only covers cattle, many of the concepts set forth can be applied to other livestock species.

Information obtained from the slaughterhouse is useful to primary production; conversely, information compiled in the primary production process makes for more efficient use of slaughterhouse resources.

This information makes it possible to carry out risk-based inspections, which will gradually replace traditional procedures. Conventional inspections are often very rigid and mechanical and incapable of measuring the seriousness of hazards or of determining the probability that they will occur.

Emerging biological, physical and chemical hazards, as well as new technologies, mean that we cannot become complacent about inspection procedures but must continue to be alert and to keep pace with the constant changes in food safety sciences.

Another new trend is the active participation of operators, who must shoulder primary responsibility in upholding the safety of the food they produce.

Official veterinary inspection in the slaughterhouse plays several roles: the detection of animal diseases, the inspection of meat and meat products and the verification of audits carried out by the private sector.

In recent years, the bovine spongiform encephalopathy crisis and cases of dioxin poisoning have highlighted the need for traceability of foodstuffs, i.e. giving consumers the opportunity to obtain information about the origin of their food and the different stages of its production (commonly referred to as the 'farm-to-fork' chain).

Finally, the slaughterhouse veterinarian, as a professional devoted to providing care to animals, is also responsible for ensuring animal welfare; this is an inherent part of his professional ethics.

Keywords

Food-borne disease – Food safety – Good manufacturing practice – Guideline – Hazard analysis and critical control point – Hygiene – Slaughterhouse – Veterinary inspection.

■

Rev. sci. tech. Off. int. Epiz., **25** (2)

859

Lignes directrices pour les procédures d'inspection des animaux et de la viande à l'abattoir

A. Schnöller

Résumé

Nous assistons depuis quelques décennies à des transformations radicales des systèmes d'inspection applicables aux animaux d'élevage et à la viande dans les abattoirs.

Les pays développés ont intégré ces changements dans leurs législations ; le Codex alimentarius les reflète dans ses Codes de bonnes pratiques, qui visent à harmoniser les échanges internationaux de denrées alimentaires.

L'auteur décrit les différents aspects à prendre en compte lors de l'inspection vétérinaire des animaux et de leurs produits à l'abattoir, en vue de préserver la santé publique mais aussi la santé animale. Les critères exposés, qui concernent essentiellement l'espèce bovine, s'appliquent également, pour la plupart, aux autres espèces d'animaux d'élevage.

Les informations obtenues à l'abattoir s'avèrent utiles pour la production primaire ; réciproquement, l'information recueillie lors de la production primaire peut rendre plus efficiente l'utilisation de ressources à l'abattoir.

Cette nouvelle conception permet de conduire des procédures d'inspection basées sur les risques, au lieu des systèmes traditionnels, souvent trop rigides et mécaniques et incapables de mesurer la gravité des risques.

Les dangers émergents, biologiques, physiques ou chimiques et les nouvelles technologies utilisées ne permettent pas de s'en tenir à des actions de simple routine ; il convient désormais d'adopter une attitude d'alerte, adaptée à l'évolution permanente des connaissances scientifiques en matière de sécurité sanitaire des aliments.

Une autre tendance est la participation active des opérateurs, désormais les premiers responsables de l'innocuité des aliments qu'ils produisent.

L'inspection vétérinaire officielle exerce ainsi plusieurs fonctions telles que la détection des maladies animales, le contrôle des viandes et des produits d'origine animale ainsi que la vérification des systèmes d'audit mis en œuvre dans les entreprises.

Tout dernièrement, après les crises dues à l'encéphalopathie spongiforme bovine et aux intoxications par les dioxines, il est apparu nécessaire de mettre en œuvre la traçabilité/le traçage, c'est-à-dire d'offrir aux consommateurs la possibilité de connaître l'origine des produits tout au long de la chaîne « de la fourche à la fourchette ».

Enfin, le vétérinaire de l'abattoir est également responsable du bien-être des animaux, envers lesquels il a une obligation éthique inaliénable en tant que professionnel des soins apportés aux animaux.

Mots-clés

Abattoir – Analyse des risques et maîtrise des points critiques – Bonne pratique de manufacture – Ligne directrice – Sécurité sanitaire des aliments – Inspection vétérinaire – Toxi-infection alimentaire – Hygiène.

■

860

Rev. sci. tech. Off. int. Epiz., **25** (2)

Bibliografía

1. Acha P. & Szyfres B. (2003). – Zoonosis y enfermedades transmisibles comunes al hombre y los animales, 3ª edición. Organización Panamericana de la Salud, Washington, DC.

2. Brackett R.H. & Doyle M.P. (1994). – Ineffectiveness of hot acid sprays to decontaminate *Escherichia coli* O157:H7 on beef. *J. Food Protec.*, **57**, 198-203.

3. Callaway T.R., Anderson R.C., Edrington T.S., Elder R.O., Genovese K.J., Biachoff K.M., Pool T.L., Yung Y.S., Harvey R.B. & Nisbet D.J. (2003). – Pre-slaughter intervention strategies to reduce food-borne pathogens in food animals. *J. Anim. Sci.*, **81**, E17-E23.

4. Comisión del Codex Alimentarius (1997). – Sistema de análisis de peligros y de puntos críticos de control (HACCP) y directrices para su aplicación, Apéndice al Código internacional recomendado de prácticas. Principios generales de higiene de los alimentos (CAC/RCP 1-1969; Tercera Revisión, 1997). Comisión del Código Alimentarius, Roma.

5. Comisión del Codex Alimentarius (2003). – Código internacional de prácticas recomendado para principios generales de higiene de los alimentos (CAC/RCP 1-1969; Cuarta revisión, 2003). Comisión del Código Alimentarius, Roma.

6. Comisión del Codex Alimentarius (2005). – Anteproyecto de grupo preliminar de principios para la rastreabilidad/rastreo de productos con respecto a la inspección y certificación de alimentos (CL 2005/23 FICS). Comité del Codex sobre Sistemas de Inspección y Certificación de Importaciones y Exportaciones de Alimentos (CCFICS), Roma.

7. Comisión del Codex Alimentarius (2005). – Código de prácticas de higiene para la carne (CAC/RCP 58). Comisión del Codex Alimentarius, Roma.

8. Comisión del Codex Alimentarius (2005). – Código de prácticas para reducir al mínimo y contener la resistencia a los antimicrobianos (CAC/RCP 61-2005). Comisión del Codex Alimentarius, Roma.

9. Comisión del Codex Alimentarius (2005). – Principios y Directrices para la aplicación de la gestión de riesgos microbiológicos (GRM). Apéndice III. Alinorma 05/28/13. Informe del Comité del Codex sobre Higiene de los Alimentos. Organización de las Naciones Unidas para la Agricultura y la Alimentación/Organización Mundial de la Salud, Roma.

10. Comunidades Europeas (CE) (2002). – Reglamento (CE) nº 178/2002 del Parlamento Europeo y del Consejo del 28 de enero de 2002 por el que se establecen los principios y los requisitos generales de la legislación alimentaria, se crea la Autoridad Europea de Seguridad Alimentaria y se fijan procedimientos relativos a la seguridad alimentaria. *Diario of. Comunidades eur.*, **L 31**, 1.2.2002, 1-24.

11. Conner D.E. & Kotrola J.S. (1995). – Growth and survival of *E. coli* O157:H7 under acidic conditions. *Appl. environ. Microbiol.*, **61** (1), 382-385.

12. Doyle M.P., Beuchat L.R. & Montville T.J. (1997). – Food microbiology: fundamentals and frontiers. American Society for Microbiology Press, Washington, DC.

13. European Food Safety Authority (EFSA) (2004). – Opinion of the Scientific Panel on Animal Health and Welfare on a request from the Commission related to welfare aspects of the main systems of stunning and killing the main commercial species of animals (Question no. EFSA-Q-2003-093). *EFSA J.*, **45**, 1-29.

14. European Food Safety Authority (EFSA) (2004). – Welfare aspects of animal stunning and killing methods. Scientific Report of the Scientific Panel for Animal Health and Welfare on a request from the Commission related to welfare aspects of animal stunning and killing methods, AHAW/04-027 (Question no. EFSA-Q-2003-093). EFSA, Parma.

15. Finch M.J. & Blake P.A. (1985). – Food-borne outbreaks of campylobacteriosis: the United States experience, 1980-1982. *Am. J. Epidemiol.*, **122**, 262-268.

16. Glass K.A., Loeffelholz J.M., Ford J.P. & Doyle M.P. (1992). – Fate of *Escherichia coli* O157:H7 as affected by pH or sodium chloride and in fermented, dry sausage. *Appl. environ. Microbiol.*, **58**, 2513-2516.

17. Novick R.P. (1981). – The development and spread of antibiotic-resistant bacteria as a consequence of feeding antibiotics to livestock. *Ann. N.Y. Acad. Sci.*, **368**, 23-59.

18. Organización Mundial de la Salud (OMS) (1988). – Control de la salmonelosis: importancia de la higiene veterinaria y de los productos de origen animal. Informe de un Comité de Expertos de la OMS. Serie de Informes Técnicos nº774. OMS, Ginebra.

19. Organización Mundial de la Salud (OMS) (2001). – Improved Coordination and Harmonization of National Food Safety Control Services Report on a joint WHO/Euro FSAI Meeting, Dublin, Ireland, 19-20 June. Oficina Regional de la OMS para Europa, Copenhague. Página web: http://www.euro.who.int /document/E74473.pdf (consulta del 29 de junio de 2006).

20. Rasmussen M., Cry A.W.C., Casey T.A. & Whipp S.C. (1993). – Rumen contents as a reservoir of enterohemorrhagic *Escherichia coli*. *FEMS Microbiol. Lett.*, **114**, 79-84.

21. Silvestre A. & Rey A.M. (2005). – Comer sin riesgos, tomo II. Las enfermedades trasmitidas por alimentos. Hemisferio Sur, Buenos Aires.

22. Zhao T., Doyle M.P. & Besser R.E. (1993). – Fate of enterohemorrhagic *Escherichia coli* O157:H7 in apple cider with and without preservatives. *Appl. environ. Microbiol.*, **59**, 2526-2530.

23. Zhao T. & Doyle M.P. (1994). – Fate of enterohemorrhagic *Escherichia coli* O157:H7 in commercial mayonnaise. *J. Food Protec.*, **57**, 780-783.

Nota

Nomenclature – Reference documents:
Mammal Species of the World, Second Edition, 1993
Distribution and Taxonomy of Birds of the World, 1991
Virus Taxonomy – Classification and Nomenclature of Viruses, Seventh Report of the International Committee on Taxonomy of Viruses, 1995
Approved Lists of Bacterial Names, Amended Edition, 1989 and *Index of the Bacterial and Yeast Nomenclatural Changes,* 1992

The articles published in the OIE *Scientific and Technical Review* are regularly analysed and indexed in the databases *Agris* (FAO, Italy) and *Littérature vétérinaire francophone* (Canada), in the abstract journals *Index Veterinarius* and *Veterinary Bulletin* (CABI databases, United Kingdom), in *Biosis, Capsule Report, Current Contents©/Agriculture, Biology and Environmental Sciences, Fish and Wildlife Worldwide, Focus On©: Veterinary Science & Medicine, Index Medicus, Medline* and *SciSearch©* (United States of America), in *Zoological Record* (United Kingdom), in *Electre* (France) and on the current awareness service *Veterinary journals: table of contents* of the Faculty of Veterinary Medicine of the University of Montreal, Canada.

■

Nomenclature – Ouvrages de référence :
Mammal Species of the World, deuxième édition, 1993
Distribution and Taxonomy of Birds of the World, 1991
Virus Taxonomy – Classification and Nomenclature of Viruses, Seventh Report of the International Committee on Taxonomy of Viruses, 1995
Approved Lists of Bacterial Names, édition corrigée, 1989 et *Index of the Bacterial and Yeast Nomenclatural Changes,* 1992

Les articles publiés dans la *Revue scientifique et technique* de l'OIE sont régulièrement analysés et indexés dans les bases de données *Agris* (FAO, Italie) et *Littérature vétérinaire francophone* (Canada), dans les bulletins signalétiques *Index Veterinarius* et *Veterinary Bulletin* (bases de données du CABI, Royaume-Uni), dans *Biosis, Capsule Report, Current Contents©/Agriculture, Biology and Environmental Sciences, Fish and Wildlife Worldwide, Focus On©: Veterinary Science & Medicine, Index Medicus, Medline* et *SciSearch©* (États-Unis d'Amérique), dans *Zoological Record* (Royaume-Uni), ainsi que dans *Électre* (France) et sur le service d'alerte *Veterinary journals: table of contents* de la Faculté de médecine vétérinaire de l'Université de Montréal, Canada.

■

Nomenclatura – Obras de referencia:
Mammal Species of the World, Segunda edición, 1993
Distribution and Taxonomy of Birds of the World, 1991
Virus Taxonomy – Classification and Nomenclature of Viruses, Seventh Report of the International Committee on Taxonomy of Viruses, 1995
Approved Lists of Bacterial Names, edición corregida, 1989 e *Index of the Bacterial and Yeast Nomenclatural Changes,* 1992

Los artículos publicados en la *Revista científica y técnica* de la OIE son analizados e indicados regularmente en las bases de datos *Agris* (FAO, Italia) y *Littérature vétérinaire francophone* (Canadá), las fichas descriptivas *Index Veterinarius* y *Veterinary Bulletin* (bases de datos del CABI, Reino Unido), en *Biosis, Capsule Report, Current Contents©/Agriculture, Biology and Environmental Sciences, Fish and Wildlife Worldwide, Focus On©: Veterinary Science & Medicine, Index Medicus, Medline* y *SciSearch©* (Estados Unidos de América), en *Zoological Record* (Reino Unido), en *Electre* (Francia) y en el servicio de alerta *Veterinary journals: table of contents* de la Facultad de veterinaria de la Universidad de Montreal, Canadá.

──

Notes / Apuntes

Notes / Apuntes

Directeur de la publication : B. Vallat

Directeur de la rédaction : P.-P. Pastoret